A Gardener's Book of Plant Names

A Gardener's Book of Plant Names

A Handbook of the Meaning and
Origins of Plant Names

A. W. Smith

Harper & Row, Publishers
New York, Evanston, and London

FIRST EDITION I-N

LIBRARY OF CONGRESS CATALOG CARD NUMBER: 62-9906

AN ORCHARD INNOVATIONS REPRINT EDITION
Printed in the United States of America

ISBN: 978-1951682316

Ver. 1.0 (4/16/2020)

His helmet now shall make a hive for bees.

—GEORGE PEELE

in *Polyhymnia: The Aged Man at Arms*

Contents

Introduction

Literally hundreds of thousands of plants have been given botanical names. Of this huge number very few have English names, and these have become established more by use than anything else. Often one name refers to a number of different plants, depending on where one lives. A bluebell is a *Campanula* in Scotland and in England an *Endymion*. Across the Atlantic it becomes *Polemonium, Eustoma, Muscari,* or *Mertensia*—all on a purely regional basis. In France it is *jacinthe des prés*—*Hyacinthus*, in fact.

Botanical names cut across all local preferences. They are used by professional and amateur alike in all countries. They are precise, in that they fix the plant exactly without possibility of doubt.

Two hundred years ago, when the foundations were laid for the present system of naming plants, Latin was the international language of science and of scholarship generally. So, today, plant names are in a Latin form. But botanical Latin has little to do with the classical. Words have been given new botanical meanings so that a Latin dictionary is often not very helpful.

Classification and the subsequent naming of a plant begins with placing it in its proper plant family or order. This is a grouping of related genera, of which there are only a few dozen of consequence to most general gardeners and, in any case, their interest is more botanical than horticultural. Plant family names are easily recognized by their ending which is nearly always *-aceae*, which means "of the family of" (as in *Rosaceae*, of the rose family). One of the rare exceptions is *Compositae*, of the daisy family.

Although necessary for classification, the name of the family is not part of the plant's name. This regularly consists of the genus name which is followed by the species name, or specific, which gives the sub-division within the genus, sometimes followed by one and, occasionally, by more specific words when closer definition becomes essential. The plant name thus stated—genus name followed by one or more specifics—is complete and precise in itself and enough to identify it exactly among several hundred thousand other known plants in the botanical world.

Nearly all genus names have been given an ending to make them look like Latin. While a few are genuine Latin, the majority consists of Greek words either singly or in combination. Of the remainder there are Latinized names commemorating people, vernacular names, geographic names, and so on. A few have no detectable parentage but it is hard to believe that they are meaningless.

Species names are often genuine Latin, generally in the form of an adjective, of which a few have been given special botanical meanings. They often give some clue regarding the plant—its color, size, shape, habit of growth, or native habitat. Otherwise, like genus names, species names may commemorate people or be geographic or vernacular names and so on.

This is the so-called binomial or two-name system which was originated by the Swedish botanist Linnaeus about two hundred years ago. Before he laid his orderly hand on it the situation was chaotic; precision could be achieved only by adding descriptive Latin words in the hope that in the end there could be no doubt as to exactly what plant was intended.

The result was cumbersome and confusing and lacked universal acceptance. What today is called *Dianthus caryophyllus* (clove pink) was then *Dianthus floribus solitaris, squamis calycinis subovatis brevissimis, corollis crenatis,* meaning Dianthus with solitary flowers with very short inverted egg-shaped scaled calyces and crown-shaped corollas. As a total description this was fairly accurate, but Linnaeus cut the whole thing back with his new binomial system to two Latin words meaning clove-flowered pink.

Linnaeus also proposed a system of classification and, although his method of naming has persisted, it was too much to expect that his system of classification could remain unmodified for a couple of hundred years. Linnaeus, who seems to have had something of an obsession about sex, based his classifications solely on the sexual characteristics of the plant. Since that day the system has been rationalized and other things are now taken into account in classification.

The binomial or two-name system is sometimes a misnomer. Plants often require three or more names to be identified with complete precision. Thus the familiar *Alyssum saxatile* or basket-of-gold becomes *Alyssum saxatile* var. *compactum citrinum* when it is the low-growing lemon-yellow form of the species. The abbreviation 'var.,' for variety, can be omitted. It is largely a matter of taste.

There is nothing intrinsically difficult about botanical names. They are merely words in another language which become easier to memorize when one knows their meaning. Used as a kind of almost meaningless jargon, as one suspects they sometimes are, they are hard to remember and to reproduce correctly.

Apart from their precision, botanical names often hold useful clues regarding the plant itself which can be helpful in recognizing it. Sometimes, too, the names have stories behind them which give an additional handle to the memory.

In addition to their botanical names, some plants acquire another kind of name. These are mostly the garden plants and other cultivated species that have been especially bred to produce finer forms. These are the "named varieties" or "cultivars" of the nurseryman and the florist. They include such things as practically all apples, pears, and other orchard fruits, the hybrid roses as well as a very large share of border plants and vegetables. Examples are such things as *Philadelphus virginalis* 'Albatros', *Phlox drummondii* 'Twinkle', and so on.

The parentage of these plants is often so confused that only by some extraordinary coincidence involving the genes will any of them come true from seed. For instance, it is of little use to plant the seeds of a named variety of border phlox, *Phlox paniculata*. The seedlings are almost certain to come up in any color or form but that of the parent plant and be generally quite worthless. Propagation of hybrids like these must be by other methods— division, layering, grafting, budding, and so on.

Yet in many cases it is only by painstaking and controlled crossing of named varieties that new and more desirable forms can be obtained. Many hundreds and even thousands of seedlings may have to be discarded by the breeder before he finds what he is seeking. It may, for instance, be such a thing as an odorless marigold. This has been an objective of one famous seed-grower for many years and hired help spends many hours on hands and knees sniffing up and down the rows.

Very occasionally a hybrid, sometimes of known parentage, will establish itself, coming true to seed and in all respects behaving as a species. For example, the accidental cross *Gentiana farreri* × *G. sino-ornata* resulted in a new species which has been named *Gentiana* × *macaulayi*.

Most good catalogues tend to list species apart from hybrids and named varieties. Less good suppliers seem sometimes to make every effort to depart as far as possible from botanical names. The fanciful names given by them to good honest species are generally unhelpful and may be downright misleading.

Within reasonable limits, nobody need be too disturbed about pronunciation. There are no particular difficulties and so long as the accent or emphasis is put on the preferred syllable, the rest is fairly easy. But even the question of accent is to some extent a matter of taste, particularly where the names of people are concerned. It does not matter very much if one prefers Hales-ia to Hal-ee-sia, James-ia to Jam-ee-sia.

It is not as if botanical names were in classical Latin with an accepted pronunciation. While certain pronunciations may be preferred by usage, much must remain as a matter of personal taste and of what sounds right. This itself will depend to some extent on where one was brought up. English speech sounds odd to Kansas ears and vice versa. And does one say americahna, americayna, or americanna? Daylia, dallia, or dahlia? Who is to decide which is correct?

The important thing is to be intelligible. It is probably advisable therefore to follow the convention of English-speaking gardeners and pronounce botanical names as if they were English words instead of trying to pretend that they are Latin. This is all very well among English-speaking gardeners, but the system is likely to be unintelligible to Continental Europeans who tend to pronounce botanical names as if they were classical Latin tinged with the accent of their own native language—be it Dutch, Danish, or what-have-you.

There are compilations of preferred pronunciations and these have been followed as far as practicable, relying on that physical and mental giant of American botany, Liberty Hyde Bailey, for the most informed guidance. Bailey himself, who died at over ninety a few years back, would have been the last to be dogmatic on these matters.

Possibly the final word on the matter of pronunciation was said by the Latin author, Pliny, who as commander-in-chief of the Roman navy had himself rowed across the Bay of Naples in a galley to study close at hand the eruption of Vesuvius which destroyed Pompeii. He lost his life in the lava flow in the interests of science. As an author he had set himself the monumental task of writing down all the known natural history of his time. In order not to miss a moment he had himself read to by slaves through his meals. On one of these occasions a guest stopped the slave in his reading to correct some error in pronunciation. Pliny, annoyed at the interruption, asked the guest whether he had understood what the slave had read, and, that being the case, why he had wasted so much precious time over something which was of no consequence whatsoever.

The privilege of selecting and bestowing a name on a new plant lies with the person who first classifies it and publishes an adequate description of it in botanical terms. He may name it more or less what he pleases within the rather broad generally accepted limits of a very few botanical rules. For one thing, it is not regarded as proper to name a discovery after oneself. For another, the selected name must conform to the binomial system as a precise internationally current scientific term not duplicated elsewhere.

The same privilege of selecting a name also belongs to the individual who manages, as is sometimes the case, to uncover a case of faulty previous classification of a known plant. To the layman, some of these rechristenings sometimes seem rather fickle and unnecessarily pedantic. Often, however, as much of the old binomial as possible is incorporated in the new name, which is only sensible, and certainly welcome to those who are conscious of increasingly short memory.

Conforming to the fiction that botanical names are Latin, the rules of Latin grammar are observed. All generic names are treated as nouns. They may be masculine, feminine, or neuter. The species name is often an adjective which must agree in gender with the generic. It is often possible to make a fair guess at the gender of a generic from its ending but there may be traps for the unwary. Fortunately these exceptions are rather few and they too are subject to a few simple rules.

(a) Generics ending in -us are nearly all masculine. The few feminine exceptions are tree names and include *Pinus, Quercus, Laurus*.

(b) Generics ending in -a are generally feminine (*Campanula, Viola*) and always so if they are Latin. There is a small group ending in -ma which derive from Greek and are neuter (*Aethionema, Ceratostigma*).

(c) Generics ending in -um are neuter.

(d) Generics ending in -es, -e, and -is are feminine with the single exception of *Cucumis* (cucumber), which is masculine.

(e) Generics ending in -codon, -pogon, and -stemon are Greek and masculine.

(f) Generics ending in -dendron (*Philodendron*), -nema, or -stigma (*Aethionema, Ceratostigma*) are neuter.

(g) Generics ending in -daphne and -mecon are Greek and feminine.

(h) *Acer* (maple) is neuter.

Most species names are Latin adjectives or, at least, are in a recognizable Latin form. With the exception of those adjectives whose masculine and feminine forms both end in -is (*humilis*, low-growing), all Latin adjectives have different endings for masculine, feminine, and neuter; there are, however, a few exceptions such as the adjectives *felix* (happy) and *simplex* (simple), which remain the same in all genders.

The rules for Latin adjectives are few and simple. There are four main categories.

(a) Adjectives ending in:

MASCULINE -us	FEMININE -a	NEUTER -um
alb-us (white)	*alb-a*	*alb-um*
parv-us (small)	*parv-a*	*parv-um*
nive-us (snowy)	*nive-a*	*nive-um*

(b) Adjectives ending in:

MASCULINE -er	FEMININE -ra	NEUTER -rum
nig-er (black)	nig-ra	nig-rum
rub-er (red)	rub-ra	rub-rum

An exception is *asper, aspera, asperum* (rough).

(c) Adjectives ending in:

MASCULINE -er	FEMININE -ris	NEUTER -re
ac-er (sharp)	ac-ris	ac-re
campest-er (of fields)	campest-ris	campest-re

(d) Adjectives ending in:

MASCULINE -is	FEMININE -is	NEUTER -e
trist-is (sad)	trist-is	trist-e
humil-is (low-growing)	humil-is	humil-e

Certain species names are participles. They end in *-ens* (*reptens*, creeping) or in *-ans* (*radicans*, rooting). They are the same for all genders.

A few specifics are nouns in the nominative case (*Sedum rosea*, the Rose sedum or rose-colored sedum). They are the same in all genders.

Another group of specifics is of nouns in the genitive singular. Generally they commemorate people as in *Gentiana farreri* (Farrer's gentian) and *Rhododendron fortunei* (Fortune's rhododendron.) Here again there can be no agreement in gender.

Some specifics are nouns in the genitive plural as in *Sempervivum tectorum* or house-leek—literally, Sempervivum of house roofs. These also remain unchanged by gender.

Specifics taken directly from the Greek keep the same forms in all genders. They end in *-yx, -ys,* and *-ops,* as in *trichocalyx* (with a hairy calyx), *leucobotrys* (with white clusters), and *cyclops* (gigantic). There are a few others such as *-ripes* (*lateripes*, lateral stalked) and *-lepis* (*lasiolepis*, with woolly scales).

Constantly recurring is the ending *-oides*, signifying "resembling" or "similar to" (*primuloides*, resembling primrose). This sometimes appears as *-odes* (*sarcodes*, fleshlike).

Lastly there is a small category of specifics taken directly from other languages such as *Pinus mugo*, the latter simply being the Italian name for this pine.

All genus names should be capitalized. When they become English vernacular names they are given small letters. Thus, *Gentiana* becomes gentian.

As far as specific names are concerned, many people nowadays give them all small letters irrespective of their derivation. This system seems logical. It is legitimate usage and it is the pattern followed in this book.

For those who prefer capitals for certain specifics here are some categories where they may legitimately be employed:

(*a*) If the specific is a descriptive adjective (*parvus*, small) or a common noun (*tectorum*, of house roofs) there is no question that it rates only a small letter.

(*b*) If the specific is geographical (*canadensis*, *africanus*, *braziliensis*) the custom is to give it a small letter although some people still prefer, incorrectly, to capitalize it.

(*c*) When specifics commemorate people, generally in the form of a proper noun in the genitive singular, the permissibility of a capital is admitted by the International Code of Botanical Nomenclature. But many people prefer to do otherwise and here the small letter has been used in the interest of consistency, as in *Rhododendron fortunei* (Fortune's rhododendron) and *Gentiana* × *macaulayi* (Macaulay's gentian). When the name ends in a consonant, the letters *ii* are added (as see *jackmanii* and *engelmannii*); except when the name ends in *er*, when *i* is added. When the name ends in a vowel, *i* is added; except when the vowel is *a*, when *e* is added.

(*d*) Vernacular plant names used as specifics are sometimes awarded capitals. Here the pattern used is a small letter (*Pinus mugo*). The Italian name for this pine is *mugo* and as a Latin name it should be spelled in this way.

(*e*) There is a small class of generic names which are also used as specifics. The firm rule used to be that all these words be spelled with capitals. Many of them are old generic names which have passed out of use and whose origins are obscured. Because they are nouns they sometimes appear not to agree in gender with the generic, as in *Sedum rosea*. Here the modern trend is followed and they are given small letters but that is a matter of taste.

In this book an attempt has been made to reproduce in a practical way what seems to be the preferred pronunciation of botanical names among English-speaking gardeners.

(*a*) Emphasis, which is more important than pronunciation, has been indicated by using capitals for the syllable to be stressed.

(*b*) The only infallible way of indicating pronunciation is to use the systems of phonetics which in extreme forms become almost unintelligible to all but lexicographers. Here reliance has been placed on spelling out words by syllables, using normally accepted vowel sounds.

(*c*) In classical Latin every vowel is pronounced separately so that there are as many syllables as vowels— except in the case of diphthongs (æ and œ) which are treated as single syllables. Here, in the interests of brevity and simplicity, no attempt has been made to sort out the classical pronunciation of such common endings as *-ea*, *-ia*, *-eus*, *-eum*, and so on. They are normally elided in speech to sound like *-ya*, *-ya*, *-yus*, and *-yum*. In a few words of Greek origin like *giganteus* the accent is on the *-e* which is long (thus jy-gan-TEE-us).

The rules for accenting or stressing syllables are both brief and simple:

(*a*) In two-syllable words the emphasis falls on the first syllable (AL-bus; RU-ber; BO-nus).

(*b*) In Latin words of more than two syllables the emphasis usually is on the penultimate syllable when the vowel is long (*montanus*, mon-TAY-nus; *alpinus*, al-PY-nus).

(*c*) In words of more than two syllables, if the next to the last syllable has a short vowel the emphasis may be either on that syllable or on the one preceding it (*campestris*, kam-PEST-ris; *angustissimus*, an-gus-TISS-im-us). There is no hard and fast rule. When at a loss, use the one that sounds best.

(*d*) In no case in a Latin word does the emphasis occur before the antepenultimate, or the last syllable but two of a word.

Some Botanical Definitions

1

ACHENE

A dry, one-seeded fruit that does not split. The "seeds" of a strawberry are achenes, and, correctly, are the fruit rather than the edible pulp in which they are embedded.

ADVENTIVE

A plant that has become accidentally established in the wild, sometimes only for a brief period. Many of the commonest American wildflowers—including chicory, dandelion, and all the clovers—are foreigners and therefore adventives. Some wildflower books tend to banish all adventives from the select company of the strictly native, often to the confusion of identification. However, it is not wise to be too national about wildflowers. Seeds have an extraordinary power of survival and seize any opportunity for travel—in the coats of animals and clothing of men, in the bellies of birds and beasts, on sea drifts. The means are limitless.

There is, for instance, in Scotland a stream warmed by water from a woolen mill where Australian flowers once flourished in temperate conditions, having arrived as seeds in the baled fleeces. The wool nowadays arrives in much cleaner condition. Although many of the "introductions" have now died out, there remain one or two survivors.

ANNUAL

A plant which lasts only one year, perpetuating itself by seed.

ANTHER

The pollen-bearing part of the stamen. Supported by the filament, it forms the male portion of a flower.

AQUATIC

A plant living in or growing near water.

BIENNIAL

A plant which fruits and dies in its second year.

BLOOM

The delicate powdery deposit on certain fruits like grape and plum and on some leaves, giving the latter a bluish or gray-bluish tint (see *glaucous*).

3

BRACT

The leaflike or membranous leaf or scale growing below the calyx or peduncle of many flowers. It is sometimes brightly colored and is, visually, of more importance than the flower. The scarlet petals of poinsettia and the pink or white petals of dogwood are all bracts.

BULB

Swollen stem and leaf bases forming a spherical mass.

CALYX

The whorl of "leaves" (sepals) forming the outer covering of the flower bud.

CARPEL

One of the cells of a compound fruit or pistil, or the single cell of a simple fruit or pistil.

CILIATE

Fringed with hairs (cilia).

CLAMMY

Moist or sticky.

CONNECTIVE

The portions of a filament which support the lobes of the anther.

COROLLA

The petals of a flower collectively.

CORM

Stem-base swollen to bulbous shape.

CORYMB

A flower cluster in which the individual outer-flower stalks are elongated to make the cluster flat-topped or nearly so. It blooms from the outside inward toward the center.

CRYPTOGAM

Literally, a hidden marriage. A plant which does not produce flowers or seeds in the ordinarily understood sense, such as ferns, mosses, lichens, and fungi.

CYME

A broad, branching, often flat-topped flower cluster blooming from the center to the edges. The main stalk is always topped by a flower.

DECIDUOUS

Dropping leaves, petals, fruit, etc., in a particular season, as opposed to persistent or evergreen.

DEHISCENT

The splitting or other mode of opening of a seed pod to discharge seeds. Dehiscence can be quite violent, as in castor oil plant and common broom.

DIOECIOUS

Having unisexual male and female flowers borne on separate plants (e.g., holly).

DISK (ALSO DISC)

A flattened round part of a plant. The group of tubular florets forming the flower center of plants of the daisy family (*Compositae*).

DRUPE

A stone fruit, such as peach, cherry, olive, plum.

EPIPHYTE

A plant which grows on another, but which is generally not parasitic in the sense of drawing nourishment from the host but only in using it as a growth site. Included are the air plants and other perchers which are fed from the air and often establish on fence and telephone wires.

FILAMENT

In a flower, that slender part of the stamen which supports the anther.

FLORET

One of the individual and often small flowers which comprise the flower head of plants of the daisy family (*Compositae*). Also, more generally, any small flower which is part of a dense cluster.

FOLLICLE

A dry, one-chambered fruit splitting along one seam (peony, milkweed, monkshood).

GLABROUS

Smooth, without hair.

GLAUCOUS

Of bluish or gray-green color due to a covering of fine whitish or grayish powder called bloom.

GLOMERULE

A cluster or head of flowers.

GLUME

The chaff-like bract which forms an outer envelope in the inflorescence of grasses and sedges or in the husks of wheat and other grain.

HERB

A plant of which the stem does not become woody and persistent but dies down to the ground (or entirely) after flowering. Also applied to plants which are used for medicine or for their scent or flavor.

INDUSIUM

The membranous scale covering the sorus of a fern.

INFLORESCENCE

An arrangement of flowers in a cluster.

INVOLUCRE

A rosette or whorl of bracts surrounding the base of an inflorescence, as in cornflower.

MONOECIOUS

Having separate male and female flowers on the same plant (cucumber, pumpkin, melon).

NECTARY

The part of the flower which secretes nectar, the chief source of honey.

PANICLE

A loose, irregularly spreading flower cluster, blooming from the center or bottom to the edges or top.

PAPPUS

The feathery or bristly appendage on the seeds of *Compositae*.

PEDICEL

A small stalk, but especially the subordinate stalk bearing the individual flowers of an inflorescence.

PEDUNCLE

The main stalk of a flower cluster or the stalk of a solitary flower.

PERENNIAL

Plants which remain alive through a number of years.

PERIANTH

Collective term for the calyx and corolla, especially when these are more or less indistinguishable as in many monocotyledons (e.g., lilies).

PISTIL

The complete female organ of reproduction.

PLANT

A member of the vegetable kingdom. In common use, usually excluding trees and shrubs.

PYRENE

The stone of stone fruits (e.g., olive, plum, peach).

RACEME

An elongated inflorescence in which the flowers are arranged on short, nearly equal pedicels blooming from the bottom up (lily-of-the-valley, squill).

RAY

One of the petals radiating from the disk in such flowers as daisy, sunflower, aster.

RHYZOME

Creeping, usually thickened, underground stem.

SAPROPHYTIC

Living on decayed vegetable matter.

SCAPE

A flower stalk, generally leafless, rising straight from the ground (e.g., tulip, primrose).

SECUND

With flowers or leaves arranged on one side only of a stalk.

SESSILE

Lacking a stalk.

SHRUB

A woody plant smaller than a tree.

SORUS

The collection of spore cases in or under which are the spores of ferns.

SPADIX

The thick, often fleshy, spike of flowers in members of the *Arum* family and certain other genera.

SPORE

The minute reproductive organ of flowerless plants such as ferns and mosses.

STAMEN

The male organ in a flower.

STIGMA

The organ at the termination of style and ovary which receives pollen and pollination.

STIPULE

The small leaflike or membranous organ found at the base of many leaf stalks.

STOLON

A horizontal stem on or just below the ground from the tip of which a new plant grows. Also a bent shoot that takes root.

STYLE

The shanklike connection between ovary and stigma.

SUCCULENT

Herbs with a juicy structure adapted to dry situations.

TERRESTRIAL

Growing in the soil.

TREE

A woody perennial plant having a trunk for its main stem and growing to a considerable size.

TRUSS

A non-technical term for a compact flower cluster at the end of a stalk, as in lilac.

TUBERCLE

A small tuber. Also the nodules on the roots of most legumes; also the knoblike growths on many cacti.

UMBEL

A flower cluster in which all the individual flower stalks arise from one point to form a flat-topped or ball-like cluster (onion).

Meanings and Origins of Plant Names

2

A

a-

Prefix in compound words of Greek origin signifying a negative, lacking, or contrary to. Thus *apetalus,* lacking petals; *Alyssum,* against madness.

abbreviatus, -a, -um [ab-ree-vi-AY-tus]
Shortened; abbreviated.

Abelia [ab-EE-lia]
Ornamental shrubs named for Dr. Clarke Abel (1780-1826), who, at the suggestion of Sir Joseph Banks, accompanied Lord Amherst on his embassy to Peking (1816–1817) as botanist. Much of his collection was lost by shipwreck on the way home to Kew. Except for a Russian ecclesiastical mission, no European naturalist was to visit China for nearly thirty years thereafter, Robert Fortune (see *Fortunella*) being among the first to follow. Abel died in India while serving as personal physician to Lord Amherst, who was by that time Governor-General.

Abies [AB-i-eez]
Fir. The classical Latin name.

abietinus, -a, -um [ab-i-ee-TY-nus]
Resembling the fir tree.

Abobra [ab-o-bra]
Latinized form of the Brazilian name for this vine of the cucumber family.

abortivus, -a, -um [ab-or-TY-vus]
With parts missing; imperfect.

abricock [ab-RI-cock]
Antique English spelling of apricot.

Abroma [ab-RO-ma]
Gr. *a,* not; *broma,* food. These evergreen trees are mildly poisonous.

Abronia [ab-RO-nia]
Sand verbena, wild lantana. Gr. *abros,* delicate; in allusion to the appearance of the bracts beneath the flower of these herbs.

11

Abrophyllum [ab-ro-FILL-um]

Gr. *abros*, delicate; *phyllon*, a leaf. The leaves of these Australian shrubs have a delicate appearance.

abrotanifolius, -a, -um [ab-ro-tay-ni-FO-lius]

Having leaves resembling southernwood.

abrotanum [ab-ro-TAY-num]

Ancient Latin name and now the specific name of southernwood (*Artemisia abrotanum*, orginally spelled *abrotonum*).

abruptus, -a, -um [ab-RUP-tus]

Ending suddenly; abrupt.

Abrus [AB-rus]

Wild licorice. Gr. *abros*, delicate; in allusion to the soft leaves. The root has the property of licorice of poor quality. The seeds, bright scarlet with black spots, are used in India as weights and are strung as beads.

abscissus, -a, -um [ab-SISS-us]

Ending abruptly; cut off.

absinthium [ab-SIN-thi-um]

Latin and pre-Linnaean name for wormwood, the botanical name for which is now *Artemisia absinthium*. It gives the flavor to absinthe. In biblical days it was a symbol of calamity and sorrow.

Abutilon [ab-YEW-til-on]

Flowering maple. From the Arabic name for a mallowlike plant.

abyssinicus, -a, -um [ab-iss-IN-ik-us]

Abyssinian.

Acacia [ak-AY-sha]

The Greek name for the tree. Derived from Gr. *akis*, a sharp point.

Acaena [ass-EE-na]

New Zealand bur. Gr. *akaina*, a thorn. The name derives from the spines on the calyx of these low-growing shrubs or herbs.

Acalypha [ak-al-LY-fa]

Copper leaf. Ancient Greek name for nettle but applied by Linnaeus to this genus of shrubs or herbs because of the nettlelike appearance of the leaves.

Acampe [ak-AM-pe]

Gr. *akampes*, inflexible or brittle. The flowers of these epiphytic orchids are brittle and break off easily.

acanth [ak-anth]
In compound words signifying spiny, spiky, or thorny.

acanthifolius, -a, -um [ak-anth-i-FO-lius]
With leaves like *Acanthus*.

Acanthium [ak-ANTH-ium]
Pre-Linnaean name for the Scotch thistle.

Acanthocereus [ak-anth-o-SEE-reus]
Trailing or climbing cactus. Gr. *akanthos*, a thorn; *Cereus*, cactus.

acanthocomus, -a, -um [ak-an-tho-KO-mus]
Having spiny hairs.

Acantholimon [ak-an-tho-LY-mon]
Prickly thrift. Gr. *akanthos*, a thorn; *limon*, Statice or sea-lavender, which it resembles.

Acanthopanax [ak-an-tho-PAY-nax]
Gr. *akanthos*, a thorn; *Panax*, ginseng, which this genus of trees and shrubs resembles.

Acanthophoenix [ak-an-tho-FEE-nix]
Spine-areca. Gr. *akanthos*, a thorn; *Phoenix*, which is both the Greek and the modern genus name for the date palm, which *Acanthophoenix* resembles.

Acanthorhiza [ak-an-tho-RY-za]
Gr. *akanthos*, a thorn; *rhiza*, a root. The rootlets of these palms are spiny.

Acanthus [ak-AN-thus]
Greek name meaning thorn. In America it is called "bear's breech" from the size and appearance of the leaf which is very big, broad, and distinctly hairy. The acanthus leaf was a favorite decoration in classical sculpture, as in the capital of the Corinthian column. In England the bear has been dressed up and it is now called "bear's breeches" despite long-standing authority to the contrary.

acaulis, -is, -e [ak-AW-lis]
Stemless or with only very short stems.

-aceae [-AY-se-ee]
An ending used in the names of plant families denoting "belonging to the family of." Thus "Rosaceae," belonging to the rose family. Of a total of nearly three hundred plant families, only a few dozen concern the general gardener and the interest is largely botanical. This ending is almost universal, a few of the eight exceptions being "Compositae" (daisies),

"Gramineae" (grasses), "Leguminoseae" (legumes). The English equivalent is -aceous, as in rosaceous.

acephalus, -a, -um [ay-SEFF-al-us]
Without a head.

Acer [AY-ser]
Latin name for the maple tree. The word also means sharp and is in reference to the hardness of the wood, which the Romans used for spear hafts.

acer, acris, acre [AY-ser, AY-kris, AY-kree]
Sharp; pungent. Used both in the sense of keen and in relation to taste.

Aceranthus [ay-ser-ANTH-us]
Maplewort. L. *Acer*, maple; Gr. *anthos*, a flower.

acerbus, -a, -um [as-ERB-us]
Bitter; sour. Also rough to touch.

acerifolius, -a, -um [ay-ser-i-FO-lius]
With leaves resembling maple.

aceroides [ay-ser-OY-deez]
Resembling maple.

acerosus, -a, -um [ay-ser-o-sus]
Chaffy; needlelike.

acetosa, acetosella [ay-se-TO-sa]
Pre-Linnaean names for common sorrel and other plants with acid leaves. From L. *acetum*, vinegar.

Achillea [ak-il-EE-a]
Yarrow or sneezewort. The Greek name honors Achilles, the heroic warrior of the Trojan wars. As a youth, he was taught the properties of this plant in healing wounds by his tutor Cheiron the Centaur who was half horse and half man. This useful piece of knowledge was highly regarded and was regularly applied in medicine until relatively recent times. Achilles himself had the good fortune to be almost entirely invulnerable—his mother, Thetis, having dipped him as a baby into the River Styx. As a result he was vulnerable only in the heel where his mother's forefinger and thumb had held him during the process of immersion. In the end, the god Apollo directed the arrow of Paris to this one spot and it proved fatal.

"Sneezewort" derives from the fact that since ancient times one common species *Achillea ptarmica* (Greek for sneeze-making) has been used as a kind of snuff.

achilleifolius, -a, -um [ak-ill-eye-FO-lius]
With leaves resembling *Achillea millefolium* or milfoil.

Achimines [ak-i-MEE-neez]
Gr. *a*, not; *cheimino,* to suffer from cold. This genus of tropical American herbs will not stand any chilling.

Achlys [AK-lis]
Deer-foot. Vanilla leaf. Named for a minor Greek goddess of hidden places—an allusion to the woodland habitat of this genus of perennial herbs.

Achras [AK-ras]
A tropical evergreen tree with edible fruit. Name of Greek derivation for a kind of wild pear and applied to the sapote or marmalade plum which has been described as "melting and has the sweet perfumes of honey, jasmine, and lily-of-the-valley."

acicularis, -is, -e [ay-sik-you-LAIR-is]
Shaped like a needle; needlelike.

aciculus, -a,-um [ay-SIK-you-lus]
Sharply pointed.

Acidanthera [as-id-AN-the-ra]
Gr. *akis,* a point; *anthera,* anthers. The flower of these cormous plants has pointed anthers.

acidissimus, -a, -um [as-id-ISS-im-us]
Very sour, indeed.

acidosus, -a, -um [as-id-O-sus]
Acid; sour.

acidus, -a, -um [ASS-id-us]
Acid; sour.

acinaceus, -a, -um [ass-in-AY-seus]
Shaped like a curved sword or scimitar.

acinacifolius, -a, -um [ass-in-ay-si-FO-lius]
With leaves shaped like a curved sword or scimitar.

acinaciformis, -is, -e [ass-in-ay-si-FORM-is]
Like a curved sword or scimitar.

Acineta [ass-in-EE-ta]
Gr. *akineta,* without movement, in reference to the immobile lip of the flower of these epiphytic orchids.

Ackama [ak-AY-ma]
Derivation not certain but probably from the trees' native antipodean name.

Acoelorraphe [as-ee-lo-RAFF-ee]
Saw cabbage palm of Florida. Derivation obscure.

Acokanthera [ak-o-KAN-the-ra]
Gr. *akis*, a spike; *anthera*, anthers. The anthers are pointed. Certain species of these shrubs and small trees are the source of deadly arrow poisons used by some African tribes.

aconitifolius, -a, -um [ak-on-eye-ti-FO-lius]
With leaves like aconite or monkshood.

Aconitum [ak-o-NY-tum]
The ancient Latin name for these poisonous herbs. The English names, aconite, monkshood, and wolf's-bane, are derived from the shape of the flower and the fact that the plant was supposed to keep away wolves. The leaves and roots of all species are the source of a strong alkaloid poison which has uses in pharmacy. Care must be taken on all occasions when handling the roots, which have sometimes been mistaken for horse-radish with disastrous results.

Acorus [AK-or-us]
Sweet flag. The Latin name. The root stocks yield the sweet-scented calamus root once much used in making cosmetics.

acre, -is [AY-kre]
Neuter and feminine of *acer* (*q.v.*).

Acrocomia [ak-ro-KO-mia]
Gr. *akron*, extremity; *kome*, a tuft of hair. The leaves of this tropical American feather palm are at the top of the stem.

Acronychia [ak-ro-NY-kia]
Gr. *akron*, extremity; *onux*, a claw. The points of the petals of these trees and shrubs are curved and look like claws.

acrostichoides [ak-ros-ti-KOY-deez]
Resembling *Achrostichum*, a tropical fern.

Actaea [ak-TEE-a]
Baneberry. Cohosh. Named by Linnaeus although this is the Latin for the elder, which the leaves resemble. The fruit is poisonous; hence the English name.

Actinidia [ak-tin-ID-ia]
From Gr. *actis*, a ray, in allusion to the styles of these climbing shrubs which radiate like the spokes of a wheel.

Actinophloeus [ak-tin-o-FLEE-us]
Australasian feather palms. From Gr. *actis*, ray; *phleos*, a reed; in allusion to the arrangement of the fronds.

Actinostrobus [ak-tin-o-sᴛʀo-bus]
From Gr. *aktis*, a ray; *strobos*, a cone; in reference to the structure of the cone scales on these shrubs.

acu- [ak-yew-]
In compound words signifying sharply pointed, thus:

aculeatus	prickly
aculeatissimus	very prickly
aculeolatus	with small prickles
acuminatus	tapering into a long narrow point
acuminatifolius	with leaves tapering quickly into long narrow points
acutifolius	with leaves tapering quickly into sharp points
acutilobus	with sharply pointed lobes
acutipetalus	with sharp pointed petals
acutus	with a sharp but not a tapering point
acutissimus	very acutely pointed

Adansonia [ad-an-so-nia]
Baobab or monkey-bread tree of Africa. Named in honor of a French botanist, Michel Adanson (1727-1806), who traveled extensively in that continent.
As a tree, the baobab is frequently a remarkable sight. Although seldom as much as forty feet in height it may be thirty feet in diameter at the bottom. With this enormous girth, so disproportionate to the height, it ranks as one of the largest trees in the world. Its appearance is often that of a huge bottle with a few branches with sparse leaves stuck into the top.

aden- [ad-en-]
Prefix which in compound Greek words signifies stickiness or what botanists describe as clammy. The word means gland and refers to the minute bodies common on several parts of many plants, sometimes making them very sticky indeed.

Adenanthera [ad-en-ᴀɴ-the-ra]
Red sandalwood tree of India. From Gr. *aden*, gland; *anthera*, anthers. The anthers are tipped with a gland. The red, lens-shaped seeds are used in necklaces.

Adenocarpus [ad-en-o-ᴋᴀʀ-pus]
From Gr. *aden*, gland; *karpos*, fruit. The pods of these shrubs are sticky.

Adenophora [ad-en-OFF-or-a]
Gland bellflower. From Gr. *aden,* gland; *phoreo,* to bear.
A sticky nectary surrounds the base of the style on these
perennial herbs.

adenophorus, -a, -um [ad-en-OFF-or-us]
Gland-bearing, generally in reference to a nectary.

adenophillus, -a, -um [ad-en-off-ILL-us]
Having sticky leaves.

adenopodus, -a, -um [ad-en-o-pod-us]
Having sticky pedicels.

adenostoma [ad-en-o-STO-ma]
Gr. *aden,* gland; *stoma,* mouth; in allusion to the glands at
the mouth of the calyx of these evergreen shrubs.

Adhatoda [ad-hat-o-da]
Latinized version of the native Brazilian name for these
shrubs.

adiantifolius, -a, -um [ad-i-ant-i-FO-lius]
Having leaves like *Adiantum* or maidenhair fern.

adiantoides [ad-i-ant-OY-deez]
Resembling *Adiantum* or maidenhair fern.

Adiantum [ad-i-ANT-um]
Maidenhair fern. Gr. *adiantos,* dry. So named because the
leaflets shed water in a remarkable way—if plunged into
water the fronds remain dry.

adlamii [AD-lam-my-i]
Species named for R. W. Adlam of Johannesburg who sent
South African plants to Kew Gardens in the 1890's.

Adlumia [ad-LUM-ia]
Climbing fumitory, Allegheny vine. Named for John Adlum
(1759-1836), a native of Pennsylvania and a well-known
grape breeder. In 1819 he put Catawba, the first great
American grape, on the market from his Georgetown, D. C.
nursery. It is still a leading American grape for both wine
and table.

admirabilis, -is, -e [ad-mi-RAY-bil-is]
Noteworthy.

adnatus, -a, -um [ad-NAY-tus]
Adnate; joined together. Usually used in connection with
two unlike structures growing together naturally but in a
way which appears to be abnormal, such as a leaf growing
along a stem.

adonidifolius, -a, -um [ad-o-nid-i-ᴘᴏ-lius]
With leaves like *Adonis* or pheasant's-eye.

Adonis [ad-o-nis]
Pheasant's-eye. The Greek name.
The flower is supposed to have sprung from the blood of Adonis who was gored to death by a wild boar. He was beloved by Aphrodite and by some accounts was unsuccessfully wooed by her. Adonis was regarded by the Greeks as the god of plants. It was believed that he disappeared into the earth in autumn and winter only to reappear in spring and summer. To celebrate his return, the Greeks had the custom of making Adonis gardens, consisting of clay pots of quickly growing seeds which were set around his statue—the forerunner of much in modern custom, both horticultural and otherwise.

adpressus, -a, -um [ad-ᴘʀᴇss-us]
Adpressed or appressed; signifying the manner in which scales are pressed against a cone or certain leaves against a stem.

adscendens [ad-sᴇɴᴅ-ens]
Ascending; mounting, generally implies a somewhat gradual rise or upward curve from a nearly prostrate base.

adsurgens [ad-sᴇʀ-jens]
Rising erect; pushing straight upwards.

aduncus, -a, -um [ad-ᴜɴᴋ-us]
Hooked. The uncus was the hook used by Roman executioners to drag away the bodies of victims.

advenus, -a, -um [ad-ᴠᴇᴇ-nus]
Adventive; newly arrived; not native.

Aechmea [ᴇᴇᴋ-mea]
Gr., *aichme*, a point, in reference to the stiff points of the sepals of these epiphytic herbs.

aegeus, -a, -um [ᴇᴇ-jeus]
From the shores of the Aegean Sea and therefore of Greek origin.

Aegle [ᴇᴇɢ-le]
Bael fruit of India. Named for one of the naiads, those female divinities of Greek mythology who presided over springs, rivers, and lakes. The bael tree, sacred to the god Siva, is widely cultivated in India for its fruit which, besides being edible, is regarded as a specific against dysentery.

Aegopodium [ee-go-PO-dium]

Goutweed, bishopsweed. Gr. *aix*, a goat; *podion,* a foot; in allusion to the shape of the leaf. It was once thought to cure gout.

aegyptiacus, -a, -um [ee-jip-TY-ak-us]

Egyptian.

aemulus, -a, -um [EE-mew-lus]

Rivaling; imitating.

aeneus, -a, -um [EE-neus]

Of a bronze color.

Aeonium [ee-o-nium]

Latin name for one of this genus of succulents which some botanists feel should be classified under *Sempervivum.*

aequalis, -i, -e [ee-KWAY-lis]

Equal.

aequinoctialis, -is, -e [ee-kwi-nox-i-AY-lis]

Belonging to the equinoctial zone; from the equatorial regions.

aequitrilobus, -a, -um [ee-kwi-try-LO-bus]

With three equal lobes.

Aerangis [air-ANG-gis]

Gr. *aer,* air; *aggeion,* a vessel. These orchids are epiphytes, which are sometimes called air plants or tree perchers. They draw their sustenance from the air and are quite capable of growing on such unlikely hosts as telephone wires. They are parasites only to the extent that all they steal from their hosts is a growth site. They are common in the tropics.

Aerides [AIR-id-eez]

From Gr. *aer,* air. These orchids are epiphytes.

aerius, -a, -um [AIR-ius]

Lofty.

aeruginosus, -a, -um [air-roo-jin-o-sus]

Rust-colored.

Aerva [AIR-va]

From the Arabic name of the plant.

Aesculus [EES-kew-lus]

Horse-chestnut, buckeye. The Latin name for a kind of oak bearing edible nuts but taken by Linnaeus for this genus.

aestivalis, -is, -e [eest-iv-AY-lis]

Pertaining to summer.

aestivus, -a, -um [ee-STY-vus]
Ripening or developing in summer.

Aethionema [ee-thi-o-NEE-ma]
Stone cress. Gr. *aitho*, to scorch; *nema*, a thread. Possibly in allusion to the brown color of the stamens in some of the species of these shrubby herbs.

aethiopicus, -a, -um [ee-thi-o-pik-us]
African.

afer, afra, afrum [AFF-er]
From the North African coast (Algeria, Tunis, etc.)

affinis, -is, -e [af-FY-nis]
Related or similar to.

africanus, -a, -um [aff-rik-AY-nus]
African.

Agapanthus [ag-a-PAN-thus]
African lily. Lily-of-the-Nile. From Gr. *agape*, love; *anthos*, a flower.

Agaricus [ag-GAIR-ik-us]
Old generic name for field and other mushrooms many of which are now reclassified in other genera.

Agastache [ag-as-TAY-ke]
Gr., *agan*, very much; *stachys*, an ear of wheat; in reference to the form of the many flower spikes of these perennial herbs.

agastus, -a, -um [ag-AST-us]
Charming.

Agathis [AG-a-this]
Dammar or kauri pine. Gr. *agathis*, a ball of thread; from the appearance of the catkin on the female trees. The dammar pine is the source of gum dammar or copal used in the manufacture of varnish.

Agathosma [ag-ath-os-ma]
From Gr. *agathos*, good; *osma*, fragrance. Some of the species of these evergreen shrubs are aromatic.

Agave [ag-AH-ve]
Century plant, sisal. Gr. *agauos*, admirable, in allusion to the splendid appearance of the plants in flower. These plants are used for rope and fiber. They are also the source of both tequila and pulque, the distilled and fermented liquors much appreciated in Mexico. The cloudiness in the latter is an important source of vitamins.

agavoides [ag-av-OY-deez]
Resembling *Agave.*

ageratifolius, -a, -um [aj-er-ay-ti-FO-lius]
With leaves like *Ageratum.*

ageratoides [aj-er-ay-TOI-deez]
Like *Ageratum.*

Ageratum [aj-er-AY-tum]
Gr. *a,* not; *geras,* old age; presumably because the flowers of these annuals or perennials retain their clear color for a long time.

agetus, -a, -um [aj-EE-tus]
Wonderful.

aggregatus, -a, -um [ag-greg-AY-tus]
Aggregate; clustered in a dense mass. The raspberry and strawberry are aggregate fruits, being the massed product of several ovaries.

Aglaia [ag-LAY-ia]
Evergreen trees and shrubs named for one of three Graces because of the beauty and sweet scent of the flowers.

Aglaonema [ag-lay-o-NEE-ma]
Gr. *aglaos,* bright; *nema,* a thread. Probably from the bright color of the stamens of these foliage plants.

Agonis [ag-o-nis]
Gr. *agon,* a gathering or a collection, in allusion to the number of the seeds on these Australian evergreen trees and shrubs.

agrarius, -a, -um [ag-RAY-rius]
Of the open fields.

agrestis, -is, -e [ag-REST-is]
Growing in the fields.

agrifolius, -a, -um [ag-rif-o-lius]
With rough or scabby leaves.

Agrimonia [ag-rim-o-nia]
Agrimony. From the Greek name *Argemone.* It yields a yellow dye. This herb is used in medicine as an astringent and tonic.

Agrostis [ag-ROS-tis]
Bent grass. The classical name for a kind of grass.

Aichryson [ay-CRY-son]
Classical Greek name for another plant than these herbs from the Canary Islands.

Ailanthus [ay-LAN-thus]
Tree-of-heaven. The Latinized version of the native Moluccan name for this tree.

aiolosalpinx [ee-o-lo-SAL-pinks]
Species name meaning the trumpet of Aeolus, the god of the winds.

Aiphanes [AY-fan-eez]
Gr. *aiphnes*, ragged or jagged. The leaves of these palms have jagged tips.

Aira [AY-ra]
Hair grass. From the classical Greek name for another plant.

aitchisonii [AITCH-iss-on-i-eye]
In honor of Dr. J. E. T. Aitchison (1836-1898), British physician and botanist who served with the delimitation commission in Afghanistan (1884-1885).

aizoides [ay-eye-ZOI-deez]
Like *Aizoon*, a genus related to the ice plants. Not of garden interests.

ajacis [aj-AY-kiss]
In honor of Ajax, the Greek hero who at the siege of Troy committed suicide in a fit of pique because the armor of Achilles was awarded to Odysseus. This is the species name of the rocket larkspur (*Delphinium ajacis*) because of the marks like shields on the petals.

ajanensis, -is, -e [aj-an-EN-sis]
From Ajan on the coast of Siberia.

Ajuga [aj-oo-ga]
Bugle. Gr. *a*, not; *zeugon*, yoke; an allusion to the fact that the calyx of these perennials is not divided and is in fact a single sepal.

Akebia [ak-EE-bia]
Latinized version of the Japanese name for these twining shrubs.

alabamensis, -is, -e [al-ab-am-EN-sis]
From the state of Alabama.

alatus, -a, -um [al-AY-tus]
Winged, e.g., the seed of the maple.

albanensis, -is, -e [al-ban-EN-sis]
From St. Albans in Hertfordshire, England.

alb-, albi-, albo-
In compound words signifying white, thus:

albescens	whitish
albicans	off-white
albicaulis	white-stemmed
albidus	white
albiflorus	white-flowered
albifrons	with white fronds
albiplenus	with double white flowers
albispinus	with white thorns
albocinctus	with a white crown or girdle
albomaculatus	spotted with white
albopictus	painted with white
albopilosus	with white hairs; shaggy white
albopleno	with double white flowers
albospicus	white spiked
albovariegatus	variegated with white
albulus	whitish

Albizzia [al-BIZZ-ia]
Pink siris. Nemu tree. In honor of the Albizzi, an old Tuscan family.

albus, -a, -um [AL-bus]
White.

Alchemilla [al-kem-ILL-a]
Lady's mantle. The Latinized version of the Arabic name, in allusion to the use of these herbs in alchemy.

alcicornis, -is, -e [al-sik-ORN-is]
Palmated like the horns of the European elk, called moose in America.

alcockianus, -a, -um [awl-kok-i-AY-nus]
In honor of Sir Rutherford Alcock (1809-1897), British consular official in China.

aldenhamensis, -is, -e [awl-den-ham-EN-sis]
Originated at Aldenham near London, once one of the great houses of England.

aleppicus, -a, -um [al-EP-ik-us]
Of Aleppo in Syria.

Aletris [AL-et-ris]
Greek word meaning the female slave who grinds the meal. The name refers to the powdered appearance of these herbs.

Aleurites [al-yew-RY-teez]
Gr. *aleuron*, floury. Some of the species appear to be dusted

with flour. The genus includes the Tung Oil or China Oil tree, the seed of which produces an oil valuable in making varnish and high-quality paint. A more recent use, at least as far as Western medicine is concerned, is the use of Tung Oil in treating leprosy.

aleuticus, -a, -um [al-YEW-tik-us]
Of the Aleutian Islands off the coast of Alaska.

alexandrae [al-ex-AND-ree]
Of Queen Alexandra, wife of Edward VII of England.

alexandrinus, -a, -um [al-ex-an-DRY-nus]
Of Alexandria in Egypt.

algeriensis, -is, -e [al-jeer-i-EN-sis]
Algerian.

algidus, -a, -um [al-JY-dus]
Cold; originating in high mountains.

alienus, -a, -um [ay-li-EEN-us]
Foreign.

Alisma [al-IZ-ma]
Water plantain. The classical Greek name for this plant.

Allamanda [al-am-AN-da]
In honor of Dr. J. N. S. Allamand of Leyden, Holland, who sent seeds of this climbing plant to Linnaeus.

alliaceus, -a, -um [al-ee-AY-sius]
Like onion or garlic in flavor or appearance.

alliariaefolius, -a, -um [al-i-air-ee-FO-lius]
With leaves like *Alliaria,* a plant of practically no gardening interest.

Allionia [al-li-o-nia]
A North American herb named in honor of Carlo Allioni (1705-1804), Italian botanist.

Allium [AL-lium]
Onion, chive, and garlic. From the classical Latin name for garlic. The whole group was prized by the ancients as possessing medicinal and aphrodisiac qualities as well as flavor.

Alloplectus [al-o-PLEK-tus]
Gr. *allos,* diverse; *pleco,* to plait. The allusion is to the appearance of the calyx of these evergreen shrubs, which seems to be plaited in a complicated pattern.

alnifolius, -a, -um [al-ni-FO-lius]
With leaves like the alder.

Alnus [AL-nus]
Alder. The classical Latin name.

Alocasia [al-o-KAY-sia]
An unexplained variant of *Colocasia*, the name of a closely allied genus. Both of these foliage plants are very closely related to the genus *Caladium*.

Aloe [AL-lo, preferably al-o-ee]
From the Arabic name of these perennial succulents.

aloides (sometimes **alooides**) [al-OY-deez, al-o-OY-deez]
Aloe-like.

aloifolius, -a, -um [al-o-i-FO-lius]
With leaves like an aloe.

Alonsoa [al-on-ZO-a]
Mask-flower. Andean plants named in honor of Alonzo Sanoni, Secretary of State of Columbia when it was a Spanish colony in the 18th century.

Alopecurus [al-o-pek-YEW-rus]
Lamb's tail grass. Meadow foxtail. Gr. *alopekouros*, a fox's tail.

alpestris, -is, -e [al-PEST-ris]
Of the lower mountains, with the implication of coming from below timber line, although not invariably.

Alphitonia [al-fit-o-nia]
From Gr. *alphiton*, barley meal, in reference to the dry, mealy quality of the fruit pulp or mesocarp of these tall trees.

alpicola [al-pik-o-la]
Dwelling in high mountains.

alpigenus, -a, -um [al-pij-EN-us]
Originating in the mountains.

Alpinia [al-PIN-ia]
Perennial tropical herbs, named in honor of Prosper Alpino (1553-1616), Italian botanist.

alpinus, -a, -um [al-PY-nus]
Alpine; from high mountains above timber line.

Alseuosma [al-su-OS-ma]
Gr. *alsos*, a grove; *euosmos*, fragrant. The flowers of these shrubs are strongly fragrant.

Alsophila [al-SOFF-ill-a]
Gr. *alsos*, a grove; *philos*, loving. They are shade-loving tree ferns.

Alstonia [al-STO-nia]
Evergreen shrubs or trees with milky juice, named in honor of Dr. Charles Alston (1685-1760), Professor of Botany, Edinburgh University, 1716-1760.

Alstroemeria [al-stree-MEER-ia]
Peruvian lily. In honor of Baron Claus Alstroemer (1736-1794), a friend of Linnaeus.

altaicus, -a, -um [al-TAY-kus]
From the Altai Mountains in Mongolia.

alternans [AL-ter-nans]
Alternating.

Alternanthera [al-ter-nan-THEE-ra]
Joy-weed. L. *alternans*, alternating; Gr. *anthera*, anthers. Alternate anthers in this genus of colored-leaved perennials are barren.

alternifolius, -a, -um [al-ter-ni-FO-lius]
Having alternate leaves; the leaves on each side of a stem not opposite to each other.

alternus, -a, -um [al-TERN-us]
Alternate; not opposite.

Althaea [al-THEE-a]
Hollyhock. Gr. *althaia*, a cure, something that heals; in allusion to the use of some species in medicine.

althaeoides [al-thee-OY-deez]
Resembling hollyhock.

altifrons [AL-ti-frons]
Having tall fronds or foliage.

altissimus, -a, -um [al-TISS-im-us]
Very tall; tallest.

altus, -a, -um [AL-tus]
Tall.

alulatus, -a, -um [al-yew-LAY-tus]
Small or narrow-winged.

Alyssum [al-LISS-um]
Madwort. From Gr. *a*, not or against; *lyssa*, rage or madness. This herb was one regarded as a specific against madness and the bites of mad dogs.

Alyxia [al-IX-ia]
Latinized version of the East Indian vernacular name for these glabrous shrubs.

amabilis, -is, -e [am-AB-ill-is]
Lovely.

amaranthoides [am-a-ranth-OY-deez]
Resembling amaranth.

Amaranthus [am-ar-ANTH-us]
Love-lies-bleeding. From Gr. *amarantos*, unfading. The flowers of some of the species of these annuals retain their color for a long time in the manner of everlastings.

amaranticolor [am-ar-an-TIK-ol-or]
Color of amaranth or purple.

Amarcrinum [am-ar-CRY-num]
From a contraction of *Amaryllis* and *Crinum*, this being a hybrid of these two. The earlier and more correct name is *Crinodonna*.

amaricaulis, -is, -e [am-ar-ik-AWL-is]
Having a bitter-tasting stem.

amarella [am-ar-ELL-a]
Bitter.

amarus, -a, -um [am-AY-rus]
Bitter.

Amaryllis [am-ar-ILL-is]
Showy, bulbous plants, given this girl's name, a favorite in classical poetry and equally irresistible to the English pastoral poets of the 17th and 18th centuries.

Amasonia [am-as-o-nia]
Tropical American sub-shrubs, named in honor of Thomas Amason, a traveler in America in colonial days.

amazonicus, -a, -um [am-az-ON-ik-us]
From the region of the Amazon River.

ambiguus, -a, -um [am-big-YEW-us]
Uncertain; doubtful.

amboynensis, -is, -e [am-boy-NEN-sis]
From the island of Amboina in the Malayan archipelago.

Ambrosia [am-BRO-sia]
Of excellent flavor. In ancient mythology, ambrosia was the substance which, with nectar, provided the food and drink of the gods, making immortal those who partook of them. Now the generic name of some weedy herbs.

ambrosioides [am-bro-si-OY-deez]
Resembling *Ambrosia*, a genus which includes ragweed and which is of no garden interest.

Amelanchier [am-el-ANK-ier]
June berry; shadbush or shadblow. (These small trees and shrubs bloom when the shad are running.) From *amelancier*, the French Provençal name of one of the species. It is also called "sarvis" or "servis berry" from its resemblance to the service, a forgotten English fruit rather like a pear which was eaten overripe like a medlar.

amelloides [am-ell-OY-deez]
Resembling *Amellus*, a genus of no gardening interest.

amellus [am-ELL-us]
Species name of an aster, named after the river Mellus, near Rome, where a plant like it grew in classical times.

americanus, -a, -um [am-er-ik-AY-nus]
From America, North or South.

amesianus, -a, -um [aims-i-AY-nus]
In honor of two members of the Ames family of Boston. Frederick Lothrop Ames (1835-1893) was a well-known horticulturalist and amateur grower of orchids. Oakes Ames (1874-1950) was Supervisor of the Arnold Arboretum and Professor of Botany at Harvard. His teaching of economic botany was deeply interesting to generations of students. On his death he left his orchid herbarium of 64,000 specimens to Harvard.

amethystinus, -a, -um [am-e-THIS-tin-us]
Violet-colored.

Amherstia [am-HERST-ia]
A handsome flowering tree, native to India, named after the Countess Amherst (d. 1838), wife of the Earl who took Clarke Abel (for whom *Abelia* was named) on his mission to Peking (1816) and who later became Governor-General in India. An amateur botanist, she collected plants on her travels.

Amicia [am-ITCH-ia]
In honor of Jean Baptiste Amici, Italian scientist of the early 19th century.

amicorum [am-my-KOR-um]
Of the Friendly or Tonga Islands in the South Pacific.

Ammobium [am-o-bium]
Winged everlasting. Gr. *ammos*, sand; *bio*, to live; in reference to the native habitat of these Australian annuals and perennials.

Ammocharis [am-OCK-ar-is]
Gr. *ammos,* sand; *charis,* beauty; an allusion both to the habitat and to the quality of these bulbous plants.

Ammophila [am-OFF-ill-a]
Beach or Marram grass. Gr. *ammos,* sand; *philos,* loving.

ammophilus, -a, -um [am-OFF-ill-us]
Sand-loving.

amoenus, -a, -um [am-EEN-us]
Pleasant; delightful.

Amomum [am-o-mum]
From the East Indian vernacular name for these herbs. *A. cardamon* is not true cardamon but provides a cheap and fairly acceptable substitute.

Amorpha [am-OR-fa]
False indigo. Gr. *amorphos,* shapeless or deformed; in allusion to the small imperfectly developed flowers of these shrubs.

Amorphophallus [am-or-fo-FAL-us]
Gr. *amorphos,* shapeless or deformed; plus *phallus;* in allusion to the form and shape of the tubers of these herbs.

Ampelopsis [am-pel-OP-sis]
Pepper vine. Gr. *ampelos,* a vine; *opsis,* likeness. It looks like and is closely related to the grape vine.

amphibius, -a, -um [am-FIB-ius]
Growing both in water and on land; amphibious.

Amphicome [am-fik-o-me]
Gr. *amphi,* both; *kome,* a head of hair. The seeds of these herbaceous plants have a hairy tuft at each end.

amplexicaulis, -is, -e [am-plex-ik-AW-lis]
Stem-clasping.

amplexifolius, -a, -um [am-plex-i-FO-lius]
Leaf-clasping.

ampliatus, -a, -um [am-pli-AY-tus]
Enlarged.

amplissimus, -a, -um [amp-LISS-im-us]
Very large.

amplus, -a, -um [AMP-lus]
Large.

Amsonia [am-SO-nia]
Blue-flowered herbaceous perennials named in honor of Dr. Charles Amson, 18th-century Virginia physician.

amurensis, -is, -e [am-oor-EN-sis]
From the area of the Amur River which forms the boundary
between Manchuria and Soviet Russia in eastern Asia.

amygdaliformis, -is, -e [am-ig-dal-i-FORM-is]
Shaped like an almond.

amygdalinus, -a, -um [am-ig-dal-EYE-nus]
Almond-like.

amygdaloides [am-ig-dal-OY-deez]
Resembling almond.

Amygdalus [am-IG-dal-us]
Greek name for almond, but now generally classified under
Prunus.

Anacampseros [an-a-KAMP-ser-os]
Gr. *anakampto,* to cause to return; *eros,* love. Some of
these African plants are considered to be the effective ingredient in love potions.

anacanthus, -a, -um [an-ak-ANTH-us]
Without thorns.

anacardioides [an-a-kar-di-OY-deez]
Resembling the cashew or *Anacardium.*

Anacardium [an-a-KARD-ium]
Cashew nut. The origin of the word is doubtful although
it is suggested that it may be connected with the Greek
kardia, meaning a heart, in allusion to the shape of the
cashew apple which bears the nut. There is a poisonous
oil in the shell which makes harvesting disagreeable. The
nut itself must be roasted before it can be eaten. The wood
yields a gum used in making varnish.

Anacharis [an-a-KAIR-is]
Gr. *ana,* without; *charis,* beauty. A family of North American water plants whose principal importance is to act as
oxygenators in aquaria and to provide shelter for young fish.

Anagallis [an-a-GAL-is]
Gr. *anagelao,* to delight. The genus of low herbs includes
scarlet pimpernel or poor man's weather glass. So called because it opens only in fine weather.

Ananas [an-NAN-as]
Pineapple. From the South American Indian name. Many
languages use this or some related form of this word.

Anaphalis [an-AFF-al-is]
Pearly everlasting. From the classical Greek name for another of the everlastings.

Anastatica [an-as-TAT-ik-a]
Rose of Jericho, resurrection plant. From Gr. *anastasis*, resurrection, in allusion to the fact that no matter how dry it may have become, the plant recovers its shape on being placed in water.

anatolicus, -a, -um [an-at-o-lik-us]
From Anatolia, a province of Turkey in Asia Minor.

anceps [AN-seps]
Two-headed, implying more than one stem.

Anchusa [an-KOO-sa]
Bugloss, alkanet. From Gr. *ankousa*, cosmetic paint. Some species of these plants can be used to make rouge.

andicolus, -a, -um [an-DIK-o-lus]
Native of the Andes.

andinus, -a, -um [an-DY-nus]
Belonging to the Andes.

Andira [an-DY-ra]
Cabbage tree. The Latinized form of the Brazilian name for these ornamental evergreen trees.

androgynous [an-DROG-in-us]
Having both male and female flowers separate but on the same spike; hermaphrodite.

Andromeda [an-DROM-ed-a]
Bog rosemary. Named after the mythological maiden who was chained to a rock as an offering to the sea monster and who was rescued by Perseus. The name has been used at various times for a confusing variety of plants. Today, among the plants wrongly so called in some nursery catalogues and by gardeners are *Pieris japonica, Pieris floribunda, Enkianthus, Gaultheria,* and *Leucothoë.*

Andropogon [an-dro-PO-gon]
Beard grass. From Gr. *aner,* a man; *pogon,* a beard; in reference to the hairs on the spikelets of some species of these grasses.

Androsace [an-DROSS-as-ee]
Rock jasmine. From Gr. *aner,* a man; *sakos,* a shield; from the resemblance of the anther to a shield.

androsaemifolius, -a, -um [an-dro-SEEM-i-fo-lius]
With leaves like *Androsaemum,* an old generic name of *Androsace.*

androsaemum [an-dro-SEE-mum]
With sap the color of blood.

Androstephium [an-dro-STEE-fium]
Gr. *aner*, man; *stephanos*, a crown. The stamens form a corona or crown within the flower of these bulbous plants.

Anemone [correctly, an-em-o-ne; popularly, an-EM-on-e]
Gr. *anemos*, wind, the classical Greek name exactly approximating the English name of wind flower. There was an old belief that it would bloom only when the wind blew. In Greek mythology, Anemone was the name of the daughter of the winds.

anemoneflorus, -a, -um [an-em-o-ne-FLOW-rus]
Anemone-flowered.

Anemonella [an-em-o-NELL-a]
Diminutive of *Anemone*, from which the plant differs only technically.

Anemonopsis [an-em-o-NOP-sis]
From Gr. *anemos*, wind; *opsis*, like or similar to; because of this perennial's resemblance to *Anemone*.

Anemopaegma [an-em-o-PEEG-ma]
From Gr. *anemos*, wind; *paigma*, sport. These are rampant climbing shrubs.

Anemopsis [an-em-OP-sis]
From Gr. *anemos*, wind; *opsis*, similar to; from a resembalance of the flower to *Anemone* in this aquatic herb.

Anethum [an-EE-thum]
Greek name for dill. Best known in pickles, dill seeds are also used in making gin and in pharmacy.

anfractuosus, -a, -um [an-frak-tew-o-sus]
Bent; twisted.

Angelica [an-JELL-ik-a]
So named on account of its supposed angelic qualities in medicine. This showy herb was regarded as an aphrodisiac, a specific against plague, an antidote to poisons, and the root, chewed, protected against witches. Deep green in color, the candied stalks of *A. archangelica* have a delectable and unusual flavor more appreciated by Europeans than by Americans.

Angelonia [an-JELL-o-nia]
Latinized version of the South American vernacular name of one of the species of these perennial herbs and sub-shrubs.

anglicus, -a, -um [ANG-lik-us]
From England; English.

Angiopteris [an-ji-OP-ter-is]
Gr. *aggeion,* a vessel; *pteros,* a wing; in allusion to the form of the receptacle in which the spores of these ferns are produced.

Angophora [ang-OFF-or-a]
Gum myrtle. From Gr. *aggeion,* a vessel; *phoreo,* to carry; in allusion to the form of the fruit of these Australian trees and shrubs.

Angraecum [an-GREE-kum]
Latinized version of the Malayan name (*angurek*) for air plants. Now the name of a large genus at epiphytic orchids.

anquicidus [an-qwi-SY-dus]
Snake-killing.

anguina [an-GWI-na]
Serpentine.

angularis, -is, -e [ang-gew-LAY-ris]
angulatus, -a, -um [ang-gew-LAY-tus]
Angular.

angulidens [an-GEW-lid-ens]
Having hooked teeth.

anguligerus [an-gew-LIJ-er-us]
Having hooks.

angulizans [an-GEW-liz-ans]
Hooked.

angulosus, -a, -um [an-gew-LO-sus]
Full of corners; many-angled.

Anguloa [an-gew-LO-a]
Terrestrial orchids named in honor of Don Francisco de Angulo, Spanish botanist of the latter part of the 18th century.

angustifolius, -a, -um [an-gus-ti-FO-lius]
Having narrow leaves.

angustus, -a, -um [an-GUS-tus]
angustatus, -a, -um [an-gus-TAY-tus]
Narrow.

anguria [an-GEW-ria]
A specific name derived from the Greek for a cucumber.

Anigozanthus [an-eye-go-ZAN-thus]
Kangaroo's paw. Australian sword lily. Gr. *anoigo,* to open; *anthos,* a flower. The petals of these perennials flare open almost to the base.

anisatus, -a, -um [an-is-AY-tus]
Anise-scented.

anisodorus, -a, -um [an-is-o-DOR-us]
Anise-scented.

anisophyllus, -a, -um [an-eye-so-FILL-us]
With unequal leaves, generally implying one of a pair of opposite leaves much larger than the other.

Anisotome [an-eye-so-to-me]
Gr. *anisos,* unequal; *tome,* cut; in allusion to the manner in which the edges of the leaves are cut on these New Zealand herbaceous plants.

anisum [an-EYE-sum]
The old name as well as the species name for anise *(Pimpinella anisum),* much used for flavoring in various condiments, sweets, medicines, and liqueurs to say nothing of providing a distinctive scent for fox and other hounds to follow in drag-hunting. The leaves are said to remove freckles.

annamensis, -is, -e [an-am-EN-sis]
Of Annam in southeastern Asia.

Annona [an-o-na]
Latinized version of the vernacular name for the *Cherimoya,* soursop or custard-apple.

annularis, -is, -e [an-yew-LAIR-us]
Ring-shaped.

annulatus, -a, -um [an-yew-LAY-tus]
Furnished with rings.

annuus, -a, -um [AN-yew-us]
Annual.

Anoda [an-o-da]
L. *anodus,* without a knot or joint; in allusion to the lack of a node on the pedicel of these herbs and sub-shrubs.

anomalus, -a, -um [an-OM-al-us]
Deviating from the normal in the light of related plants.

anopetalus, -a, -um [an-o-PET-al-us]
With erect petals.

Anopteris [an-OP-ter-is]
From Gr. *ana*, upward; *pteron*, a wing; in allusion to the appearance of the flap, or indusium, over the sori or spore-producing part of this fern.

anosmus, -a, -um [an-OS-mus]
Lacking scent.

Ansellia [an-SEL-ia]
Epiphytic orchids named in honor of Ansell, a 19th-century English botanist of the Chiswick Gardens of the Royal Horticultural Society who accompanied an expedition (1841-1842) to the river Niger in Africa.

antarcticus, -a, -um [ant-ARK-tik-us]
Of the South Polar regions.

Antennaria [an-ten-AY-ria]
Everlasting. Pussy's toes. L. *antenna*, literally, the yard of a sailing ship. The pappus of the flower of these silvery leaved plants is supposed to look like the antennae of a butterfly.

Anthemis [AN-them-is]
Chamomile. Also spelled camomile. Mayweed. From Gr. *chamos*, ground; *melos*, apple. The foliage is strongly scented. *Anthemis* is the Greek name for this plant which has a long history, as a flavoring herb and, in medicine, where known for its bitter and tonic properties, with chamomile tea an old household remedy. The Elizabethans used chamomile (*A. nobilis*) in lawns, and it is used occasionally for this purpose in England today. It stands mowing and produces a strong turf with a characteristic odor provided the climate is not too dry.

anthemoides [an-them-OY-deez]
Resembling chamomile.

Anthericum [an-THER-ik-um]
St. Bernard's lily. From Gr. *anthos*, a flower; *kerkos*, a hedge; in allusion to the tall flower stems of these herbs.

anthocrene [an-tho-KREE-ne]
Flower fountain.

Antholyza [an-tho-LY-za]
Gr. *anthos*, flower; *lyssa*, rage. The opened flower of these cormous plants looks like the mouth of an angry animal.

Anthoxanthum [an-thox-ANTH-um]
Sweet vernal grass. From Gr. *anthos*, a flower; *xanthos*,

yellow; in allusion to the yellow of the spikelets when ripe.

Anthriscus [an-THRIS-kus]
Salad chervil. From the Latin name for another unidentified plant.

Anthurium [an-THOO-rium]
Flamingo flower. From Gr. *anthos,* a flower; *oura,* a tail; in allusion to the prominent spadix of these foliage plants.

anthyllidifolius, -a, -um [an-thill-id-i-FO-lius]
With leaves like woundwort or ladies' fingers.

Anthyllis [an-THILL-is]
Kidney vetch. Woundwort. Ladies' fingers. The ancient Greek name. This herb once had a place in medicine as a vulnerary.

Antiaris [an-ti-AY-ris]
Upas tree of the East Indies. From the Javanese word for the immensely poisonous juice of the tree which is used as an arrow poison. There is a fabulous legend that it is deadly merely to sleep in the shade of the upas tree.

Antidesma [an-ti-DESS-ma]
Gr. *anti,* like; *desmos,* a band or ligament. The bark of these trees is used for cordage.

Antigonon [an-TIG-o-non]
Coral vine. From Gr. *anti,* like; *gonia,* an angle; in allusion to the growth habit of the stem which takes a series of rather sharp angles.

antillanus, -a, -um [an-til-AY-nus]
 antilleris, -is, -e [an-til-AY-ris]
Of the Antilles, the two groups of islands (Greater and Lesser) which comprise the West Indies.

antipodus, -a, -um [an-TIP-o-dus]
Of the Antipodes.

antiquorum [an-tik-KWOR-um]
Of the ancients.

antiquus, -a, -um [an-TIK-wus]
Ancient, antique.

antirrhiniflorus, -a, -um [an-ti-ry-ni-FLO-rus]
With flowers resembling snapdragon.

antirrhinoides [an-ti-ry-NOY-deez]
Resembling snapdragon.

Antirrhinum [an-ti-RY-num]
Snapdragon. From Gr. *anti,* like; *rhis,* a nose or snout. This

is an allusion to the appearance of the flower, which looks like a snouted dragon. The mouth can be made to open very satisfactorily by gently pinching the sides of the corolla.

anulatus, -a, -um [an-yew-LAY-tus]
Ringed. The original correct spelling. Now with two n's.

apenninus, -a, -um [ap-en-NY-nus]
Of the Apennine Mountains in central Italy.

apertus, -a, -um [ap-ERT-us]
Exposed; bare; open.

apetalus, -a, -um [a-PET-al-us]
Without petals.

Aphanostephus [aff-an-os-tef-us]
Gr. *aphanes*, inconspicuous; *stephanos*, a crown; from the small size of the flower heads of these herbs.

Aphelandra [aff-el-AND-ra]
Gr. *apheles*, simple; *aner*, male; an allusion to the fact that the anthers of these flowering shrubs and herbs are one-celled.

aphyllus, -a, -um [a-FILL-us]
Without leaves or apparently so.

apiatus, -a, -um [ap-i-AY-tus]
Beelike.

apicatus, -a, -um [ay-pik-AY-tus]
Tipped with a sharp point.

apiculatus, -a, -um [ay-pik-yew-LAY-tus]
Terminating abruptly in a short and often sharp point.

apiferus, -a, -um [ay-PIFF-er-us]
Literally, bee-bearing. Species name of *Ophrys apifera*, the bee orchid, the labellum of whose flower so resembles a bee that drones attempt copulation.

apiifolius, -a, -um [a-pi-eye-FO-lius]
Having leaves like celery (*Apium*).

Apios [AY-pios]
Potato-bean. Groundnut. Gr. *apion*, a pear; from the shape of the tubers which were eaten sometimes by North American Indians.

Apium [AY-pium]
Celery. The classical Latin name for parsley, from Gr. *apon*, water; in reference to what was regarded as the plant's natural habitat.

38

Aplectrum [ay-PLEK-trum]
Adam and Eve. Puttyroot. Gr. *a,* without; *plektron,* a spur.
The flower of this small North American terrestrial orchid
has no spur.

Apocynum [ap-oss-in-um]
Dogbane. The classical Greek name for this or a related
plant. From *apo,* away; *kyon,* a dog. Supposed to have been
poisonous to dogs. The root of one species, *A. canabinum*
(Choctaw root or Indian hemp) furnishes an emetic and
cathartic.

apodus, -a, -um [AP-o-dus]
Having flowers without a stalk.

Apogon [ap-o-gon]
From Gr. *a,* not; *pogon,* a beard; applied to the genus of
beardless irises.

Aponogeton [ap-o-no-JEE-ton]
Cape pondweed. Derivation uncertain but may come from
the Latin name of a town in Italy, Aquae Aponi (now
Abano), plus *geiton,* a neighbor. It is found in the surrounding marshes.

Aporocactus [ap-or-o-KAK-tus]
Rat-tail cactus. From the Greek, meaning impenetrable
cactus.

appendiculatus, -a, -um [ap-en-dik-yew-LAY-tus]
Having appendages, such as a crown, crest, or hairs.

applanatus, -a, -um [ap-lan-AY-tus]
Flattened out.

Apple
All domestic apples are varieties of the species *Malus
pumila,* a crab with very wide distribution—growing wild
from Norway to the Himalayas and from Asia to Spain. It
is true that there may have been some minor intervention
of other species (such as *M. prunifolia* or *M. sylvestris*) but
for practical purposes apples have been developed over
centuries of cultivation and selection from the one species.
Over the years innumerable varieties have been brought
into cultivation—several thousand in the United States
alone. The majority have been discarded as better and
more productive sorts have come on the scene. But around
the world in both temperate zones apple varieties are grown
in great numbers. While this is in part the result of local

taste and custom, relatively small differences in climate, soil, and elevation materially affect both quality and fruit production.

Existing varieties must be propagated by vegetative means —nursery stock generally by budding or, otherwise, by grafting. The odds are enormously against any seedling resembling the parent tree. In fact, the chances are against its being of any real value at all. Thus, while new varieties are generally the result of careful selection in a deliberate and planned attempt to combine the good qualities of both parents the grower is almost inevitably faced with the frustrations of having to discard possibly hundreds of seedling trees before one can be found which might be worth a further try.

A great many of today's best apples are of known parentage and are the result of careful selection and roguing. There still remain, however, quite a large number of admirable varieties which were discovered first as more or less chance seedlings and which have stood the test of time. Among the oldest of apples in America is the Sweet Rhode Island Greening. The first named variety in America, it was introduced by the Reverend William Blaxton around 1640 as Blaxton's Yellow Sweeting. Blaxton originally planted an orchard in Boston around 1625, approximately at what is now the corner of Beacon and Charles Streets. One of the best gardeners of his day, he also trained a bull to the saddle and used it to ride around Boston on his daily business.

Among other American apples, Rhode Island Greening appeared around 1748 at a Rhode Island village now known as Green's End. The tree was killed by being stripped of scions for grafting purposes. The Baldwin arrived as a chance seedling soon after 1740 on the farm of John Ball of Wilmington, Massachusetts, where it was originally known as Woodpecker or Butters. It was brought to the notice of Colonel Loammi Baldwin who introduced it widely about 1784. Similarly, McIntosh was found as a wild seedling on the Ontario farm of John McIntosh in 1796 and rapidly spread from there.

Green Newtown, which originated along the Hudson, was sent to England by Benjamin Franklin in 1759. It is seldom seen today in Eastern markets which are dominated by color and size at the expense of flavor and other qualities. It is exported in considerable quantity to England where people seem to be prepared to sacrifice appearance to quality. In fact, the distinctions, so carefully drawn in England, of dessert, cooking, and cider apples are hardly known in America and certainly the terms are quite unfamiliar. This may account in part for the insipid flavor (save the heresy) of most American apple pies.

In the English West Country there are cider-apple varieties which are known to have been in cultivation for six or seven centuries. Of the cookers, Bramley's seedling has been estimated to account for about 75 per cent of the apples in that category. It seems to have been raised from one of several pips sown by a Miss Brailsford in a flower pot and later planted in the garden of Matthew Bramley, a Nottinghamshire innkeeper and butcher, about 1850.

Ribston Pippin appears to be the sole survivor of a planting of apple pips brought from Normandy to England about 1688. The original tree is known to have lived for possibly 240 years. It was finally blown down in 1928.

That most delectable of all English eating apples, Cox's Orange Pippin, originated in 1830, probably as a pip from Ribston Pippin. Richard Cox was a brewer of Bermondsey who retired to Colnbrook where the apple was grown.

The word "seedling" in the name of an apple is understood generally to mean that the apple appeared more or less by chance—either volunteered or as one from an unknown source. "Pippin" and "Pearmain" merely mean a kind of apple and their inclusion in any varietal name is largely decoration.

appressus, -a, -um [ap-RESS-us]
Pressed close to; lying flat against, as some leaves against a stem or the scales of a fir cone.

apricus, -a, -um [AP-rik-us]
Sun-loving; open to the sun.

apterus, -a, -um [AP-ter-us]
Wingless.

aquaticus, -a, -um [ak-WAT-ik-us]
  aquatalis, -is, -e [ak-WAT-al-is]
Growing in or near water.

Aquifolium [ak-kwi-FO-lium]
Classical name for holly, now under the genus *Ilex*.

Aquilegia [ak-wil-EE-jia]
Columbine. From L. *aquila,* an eagle, from the form of the petals. The English name is also in allusion to the form of the flower which has the appearance of doves (L. *columba*) drinking—especially the short spurred varieties of these perennial herbs.

aquilegifolius, -a, -um [ak-wil-ee-ji-FO-lius]
With leaves like columbine.

aquilinus, -a, -um [ak-wil-LY-nus]
Eaglelike; aquiline.

arabicus, -a, -um [a-RAB-ik-us]
arabus, -a, -um [A-rab-us]
Of Arabia.

Arabis [a-RAB-is]
Rock-cress. From L. *Arabia,* where some species of these herbs originated, although none of the garden ones.

Arachis [a-RAK-is]
Peanut, groundnut, monkeynut. Gr. *a,* without; *rachis,* a branch, of uncertain application here. One of the most valuable oil seeds. After flowering, the stalks bend down forcing the fruits into the soil where they develop and ripen.

Arachnanthe [a-rak-NAN-the]
Gr. *arachnis,* a spider, *anthos,* a flower; from the shape of the flower of these orchids.

arachnoides [a-rak-NOY-deez]
arachnoideus, -a, -um [a-rak-NOY-deus]
Covered with hairs giving the appearance of a spider's web.

aragoanus, -a, -um [a-rag-o-AY-nus]
In honor of J. E. V. Arago (1790-1855), French botanist who accompanied Admiral de Freycinet in his explorations, 1817-1820.

aragonensis, -is, -e [a-rag-on-EN-sis]
From the province of Aragon in northeastern Spain.

Aralia [a-RAIL-ia]
Derivation of the name of these herbs, shrubs, and trees is unknown. The genus includes wild sarsaparilla.

araliaefolius, -a, -um [a-ray-li-ee-FO-lius]
With leaves like *Aralia*.

araucana [a-raw-KAY-na]
The name both of a district and of an Indian tribe in southern Chile where the monkey-puzzle tree was discovered.

Araucaria [a-raw-KAY-ria]
Monkey-puzzle tree. Derived from the district in Chile where one species was first found.

Araujia [a-RAW-jia]
From the Brazilian vernacular name of these vines.

arborescens [ar-bor-ESS-ens]
arboreus, -a, -um [ar-BOR-eus]
Tending to be woody; growing in treelike form.

arbor-tristis, -is, -e [ar-bor-TRIST-is]
Grayish in color. Literally, sad tree.

arbusculus, -a, -um [ar-BUSS-kew-lus]
Resembling a small tree.

arbutifolius, -a, -um [ar-bew-ti-FO-lius]
Having leaves like *Arbutus*.

Arbutus [AR-bew-tus; popularly, ar-BEW-tus]
Strawberry tree. The Latin name. Mayflower (*Epigaea repens*) is often popularly called trailing arbutus.

Archontophoenix [ar-kon-to-FEE-nix]
Gr. *archontos*, a chieftain; *Phoenix*, the date palm. The allusion is to the majestic appearance of these feather palms.

arcticus, -a, -um [ark-TIK-us]
From the polar regions; arctic.

Arctostaphylos [ark-to-STAFF-il-oss]
Bearberry. Gr. *arktos*, a bear; *staphylos*, a grape.

Arctotis [ark-TO-tis]
African daisy. Gr. *arktos*, a bear; *otos*, an ear. The scales of the pappus are supposed to look like the ears of a bear.

arcturus, -a, -um [ark-TEW-rus]
Species name after the star.

arctuatus, -a, -um [ark-tew-AY-tus]
Bent like a bow; arched.

ardens [AR-denz]
Glowing.

Ardisia [ar-DIZ-ia]

Spearflower. Marlberry. From Gr. *ardis*, a point; in allusion to the spear-pointed anthers of these flowering trees and shrubs.

Areca [a-REE-ka]

Betelnut. From the vernacular name of the palm used by the natives of Malabar on the southwest coast of India. The sliced nut, wrapped in a pan leaf smeared with lime, is chewed by people throughout tropical Asia. It gives the blood-red color to their frequent and copious expectorations. It stains the teeth black but is considered to aid digestion.

Arecastrum [a-ree-KAS-trum]

Queen palm. From L. *Areca*-like.

Aregelia [a-reg-ELL-ia]

Ornamental epiphytic plants named in honor of E. A. von Regel (1815-1892), Russian botanist, Director of the Imperial Botanical Gardens at what was then called St. Petersburg, now Leningrad.

Arenaria [a-ren-AIR-ia]

Sandwort. From L. *arena*, sand; an allusion to the fact that most of the species of these herbs prefer sandy places.

arenarius, -a, -um [a-ren-AIR-ius]
arenicolus, -a, -um [a-ren-IK-o-lus]
arenosus, -a, -um [a-ren-o-sus]

Growing in sandy places.

Arenga [a-RENG-ga]

From the Malayan name, *areng*, for this palm from which palm-sugar or jaggery is made as well as palm wine.

areolatus, -a, -um [a-reo-LAY-tus]

Pitted.

Arethusa [a-reth-EU-sa]

Bog-orchid. Named in honor of Arethusa, a wood nymph, who, pursued by Alpheus, a river god, was changed by Artemis (L. Diana) into a stream, which, running under the sea, came up in Sicily as a fountain.

Argania [ar-GAY-nia]

Latinized version of the local Moroccan name for this tree whose kernels provide a substitute for olive oil.

Argemone [ar-JEM-o-ne]

Prickly or crested poppy. Once reputed to cure cataract of

the eye, the name derives from the Greek for another plant with the same virtue. The word *argema* is Greek for cataract.

argentatus, -a, -um [ar-jen-TAY-tus]
argenteus, -a, -um [ar-JEN-teus]
Silvery.

argenteoe- [ar-JEN-teo-]
In compound words signifying silver, thus:

argenteoguttatus	spotted with silver
argenteomarginatus	with silver edges
argenteovariegatus	silver-variegated

argentinus, -a, -um [ar-jen-TY-nus]
Of Argentina.

argillaceus, -a, -um [ar-jill-AY-shus]
Whitish. Literally, pertaining to white or potter's clay.

argophyllus, -a, -um [ar-go-FILL-us]
Silver-leaved.

argutus, -a, -um [ar-GEW-tus]
Sharply toothed or notched.

argyraeus, -a, -um [ar-jy-REE-us]
Silvery.

Argyreia [ar-jy-REE-a]
Silver morning-glory. Gr. *argyreios*, silvery. The undersides of the leaves are silvery.

argyro- [ar-JY-ro-]
In compound words signifying silver, thus:

argyrocomus	silver-haired
argyroneurus	with silver veins
argyrophyllus	silver-leaved

aridus, -a, -um [AIR-id-us]
Growing in dry places.

arietinus, -a, -um [a-ri-ee-TY-nus]
Like a ram's head; horned like a ram.

arifolius, -a, -um [a-ri-FO-lius]
With leaves like *Arum*.

Ariocarpus [a-rio-KAR-pus]
Gr. *aria*, the whitebeam; *karpos*, fruit. The fruits of these cacti resemble those of whitebeam, a kind of mountain ash.

Arisaema [a-riss-EE-ma]
Jack-in-the-pulpit. Indian turnip. Dragon arum. Gr. *aron,*
Arum; *haima,* blood; in allusion to the leaf color of some
of the species.

aristatus, -a, -um [a-ris-TAY-tus]
Bearded; furnished with an awn, e.g., oats.

Aristolochia [a-riss-to-LO-kia]
Dutchman's pipe, snakeroot. Gr. *aristos,* best; *lochia,* child-
birth. Sometimes called birthwort, snakeroot was supposed
to ease difficulties in parturition. The form of the root suggested it as a remedy for snake bite. In modern pharmacy
it is the source of an astringent bitter.

aristosus, -a, -um [a-ris-TOE-sus]
Bearded; awned.

Aristotelia [a-ris-tot-EE-lia]
A genus of trees and shrubs named in honor of Aristotle
(384-322 B.C.), Greek philosopher in whom is said to have
reposed all the knowledge of his time.

arizonicus, -a, -um [a-riz-ON-ik-us]
Of Arizona.

armatus, -a, -um [ar-MAY-tus]
Armed with thorns, spines, and other such features.

Armeria [ar-MEER-ia]
Statice, thrift, sea-pink. The Latin name for a kind of
dianthus.

armenus, -a, -um [ar-MEE-nus]
Armenian.

armillaris, -is, -e [ar-mill-AIR-is]
Encircled, as with a bracelet or collar.

armillatus, -a, -um [ar-mill-AY-tus]
Like a bracelet or collar.

Amoracia [ar-mor-AY-sia]
Horse-radish. The classical Latin name.

Arnebia [ar-NEEB-ia]
Prophet flower. Arabian primrose. Latinized version of the
Arabic name for the Arabian primrose, an attractive annual.

Arnica [AR-nik-a]
The classical name for this plant. From Gr. *arnakis,* lamb-
skin; in allusion to the soft texture of the leaves. Tincture
of arnica is obtained from the roots of *A. montana,* called

mountain tobacco. It has popular use in the treatment of bruises and sprains.

arnoldianus, -a, -um [ar-nol-di-AY-nus]
Originated at the Arnold Arboretum, Boston, Massachusetts.

arnoldii [ar-NOL-di-eye]
Of Joseph Arnold, M.D. (1782-1818), naturalist under Sir Stamford Raffles, who built Singapore out of a swamp.

aromaticus, -a, -um [a-ro-MAT-ik-us]
Fragrant; aromatic.

Aronia [a-RO-nia]
Chokeberry, from *aria*, the Greek name for whitebeam (a species of mountain ash) whose fruits resemble chokeberry.

Arpophyllum [arp-o-FILL-um]
Gr. *arpe*, a sickle; *phyllon*, a leaf; in reference to the shape of the leaves of these epiphytic orchids.

Arracacia [a-rak-AY-sia]
From the Spanish name of these South American perennial herbs.

arrectus, -a, -um [ar-RECT-us]
Upright; erect.

Arrhenatherum [a-ree-na-THEE-rum]
Gr. *arren*, male; *anther*, a bristle. The male or staminate flowers of this genus of perennial grasses are furnished with awns or bristles.

Artabotrys [ar-TAB-ot-ris]
Gr. *artao*, to support; *botrys*, a bunch of grapes. The bunched fruits are suspended by a tendril. In the East Indies, notably Java, the leaves of these woody climbers are regarded as a preventive of cholera.

Artemisia [ar-tem-IS-ia]
Wormwood. Named in honor of Artemis, the Greek goddess of chastity. Of considerable medicinal value, plants of the genus yield vermifuges, stimulants, and a vulnerary, as well as the active principle of absinthe.

artemisioides [ar-tem-is-i-OY-deez]
Resembling *Artemisia*.

articulatus, -a, -um [ar-tik-yew-LAY-tus]
Jointed, e.g., some bamboos and grasses.

Artocarpus [ar-to-KARP-us]
Breadfruit. From Gr. *artos*, bread; *karpos*, fruit. The bread-

fruit when baked and warm has some resemblance to fine white bread. The 18th-century explorers thought it delicious as, indeed, it must have seemed after several months voyaging and a prolonged diet of salt meat and hard weevily biscuit. It was the idea of Sir Joseph Banks, who accompanied Captain James Cook, to introduce it into Jamaica and the West Indies generally where food for the slaves was always short. He organized the expedition of Captain Bligh in the *Bounty* to bring plants from Tahiti to Jamaica.

Arum [AY-rum]
Lords-and-ladies. Cuckoo-pint. From *aron*, the Greek name for these poisonous plants which are closely related to jack-in-the-pulpit.

Aruncus [a-RUNK-us]
Goat's-beard. The classical name for these herbs.

arundinaceus, -a, -um [a-run-din-AY-seus]
Resembling a reed.

Arundinaria [a-run-din-AIR-ia]
Southern cane of the cane brakes of southeast United States. From Gr. *arundo*, a reed.

Arundo [a-RUN-do]
Genus of ornamental grasses. From Gr. *arundo*, a reed.

arvalis, -is, -e [ar-VAY-lis]
arvensis, -is, -e [ar-VEN-sis]
Growing in or pertaining to cultivated fields.

asarifolius, -a, -um [ass-a-ri-FO-lius]
With leaves resembling *Asarum* or wild ginger.

Asarum [ASS-a-rum]
Wild ginger. The derivation of the name for these low, nearly stemless herbs is uncertain.

ascalonicus, -a, -um [ass-kal-ON-ik-us]
From the neighborhood of Ascalon, seaport city in Palestine.

ascendens [ass-END-ens]
Rising upwards in a sloping fashion.

asclepiadeus, -a, -um [ask-klee-pia-DEE-us]
Resembling milkweed or *Asclepias*.

Asclepias [ass-KLEE-pias]
Milkweed. Butterfly-weed. The Greek name for these plants, in honor of Asclepias, god of medicine, who in Latin

was called Aesculapius. Some of the species were used in medicine. Asclepias was generally shown flanked on one side by Hygeia, goddess of wise living, and on the other by Panakeia, goddess of cure-alls. In hygiene and panaceas or wonder drugs, the cult of both is still widely observed.

Asclepiodora [as-klee-pio-DOOR-a]
These plants closely resemble *Asclepias*.

Ascyrum [as-SY-rum]
From Gr. *a*, not; *skyros*, rough; thus, smooth or soft to touch. Of uncertain application to these herbs and sub-shrubs.

aselliformis, -is, -e [as-ell-i-FORM-is]
In the shape of a wood louse.

asiaticus, -a, -um [ay-si-AT-ik-us]
Asian.

Asimina [as-IM-in-a]
Paw-paw. The Latinized version of what is said to be the French form of the Indian name for this North American genus of shrubs and small trees.

asparaginus, -a, -um [as-par-ag-EYE-nus]
asparagoides [as-par-ag-OY-deez]
Resembling asparagus.

Asparagus [as-PA-rag-us]
Classical name for the plant which was well known to the ancients. Old English gardeners called it "Sperage" and regarded it as a mild aphrodisiac. Nowadays it is often referred to vulgarly as sparrow-grass.

asper, aspera, asperum [AS-per]
asperatus, -a, -um [as-per-AY-tus]
Rough.

aspericaulis, -is, -e [as-per-ik-AW-lis]
Rough-stemmed.

asperifolius, -a, -um [as-per-i-FO-lius]
Rough-leaved.

asperrimus, -a, -um [as-PER-im-us]
Very rough.

Asperula [as-PER-u-la]
Woodruff. Diminutive of asper; an allusion to the rough stems. *A. odorata* is very fragrant and is used by Germans to flavor May wine.

Asphodeline [as-fo-de-LY-ne]
Jacob's rod. The word means one of the asphodels. This genus of herbaceous plants includes the traditional asphodel, *Asphodeline luteus*. The plant often called asphodel today is *Asphodelus ramosus*. The two bear a close resemblance to each other.

asphodeloides [as-fo-del-OY-deez]
Resembling asphodel.

Asphodelus [as-FO-del-us]
Greek name for the true asphodel.

Aspidistra [as-pid-ISS-tra]
Gr. *aspideon*, a small round shield; in reference to the shape of the stigma. This foliage plant is often used as decoration in bars, movie houses, and the front windows of rooming houses. Because of its ability to withstand unlimited ill-treatment it is called the cast-iron plant and, sometimes, the beerplant for the reason that bartenders often water it with beer dregs as the most readily available liquid. The flowers which appear at ground level are said to be pollinated by slugs.

asplenifolius, -a, -um [as-plee-ni-FO-lius]
With leaves like spleenwort which are fine, feathery, and fernlike.

Asplenium [as-PLEE-nium]
Spleenwort. Gr. *a*, not; *splen*, the spleen; a reference to this fern's traditional virtues in afflictions of the spleen and liver. It could not, however, be given to women because it was supposed to cause barrenness.

Aspris [AS-pris]
Classical Greek name for these ornamental grasses.

assimilis, -is, -e [as-SIM-ill-is]
Similar; like unto.

assurgens [as-SER-jens]
Ascending.

assurgentiflorus, -a, -um [as-ser-jen-ti-FLOR-us]
With flowers in ascending clusters.

Aster [AS-ter]
Starwort. Michaelmas daisy. L. *aster*, a star; an allusion to the form of the flower.

asteroides [as-ter-OY-deez]
Resembling aster.

Astilbe [as-TIL-be]
Gr. *a*, without; *stilbe*, brightness; in allusion to the dullness of the leaves of these ornamental perennial herbs.

astilboides [as-til-BOY-deez]
Resembling *Astilbe*.

Astragalus [as-TRAG-al-us]
Milk vetch. Greek word for some leguminous plant but well applicable to this enormous genus of plants of the pea family.

Astrantia [as-TRAN-shia]
Gr. *aster*, a star; in allusion to the star-shaped bracts of these perennial herbs.

Astrophytum [as-tro-FY-tum]
Gr. *aster*, a star; *phytos*, a plant; in allusion to the flattened form of these Mexican cacti.

asturicus, -a, -um [as-TEW-rik-us]
asturiensis, -is, -e [as-tew-ri-EN-sis]
From the province of Asturia in Spain.

Atalantia [at-a-LAN-tia]
Woody plants, useful as stocks for citrus fruits. Named in honor of Atalanta, daughter of King Schoenus of Scyros. The fruit of the plant is golden-colored. The allusion is to the story that Atalanta consented to accept in marriage any suitor who could outrun her. Hippomenes did so, but only by a ruse. He threw down three of Aphrodite's golden apples in front of her. In stopping to gather them up she lost the race.

ater, atra, atrum [AY-ter]
Dead-black.

Athamanta [ath-a-MAN-ta]
Candy carrot. After Mount Athamas in Sicily where some of the species of these herbaceous plants are found.

Athyrium [a-THI-rium]
Lady fern, swamp spleenwort. Derivation unknown.

atlanticus, -a, -um [at-LAN-tik-us]
From the shores of the Atlantic, or, alternatively, from the Atlas Mountains in North Africa.

Atriplex [AT-rip-lex]
The Greek name for orach, a species of this genus of herbs and shrubs which can be used like spinach but which is

generally regarded as a weed. The genus also includes salt-bush which is much appreciated by Australian sheep.

atriplicifolius, -a, -um [at-rip-liss-i-FO-lius]
With leaves like salt-bush.

atrocarpus, -a, -um [at-ro-KARP-us]
With black or very dark fruit.

atrocaulis, -is, -e [at-ro-KAW-lis]
With black or very dark stems.

Atropa [AT-ro-pa]
Deadly nightshade, belladona. Named for Atropos, one of the three Fates whose particular business it was to snip the thread of life. This genus of herbs, while very poisonous, has important uses in medicine. The specific name belladonna, meaning pretty lady, arises from the fact that it was used in cosmetics to make the eyes appear larger and brighter.

atro- [at-ro-]
In compound words signifying dark, thus:

atropurpureus	dark purple
atrorubens	dark red
atrosanguineus	dark blood red
atroviolaceus	dark violet
atrovirens	dark green

Attalea [at-TAY-lea]
L. *attalus,* splendid or magnificent; in allusion to the beauty of these palms.

attenuatus, -a, -um [at-ten-yew-AY-tus]
Narrowing to a point; attenuated.

atticus, -a, -um [AT-tik-us]
From Attica, the classical name for that part of Greece in the neighborhood of Athens.

Aubrietia [aw-BREE-shia]
Purple rock-cress. Perennial trailers named in honor of Claude Aubriet (1668-1743), French botanical artist.

aubrietioides [aw-bree-she-oy-deez]
Resembling *Aubrietia.*

Aucuba [aw-KEW-ba]
Latinized version of the Japanese name of these ornamental evergreen shrubs.

aucuparia [aw-kew-PAY-ria]
Species name for the rowan tree, *Sorbus aucuparia*. It implies bird-catching, the fruit being much enjoyed by birds.

Audibertia [aw-di-BER-shia]
Herbs and small shrubs named for Urbain Audibert, well-known nurseryman of Tarascon, France, in the 19th century.

Audouinia [aw-doo-IN-ia]
Small shrubs from South Africa named for J. V. Audouin (d. 1841) Professor of Natural History at the Sorbonne in Paris.

augustissimus, -a, -um [aw-gus-TISS-im-us]
Very notable or majestic.

augustus, -a, -um [aw-GUS-tus]
Majestic; notable.

aurantiacus, -a, -um [aw-ran-TY-ak-us]
aurantius, -a, -um [aw-RAN-ti-us]
Orange-colored.

aurantifolius, -a, -um [aw-ran-ti-FO-lius]
With orange-red leaves.

auratus, -a, -um [aw-RAY-tus]
aureolus, -a, -um [aw-re-o-lus]
aureus, -a, -um [AW-reus]
Golden.

aureo- [aw-reo-]
In compound words signifying golden, thus:

aureomaculatus	golden-spotted
aureomarginatus	edged with gold
aureoregina	golden queen
aureoreticulatus	veined with gold
aureovariegatus	gold-variegated

auricomus, -a, -um [aw-rik-o-mus]
Having golden hair.

Auricula [aw-RIK-yew-la]
Pre-Linnaean name for plants now included in the genus *Primula* but still commonly used in England where auriculas are favorites both for show and in Alpine gardens.

auriculatus, -a, -um [aw-rik-yew-LAY-tus]
Eared; with an ear-shaped appendage.

auritus, -a, -um [aw-RY-tus]
Eared; having an ear.

aurum
Gold (the metal), represented by the symbol *Au*. It was

once believed that gold was of botanic origin, the reason being that the metal chiefly occurs embedded in igneous rocks in a crystalline, wiry, branchlike form which gives it the appearance of a plant in the rocks. This pleasant misconception persisted sufficiently strongly until the 16th century when Agricola, the Swiss metallurgist, refuted it.

australiensis, -is, -e   [aw-stray-li-EN-sis]
Australian.

australis, -is, -e   [aw-STRAW-lis]
Southern.

austriacus, -a, -um   [aw-STRY-ak-us]
Austrian.

austrinus, -a, -um   [aw-STRY-nus]
Southern.

autumnalis, -is, -e   [aw-tum-NAY-lis]
Pertaining to autumn.

Avena   [av-EE-na]
Oats. The classical name.

Averrhoa   [av-er-o-a]
Ornamental trees, named after a Moorish physician, Averrhoes, who lived in Cordoba, Spain, during the 12th century. He translated Aristotle into Arabic.

avicularis, -is, -e   [av-ik-yew-LAIR-is]
Relating to small birds.

avium   [AY-vium]
Of the birds. Appropriately, the common sweet cherry is *Prunus avium.*

axillaris, -is, -e   [ax-ill-AIR-is]
Borne in the axil; axillary.

Azalea   [az-AY-lea]
Gr. *azaleos*, dry; in allusion to an old-fashioned idea that these shrubs demand a dry situation. Nowadays, while azaleas are technically classified as rhododendrons, they are generally kept apart by gardeners and often by nurserymen.

azaleoides   [az-ay-le-oy-deez]
Resembling Azalea.

Azara   [az-AIR-ra]
Evergreen shrubs with fragrant flowers, named in honor of J. N. Azara, a Spanish patron of science of the early 19th century.

azedarach [az-ed-AY-rak]
Specific name of uncertain origin for chinaberry, *Melia azedarach.*

Azolla [az-OLL-a]
Genus of minute but quickly spreading aquatics. From Gr. *azo,* to dry; *ollo,* to kill; the plants die when they become dry.

azoricus, -a, -um [az-AW-rik-us]
From the Azores Islands in the eastern Atlantic.

azureus, -a, -um [a-ZUR-eus]
Sky-blue; azure.

B

Babiana [babbi-AY-na]
Latinized version of an Afrikaans word, babiaan, (baboon). Baboons are said to eat this bulbous plant, which is sometimes called baboon-root.

babylonicus, -a, -um [bab-ill-ON-ik-us]
Babylonian. Specific name of the weeping willow (*Salix babylonicus*) which was thought by Linnaeus to be a native of southwest Asia. It belongs, in fact, to the Far East. The biblical "willows" of the waters of Babylon are generally thought to be *Populus euphratica.*

baccans [BAK-ans]
Berry-bearing.

baccatus, -a, -um [bak-AY-tus]
Fleshy; having berries with a pulpy texture.

Baccharis [BAK-a-ris]
Deciduous and evergreen trees, shrubs, and herbs named in honor of Bacchus, the god of wine. It is suggested that the roots were sometimes used to spice wine. Groundsel tree is *B. halimifolia.*

bacciferus, -a, -um [bak-IFF-er-us]
Berry-bearing.

bacillaris, -is, -e [bass-ill-AIR-is]
Stick- or staff-like.

Bactris [BACK-tris]
From Gr. *bactron,* a walking staff; suggesting the use to which the young stems of these palms are often put.

Baeria [BEAR-ia]
Herbs, mostly annuals, named in honor of Dr. von Baer,

early 19th-century Russian botanist of the University of Dorpat.

baicalensis, -is, -e [by-kal-EN-sis]
From Lake Baikal in eastern Siberia.

baileyi [BAY-li-eye]
Of Bailey, honoring one of the following:
(a) Captain F. M. Bailey, Indian Army, who collected on the borders of Tibet from 1913 on. His most celebrated contribution was the *Meconopsis betonicifolia,* for a time also known as *M. baileyi.*
(b) Major Vernon Bailey, U. S. Army, who collected cacti from 1900 on.
(c) Liberty Hyde Bailey (1858-1957) Professor of Horticulture at Cornell and author of many authoritative books (*The Cyclopedia of American Horticulture, Hortus,* etc.).

Baillonia [by-LO-nia]
Deciduous shrubs named in honor of the French botanist Henri Baillon (1827-1895).

Balaka [bal-AH-ka]
The vernacular name for these feather palms from the Fiji Islands.

balearicus, -a, -um [bal-ee-AIR-ik-us]
From the Balearic Islands off the Mediterranean coast of Spain.

Ballota [bal-o-ta]
Greek name for black horehound, one of the species of this genus of sub-shrubs or perennial herbs.

balsameus, -a, -um [bal-SAY-meus]
Similar to balsam; balsamic.

balsamiferus, -a, -um [bal-sam-IFF-erus]
Balsam-bearing.

balticus, -a, -um [BAWL-tik-us]
Of the area of the Baltic Sea.

Bambusa [bam-BOO-sa]
Bamboo. Latinized version of the Malayan vernacular name.

bambusoides [bam-boo-SOY-deez]
Resembling bamboo.

banaticus, -a, -um [ban-AT-ik-us]
From the province of Banat in southern Hungary.

56

Banksia [BANK-sia]

Australian honeysuckle. Named for Sir Joseph Banks (1743-1820), President of the Royal Society and virtual Director of Royal Botanic Gardens, Kew. Banks was a distinguished botanist in his own right as well as a wealthy and generous patron of science. A man of boundless interests, he made great contributions, both scholarly and material, to research. When he died, he left immense natural-history collections for the public good.

When Captain James Cook went to the Pacific in 1768 to observe the transit of Venus, Banks, as a young man, both outfitted the expedition at his own expense and went with it himself as a scientist. He returned three years later with a rich harvest of plants and seeds.

He made other expeditions, also at his own expense, to Labrador, Newfoundland, and Iceland. Later (1787) he promoted a scheme for bringing the breadfruit tree from Tahiti to be established in the West Indian islands where food for the slaves had become a very difficult problem. Captain William Bligh (see *Blighia*) was selected to undertake the mission in the *Bounty*. It ended in the mutiny of the crew and the loss of the ship. A later expedition, also commanded by Bligh, successfully transported the breadfruit which, however, did not provide the complete solution of the West Indian food problem which had been hoped for.

banksianus, -a, -um [bank-si-AY-nus]

banksii [BANK-si-eye]

In honor of Sir Joseph Banks (see *Banksia*).

Baphia [BAFF-ia]

Gr. *baphe*, a dye. The tree provides the bar or cam wood of commerce which yields a red dye. Violin bows are made from the wood.

Baptisia [bap-TIZ-ia]

Wild indigo of North America. From Gr. *bapto*, to dye. It has sometimes been used as a substitute for true indigo.

Barbarea [bar-bar-EE-a]

Yellow rocket. Winter or upland cress. Once generally known as herb of St. Barbara, patron saint of artillerymen and miners and protectress in thunderstorms.

barbarus, -a, -um [BAR-bar-us]

Foreign.

barbatulus, -a, -um [bar-BAT-u-lus]
Somewhat bearded.
barbatus, -a, -um [bar-BAY-tus]
Bearded; furnished with long weak hairs.
barbigerus, -a, -um [bar-BIJ-er-us]
Bearing barbs or beards.
barbinervis, -is, -e [bar-bin-NERV-is]
With veins barbed or bearded.
barbinodis, -is, -e [bar-bin-o-dis]
With beards at the nodes or joints.
barbulatus, -a, -um [bar-bew-LAY-tus]
Somewhat bearded or with a short beard.
barcinonensis, -is, -e [bar-sin-o-NEN-sis]
From the neighborhood of Barcelona, Spain.
Barklya [bark-LY-a]
A large tree, a native of Australia, named in honor of Sir
Henry Barkly (1815-1898), once Governor of Cape Colony
in South Africa, who was deeply interested in plants.
Barleria [bar-LEER-ia]
Evergreen shrubs named in honor of Jacques Barrelier,
French botanist (d. 1673).
barometz [bar-o-metz]
Species name of *Cibotium barometz*, woolly fern or Scythian
lamb. Barometz is from a Tartar word meaning lamb. What
we now know as cotton was for centuries supposed to be de-
rived from this fern which was commonly supposed to be
half animal and half plant.
Barosma [bar-os-ma]
Gr. *barys*, heavy; *osma*, odor; in reference to the powerful
scent of the leaves of these evergreen shrubs.
Barringtonia [bar-ing-TO-nia]
Evergreen trees and shrubs, named after the Hon. Daines
Barrington (1727-1800), English jurist, antiquary, and botanist.
Basella [bas-ELL-a]
Malabar nightshade. The Latinized version of the vernacu-
lar name. The plant is edible and is cultivated in India and
elsewhere in the tropics for use as a potherb.
baselloides [bas-ell-OY-deez]
Resembling *Basella*.

58

basilaris, -is, -e [bay-sill-AIR-is]
Pertaining to the base or bottom.

basilicum [bas-ILL-ik-um]
Princely, royal. The classical and now the species name for the herb sweet basil in allusion to its reputed healing qualities.

batatas [bat-AY-tas]
Specific name for the sweet potato, *Ipomoea batatas*. The word is the vernacular Carib (Haitian) Indian name for sweet potato. From it derives the English word potato.

batrachoides [bat-rak-OY-deez]
Resembling water-buttercup.

Bauera [bow-EER-a]
Small evergreen shrubs named by Sir Joseph Banks after Franz (1758-1840) and Ferdinand (1760-1826) Bauer, Austrian brothers, both botanical artists.

bauerianus, -a, -um [bow-eer-i-AY-nus]
In honor of Ferdinand Bauer who was botanical artist on Captain Flinders' expedition to Australia.

Bauhinia [baw-HIN-ia]
Evergreen shrubs named after two illustrious Swiss botanists, the brothers John and Caspar Bauhin. John (1541-1613) was responsible among other works for the great *Historia Plantarum*, published nearly forty years after his death. Caspar (1560-1624) produced a valuable collection of synonyms. It has been suggested that the twin leaflets of the plant typify the two brothers.

bavaricus, -a, -um [bav-AIR-ik-us]
Bavarian.

Beaufortia [bow-FORT-ia]
Flowering, heathlike shrubs named after Mary, Duchess of Beaufort, patroness of botany early in the 19th century.

Beaumontia [bow-MONT-ia]
Nepal trumpet-flower. Heralds-trumpet. Trees, shrubs, and climbers with showy white flowers, named in honor of Lady Diana Beaumont (d. 1831) of Bretton Hall, Yorkshire.

Befaria [beff-AIR-ia]
Evergreen shrubs named in honor of Dr. Bejar, 17th-century Spanish botanist whose name is supposed to have been erroneously Latinized by Linnaeus. Older books refer to the plant as Bejaria.

Begonia [beg-o-nia]
A great group of cultivated ornamental plants named for Michel Begon (1638-1710), Governor of French Canada and a patron of botany.

Belamcanda [bel-am-CAN-da]
Blackberry lily. Leopard flower. Latinized version of the East Asiatic vernacular name for this tuberous-rooted, herbaceous perennial.

belgicus, -a, -um [BEL-jik-us]
Belgian.

belladonna [bell-a-DONN-a]
Italian word meaning beautiful lady. Species name of *Atropa* and *Amaryllis*. In regard to the first the allusion is to its cosmetic use. Ladies used it to give brilliancy to the eyes— a property of the plant being to dilate the pupil. That vision was affected was probably not important.

bellidifolius, -a, -um [bel-id-i-FO-lius]
With beautiful leaves; with leaves like *Bellis*.

bellidiformis, -is, -e [bel-id-i-FORM-is]
Daisy-like.

bellidioides [bel-id-i-OY-deez]
Resembling *Bellium*.

Bellis [BELL-is]
Daisy. L. *bellus*, pretty.

Bellium [BELL-ium]
From *Bellis*, daisy. Only for technical reasons is it not included in *Bellis* which it much resembles.

belloides [bel-OY-deez]
Resembling *Bellis* or daisy.

bellus, -a, -um [BELL-us]
Beautiful, handsome.

Beloperone [bel-o-per-o-ne]
Gr. *belos*, an arrow; *perone*, a band or strap; in allusion to the arrow-shaped connective, the part of the filament of the stamen connecting the anther lobes of the evergreen flowering shrubs.

benedictus, -a, -um [ben-ni-DIK-tus]
Blessed; well spoken of.

bengalensis, -is, -e (sometimes **benghalensis**) [ben-gawl-EN-sis]
From Bengal, India.

Benincasa [ben-in-KAY-sa]
Annual running squash-like herbs with edible fruits named
for Count Guiseppe Benincasa (d. 1596), Italian botanist
who founded the Botanic Garden in Pisa.

Benzoin [BEN-zoyn]
From an Arabic vernacular word meaning aromatic gum.
See *Lindera.*

Berberidopsis [ber-berry-DOP-sis]
From *Berberis,* barberry, and Gr. *opsis,* similar to.

Berberis [BER-ber-is]
Barberry. The Latinized form of the Arabian name for the
fruit. This large genus of shrubs comprises several hundred
species.

Berchemia [ber-KEE-mia]
Deciduous shrubs named for M. Berchem, French botanist
of the 17th century.

Bergenia [ber-GEN-ia]
Decorative perennials formerly called *Saxifraga* named for
Karl August von Bergen (1704-1760), Frankfurt botanist.

Bergerocactus [ber-jer-o-KAK-tus]
Named for Alwyn Berger (1871-1931), American horticulturist and botanist with a special interest in succulents. He
became Superintendent of the Hanbury Garden, La Mortola,
Italy.

Berlandiera [ber-lan-DEER-a]
Perennial herbs and sub-shrubs named for J. L. Berlandier
(d. 1851), Genoese botanist, who explored in Texas and
New Mexico.

bermudianus, -a, -um [ber-mew-di-AY-nus]
From Bermuda.

berolinensis, -is, -e [ber-o-lin-EN-sis]
Of Berlin.

Berteroa [ber-ter-o-a]
Dwarf herbs named for C. G. L. Bertero (1789-1831),
Italian physician who botanized in Guadaloupe and other
West Indian islands.

Bertholletia [ber-to-LEE-shia]
Brazil-nut. Named for Claude-Louis Berthollet (1748-1822),
French chemist, who discovered the bleaching qualities of
chlorine. The Brazil-nut tree (*B. excelsa*) grows to great
size. The globular fruits, consist of a hard, woody casing

packed with about twenty of the nuts of commerce, each in its own shell.

Bertolonia [ber-to-LO-nia]
Foliage plants named for A. Bertoloni (1775-1869), Italian botanist.

bessarabicus, -a, -um [bess-a-RAY-bik-us]
From Bessarabia in eastern Rumania.

Beta [BEE-ta]
Latin name. Cultivated from remote times, the genus includes the familiar red and the white sugar beet—both varieties of *B. vulgaris,* and Swiss chard (var. *cicla*). About half of the world's sugar supplies derive from beet.

betaceus, -a, -um [bee-TAY-seus]
Beetlike.

betonicifolius, -a, -um [bet-on-iss-i-FO-lius]
With leaves like betony.

Betula [BET-yew-la]
Birch. The Latin name. The tree has special emotional appeal for the Northern peoples and is surrounded with legend and symbolism. Oil of birch gives to Russia leather its particular fragrance.

betulaefolius, -a, -um [bet-yew-lee-FO-lius]
Having leaves like birch.

betulinus, -a, -um [bet-yew-LY-nus]
betuloides [bet-yew-LOY-deez]
Resembling birch.

bicolor [BY-coll-or]
Of two colors.

bicornis, -is, -e [by-CORN-is]
bicornutus, -a, -um [by-cor-NEW-tus]
Two-horned; having two horns or hornlike spurs.

Bidens [BY-dens]
Tickseed. Beggar's ticks. L. *bis,* twice; *dens,* a tooth; in reference to the two teeth on what is commonly called the seed but which, correctly, is the achene or dry one-seeded fruit. Other names are stick-tight and bur-marigold.

bidentatus, -a, -um [by-den-TAY-tus]
Having two teeth.

biennis, -is, -e [by-ENN-is]
Biennial.

bifidus, -a, -um [BY-fid-us]
Cleft into two parts.
biflorus, -a, -um [by-FLOR-us]
Twin-flowered.
bifolius, -a, -um [by-FO-lius]
Twin-leaved.
Bifrenaria [by-free-NAIR-ia]
L. *bis*, twice; *frenum*, a bridle; in allusion to the double band
by which the pollen masses are connected with their gland
in these epiphytic orchids.
bifurcatus, -a, -um [by-fur-KAY-tus]
Bifurcate; forked into two generally almost equal stems or
branches.
Bigelovia [big-el-LO-via]
Plumed goldenrod. A North American shrubby and herbaceous perennial named in honor of Dr. John M. Bigelow
(1787-1879), Boston physician who assisted Engelmann
(see *engelmannii*) on the U. S.–Mexican boundary mission.
He collected regularly while visiting his patients in the
Boston area on horseback. One plant collected and described
by him, *Rubus sempervirens,* does not seem to have been
noted since. Professor Liberty Hyde Bailey who was reclassi-
fying the genus *Rubus* at the close of his life, had Bigelow's
herbarium specimen and would encourage anyone he knew
to be going to the Boston area to hunt for the plant—even
offering to pay for a collect telegram if it were found. It is
not, however, a very noticeable plant and it would take the
eye of a Bigelow or Bailey to detect it.
Bignonia [big-NO-nia]
Trumpet-creeper or cross vine. Named in honor of Abbé
Jean Paul Bignon (1662-1723), Librarian to Louis XIV.
bignonioides [big-no-ni-OY-deez]
Resembling *Bignonia.*
bihai [bi-HAI]
Tropical American vernacular name for the wild plantain.
bijugus, -a, -um [by-JOO-gus]
Double-yoked; two pairs joined.
Billardiera [bill-ar-DEER-a]
Apple berry. Evergreen climbers named in honor of Jacques
Julien Houton de la Billardière (1775-1834), French
botanist.

Billbergia [bill-BERJ-ia]
Epiphytic evergreen plants named in honor of J. G. Billberg
(1772-1844), Swedish botanist.

bipinnatus, -a, -um [by-pin-AY-tus]
Two-pinnated. A compound leaf is pinnate when the leaflets
are arranged feather fashion. It is bipinnate when the leaflets
themselves have leaflets arranged feather fashion.

Bischofia [bish-o-fia]
An ornamental tropical tree named in honor of G. W.
Bischof, German Professor of Botany.

Biscutella [bis-kew-TELL-a]
L. *bis*, twice; *scutella*, a small flat dish; in allusion to the
form of the fruits of these annual and perennial herbs.

bisectus, -a, -um [by-SEK-tus]
Divided into two equal parts.

biserratus, -a, -um [by-ser-AY-tus]
Double-toothed, i.e., with the teeth on the leaves being
themselves toothed.

Bismarckia [biz-MARK-ia]
A palm, named in honor of Prince Otto von Bismarck (1815-
1898), first Chancellor of the German Empire.

biternatus, -a, -um [by-ter-NAY-tus]
Twice ternate. When leaflets are borne in threes, as in
clover, they are described as ternate. A plant is biternate
when the three divisions each bear three leaflets.

bituminosus, -a, -um [by-tew-min-o-sus]
Sticky.

bivalvis, -is, -e [by-VAL-vis]
Having two valves. The two sides of a pea-pod are the
valves.

Bixa [BIX-a]
Latinized version of the South American vernacular name
for this evergreen flowering tree, the source of annatto dye.

blandus, -a, -um [BLAND-us]
Mild; not strong or bitter.

Blechnum [BLEK-num]
From the classical Greek name for a fern, probably not this
one.

bleo [BLEE-o]
Brazilian vernacular name for *Pereskia bleo.*

blepharophyllus, -a, -um [bleff-a-ro-FILL-us]
With leaves fringed like eyelashes.

Bletilla [blet-ILL-a]
Diminutive of *Bletia*, a genus of terrestrial orchids of no horticultural interest which it closely resembles. Named in honor of Louis Blet, a Spanish apothecary who had a botanic garden in Algeciras toward the end of the 18th century.

Blighia [BLY-ya]
Akee tree. A tropical tree with edible fruit named in honor of William Bligh, Captain of the *Bounty*, notorious for the mutiny which occurred in that ship and less well known for his extraordinary feat of navigating 4,000 miles across the Pacific to the island of Timor in an open boat with the loyal remnant of his crew, virtually without loss of a man. Bligh's original mission was to bring the breadfruit tree from Tahiti to the West Indies, an idea of Sir Joseph Banks (see *Banksia*) with whom he had sailed as shipmates on a previous voyage with Captain Cook. Subsequently, Bligh fulfilled his mission in another voyage and the breadfruit is now established in the West Indies. Later Bligh became Governor of New South Wales where, in 1808, he was again the target of a mutiny.

blitoides [bly-TOY-deez]
Resembling *Blitum* (an old name for strawberry-blite), a coarse weed with a red fruit.

Bloomeria [bloo-MEER-ia]
Bulbous plants named in honor of Dr. H. G. Bloomer (1821-1874), pioneer Californian botanist.

Blumenbachia [bloo-men-BACK-ia]
Plants covered with stinging hairs. Named in honor of Johann Friederich Blumenbach (1752-1840), Professor of Medicine at Göttingen.

Bocconia [bok-o-nia]
Plume poppy. Named in honor of Paolo Bocconi (1633-1703), Sicilian physician and botanist.

Boehmeria [bo-MEER-ia]
China-grass. Named in honor of George Rudolph Boehmer (1723-1803) Professor of Botany at Würtemberg. One of the species, *B. nivea*, is the source of ramie, a very fine

fiber, taken from the inner bark. Ramie is one of the strongest fibers known but, owing to certain technical drawbacks, it is not widely used commercially. Its principal use is in the manufacture of gas mantles.

boldus [BOWL-dus]
Latinized form of a Chilean vernacular name.

Boltonia [bowl-TOE-nia]
False chamomile. Herbaceous perennials and annuals, named in honor of James Bolton (d. 1799), British botanist.

Bomarea [bo-MAIR-ea]
Handsome flowering climbers, named after Jacques Christophe Valmont de Bomare (1731-1807), French patron of science.

Bombax [BOM-bax]
From Gr. *bombyx*, silk; in allusion to the fluffy, silky hairs which fill the seed capsule. This is the cotton-tree of the East Indies.

bona-nox [BO-na-nox]
Good-night. Species name for one of the morning glories.

bonus, -a, -um [BO-nus]
Good.

bonus-henricus [bo-nus-hen-RY-kus]
Literally, good Henry. Species name of a *Chenopodium* called good-King-Henry and sometimes mercury. It is a hardy, rank vegetable which may be eaten like spinach.

Borago [bo-RAY-go]
The herb borage (pronounced burrij) possibly from *L. burra*, a hairy garment; in allusion to the hairy leaves. The leaves have a fragrance like cucumber and are used in such mixtures as claret-cup, giving a delicate but distinctive flavor and coolness.

Borbonia [bor-BO-nia]
Evergreen shrubs named for Gaston de Bourbon, Duke of Orleans and son of Henry IV of France, a patron of botany.

borbonicus, -a, -um [bor-BON-ik-us]
(*a*) From the island of Réunion in the Indian Ocean, once called Bourbon Island.
(*b*) In honor of the Bourbon kings of France.

borealis, -is, -e [bor-ee-AY-lis]
Northern.

borinquenus, -a, -um [bo-rin-KWEE-nus]
From the island of Puerto Rico, called Borinquen by the Spanish.
borneensis, -is, -e [bor-ne-EN-sis]
From Borneo.
Boronia [bo-RO-nia]
Fragrant-flowered evergreen shrubs named for Francesco Boroni who appears to have been a servant of John Sibthorp (1758-1796), an English botanist who collected in Greece. Boroni died of an accident in Athens.
Bossiaea [boss-EE-ya]
Evergreen shrubs, usually with yellow flowers, named in honor of Boissier Lamartinière, French botanist, who sailed with La Pérouse, noted French navigator, who was lost off the New Hebrides in 1789.
Boswellia [bos-WELL-ia]
Evergreen trees, source of the biblical resin, frankincense. Named in honor of James Boswell (1740-1795), friend and biographer of Dr. Samuel Johnson, who only recently has begun to be accorded the recognition he deserves as a man of distinction and stature in his own right.
Botrychium [bot-RY-kium]
Moonwort. Grape fern. From Gr. *botrys*, a bunch of grapes; a reference to the bunchlike formation of the spore-bearing organs of these deciduous ferns.
botryoides [bot-ri-OY-deez]
Resembling a bunch of grapes.
Bougainvillea [boo-gen-VILL-ea]
Perhaps the handsomest and most widely planted tropical vine. Named in honor of Louis Antoine de Bougainville (1729-1811), who made various voyages of exploration, his name being commemorated in several South Pacific place names. He was a noted mathematician, scientist, lawyer, soldier, and author besides being a Fellow of the Royal Society in London.
Boussingaultia [boo-sin-GAUL-tia]
Madiera vine. Named for J. B. Boussingault (1802-1887) noted French chemist.
Bouvardia [boo-VARD-ia]
Flowering evergreen shrubs named for Dr. Charles Bouvard (1572-1658), Superintendent of the Jardin du Roi, Paris.

Bowkeria [bo-KERR-ia]

Evergreen shrubs named for James Henry Bowker (d. 1900) and his sister Mrs. Mary Elizabeth Barber (d. 1899), South African botanists. *Aloe barberae* was named after the latter.

Boykinia [boy-KIN-ia]

Perennial herbs named in honor of an American field botanist, Dr. Boykin of Milledgeville, Georgia.

brachiatus, -a, -um [brak-i-AY-tus]

Branched at right angles; armlike.

brachy- [brack-i-]

In compound words signifying short, thus:

brachybotris	short-clustered
brachycerus	short-horned
brachypetalus	short-petaled
brachyphyllus	with short leaves

Brachychiton [brak-i-KY-ton]

Bottle tree. From Gr. *brachys*, short; *chiton*, a tunic; a reference to the overlapping scales.

Brachycome [brak-ik-o-me]

Swan River daisy. From Gr. *brachys*, short; *kome*, hair; in allusion to the short bristles of the pappus.

bracteatus, -a, -um [brak-tee-AY-tus]

bracteosus, -a, -um [brak-tee-o-sus]

bractescens [brak-TESS-ens]

Having bracts. A bract is a leaflike and often a brightly colored organ generally just below the flower cluster. The red "flower" of the poinsettia is, in fact, composed of bracts, the real flower being somewhat insignificant and generally yellow. Other showy bracts are the "flowers" of dogwood and *Bougainvillea*.

Brahea [bra-HEE-a]

Fan-leaved palms, named in honor of Tycho Brahe (1546-1601), noted Danish astronomer, who was responsible for some of the great scientific advances of his day.

Brasenia [bras-EEN-ea]

Water-shield. The origin of the botanical name for this aquatic plant is obscure.

brasiliensis, -is, -e [braz-ill-i-EN-sis]

Brazilian.

Brassavola [brass-AV-o-la]
A genus of epiphytic orchids. Named after A. M. Brassavola (1500-1555), Venetian botanist.

Brassia [BRASS-ia]
A genus of epiphytic orchids named after William Brass, English botanist, who collected in West Africa for Sir Joseph Banks (see *Banksia*) in the latter part of the 18th century.

Brassica [BRASS-ik-a]
The cabbage tribe. The classical Latin name for cabbage.

brevis, -is, -e [BREV-is]
Short. Also:—

brevifolius, -a, -um [brev-i-FO-lius]
With short leaves.

brevipedunculatus, -a, -um [brev-i-pee-dunk-ew-LAY-tus]
With a short flower stalk.

breviscapus, -a, -um [brev-i-SKAY-pus]
With a short scape.

Brevoortia [brev-VOOR-tia]
Floral firecracker. Named for J. C. Brevoort, Regent of New York State University. The single species, *B. ida-maia*, is named for Ida May Burke, daughter of a California stagecoach driver, who brought it to the attention of Alphonso Wood (1810-1881), American botanist.

Breynia. [BRY-nia]
A genus of shrubs and small trees. Named in honor of Johann Philip Breyn, 17th-century German botanist.

Brickellia [brik-ELL-ia]
Herbs or small shrubs named in honor of Dr. John Brickell, 18th-century American naturalist, who published *A Natural History of North Carolina* (1737).

Briza [BRY-za]
Quaking grass. The Greek name for one of the food grains, possibly rye.

brizaeformis, -is, -e [bry-zee-FORM-is]
brizoides [bry-ZOY-deez]
Resembling quaking grass or *Briza*.

Brodiaea [bro-di-EE-a]
Cormous plants named for John Brodie (1744-1824), Scottish botanist.

Bromelia [bro-MEE-lia]
Perennial herbs with stiff, pineapple-like leaves, named in honor of Olaf Bromel (1629-1705), Swedish botanist.

bromoides [bro-MOY-deez]
Resembling brome grass or *Bromus.*

Bromus [BRO-mus]
Brome grass. From Gr. *bromos,* fodder.

bronchialis, -is, -e [bronk-i-AY-lis]
Useful in treating bronchitis.

Brosimum [BRO-sim-um]
From Gr. *brosimos,* edible. The genus includes the West Indian bread-nut which also provides the beautifully marked snake-wood. Another species of the genus is the cow-tree, the *palo de vaca,* of South America whose milky sap is reputed to be as rich and wholesome as cow's milk. Altogether it is a genus almost as versatile as Al Capp's concept of the Shmoo.

Broughtonia [broo-TOE-nia]
Epiphytic orchids named for Arthur Broughton, English botanist and physician (d. 1796).

Broussonetia [broo-so-NESH-ia]
Named for Pierre Marie August Broussonet (1761-1807), Professor of Botany at Montpellier, France. One species is the paper mulberry whose bark yields a kind of paper. It is a good street tree, and a few specimens may be seen in New York.

Browallia [brow-WALL-ia]
Shrubs or herbs with blue or white flowers, named in honor of John Browall, Bishop of Abo, Sweden, a botanist, who in 1739 defended the sexual system of classification proposed by Linnaeus.

Brownea [BROWN-ea]
Evergreen flowering trees and shrubs named for Patrick Browne (1720-1790), Irish physician and author of *A History of Jamaica.*

Bruckenthalia [bruk-en-THAY-lia]
Spike heath. Named in honor of S. von Bruckenthal (1721-1803), an Austrian nobleman.

brumalis, -is, -e [broo-MAY-lis]
Winter-flowering. Literally, pertaining to the winter solstice.

Brunfelsia [brun-FEL-sia]
Evergreen, free-flowering shrubs named for Otto Brunfels
(1489-1534), Carthusian monk and one of the earliest
German botanists, who in 1530 published the first good
figures of plants.
Brunnera [BRUNN-er-a]
Perennial herbs named for Samuel Brunner (1790-1844),
Swiss botanist.
brunneus, -a, -um [BRUNN-eus]
Brown.
Brunsvigia [bruns-VIGG-ia]
Bulbous plants named in honor of the Royal House of
Brunswick. This is Josephine's lily of South Africa which
differs only technically from *Amaryllis.*
bryoides [bry-OY-deez]
bryolophotus, -a, -um [bry-o-lo-FO-tus]
Resembling moss.
bryolophytus, -a, -um [bry-o-lo-FY-tus]
Mossy; plumed; like a moss plant.
Bryonia [bry-o-nia]
Bryony. From Gr. *bryo,* to sprout; in allusion to the annual
growth from the tuber of these climbing plants.
Bryophyllum [bry-o-FILL-um]
From Gr. *bryo,* to sprout; *phyllon,* a leaf; in allusion to the
vegetative buds on the edges of the leaves of these succulents which need only to be laid on damp sand to start new
plants.
Their sturdy constitution and ease of propagation makes
them popular house plants, with such English names as air
plant, life-plant, and floppers.
bucinatorius, -a, -um [bew-sin-ay-TOR-ius]
bucinatus, -a -um [bew-sin-AY-tus]
Shaped like a crooked trumpet or horn.
Buckleya [BUK-lia]
A parasitic shrub. After S. B. Buckley (1809-84), American
botanist.
Buddleia [BUD-lia]
Butterfly bush. Ornamental small trees and shrubs. Named
in honor of the Reverend Adam Buddle (1660-1715),
English botanist and vicar of Farnbridge in Essex. Strictly,
the name should be spelled "Buddleja" as first proposed.

buddleoides [bud-le-oy-deez]
Resembling *Buddleia.*

bufonius, -a, -um [bew-FO-nius]
Pertaining to toads; growing in damp places.

bulbiferus, -a, -um [bul-BIFF-er-us]
Bulb-bearing.

bulbiformis, -is, -e [bul-bi-FORM-is]
Shaped like a bulb.

Bulbine [bul-BY-ne]
Herbaceous plants of the Lily family. From Gr. *bolbos,*
a bulb.

Bulbinella [bul-bin-ELL-a]
Diminutive of *Bulbine,* now used for the name of a particular herbaceous tuberous-rooted perennial.

Bulbocodium [bul-bo-KO-dium]
Gr. *bolbos,* a bulb; *kodion,* wool; in allusion to the woolly
bulbs of this crocus-like plant.

Bulbophyllum [bul-bo-FILL-um]
From Gr. *bulbos,* a bulb; *phyllon,* a leaf. The leaves of
these epiphytic orchids grow from a pseudobulb.

bulbosus, -a -um [bul-BO-sus]
Bulbous; may be applied to any swollen underground
stem, not necessarily a bulb.

bulgaricus, -a, -um [bul-GAIR-ik-us]
Bulgarian.

bullatus, -a, -um [bul-AY-tus]
Bullate; blistered or puckered, usually applying to foliage.

Bumelia [bew-MEE-lia]
Greek name for the ash tree, but the reason is obscure for
applying it to these small trees and shrubs.

buphthalmum [bewf-THAL-mum]
From Gr. *bous,* an ox; *ophthalmos,* an eye; an allusion to
the appearance of the flower which in English is called ox-
eye.

Bupleurum [bew-PLEUR-um]
Hare's ear. Herbaceous plants or shrubs. From the Greek
name for another plant.

bursa-pastoris [bur-sa-past-OR-is]
Old generic and now the species name for the weed shepherd's purse, which is the literal translation of the words.

Bursaria [bur-SAIR-ia]
L. *bursia,* a purse; in allusion to the shape of the seed pod of these shrubs or small trees.

Buteia [BEW-tia]
Pindo palm. Named for John Stuart, third Earl of Bute (1713-1792), for whom *Stewartia* (sometimes *Stuartia*) was also named. He was British Prime Minister, 1762-1763.

Butomus [bew-TOE-mus]
Flowering rush. From Gr. *bous,* ox; *temmo,* to cut; in allusion to the sharp leaf margins which make the plant quite unsuitable for fodder. The baked root-stocks are said to be edible.

buxifolius, -a, -um [bux-i-FO-lius]
Box-leaved.

Buxus [BUX-us]
Box. The classical Latin name.

byzantinus, -a, -um [by-zan-TY-nus]
From Istanbul, classically Byzantium.

C

Cabomba [ka-BOM-ba]
Fanwort. Fish grass. Latinized version of the native Guiana name for these perennial aquatics.

cacaliaefolius, -a, -um [cass-ay-li-ee-FO-lius]
With leaves like *Cacalia,* a genus of virtually no garden interest.

cacao [KAK-ow)
Aztec name for the chocolate tree and still the name both for the tree and the chocolate in many countries. *Theobroma cacao* is the botanical name.

cachemiricus, -a, -um [kash-em-MEER-ik-us]
From Kashmir.

Cactus [KAK-tus]
Name applied by the Greeks to some spiny plant. Strictly *Cactus* is the name of one genus only, but it has been adopted loosely for the whole family, comprising about 100 genera and 2,000 species.

cadmicus, -a, -um [kad-MIK-us]
Metallic; like tin in appearance.

caerulescens [see-rool-ESS-ens]
Approaching dark blue. Often incorrectly spelled "coerulescens."

caeruleus, -a, -um [see-ROOL-eus]
Dark blue. Often incorrectly spelled "coeruleus."

Caesalpinia [see-zal-PIN-ia]
Ornamental trees and shrubs named in honor of Andreas Caesalpini (1519-1603), Italian botanist and physician to Pope Clement VIII.

caesius, -a, -um [SEE-sius]
Bluish-gray.

caespitosus, -a, -um [see-spit-o-sus]
Growing in dense clumps; cespitose.

caffer, caffra, caffrum [KAFF-er]
caffrorum [kaff-RO-rum]
Of South Africa; Kaffir.

cainito [KAY-nit-o]
West Indian vernacular for the star apple (*Chrysophyllum cainito*).

Caiophora [ky-OFF-or-a]
Gr. *kaios*, a burn; *phoreo*, to bear; in allusion to the stinging hairs of these usually climbing on trailing plants.

cajan [KAY-jan]
Adaptation of a vernacular name for the pigeon pea.

cajanifolius, -a, -um [kay-jan-i-FO-lius]
With leaves like the pigeon pea.

Cajanus [ka-JAY-nus]
Latinized version of the vernacular name for the nutritious pigeon pea which is widely grown throughout the tropics. In India it is called "dall," and is cooked into a tasty potage to be eaten with curries.

calaba [KAL-a-ba]
West Indian vernacular name of *Calophyllum calaba*.

calabricus, -a, -um [kal-AB-rik-us]
From Calabria in Italy.

Caladium [kal-AY-dium]
Derivation of the name for these perennials with ornamental leaves is uncertain.

calamifolius, -a, -um [kal-am-i-FO-lius]
With reedlike leaves.

Calamus [KAL-am-us]
Cane and rattan palms. Gr. *kalamos*, a reed.

Calandrinia [kal-an-DRIN-ia]
Rock purslane. Named in honor of J. L. Calandrini, 18th-century Genevan botanist.

Calanthe [kal-ANTH-e]
Gr. *kalos*, beautiful; *anthos*, a flower. Chiefly terrestrial orchids.

Calathea [kal-a-THEE-a]
Gr. *kalathos*, a basket; in allusion to the flower cluster of these perennial foliage plants which looks like flowers in a basket.

calathinus, -a, -um [kal-a-THY-nus]
Basketlike.

calcaratus, -a, -um [cal-car-AY-tus]
Spurred.

calcareus, -a, -um [kal-KAIR-eus]
Pertaining to lime.

Calceolaria [kal-see-o-LAIR-ia]
Slipper-wort. L. *calceolus*, a slipper; in allusion to the form of the flower.

calcicola [kal-kik-o-la]
Growing in limey soil.

Calendula [kal-END-yew-la]
Marigold. L. *calendae*, the first day of the month and also the day on which interest must be paid. The allusion is to the long flowering of some of the species. *C. officinalis* is the pot-marigold which was used in English country cooking to flavor thick soups. A single head thrown into the pan imparts a pleasing taste.

calendulaceus, -a, -um [kal-end-ew-LAY-seeus]
Like *Calendula* in color.

californicus, -a, -um [kal-iff-ORN-ik-us]
Of California.

Calimeris [cal-IM-er-is]
Gr. *kalyx*, a cup; *meris*, a part; from the form of the involucre of these daisy-like plants.

Calla [KAL-la]
Gr. *kalos*, beautiful. *C. palustris*, the water-arum, is the only species in the genus. It has nothing to do with the popu-

larly named calla-lily which belongs to the genus *Zantedes-chia.*

Calliandra [kal-i-AND-ra]
Gr. *kalos,* beautiful; *andros,* a stamen. These flowering ever-green shrubs and trees have conspicuous stamens.

callianthus, -a, um [kal-i-ANTH-us]
Having beautiful flowers.

Callicarpa [kal-i-KARP-a]
Gr. *kalos,* beautiful; *karpos,* fruit. The shrubs are some-times called beauty-berry or French mulberry.

callicarpus, -a, -um [kal-i-KARP-us]
With beautiful fruit.

Callicoma [kal-ik-O-ma]
Gr. *kalos,* beautiful; *kome,* hair; in allusion to the tufted heads of the flowers on these Australian evergreen shrubs or trees.

Callirhoë [kal-LI-ro-ee]
Poppy-mallow. Showy herbs named in honor of the daughter of a minor Greek deity, Achelous, a river god.

callistachyus, -a, -um [kal-is-TAK-yus]
With beautiful spikes.

callistegioides [kal-iss-tee-ji-OY-deez]
Resembling *Calystegia,* a genus of convolvulus which includes *C. sepium,* the vicious bindweed.

Callistemon [kal-iss-TEE-mon]
Bottlebrush tree. Gr. *kalos,* beautiful; *stemon,* a stamen; in allusion to the beauty of the flowers of these ornamental shrubs.

Callistephus [kal-ISS-tee-fuss]
China or annual aster. From Gr. *kalistos,* very beautiful; *stephanos,* a crown; from the appearance of the flowers.

callistus, -a, -um [kal-ISS-tus]
Very beautiful.

Callitris [kal-LY-tris]
Cypress pine. From Gr. *kalos,* beautiful; an allusion to the beauty of the tree.

callizonus, -a, -um [kal-iz-O-nus]
Beautifully banded or zoned.

callosus, -a, -um [kal-O-sus]
Thick-skinned; with calluses.

Calluna [kal-LOON-a]
Heather or ling. From Gr. *kalluno,* to cleanse or adorn. This seems to be an allusion to the common use of heather for making brooms.

Calocephalus [kal-o-SEFF-al-us]
Gr. *kalos,* beautiful; *cephalos,* a head; an allusion to the flower of these Australian herbs or shrubs.

calocephalus, -a, -um [kal-o-SEFF-al-us]
Beautiful head.

Calochortus [kal-o-KORT-us]
Mariposa lily. Gr. *kalos,* beautiful; *chortos,* grass.

calocomus, -a, -um [kal-OK-o-mus]
With beautiful hair or bristles.

Calodendrum [kal-o-DEND-rum]
Cape chestnut. Gr. *kalos,* beautiful; *dendron,* a tree.

Calonyction [kal-o-NIK-tion]
Moonflower. From Gr. *kalos,* beautiful; *nyktos,* night; in allusion to the beauty of these night-blooming plants.

Calophaca [kal-OFF-ak-a]
From Gr. *kalos,* beautiful; *phake,* a lentil. These are leguminous shrubs not unlike laburnum.

calophyllus, -a, -um [kal-o-FILL-us]
With beautiful leaves.

Calophyllum [kal-o-FILL-um]
Calaba tree. From Gr. *kalos,* beautiful; *phyllon,* a leaf. The leaves of these evergreen, aromatic trees are a beautiful veined green.

Calopogon [kal-o-PO-gon]
Gr. *kalos,* beautiful; *pogon,* a beard; in allusion to the fringed lip of this native North American bog-orchid.

Calothamnus [kal-o-THAM-nus]
Gr. *kalos,* beautiful; *thamnos,* a shrub.

Calpurnia [kal-PER-nia]
African trees and shrubs named after T. Julius Calpurnius, a second-rate Latin poet who imitated Virgil. The genus is closely related to and may be said to imitate the genus *Virgilia.* This botanical witticism is possibly too esoteric for these non-classical days.

Caltha [KAL-tha]
In America, cowslip; in England, marsh-marigold or king-

cup. From the Latin name for a plant with a yellow flower—
possibly *Calendula.*

calvus, -a, -um [KAL-vus]
Bald; hairless; naked.

calycanthema [kal-ik-an-THEE-ma]
Species name of *Campanula* for cup-and-saucer Canterbury
bell. Literally, blossoming in the calyx.

Calycanthus [kal-ik-ANTH-us]
Carolina allspice. Gr. *kalyx,* calyx; *anthos,* a flower. The
calyx and the petals are the same color on these North
American aromatic deciduous shrubs.

calycinus, -a, -um [kal-ISS-in-us]
Calyx-like.

Calycotome [kal-ik-OT-o-me]
Gr. *kalyx,* calyx; *tome,* a part left after cutting; a tree stump.
The upper part of the calyx drops after the flower opens on
these deciduous spiny shrubs.

Calypso [kal-IP-so]
Bog-orchid named in honor of the nymph Calypso, daughter of Atlas, who entertained Odysseus for seven years but,
even with the promise of immortality, could not overcome
his longing to return home. In the end, Zeus had to send
Hermes to bid her release him.

calyptratus, -a, -um [kal-ip-TRAY-tus]
Bearing a calyptra, any caplike covering of a flower or fruit.

Calytrix [kal-EYE-trix]
Gr. *kalyx,* calyx; *thrix,* a hair. The divisions of the calyx end
in long bristling hairs on these heathlike shrubs.

camara [kam-MARR-a]
South American vernacular name for a species of *Lantana.*

Camarotis [kam-a-RO-tis]
Gr. *kamarotos,* an arch; a reference to the arched shape of
the lip of the flower of these epiphytic orchids.

Camassia [kam-ASS-ia]
Camas or bear-grass. From the North American Indian
name, *quamash.* The bulbs formed an important part of the
local diet.

cambricus, -a, -um [KAM-brik-us]
Of Wales or Cambria.

Camellia [kam-ELL-ia, preferred in southern U.S.; kam-EE-
lia, widely accepted]

Evergreen flowering trees and shrubs named for Father Georg Josef Kamel (1661-1706), Moravian Jesuit priest, who botanized in Luzon in the Philippines, and wrote an account of the plants there. It was published in 1704 under his Latinized name, Camellus. Commercially the most important species is the tea plant, *Camellia thea* or *sinensis*. The flowering species are often referred to as japonicas, especially in England.

Camoensia [kam-o-EN-sia]
Shrubby climbers named in honor of Luis de Camoens (1524-80), celebrated Portuguese epic poet and author of *The Lusiads*.

Campanula [kam-PAN-ew-la]
Canterbury-bell. Bellflower. Harebell. Diminutive of L. *campana*, a bell; in allusion to the form of the flower.

campanularius, -a, -um [kam-pan-yew-LAY-rius]
Bell-flowered.

campanulatus, -a, -um [kam-pan-ew-LAY-tus]
Bell-shaped.

campanuloides [kam-pan-ew-LOY-deez]
Resembling *Campanula*.

campestris, -is, -e [kam-PEST-ris]
Of the fields or open plains.

camphoratus, -a, -um [kam-for-AY-tus]
Pertaining to or resembling camphor.

Camphorosma [kam-for-os-ma]
Gr. *kamphora*, camphor; *osme*, an odor. The shrub gives out an odor like camphor.

camtschatensis, -is, -e [kam-chat-EN-sis]
camtschaticus, -a, -um [kam-CHAT-ik-us]
From the Kamchatka Peninsula on the Siberian coast.

Campsidium [kamp-SID-ium]
From its likeness to *Campsis* or trumpet creeper.

Campsis [KAMP-sis]
Trumpet creeper. Gr. *kampe*, something bent. The stamens of these deciduous climbing plants are curved.

Camptosorus [kamp-toe-SOR-us]
Gr. *kamptos*, curved; *sorus*, a group of fern spore cases. The sori are curved on these ferns.

campylocarpus, -a, -um [kam-py-lo-KARP-us]
With curved fruit.

canadensis, -is, -e [kan-ad-EN-sis]
Canadian, but with a wide application to North America—a consequence of early French influence.

canaliculatus, -a, -um [kan-al-ik-ew-LAY-tus]
Channeled; grooved.

Cananga [kan-ANG-ga]
Latinized version of the Malayan vernacular name for these tropical trees, one of which yields the perfume known as macassar oil.

canariensis, -is, -e [kan-air-i-EN-sis]
From the Canary Islands.

Canarina [kan-air-EYE-na]
One of the species of these herbaceous perennials originated in the Canary Islands.

Canavalia [kan-av-AY-lia]
Jack-bean. Latinized version of the Malabar vernacular name for these climbing herbs or sub-shrubs.

canbyi [CAN-bi-eye]
In honor of William Marriott Canby (b. 1831), American botanist.

cancellatus, -a, -um [kan-sell-AY-tus]
Crossbarred.

candelabrum [kan-del-AB-rum]
Like a branched candlestick.

candicans [KAND-ik-ans]
Hairy or woolly-white.

candidissimus, -a, -um [kan-did-ISS-im-us]
Very hoary or hairy-white.

candidus, -a, -um [KAN-did-us]
Shining or pure white.

Candollea [kan-DOLL-ea]
Evergreen flowering shrubs from Australia named in honor of Augustus Pyramus de Candolle (1778-1841), Professor of Botany at Geneva, Switzerland.

Canella [kan-ELL-a]
Wild cinnamon. From L. *canna*, a reed; an allusion to the rolled bark.

canescens [can-ESS-ens]
With hairs of off-white or ashy-gray color.

caninus, -a, -um [kan-NY-nus]
Pertaining to dogs.

Canistrum [kan-ISS-trum]
L. *canistra*, a flat basket; in allusion to the appearance of the inflorescence of these Brazilian plants.

Canna [KAN-na]
Indian shot. From L. *canna*, a reed.

cannabinus, -a, um [kan-NAB-in-us]
Like *Cannabis* or hemp.

Cannabis [KAN-ab-is]
Hemp. The Latin name for the plant which, besides producing fiber, is also the source of such narcotic drugs as hashish and marijuana. For this reason cultivation is often prohibited.

cantabricus, -a, -um [kan-TAB-rik-us]
From Cantabria, a district of northern Spain.

Cantua [KAN-tua]
Latinized version of the Peruvian name for these evergreen flowering trees and shrubs.

canus, -a, -um [KAY-nus]
Off-white; ash-colored.

capensis, -is, -e [kay-PEN-sis]
From the Cape of Good Hope, South Africa.

capillaris, -is, -e [kap-ill-AIR-is]
Resembling hair; very slender.

capillatus, -a, -um [kap-ill-AY-tus]
Furnished with fine hairs.

capilliformis, -is, -e [kap-ill-i-FORM-is]
Like hair.

capillipes [kap-ILL-ip-ees]
Slender-footed.

capillus-veneris [kap-ILL-us—ven-er-is]
Venus' hair. Species name of *Adiantum*.

capitatus, -a, -um [kap-it-AY-tus]
Growing in a dense head—referring to the flowers, the fruit, or the whole plant.

capitellatus, -a, -um [kap-it-ell-AY-tus]
capitellus, -a, -um [kap-it-ELL-us]
capitulatus, -a, -um [kap-it-ew-LAY-tus]
Having a small head.

cappadocicus, -a, -um [kap-a-DO-sik-us]
From eastern Asia Minor, the ancient Province of Cappadocia.

Capparis [KAPP-a-ris]
Caper. The ancient Greek name for these evergreen shrubs. The flowerbuds of *C. spinosa* are pickled and known as capers.

capreolatus, -a, -um [kap-ree-o-LAY-tus]
Twining; winding.

capreus, -a, -um [KAP-reus]
Pertaining to goats.

capricornis, -is, -e [kap-rik-ORN-is]
(*a*) Like a goat's horn.
(*b*) From or below the Tropic of Capricorn in the Southern Hemisphere.

Capsicum [KAP-sik-um]
Peppers, both hot and sweet. From Gr. *kapto*, to bite. The true peppercorn, however, is *Piper nigra*.

capsularis, -is, -e [kaps-yew-LAIR-is]
Having capsules.

caracasanus, -a, -um [kar-ak-ass-AY-nus]
From Caracas, Venezuela.

Caragana [kar-rag-AY-na]
Latinized version of the Mongolian name for one of the species of these ornamental shrubs or small trees.

Cardamine [kar-DAM-in-ee]
Bitter cress. Cuckoo flower. Lady's smock. From the Greek name for a plant of the cress family.

cardaminefolius, -a, -um [kar-dam-in-e-FO-lius]
With leaves like *Cardamine*.

Cardiandra [kar-di-AND-ra]
Gr. *kardia*, a heart; *andros*, an anther; in allusion to the shape of the anthers of these ornamental shrubby plants.

cardinalis, is, -e [kar-din-AY-lis]
Scarlet; cardinal red.

cardiopetalus, -a, -um [kar-dio-pet-AL-us]
With heart-shaped petals.

Cardiospermum [kar-dio-SPERM-um]
Gr. *kardia*, heart; *spermum*, a seed. The black seed of these climbing herbs has a heart-shaped spot.

carduaceus, -a, -um [kar-dew-AY-seus]
Resembling a thistle.

cardunculus, -a, -m [kar-DUNK-ew-lus]
Resembling a small thistle.

Carduus [KARD-ew-us]
Thistle. The classical Latin name.

Carex [KAIR-ex]
Sedge. The classical Latin name.

caribaeus, -a, -um [kar-ib-EE-us]
Of the Caribbean area.

Carica [KA-rik-a]
Papaya. Derivation of *Carica* is obscure. The melon-like fruit, with its delicate and distinctive flavor, is a natural source of pepsin and is therefore a tenderizer. Tough meat wrapped in the rind overnight is much improved. In India pregnant women are forbidden the fruit because the black seeds are said to cause miscarriage. (See *carica.*)

carica [KA-rik-a]
Species name for fig, *Ficus carica.* The word is Latin for Caria, a district in Asia Minor where neither fig nor papaya originated.

caricinus, -a, -um [kar-i-SYN-us]
  caricosus, -a, -um [kar-ik-O-sus]
Resembling sedge or *Carex.*

caricifolius, -a, -um [kar-iss-i-FO-lius]
Sedge-leaved.

carinatus, -a, -um [kar-in-AY-tus]
  cariniferus, -a, -um [kar-in-IFF-er-us]
Having a keel.

carinthiacus, -a, -um [kar-in-THY-ak-us]
From Carinthia in Austria.

Carissa [kar-ISS-a]
Probably the Latinized version of the Indian vernacular name for these spinose shrubs with edible fruits.

carlesii [kar-LEES-i-eye]
In honor of W. R. Carles, a British consul in China, who collected *Viburnum carlesii* in Korea in 1889.

Carlina [kar-LY-na]
Carline thistle. A corruption of Carolus or Charlemagne. From a tradition that Charlemagne, having been shown the root of this thistle by an angel, used it successfully as a remedy for the plague which prevailed in his army.

Carludovica [kar-loo-do-VY-ka]
Palmlike plants named in honor of Charles IV (1748-1819) and his queen, Louise of Spain.

Carmichaelia [kar-my-KAY-lia]
Shrubs, becoming leafless when fully grown. Named in honor of Captain Dugald Carmichael (1722-1827), Scottish army officer and botanist who collected plants in New Zealand.

carminatus, -a, -um [kar-min-AY-tus]
carmineus, -a, -um [kar-MIN-eus]
Carmine.

Carnegia [kar-NEG-ia]
Giant cactus or suwarro, state flower of Arizona. Named in honor of Andrew Carnegie (1835-1919), steel magnate and philanthropist.

It is the only species in the genus. It was originally *Cereus giganteus* until it was reclassified and renamed by the botanists at the Desert Laboratory at Tucson, Arizona, which was supported by Carnegie. It was probably suitable that a great benefactor should be so honored, but the matter was handled so brashly that Carnegie took deep offense.

On the occasion of one of Carnegie's visits to Tucson, the dramatic announcement was made that the feature of his welcome was to be the magnificent plant recently named in his honor. Carnegie was much moved and looked forward with keen anticipation to seeing what he understood was a new discovery. On seeing the giant cactus blooming in profusion, it was natural for Carnegie to inquire how so enormous and conspicuous a plant could have remained unnamed. When the matter was explained, Carnegie lost interest in the festivities.

carnerosanus, -a, -um [kar-ner-o-SAN-us]
From the Carnerosa Pass in Mexico.

carneus, -a, -um [KAR-neus]
carnicolor [kar-NIK-oll-or]
Flesh-colored; deep pink.

carnicus, -a, -um [KAR-nik-us]
Fleshy.

carniolicus, -a, -um [kar-ni-o-lik-us]
From Carniola in Yugoslavia on the Italian border.

carnosulus, -a, -um [kar-NO-su-lus]
Rather fleshy.

carnosus, -a, -um [kar-NO-sus]
Fleshy.

84

carolinianus, -a, -um [kar-o-lin-i-AY-nus]
  carolinensis, -is, -e [kar-o-lin-EN-sis]
  carolinus, -a, -um [kar-o-LY-nus]
From North Carolina or South Carolina.

carpaticus -a, -um (sometimes **carpathicus**) [kar-PAT-ik-us]
From the Carpathian Mountains between Czechoslovakia and Poland.

Carpentaria [kar-pen-TAIR-ia]
An evergreen flowering shrub named in honor of Professor William M. Carpenter (1811-1848), Louisiana physician.

Carpinus [kar-PY-nus]
Hornbeam. The classical Latin name. The English name is said to derive from the use of the wood for ox-yokes.

Carpodetus [kar-POD-et-us]
Gr. *karpos*, fruit; *detos*, bound; from the fact that the fruit of these evergreen shrubs or small trees is contracted in the middle.

Carrierea [kar-i-EER-ea]
Deciduous trees with attractive foliage and flowers, named in honor of E. A. Carrière (1816-1896), French botanist.

Carthamus [KAR-tham-us]
Distaff thistle. False saffron. From an Arabis word meaning to paint—an allusion to the brilliant color yielded by the flowers.

carthusianorum [kar-thew-si-ay-NOR-um]
Of the monks of the Carthusian Monastery of Grande Chartreuse near Grenoble, France.

cartilagineus, -a, -um [kar-til-aj-IN-eus]
Resembling cartilage.

Carum [kay-rum]
Caraway. A corruption of the Latin name. Caraway, *C. carvi*, from Caria, the name of the district in Asia Minor where it was much grown, is one of the few aromatics growing widely throughout the Northern temperate zone where it is much used to flavor cakes and breads. It yields an aromatic oil.

Carya [KAY-rya]
Hickory. From Gr. *karya*, a walnut tree; so called after Carya, daughter of the King of Laconia, who was changed by Bacchus into a walnut tree.

caryophyllus, -a, -um [kar-yo-FILL-us]
Literally with clovelike leaves, but generally relating to a clovelike scent as in the clove pink (*Dianthus caryophyllus.*)

Caryopteridifolius, -a, -um [ka-ri-op-ter-id-i-FO-lius]
With leaves like *Caryopteris.*

Caryopteris [ka-ri-OP-ter-is]
Blue spiraea. From Gr. *karyon*, a nut; *pteron*, a wing. The fruit is winged.

Caryota [ka-ri-o-ta]
Gr. *karyon*, any kind of nut. *C. ureus* is the toddy palm, widely grown throughout India and the East generally. It produces sap freely—as much as three gallons daily from a mature tree. This palm "wine" quickly ferments and very soon turns into the highly intoxicating toddy, looking and tasting rather like inferior gasoline. The availability of the tree is the despair of Indian prohibitionists.

caryotaefolius, -a, -um [ka-ri-o-tee-FO-lius]
With leaves like *Caryota* or fishtail palm.

caryotideus-, -a, -um [ka-ri-o-TID-eus]
Caryota-like.

cashmerianus, -a, -um [kash-meer-i-AY-nus]
From Kashmir.

Casimiroa [kas-im-i-RO-a]
Mexican evergreen trees, named for Cardinal Casimiro Gomez de Ortego, 18th-century Spanish churchman and botanist.

caspicus, -a, -um [KAS-pik-us]
caspius, -a, -um [KAS-pius]
From the shores of the Caspian Sea.

Cassia [KASS-ia]
Senna. The Greek name for a genus of leguminous plants which provide the senna leaves and pods that are important in pharmacy. Not to be confused with the cassia of commerce which is *Cinnamomum cassia* from which is derived an adulterant for true cinnamon. It is cheaper and looks the same, though coarser in flavor.

cassia [KASS-ia]
Specific name of cinnamon. (See *Cassia.*)

cassine [KASS-syne]
North American Indian name for dahoon, *Ilex cassine.*

Cassinia [kass-IN-ia]
Evergreen shrubs, named after Count Cassini, French botanist (d. 1832).

cassinoides [kass-in-OY-deez]
Resembling *Ilex cassine*.

Castanea [kas-TAY-nea]
Sweet chestnut. Among the species are the American, Spanish, and Chinese chestnuts. This is the Latin name for these trees, after the town of Castania in Thessaly which was famous for them.

Castanopsis [kas-tan-OP-sis]
Gr., resembling chestnut; from the similarity, although these trees are evergreen.

Castanospermum [kas-tan-o-SPERM-um]
Moreton Bay chestnut. From *castanea*, chestnut, Gr. *spermum*, a seed; in allusion to the form and size of the seed.

Castilloa [kas-TILL-oa]
In honor of Juan Castillo y Lopez, Spanish botanist. One of these species, *C. elastica*, yields a milky juice which can be a commercial source of rubber when the market is high enough. This is the plant that yielded the rubber balls which astonished Columbus.

Castilleja [kas-till-EE-ya]
Indian paint brush. Named for an 18th-century botanist, D. Castillejo, of Cadiz, Spain.

castus, -a, -um [KAST-us]
Spotless; chaste.

Casuarina [kas-ew-a-REE-na]
So named because the long, drooping branches of this Australian genus are supposed to resemble the feathers of a cassowary (*Casuarinus*). Called beefwood, sheoke, and Australian pine, these trees are features of many tropical beaches where alone they seem to grow well.

Cat plants
Various plants appear to be particularly attractive to cats, such as: *Nepeta*, both, *cataria*, or catnip, and *mussini;* the valerians; *Teucrium marum;* and *Actinidia kolomikta.* These are worth avoiding by those who dislike cats. Dogs do not seem to have any such preferences and, in any case, do not have such destructive garden habits.

Catalpa [kat-ALP-a]
The North American Indian name for these trees.

catalpifolius, -a, -um [kat-alp-i-FO-lius]
With leaves like catalpa.

Catananche [kat-a-NAN-ke]
Cupid's dart. Greek name for these herbs, traditionally the basis of love potions. The Greek name means a strong incentive.

Catappa [kat-APP-a]
Malayan name for the Indian almond.

cataria [kat-AIR-ia]
Pertaining to cats.

Catasetum [kat-a-SEE-tum]
Gr. *kata*, downward; *seta*, a bristle. A reference to the two horns of the column or structure formed by the junction of stamens and pistils in some of the species of this genus of epiphytic orchids.

catawbiensis, -is, -e [kat-aw-bi-EN-sis]
From the region of the Catawba River in the Blue Ridge Mountains in southeastern United States.

catechu [KAT-etch-ew]
Vernacular name of various Asiatic plants including betel palm (*Areca catechu*).

Catesbaea [kayts-BEE-a]
Lily thorn. In honor of Mark Catesby (1674-1749), of Sudbury, England, author of *A Natural History of Carolina.*

Catha [KAY-tha]
Latinized version of the Arabian name of this evergreen shrub with edible leaves.

catharticus, -a, -um [kath-ART-ik-us]
Purgative; cathartic.

cathayanus, -a, -um [kath-ay-AY-nus]
eathayensis, -is, -e [kath-ay-EN-sis]
From China.

Cathcartia [kath-KART-ia]
A poppy named in honor of J. F. Cathcart (1802-1851), Calcutta judge and amateur botanist.

catjang [KAT-jang]
Malayan vernacular name for *Vigna catjang*.

Cattleya [KATT-lee-a]
In honor of William Cattley (d. 1832) of Barnet, England,

a wealthy patron of botany and an ardent collector of rare plants. For many people the name is synonymous with orchid, or an expensive, showy, purple-and-white bloom tied with silver ribbon.

caucasicus, -a, -um [kaw-KAS-ik-us]
From the Caucasus.

caudatus, -a, -um [kaw-DAY-tus]
Having a tail; caudate.

caulescens [kawl-ESS-ens]
Having a stem.

cauliatus, -a, -um [kaw-li-AY-tus]
Having a winged stem.

cauliflorus, -a, -um [kaw-li-FLOR-us]
Bearing flowers on the stem or trunk.

Caulophyllum [kaw-lo-FILL-um]
Blue cohosh. From Gr. *kaulon*, a stem; *phyllon*, a leaf. The stem of this perennial forms a stalk for a single leaf.

caulorapus, -a, -um [kaw-lo-RAY-pus]
With a stem like a turnip, as in kohlrabi.

causticus, -a, -um [KAW-stik-us]
Burning or caustic to taste.

cavus, -a, -um [KAY-vus]
Hollow.

Ceanothus [see-an-o-thus]
New Jersey tea. From the Greek name for a spiny plant, not this one. This genus of shrubs is more appreciated abroad than in its native North America.

Cecropia [see-KRO-pia]
Milky-juiced trees named for Cecrops, king of Attica in ancient Greece.

Cedrela [SED-reel-a, preferred; sed-REE-la, popular]
Diminutive of L. *cedrus*, a cedar; from a similarity in the appearance and fragrance of the wood. The genus includes West Indian cedar which is much in demand for making cigar boxes.

Cedronella [sed-ro-NELL-a]
Diminutive of L. *cedrus*; cedar; probably from the fragrance of *C. triphylla* (balm of Gilead) which gives out a very sweet odor when gently rubbed.

Cedrus [SED-rus; popularly, SEE-drus]
Cedar. The Latin name. The genus includes such true cedars

as Atlas, cedar of Lebanon, and deodar. The trees popularly called "cedar" in the United States are generally *Juniperus* and *Thuja*.

Ceiba [say-EE-ba]
Latinized version of the South American name for the silk cotton tree which is the source of kapok, used for stuffing life-preservers and in the upholstery trade.

celastrinus, -a, -um [see-lass-TRY-nus]
Resembling bittersweet or *Celastrus*.

Celastrus [see-LASS-trus]
Bittersweet. From the Greek name for an evergreen tree.

Celmisia [sell-MIZ-ia]
New Zealand daisy. Named after Celmisios, son of the Greek nymph Alciope, for whom a related genus was named. This represents another of those classical subtleties for which a previous generation seems to have had a fondness.

Celosia [sell-o-sia]
Cock's comb. Gr. *kelos*, burned; in allusion to the brilliant color of some of the flowers.

Celsia [SELL-sia]
Herbs and sub-shrubs named in honor of Olof Celsius (1670-1756), a professor at Uppsala and a teacher of Linnaeus.

Celtis [SELL-tis]
Hackberry. The Greek name for another tree.

cembra [SEM-bra]
Italian name of the Swiss stone pine, *Pinus cembra*.

cenisius, a-, -um [sen-IZ-ius]
From the area of Mount Cenis between France and Italy.

Centaurea [sen-TOR-ee-a]
Knapweed. Bachelor's button. From centaur, one of a race, half-man and half-horse, of Greek mythology. The genus includes sweet sultan, dusty miller, and knapweed.

Centaurium [sen-TOR-ium]
Centaury. From centaur, the half-man half-horse of Greek mythology. This herb was supposed to have excellent medicinal qualities, especially in healing wounds. In fact, Chiron the Centaur, who was famous for his knowledge of the use of plants, is said to have used centaury to heal a wound in his foot, caused when he allowed one of the arrows of Hercules to fall on it.

centifolius, -a, -um [sen-ti-FO-lius]
Many-leaved; with a hundred leaves.

Centradenia [sen-tra-DEE-nia]
Gr. *kentron*, a spur; *aden*, a gland. The anthers of these flowering evergreen shrubs have a spurlike gland.

centralis, -a, -e [sen-TRAY-lis]
Spurred.

centranthifolius, -a, -um [sen-tran-thi-FO-lius]
With leaves like *Centranthus* or red valerian.

Centranthus [sen-TRAN-thus]
Red valerian. From Gr. *kentron*, a spur; *anthos*, a flower; from the sprurred flower. Often incorrectly spelled "Kentranthus."

Centropogon [sen-tro-PO-gon]
Gr. *kentron*, a spur; *pogon*, a beard; in allusion to the fringed stigma of these shrubs and sub-shrubs.

Centrosema [sen-tro-SEE-ma]
Butterfly pea. From Gr. *kentron*, a spur; *sema*, a standard. The standard has a short spur behind it.

Cephaelis [seff-EE-lis]
Gr. *kephale*, a head; from the close arrangement of the flowers of these shrubs and herbs, from one of which ipecac is produced.

Cephalanthus [seff-al-ANTH-us]
Button bush. Gr. *kephale*, a head; *anthos*, a flower. The flowers of these shrubs are closely packed in globose clusters.

Cephalaria [seff-al-AY-ria]
Giant scabious. Gr. *kephale*, a head. The flowers of these herbs are in round clusters.

cephalatus, -a, -um [seff-al-AY-tus]
Bearing heads.

cephalidus, -a, -um [seff-al-LY-dus]
Having a head.

Cephalocereus [seff-al-o-SEER-eus]
Old-man cactus. From Gr. *kephale*, a head; *cereus*, a genus of cactus. A woolly head is produced when the plant is of flowering size.

cephalonicus, -a, -um [seff-al-ON-ik-us]
From the Grecian island of Cephalonia in the Ionian Sea.

Cephalostachium [seff-al-o-STAY-kium]
Gr. *kephale,* a head; *stachys,* a spike. These bamboo grasses have flowers on spikelets.

Cephalotaxus [seff-al-o-TAX-us]
Plum yew. From Gr. *kephale,* a head; *taxus,* yew; a reference to the appearance of the trees which resemble yews.

cephalotes [seff-al-o-tees]
Resembling a small head.

cepifolius, -a, -um [sep-i-FO-lius]
With leaves resembling onion.

ceraceus, -a, -um [ser-AY-seus]
Waxy.

ceramicus, -a, -um [ser-AM-ik-us]
Resembling pottery.

cerasiferus, -a, -um [ser-ass-IFF-er-us]
Bearing cherries or cherry-like fruit.

cerasiformis, -is, -e [ser-ass-i-FORM-is]
Shaped like a cherry.

cerasinus, -a, -um [ser-a-SY-nus]
Cherry-red.

cerastioides [ser-ass-ti-OY-deez]
Resembling *Cerastium* or chickweed.

Cerastium [ser-ASS-tium]
Mouse-ear chickweed. From Gr. *keras,* a horn; in allusion to the horned shape of the seed capsule.

cerasus [ser-AY-sus]
Latin name for cherry, and now the species name for the sour cherry, *Prunus cerasus.*

ceratocaulis, -is, -e [ser-at-o-KAW-lis]
With a stalk like a horn.

Ceratonia [ser-at-o-nia]
Carob. From Gr. *keration,* a seed pod. The seed pods, sometimes sold in stores in New York, are called St. John's bread and are supposed to be the locusts which John the Baptist ate with wild honey in the wilderness. The seeds were used as weights and from them derives the carat, the jewelers' weight for gold and precious stones.

Ceratopetalum [ser-at-o-PET-al-um]
Gr. *keras,* a horn; *petalon,* a petal. The petals of one species of these Australian trees look like stag's horns.

Ceratophyllum [ser-at-o-FILL-um]
From Gr. *keras*, a horn; *phyllon*, a leaf; from the horned appearance of the leaves of these submerged plants.

Ceratopteris [ser-at-OP-ter-is]
Gr. *keras*, a horn; *pteris*, a fern; from the horned appearance of this water fern.

Ceratostigma [ser-at-o-STIG-ma]
Gr. *keras*, a horn and stigma; from the hornlike excrescence on the stigma of the flower.

Ceratozamia [ser-at-o-ZAY-mia]
Gr. *keras*, a horn; *Zamia*, the name of another genus, which it resembles except for the fact that here the cones of these Mexican foliage plants have horned scales.

Cercidiphyllum [ser-sid-i-FILL-um]
Gr. *cercis*, redbud or Judas tree; *phyllon*, a leaf; from the resemblance of the leaves to those of one species of the genus *Cercis*.

Cercidium [ser-SID-ium]
Resembling *Cercis* or redbud.

Cercis [SER-sis]
Redbud. Judas tree. The Greek name for a European species, traditionally the tree on which Judas hanged himself. The flowers, produced along the branches and trunk before the leaves appear, resemble blood.

Cerocarpus [ser-ko-KARP-us]
Gr. *kerkos*, a tail; *karpos*, a fruit. The fruit of these trees and shrubs has a tail-like plume.

cerealis, -is, -e [seer-i-AY-lis]
Pertaining to agriculture. Ceres was the goddess of farming.

cerefolius, -a, -um [ser-i-FO-lius]
Waxen-leaved.

Cereus [SEE-reus]
L. *cereus*, a wax taper; in allusion to the shape of some of the species of this cactus.

cereus, -a, -um [SEE-reus]
Waxy.

ceriferus, -a, -um [ser-IFF-er-us]
Wax-bearing.

Cerinthe [ser-IN-the]
Honeywort. From Gr. *keros*, wax; *anthos*, a flower. It was

once supposed that bees obtained wax from these flowers of which they are very fond.

cerinthoides [ser-inth-OY-deez]
Resembling *Cerinthe* or honeywort.

cerinus, -a, -um [ser-EYE-nus]
Waxy.

cernuus, -a, -um [ser-NEW-us]
Drooping; nodding.

Ceropegia [ser-o-PEEJ-ia]
Gr. *keros*, wax; *pege*, a fountain; in allusion to the waxen appearance of the flower clusters on these vines.

Ceroxylon [ser-ox-eye-lon]
Wax palm. From Gr. *keros*, wax; *xylon*, wood. The trunks of these feather palms are coated with wax.

cerris [SER-is]
Classical Latin name for the Turkey or mossy-cup oak, and now the specific name (*Quercus cerris*).

Cestrum [SES-trum]
Bastard jasmine. Greek name for some other plant than these ornamental shrubs.

Chaenomeles [kee-NOM-ee-lees or kee-no-MEE-lees]
Japanese quince. From Gr. *chaino*, to split; *meles*, an apple; an allusion to the erroneous belief that the fruit is split.

Chaenostoma [kee-NOS-tom-a or kee-no-STOM-a]
Gr. *chaino*, to gape; *stoma*, a mouth; an allusion to the form of the corolla of these African herbs and sub-shrubs.

Chaerophyllum [kee-ro-FILL-um]
Bulbous chervil. From Gr. *chairo*, to please; *phyllon*, a leaf. The foliage is fragrant.

chalcedonicus, -a, -um [kal-sed-ON-ik-us]
From Chalcedon, the classical name for what is now Kadekoy, a district in the neighborhood of Istanbul.

chalmersianus, -a, -um [chalm-ers-i-AY-nus]
In honor of James B. Chalmers (1841-1901), traveler and author of works on New Guinea, where he was killed by cannibals.

Chamaecereus [kam-ee-SEE-reus]
Gr. *chamai*, on the ground; *cereus*, a genus of cactus; an allusion to its prostrate habit.

Chamaecyparis [kam-ee-SIP-a-ris]
False cypress. From Gr. *chamai*, on the ground; *kuparissos*,

cypress. Often sold as *Retinospora*, the genus includes such specimen and timber trees as Port Orford and Alaska cedar, Hinoki cypress, and southern white cedar.

Chamaedaphne [kam-ee-DAFF-ne]
Gr. *chamai*, on the ground; *daphne*, laurel. An inappropriate name for this upright bog shrub.

Chamaedorea [kam-ee-DOR-ea]
Gr. *chamai*, on the ground; *dorea*, a gift. The shining bright-colored fruits of these palms are very easily reached.

chamaedrifolius, -a, -um [kam-ee-dri-FO-lius]
With leaves like *Chamaedrys* or ground oak.

chamaeiris [kam-ee-EYE-ris]
Specific name for an iris meaning dwarf iris.

Chamaelaucium [kam-ee-LAW-kium]
Meaning and derivation of the name for these Australian evergreen shrubs is obscure.

Chamaelirium [kam-ee-LEER-ium]
Devil's bit. This North American perennial is also sometimes called blazing star. From Gr. *chamai*, dwarf; *lirion*, a lily.

Chamaerops [kam-EE-rops]
Dwarf fan-palm. From Gr. *chamai*, dwarf; *rhops*, a bush.

Chambeyronia [sham-bay-RO-nia]
Palms named for Captain Chambeyron, who commanded the ship in which the French explorer Vieillard explored the coasts of New Caledonia where this genus was found.

charantia [ka-RAN-shee-a]
A pre-Linnaean and now the specific name for *Momordica charantia*.

charianthus, -a, -um [karri-ANTH-us]
With elegant flowers.

Charieis [KAR-ri-ice]
Greek word for elegant—in allusion to the beauty of the flowers of this South African herb.

chathamicus, -a, -um [chat-AM-ik-us]
From Chatham Island in the South Pacific.

Cheilanthes [ky-LAN-theez]
Lip ferns. From Gr. *cheilos*, a lip; *anthos*, a flower; in allusion to the form of the membranous covering of the spore-bearing parts.

cheilanthus, -a, -um [ky-LAN-thus]
With a flower furnished with a lip.

Cheiranthus [ky-RAN-thus]
Wallflower. The meaning is obscure although some suppose that it may derive from Gr. *cheir,* a hand; *anthos,* a flower; from the custom of carrying these old-fashioned, sweetly scented favorites in the hand as a bouquet.

chelidonioides [kelli-don-i-oy-deez]
Resembling *Chelidonium* or celandine.

Chelidonium [kelli-DO-nium]
Celandine. From Gr. *chelidon,* a swallow. The tradition is that the herb flowers when the swallows arrive.

Chelone [kell-o-ne]
Turtlehead. Greek word for a tortoise; in allusion to the appearance of the flower of these North American perennial herbs.

Chenopodium [ken-o-PO-dium]
Goosefoot. From Gr. *chen,* a goose; *pous,* a foot; from the shape of the leaf of these plants, mostly weeds but including some which are edible, such as good-King-Henry.

chilensis, -is, -e [chill-EN-sis]
From Chile.

chiloensis, -is, -e [chill-o-EN-sis]
From the island of Chiloe off the Chilean coast.

Chilopsis [KY-lop-sis]
Gr. *cheilos,* a lip; *opsis,* resembling. The calyx of this low tree or shrub has a distinct lip.

chimaera [kim-EER-a]
Specific name of uncertain application. The word means a monster; and, figuratively, a wild fancy.

Chimaphila [ky-MAFF-ill-a]
Pipsissewa. From Gr. *cheima,* winter; *phileo,* to love. These small perennials are evergreen.

Chimonanthus [ky-mo-NAN-thus]
Gr. *cheimon,* winter; *anthos,* flower. These shrubs flower in winter.

chinensis, -is, -e [chy-NEN-sis]
Chinese.

Chiococca [ky-o-KOK-a]
Snowberry. Gr. *chion,* snow; *kokkos,* a berry. The berries of one species of these evergreen shrubs, mostly climbers, are snow-white.

Chiogenes [ky-oj-en-eez]
Creeping snowberry. Gr. *chion*, snow; *genos*, offspring; in allusion to the snow-white berries.

Chionanthus [ky-o-NAN-thus]
Fringe-tree. Gr. *chion*, snow; *anthos*, a flower. These shrubs have showy white flowers.

chionanthus, -a, -um [ky-o-NAN-thus]
Having snow-white flowers.

Chionodoxa [ky-o-no-DOX-a]
Gr. *chion*, snow; *doxa*, glory. Among the very earliest of spring flowers, they often bloom when snow is still on the ground.

Chionophila [ky-o-NOFF-ill-a]
Gr. *chion*, snow; *phileo*, to love. It grows at high elevations in the Rocky Mountains.

chiotilla [chy-o-TILL-a]
Mexican name for a cactus, *Escontra chiotilla*.

Chironia [ky-RO-nia]
South African plants in the gentian family named for Chiron, a centaur, son of Phyllira and Saturn. One of the beings half-man and half-horse, he was skilled in the medicinal use of plants.

chirophyllus, -a, -um [ky-ro-FILL-us]
With leaves resembling a hand.

chloodes [klo-o-deez]
Grass-green.

Chloraea [klo-REE-a]
Gr. *chloros*, green. Flowers of some of the species in this terrestrial fleshy-rooted genus in the orchid family are green.

chloraefolius, -a, -um [klo-ree-FO-lius]
With leaves like *Chlora*, a genus of no horticultural interest.

chloranthus, -a, -um [klo-RANTH-us]
With green flowers.

Chloris [KLO-ris]
Finger-grass. Ornamental flowering grasses named in honor of Chloris, the Greek goddess of flowers.

chlorochilon [klo-ro-KY-lon]
With a green lip.

Chlorocodon [klo-ro-KO-don]
Gr. *chloros*, green; *kodon*, a bell; from the shape and color of the flower of this climber from Natal.

Chlorogalum [klo-ROG-al-um]
Gr. *chloros,* green; *gala,* milk; from the green color of the
sap of these bulbous plants from California.

Chlorophora [klo-ROFF-or-a]
Gr. *chloros,* green; *phoreo,* to bear. One of the species of
these trees with milky sap produces a green dye.

Chlorophytum [klo-ro-FY-tum]
From Gr. *chloros,* green; *phyton,* a plant. Some of these
herbaceous plants are grown for their foliage.

Choisya [SHOY-sia]
Mexican orange. An evergreen flowering shrub named in
honor of M. J. D. Choisy (1799-1859), Swiss botanist.

chordatus, -a, -um [cord-AY-tus]
Cordlike.

Chorisia [kor-ISS-ia]
Floss silk tree. Named in honor of Ludwig Choris, a botani-
cal artist, who accompanied the noted Russian navigator,
Otto von Kotzbue, on his great scientific expedition to the
Pacific, 1823-1826.

Chorizema [kor-RIZ-ee-ma, or kor-riz-EE-ma]
Derivation somewhat obscure but possibly from Gr. *chora,*
a place; *zema,* a drink. This genus of evergreen flowering
shrubs was discovered by the French botanist Labillardière
in Australia in 1792. It was found growing over a spring of
sweet water discovered after several frustrating experiences
with salt springs.

Chrysalidocarpus [kirs-al-id-o-KARP-us]
Gr. *chrysos,* gold; *karpos,* fruit; in allusion to the golden
fruit of one of the species. C. *lutescens* is the *Areca* of florists,
properly cane palm.

Chrysanthemum [kris-ANTH-em-um]
Gr. *chrysos,* gold; *anthos,* flower. Comprising about 150 species, the genus runs all the way from the hothouse chrysanthemum to the common white daisy of the fields.

Chrysantheoides [kris-anth-e-OY-deez]
Resembling *Chrysanthemum.*

Chrysanthus, -a, -um [kris-ANTH-us]
With golden flowers.

chryseus, -a, -um [KRIS-eus]
Golden.

Chrysobalanus [kris-o-bal-AY-nus]

Gr. *chrysos*, gold; *balanos*, an acorn; in allusion to the yellow fruit of some of the species of these shrubs and trees.

chrysocarpus, -a, -um [kris-o-KARP-us]

With golden fruit.

Chrysogonum [kris-OG-o-num]

Golden star. Gr. *chrysos*, gold; *gonu*, a knee. The golden flowers generally occur at the stem joints.

chrysokomus, -a, -um [kris-OK-o-mus]

With golden hairs.

chrysolepis, -is, -e [kris-OLL-ep-is]

With golden scales.

chrysoleucus, -a, -um [kris-o-LEW-kus]

Gold-and-white.

chrysolobus, -a, -um [kris-ol-LO-bus]

Golden-lobed.

chrysophyllus, -a, -um [kris-o-FILL-us]

With golden leaves.

Chrysopsis [kris-OP-sis]

Golden aster. Gr. *chrysos*, gold; *opsis*, appearance. The flowers are golden.

chrysostomus, -a, -um [kris-os-to-mus]

Golden-mouthed.

Chusquea [chus-KWEE-a]

A local Jamaican name for these bamboos.

Chysis [KY-sis]

From Gr. *chysis*, melting. The pollen masses in these orchids appear to be fused into a whole.

Cibotium [sy-BO-tium]

Sythian lamb (see *barometz*). From Gr. *kibotos*, a small box; from the appearance of the seed vessels of these tree ferns.

Cicer [SY-ser]

Chick pea or garbanzo. The classical Latin name.

cichoriaceus, -a, -um [sik-or-i-AY-seus]

Resembling chicory or *Cichorium*.

Cichorium [sik-OR-ium]

Chicory, endive. The Latinized version of the Arabic name for one of the species.

Cicuta [sik-YEW-ta]

Water hemlock. The Latin name for poison hemlock (*Conium maculatum*) from which the brew was made for the execution of Socrates. Both plants are equally poisonous and have no garden interest.

cicutaefolius, -a, -um [sik-ew-tee-FO-lius]
With leaves like water hemlock or *Cicuta*.

cicutarius, -a, -um [sik-ew-TAY-rius]
Resembling water hemlock or *Cicuta*.

ciliaris, -is, -e [silly-AIR-is]
ciliatus, -a, -um [silly-AY-tus]
Fringed with hairs, on many leaves and petals; ciliate.

cilicicus, -a, -um [sy-LISS-ik-us]
From Lesser Armenia in Turkey, once called Cilicia.

ciliicalyx [silly-EYE-kal-ix]
With a fringed calyx.

ciliosus, -a, -um [silly-o-SUS]
Slightly fringed or ciliate.

Cimicifuga [sim-i-SIFF-ew-ga]
Bugbane. Black cohosh. From L. *cimex*, a bug; *fugo*, to drive away; from the use of *C. foetida* as an insect repellent. The genus includes snakeroot, regarded as useful in cases of snakebite because of the form and shape of the root.

Cinchona [sin-KO-na]
Named in honor of Countess de Chinchon, wife of the Viceroy of Peru, who, legend has it, was cured in 1638 of malaria by use of what was then called Peruvian bark. It is the source of quinine, the commercial production of which is now centered in Java. During World War II it was an important part of Japanese strategy to cut the world off from supplies of quinine. Fortunately Western medicine quickly provided an effective synthetic without which the campaigns in malarial areas could not have been fought.

cinctus, -a, -um [SINK-tus]
Girdled; girt around.

cinerariaefolius, -a, -um [sin-er-rare-i-ee-FO-lius]
With leaves like *Cineraria*.

Cineraria [sin-er-RARE-ia]
From L. *cinerea*, ash-colored; from the gray down on the leaves of these herbs and sub-shrubs.

cinerascens [sin-er-ASS-ens]
Becoming ashy-gray.

cinereus, -a, -um [sin-EER-eus]
Ash-colored.

cinnabarinus, -a, -um [sin-nab-bar-EYE-nus]
Cinnabar-red; vermilion.

cinnamomeus, -a, -um [sin-am-o-meus]
Brown like cinnamon.

cinnamomifolius, -a, -um [sin-am-o-mi-FO-lius]
With leaves like cinnamon.

Cinnamomum [sin-am-o-mum]
From the classical Greek name for cinnamon. The genus includes the camphor tree and also cassia, which is widely grown throughout the Far East as an adulterant of true cinnamon, *C. zeylanicum.*

Cipura [sy-PUR-a]
Derivation of the name of these South American bulbous plants is unknown.

circinalis, -is, -e [ser-sin-AY-lis]
  circinatus, -a, -um [ser-sin-AY-tus]
Coiled.

cirratus, -a, -um [si-RAY-tus]
  cirrhosus, -a, -um [si-RO-sus]
Equipped with tendrils.

Cirsium [SER-sium]
Plumed thistle. From the Greek for a kind of thistle. The genus includes a great many pernicious weeds and very few plants of value to the gardener.

cismontanus, -a, -um [sis-mon-TAY-nus]
On this side of the mountain—meaning the south side of the Alps, the side on which Rome stands.

cisplatinus, -a, -um [sis-plat-EYE-nus]
From the neighborhood of the River Plate in South America.

Cissus [SISS-us]
From Gr. *kissos,* ivy; an allusion to the climbing habits of these shrubs.

cistiflorus, -a, -um [sis-ti-FLOR-us]
Cistus-flowered.

cistifolius, -a, -um [sis-ti-FO-lius]
With leaves like *Cistus.*

Cistus [SIS-tus]
Rock-rose. From the Greek name for the plant.

Citharexylum [sith-ar-EX-ill-um]
Gr. *kithara,* a lyre; *xylon,* wood. The wood is used locally for making musical instruments.

citratus, -a, -um [sit-RAY-tus]
Resembling *Citrus*

citrifolius, -a, -um [sit-ri-FO-lius]
With leaves resembling *Citrus*.

citrinus, -a, -um [sit-RY-nus]
Lemon-colored or resembling citron.

citriodorus, -a, -um [sit-ri-o-DOR-us]
Lemon-scented.

citroides [sit-ROY-deez]
Resembling *Citrus*.

Citropsis [sit-ROP-sis]
Citrus plus Greek *opsis*, resembling. These small trees are somewhat like *Citrus*.

Citrullus [sit-RULL-us]
From *Citrus*, from the appearance of the fruit. Watermelon is *C. vulgaris*.

Citrus [SIT-rus]
Latin name for some other fruit but applied by Linnaeus to this genus which includes, oranges, lemons, limes, and grapefruit.

Cladanthus [klad-ANTH-us]
From Gr. *klados*, a branch; *anthos*, a flower. The flowers of this annual herb occur at the ends of the branches.

Cladastris [klad-ASS-tris]
Kentucky yellow-wood. From Gr. *klados*, a branch; *thraustos*, fragile; from the brittle nature of the twigs.

cladocalyx [klad-ok-AY-lix, or klad-o-KAY-lix]
With a club-shaped calyx.

clandestinus, -a, -um [klan-des-TY-nus]
Hidden.

Clarkia [KLAR-kia]
North American annuals named in honor of Captain William Clark (1770-1838), who with Captain Meriwether Lewis made the first transcontinental expedition, crossing the Rocky Mountains in 1806.

Clausena [klaw-SEE-na]
A genus of trees named in honor of P. Clauson, a Danish botanist, who wrote of the Algae in 1634.

clausus, -a -um [KLAW-sus]
Closed; shut.

clava-Herculis [klav-a-HER-kew-lis]
Club of Hercules. A species name of *Zanthoxylum.*

clavatus, -a, -um [klav-AY-tus]
Club-shaped.

clavellatus, -a, -um [klav-ell-AY-tus]
Shaped like a small club.

Clavija [klav-EYE-ja]
Evergreen trees and shrubs named in honor of Don Jose de
Viera y Clavijo (1731-1813), who translated the works of
Buffon in Spanish.

clavus [KLAV-vus]
A club.

Claytonia [klay-TOE-nia]
Little spring-blooming perennials named in honor of John
Clayton (1686-1773), who came to Virginia from England
in 1705. He corresponded with the botanical great of the
day—Linnaeus, Gronovius, Kalm, and John Bartram—as
well as with Benjamin Franklin and Thomas Jefferson. Collinson (see *Collinsonia*), the English Quaker botanist, described him as the greatest botanist in America. The common
spring-beauty, sometimes called good-morning spring (*C.
virginica*) is a species in the genus.

Cleistocactus [kly-sto-KAK-tus]
From Gr. *kleistos*, closed, plus *cactus*. The flowers hardly
open.

clematideus, -a, -um [klem-a-TID-eus]
Like *Clematis.*

Clematis [KLEM-at-is]
Greek name for various climbing plants.

Cleome [klee-o-mee]
Derivation unknown. Spider flower is *C. spinosa.*

Clerodendrum [kler-o-DEN-drum]
Gr. *kleros*, chance; *dendron*, a tree. Supposed to be an allusion
to the variable medicinal qualities of these shrubs, trees, and
climbers.

Clethra [KLETH-ra]
Sweet pepper bush. White alder. The Greek name for alder
and applied here because of the leaf similarity.

clethroides [kleth-ROY-deez]
Resembling *Clethra.*

Clianthus [kly-ANTH-us]
Glory Pea. Gr. *kleios*, glory; *anthos*, a flower; in allusion to the brilliantly colored flowers of these trailing shrubs.

Cliftonia [kliff-TOE-nia]
An evergreen shrub named in honor of Dr. Francis Clifton, English physician, who died in 1736.

Clintonia [klin-TOE-nia]
Bear-tongue. Low herbaceous plants named for Governor De Witt Clinton, (1769-1828) of New York, who promoted the construction of the Erie Canal.

Clitoria [kly-TOW-ria]
Butterfly pea. From *L. clitoris*, an anatomical term; an allusion to a characteristic of the flower.

Clivia [KLY-via]
Kaffir lily. Bulbous evergreen plants named after a Duchess of Northumberland, a member of the Clive family, who lived in the first half of the 19th century.

clivorum [kly-VOR-um]
Of the hills.

clypeatus, -a, -um [kly-pee-AY-tus]
Resembling a Roman shield.

clypeolatus, -a, -um [kly-pee-o-LAY-tus]
Somewhat shield-shaped.

Clytostoma [kly-TOS-tom-a]
Trumpet flower. Gr. *klytos*, beautiful; *stoma*, a mouth. A reference to the beauty of the flowers of these evergreen climbers.

Cneorum [nee-o-rum]
Spurge olive. From the Greek name for some shrub resembling olive.

Cnicus [NY-kus]
Blessed thistle. From Gr. *knikos*, a thistle.

coarctatus, -a, -um [ko-ark-TAY-tus]
Pressed or crowded together.

Cobaea [ko-BEE-a]
Tendrilar climbers named in honor of a Jesuit Father, Bernardo Cobo (1572-1659), Spanish missionary and naturalist in Mexico and Peru.

cocciferus, -a, -um [kok-IFF-er-us]
coccigerus, -a, um [kok-IJ-er-us]
Berry-bearing.

coccineus, -a, -um [kok-SIN-eus]
Scarlet.

Coccinia [kok-SIN-ia]
L. *coccineus*, scarlet; from the color of the fruits.

Coccoloba [kok-o-LO-ba]
Seaside grape. From Gr. *kokkos*, a berry; *lobos*, a lobe; in allusion to the fruit.

Coccothrinax [kok-o-THRY-nax]
From Gr. *kokkos*, a berry, and *Thrinax*, a related genus of fan palms. They have berrylike fruits.

Cocculus [kok-EW-lus]
Moonseed. Snail-seed. From the diminutive of Gr. *kokkus*, a berry; in allusion to the seed of these ever green climbers or shrubs.

Cochemiea [koch-EE-mia]
From the name of an Indian tribe which once lived in lower California, home of these plants of the *Cactus* family.

cochenillifera [koch-en-eel-IFF-er-a]
Cochineal bearing. Species name of the cochineal fig, *Nopulea cochinillifera*. Cochineal is a dyestuff made from the dried bodies of the females of a scale insect found in Mexico and Central America. It is used as a reddish or purple coloring for foodstuffs and is the source of carmine.

Cochlearia [kok-lee-AIR-ia]
Scurvy grass. From L. *cochlear*, a spoon; from the shape of the basal leaves of these herbs.

cochlearis, -is, -e [kok-lee-AY-ris]
Spoon-shaped.

cochleatus, -a, -um [kok-lee-AY-tus]
Spiral like a snail shell.

Cochlospermum [kok-lo-SPERM-um]
From Gr. *kochlos*, a spiral shell; *sperma*, seed; in allusion to the shape of the seeds of these tropical trees.

Cocos [KO-kos]
The coconut palm is so widespread that it is impossible to guess where it originated. It has spread itself by natural means over the sea coasts of the tropics wherever it could find a footing on a sandy shore. One of the important sources of vegetable oil, it is an indispensable article of diet in many places. Sailing vessels in many parts of the world are rigged with coconut-fiber ropes, the nut shells

are used as drinking and other cups, the leaves are used for thatch, while the trunks make a handsome timber commercially called porcupine wood.

Codiaeum [ko-di-EE-um]
Croton. Latinized version of the Malayan vernacular name.

Codonopsis [ko-don-OP-sis]
From Gr. *kodon*, a bell; *opsis*, resembling; from the shape of the corolla of these herbs.

coelestinus, -a, -um [see-less-TY-nus]
coelestis, -is, -e [see-LESS-tis]
Sky-blue.

coeli-rosa [see-li-RO-sa]
Species name meaning rose of the sky.

Coelia [SEE-lia]
Gr. *koilos*, hollow; from an erroneous concept that the pollen masses of these epiphytic orchids were concave within.

Coelogyne [see-LOJ-in-ee]
Gr. *koilos*, hollow; *gyne*, female; referring to the depressed stigma of these epiphytic orchids.

coerulescens [see-roo-LESS-ens]
coeruleus, -a, -um [see-ROO-leus]
The first, almost dark blue; the second, dark blue.

Coffea [KOFF-ee-a]
Coffee. From the Arabic name of the beverage. The coffee we drink is made from the ground-up seed which grows enclosed in a bright scarlet cherry. Although long thought to have come from Arabia, the plant originated in Africa.

cognatus, -a, -um [kog-NAY-tus]
Closely related to.

coggygria [kog-JIG-ria]
Greek name for the smoke-tree. (See *Cotinus*.)

Coix [KO-ix]
Job's tears. From the Greek name for a reedlike plant.

Cola [KO-la]
From the African vernacular name. Cola or goora nuts are widely used in a variety of soft drinks, being an essential ingredient in some of the best known. The nuts are said by Africans to increase endurance.

colchicus, -a, -um [KOL-chik-us]
From the Black Sea shores of Georgia, once called Colchis.

Colchicum [KOL-chik-um]

Autumn crocus. Supposed to have originated in Colchis.

Coleonema [ko-leo-NEE-ma]

From Gr. *koleos*, a sheath; *nema*, a thread; referring to the filaments of the stamens which are folded in the petals of these South African evergreen shrubs.

Coleus [KO-leus]

Gr. *koleos*, a sheath; an allusion to the manner in which the stamens are enclosed. Called simply the Foliage Plant in large areas of the United States, the leaves tend to be very colorful. The plants were once widely used for ornamental ribbon bedding, sometimes on a very large scale. In fact, sixty years ago a large and pretentious garden might use many thousands of plants annually in its formal bedding arrangements. The fashion for this kind of thing has waned and few gardeners remain as exponents of the art. Fine examples, however, may still be seen in the Boston Public Gardens—one year a recognizable profile of George Washington, another year a clock face, another the insignia of the American Legion, and so on.

Colletia [ko-LEE-shea]

Spiny shrubs named in honor of Philibert Collet (1643-1718), French botanist.

Collinsia [kol-IN-sia]

Blue-eyed Mary. Annuals named in honor of Zaccheus Collins (1764-1831), Vice President of the Philadelphia Academy of Natural Sciences.

Collinsonia [kol-in-so-nia]

Horse balm, horse weed. Coarse herbs named in honor of Peter Collinson, 18th-century English Quaker botanist, who corresponded widely with men like Linnaeus and with John Bartram and John Clayton (see *Claytonia*) in America.

collinus, -a, -um [kol-LY-nus]

Pertaining to a hill.

Collomia [kol-o-mia]

From Gr. *kolla*, glue. The seeds of these herbs are mucilaginous when wet.

Colocasia [kol-o-KAY-sia]

West Indian kale. Taro root. Elephant's ear. From the Arabic vernacular name for these herbs, some with edible tubers.

colorans [KOL-or-ans]
coloratus, -a, -um [kol-or-AY-tus]
Colored.

Colquhounia [ko-HOO-nia]
Asian shrubs named in honor of Sir Robert Colquhoun, patron of the Calcutta Botanic Gardens in the early part of the 19th century.

colubrinus, -a, -um [kol-ew-BRY-nus]
Snakelike; shaped like a snake.

columbarius, -a, -um [kol-um-BAY-rius]
Dovelike or pertaining to doves.

columbianus, -a, -um [kol-um-bi-AY-nus]
From British Columbia.

columellaris, -is, -e [kol-ew-mel-AY-ris]
Pertaining to a small pillar or pedestal.

columnaris, -is, -e [kol-um-NAY-ris]
Columnar; in the shape of a column.

Columnea [ko-LUM-nea]
Tropical American herbs and shrubs named in honor of Fibius Columna (Fabio Colonna, 1567-1640) author of the first botanical book with copper-plate illustrations, published in Naples 1592.

colurna [ko-LURN-a]
Classical name and now a species name of the hazelnut.

Colutea [ko-LEW-tea]
Bladder senna. From the Greek name for these shrubs.

Collvillea [kol-VILL-ea]
A scarlet flowering tree named in honor of Sir Charles Colville, a 19th-century governor of Mauritius.

comans [KO-mans]
comatus, -a, -um [ko-MAY-tus]
Furnished with hair; hairy.

Combretum [kom-BREE-tum]
Latin name for a climbing plant, not this genus of trees and shrubs, some of which are climbers.

Comesperma [ko-mes-PER-ma]
From Gr. *kome*, hair; *sperma*, a seed; in allusion to the tufts of hair on the seeds of these herbs and shrubs.

Commelina [ko-mel-LY-na]
Day-flower. Named for the three Commelin brothers, Dutch botanists—Johann (1629-1698), Kaspar (1667-1731), and

a third who died very young. To quote Linnaeus, "Commelina has flowers with three petals, two of which are showy, while the third is not conspicuous: from the two botanists called Commelin, for the third died before accomplishing anything in Botany."

commixtus, -a, -um [ko-MIX-tus]
Mixed together; mingled.

communis, -is, -e [ko-MEW-nis]
Common; general; growing in company.

commutatus, -a, -um [ko-mew-TAY-tus]
Changed or changing.

comosus, -a, -um [ko-MO-sus]
With long hair growing in tufts.

compactus, -a, -um [kom-PAK-tus]
Compact; dense.

complanatus, -a, um [kom-plan-AY-tus]
Flattened; leveled.

complexus, -a, -um [kom-PLEX-us]
Encircled; embraced.

complicatus, -a, -um [kom-plik-AY-tus]
Complicated; complex.

compositus, -a, -um [kow-POS-it-us]
Compound.

compressus, -a, -um [kom-PRESS-us]
Compressed; flattened.

Comptonia [komp-TO-nia]
Sweet fern. Named for Henry Compton (1632-1713), Bishop of London and patron of botany. Compton began his career as an officer of the Life Guards. As Bishop of London he was suspended by the renegade King James II for his strongly expressed religious beliefs. At the time of the Revolution of 1688, he girded on sword and pistols and personally escorted Princess Anne, soon to be Queen, out of London in his own coach.

comptus, -a, -um [COMP-tus]
Adorned; ornamented.

Conandron [ko-NAN-dron]
From Gr. *konos*, a cone; *andron*, an anther. So named because of the way in which the appendages of the anthers of this herb are arranged in a cone shape around the style.

concavus, -a, -um [KON-kav-us]
Hollowed out; basin-shaped.
concinnus, -a, -um [kon-SIN-us]
Neat; elegant; well-made.
conchaefolius, -a, -um [kon-chee-FO-lius]
With leaves like sea shells.
concolor [KON-col-or]
Of the same color throughout.
condensatus, -a, -um [kon-den-SAY-tus]
  condensus, -a, -um [kon-DEN-sus]
Crowded together.
confertiflorus, -a, -um [kon-fert-i-FLOW-rus]
With the flowers crowded together.
confertus, -a, -um [kon-FERT-us]
Crowded.
conformis, -is, -e [con-FORM-is]
Conforming to the genus type. Similar in shape or other
ways to related species.
confusus, -a, -um [kon-FEW-sus]
Confused; uncertain; apt to be taken for another species.
congestus, -a, -um [kon-JEST-us]
Arranged very closely together; congested.
conglomeratus, -a, -um [kon-glo-mer-AY-tus]
Crowded together; conglomerate.
congolanus, -a, -um [kon-go-LAY-nus]
From the Congo.
conicus, -a, -um [KON-ik-us]
Cone-shaped.
coniferous, -a, -um [ko-NIFF-er-us]
Cone-bearing.
Coniogramme [kon-i-o-GRAM-me]
Gr. *konion,* dust; *gramme,* a line; in reference to the way
the spore cases are arranged along the veins of these ferns.
Conium [kon-EYE-um]
Poison hemlock. The Greek name for both the plant and
the poison derived from it. The latter was administered to
those condemned in Athens to die for certain offenses
against the state. Plato's description of Socrates taking the
poison remains one of the most moving passages in literature.
connatus, -a, -um [kon-NAY-tus]

110

United; twin; having opposite leaves joined together at their bases.

conjunctus, -a, -um [kon-JUNK-tus]
Joined.

conjugatus, -a, -um [kon-joo-GAY-tus]
conjugialis, -is, -e [kon-joo-gi-AY-lis]
Joined in pairs; wedded.

conoideus, -a, -um [kon-OY-deus]
Conelike.

Conophytum [kon-OFF-it-um]
Cone-plant. From Gr. *konos,* a cone; *phyton,* a plant; an allusion to the shape of these succulents.

conopseus, -a, -um [kon-OP-seus]
Canopied.

consanguineus, -a, -um [kon-sang-WIN-eus]
Related.

consolidus, -a, -um [kon-SOL-id-us]
Solid; stable.

conspersus, -a, -um [kon-SPER-sus]
Scattered.

conspicuus, -a, -um [kon-SPIK-ew-us]
Conspicuous.

constrictus, -a, -um [kon-STRIK-tus]
Constricted.

contiguus, -a, -um [kon-TIG-ew-us]
(*a*) Near together—so close as to touch one another.
(*b*) Closely related.

continentalis, -is, -e [kon-tin-en-TAY-lis]
Continental.

contortus, -a, -um [kon-TORT-us]
Twisted; bent irregularly; contorted.

contractus, -a, -um [kon-TRAKT-us]
Drawn together; contracted.

controversus, -a, -um [kon-tro-VERS-us]
Doubtful; controversial.

Convallaria [kon-val-AIR-ia]
Lily-of-the-valley. From L. *convallis,* a valley.

convallaroides [kon-val-a-ROY-deez]
Resembling lily-of-the-valley.

convolvulaceus, -a, -um [kon-vol-vew-LAY-seus]
Similar to *Convolvulus.*

Convolvulus [kon-VOL-vew-lus]
Bindweed. From L. *convolvo,* to twine around.

conyzoides [kon-eye-ZOY-deez]
Resembling *Conyza,* a genus of no garden interest.

Cooperia [koo-PEER-ia]
Evening-star. Night-flowering bulbous plants named in honor of Joseph Cooper, gardener to Earl FitzWilliam at Wentworth, Yorkshire, c. 1830.

Copaifera [ko-PY-fer-a]
From copaiba, the Brazilian name for a balsam, plus L. *fero,* to bear. The trees yield copal, a commercial gum used in making varnish.

copallinus, -a, -um [ko-pal-LY-nus]
Gummy; resinous.

Copernicia [kop-er-NISH-ia]
Carnanba palm, named for Copernicus (Nicolaus Koppernigk, 1473-1543), Polish astronomer, physician, economist, and theologian. His greatest modern fame rests on the first. He propounded and proved the heliocentric theory which placed the sun as the center of our solar system around which the planets, including the earth, revolve. Thus, once and for all he upset the Ptolomaic system which had been accepted for 1500 years.

Coprosma [kop-ROS-ma]
Gr. *kopros,* dung; *osme,* a smell; in allusion to the fetid odor of many of these small trees and shrubs when bruised.

Coptis [KOP-tis]
Gold thread. From Gr. *kopto,* to cut; a reference to the deeply cut leaves of these perennial herbs.

coralliflorus, -a, -um [kor-al-i-FLOW-rus]
With flowers of coral-red.

corallinus, -a, -um [kor-al-LY-nus]
Coral-red.

corallodendron [kor-al-o-DEND-ron]
Specific name of the coral-tree (*Erythrina*).

Corchorus [KORK-o-rus]
Derivation obscure. Jute is *C. capsularia.*

cordatus, -a, -um [kor-DAY-tus]
Heart-shaped.

Cordia [KORD-ia]
Trees and shrubs, named in honor of Enricus Cordus (1486-1535) and his son Valerius (1515-1544), German botanists.

cordifolius, -a, -um [kord-i-FO-lius]
With heart-shaped leaves.

cordiformis, -is, -e [kord-i-FORM-is]
Heart-shaped.

Cordyline [kor-dil-LY-ne]
Gr. *kordyle,* a club; in allusion to the fleshy roots. Often offered as *Dracaena* to which this genus of flowering trees and shrubs is closely related.

coreanus, -a -um [kor-ee-AY-nus]
From Korea.

Corema [kore-EE-ma]
Gr. *korema,* a broom; from the habit of these heathlike shrubs.

Coreopsis [ko-ree-OP-sis]
Tickseed. From Gr. *koris,* a bug; *opsis,* like. The seed of these herbs looks like a bug or tick.

coriaceus, -a, -um [kor-i-AY-seus]
Thick and tough; leathery.

Coriandrum [kor-ri-AND-rum]
Coriander. The Greek name for the plant which has a long history of use as a flavoring. Today coriander seed is used in such diverse things as gin, confectionery, bread, curry powder, and so on. When unripe the seed has an unpleasant odor which disappears when dry.

Coriaria [ko-ri-AY-ria]
L. *corium,* leather. Some species of these shrubs and herbs are used in tanning.

coriarius, -a, -um [ko-ri-AY-rius]
Like leather.

coridifolius, -a, -um [ko-rid-i-FO-lius]
corifolius, -a, -um [ko-ri-FO-lius]
coriophyllus, -a, -um [ko-ri-o-FILL-us]
With leaves like *Coris,* a plant of no garden interest.

coris [KO-ris]
Specific name for a St. John's-wort (*Hypericum*), from a similarity to *Coris.*

corneus, -a, -um [KOR-neus]
Horny.

corniculatus, -a, -um [kor-nik-ew-LAY-tus]
Horned.

corniferus, -a, -um [kor-NIFF-er-us]
corniger, -ra, -rum [KOR-nij-er]
Bearing or being furnished with a horn.

cornucopiae [kor-new-KO-pi-ee]
Shaped like a cornucopia or horn of plenty.

Cornus [KOR-nus]
Dogwood or cornel. Bunchberry. The Latin name for the cornelian cherry (*Cornus mas*).

cornutus, -a, -um [kor-NEW-tus]
Horned or horn-shaped.

Corokia [ko-RO-kia]
From the Maori name for these evergreen shrubs.

corollatus, -a, -um [ko-rol-AY-tus]
Like a corolla.

coromandelianus, -a, -um [kor-o-man-del-i-AY-nus]
From the Coromandel Coast, that part of the southeastern coast of the Indian peninsula south of the Kistna River.

coronans [KO-ro-nans]
coronatus, -a, -um [ko-ro-NAY-rius]
Crowned.

coronarius, -a, -um, [ko-ro-NAY-rius]
Used for garlands, or pertaining to garlands.

Coronilla [ko-ro-NILL-a]
Crown vetch. Diminutive of L. *corona,* a crown; in reference to the umbels of these shrubs and herbs.

coronopifolius, -a, -um [ko-ro-no-pi-FO-lius]
With leaves like *Coronopus,* a rather weedy plant.

Corozo [ko-RO-zo]
Native South American name for this palm.

Correa [ko-REE-a]
Australian shrubs named in honor of Jose Francesco Correa da Serra (1750-1823), Portuguese botanist.

corrugatus, -a, -um [ko-roo-GAY-tus]
Corrugated; wrinkled.

corsicus, -a, -um [KOR-sik-us]
From Corsica.

Cortaderia [kor-ta-DEER-ia]
Pampas grass. From the Argentinian name.

corticosus, -a, -um [kor-ti-o-sus]
With bark like a cork tree; heavily barked.

Cortusa [kor-TEW-sa]
Perennial herbs named in honor of Jacobi Antonii Cortusi (1513-1593), Director of the Botanic Garden at Padua.

cortusoides [kor-tew-soy-deez]
Resembling *Cortusa*.

coruscans [ko-RUSK-ans]
Glittering; corruscating.

Coryanthes [ko-ri-ANTH-ees]
Helmet flower or bucket orchid. From Gr. *korys*, a helmet; *anthos*, a flower.

Corydalis [ko-RY-dal-is]
Greek word meaning a lark; the flowers of these annual and perennial herbs have spurs like larks.

corylifolius, -a, -um [ko-ry-li-FO-lius]
With leaves like *Corylus* or hazelnut.

Corylopsis [ko-ry-LOP-sis]
Gr. *korylos*, hazel; *opsis*, like; from the resemblance of these deciduous flowering shrubs to *Corylus* or hazel.

Corylus [KO-ry-lus]
Hazel. The Greek name. Now the name for a large genus of shrubs and trees which includes cob-nut and filbert.

corymbiferus, -a, -um [ko-rim-BIFF-er-us]
Corymb-bearing. A corymb is a cluster of flowers in which the outer stalks or pedicels are longer than the inner ones. The blossom of the sweet cherry is an example.

corymbiflorus, -a, -um [ko-rim-bi-FLOW-rus]
With flowers produced in a corymb.

corymbosus, -a, -um [ko-rim-BO-sus]
Provided with corymbs; corymbose.

corynocalyx [ko-ry-no-KAY-lix]
With a calyx like a club.

Corynocarpus [ko-ry-no-KARP-us]
New Zealand laurel. From Gr. *koryne*, a club; *karpos*, fruit; from the shape of the fruit of this tree.

Corypha [ko-RY-fa]
Gr. *koryphe*, a summit or hilltop; in reference to the terminal crown of leaves of this palm.

Coryphantha [ko-ry-FAN-tha]
From Gr. *koryphe*, a summit; *anthos*, a flower. The flowers

are produced on the top of these globular or cylindrical cacti.

cosmophyllus, -a, -um [kos-mo-FILL-us]
With leaves like *Cosmos.*

Cosmos [KOS-mos]
Greek word meaning beautiful. These annual and perennial herbs appear in a variety of colors.

costatus, -a, -um [kos-TAY-tus]
Ribbed, e.g., the mid-rib of a leaf.

Costus [KOS-tus]
Spiral-flag. The Latin name for these perennial herbs.

cotinifolius, -a, -um [ko-ty-ni-FO-lius]
With leaves like *Cotinus* or smoke-tree.

cotinoides [ko-tin-OY-deez]
Resembling *Cotinus* or smoke-tree.

Cotinus [ko-TY-nus]
Smoke-tree. From Greek for the wild-olive but of uncertain application here.

Cotoneaster [ko-to-nee-AS-ter]
L. *cotoneum,* quince; *instar,* a likeness. From a similarity of the leaves to quince in some species of these handsome-fruited shrubs and small trees.

Cotula [KO-tew-la]
Greek word meaning a small cup. The bases of the leaves of these small herbs form cups.

Cotyledon [kot-ee-LEE-don]
From Gr. *kotyle,* a cavity or small cup; in reference to the cuplike leaves of some species of these succulent plants.

Coutarea [koo-TAY-rea]
Latinized version of the vernacular name in Guiana for these evergreen trees and shrubs.

Cowania [kow-AY-nia]
Flowering evergreen shrubs named in honor of James Cowan, early Victorian London merchant who introduced many plants from Mexico and Peru.

Crambe [KRAM-be]
Seakale. The Greek name for cabbage.

Craspedia [kras-PEE-dia]
Gr. *kraspedon,* a fringe; in allusion to the feathery pappus of these perennial herbs.

116

crassicaulis, -is, -e   [krass-ik-KAW-lis]
Thick-stemmed.
crassifolius, -a, -um   [krass-i-FO-lius]
Thick-leaved.
crassipes   [KRASS-i-pees]
Thick-footed or thick-stemmed.
crassiusculus, -a, -um   [krass-i-US-kew-lus]
Somewhat thick.
Crassula   [KRASS-ew-la]
Diminutive of L. *crassus*, thick; from the somewhat thick
leaves of these shrubs and herbs.
crassus, -a, -um   [KRASS-us]
Thick; fleshy.
crataegifolius, -a, -um   [krat-ee-gi-FO-lius]
With leaves like *Crataegus* or hawthorn.
crataegoides   [krat-ee-GOY-deez]
Resembling hawthorn.
Crataegus   [krat-EE-gus]
Hawthorn. The Greek name for the tree. From *kratos*,
strength; an allusion to the strength and hardness of the
wood.
creber, -ra, -rum   [KREE-ber]
Thickly clustered; repeated; frequent.
crebiflorus, -a, -um   [kree-bi-FLOW-rus]
With thickly clustered flowers.
crenatus, -a, -um   [kree-NAY-tus]
Cut in rounded scallops; crenate.
crenatiflorus, -a, -um   [kree-nay-ti-FLOW-rus]
With flowers cut in rounded scallops.
crenulatus, -a, -um   [kren-ew-LAY-tus]
Somewhat scalloped.
crepidatus, -a, -um   [krep-id-AY-tus]
Shaped like a sandal or slipper.
Crepis   [KREE-pis]
Hawk's-beard. A large genus of herbs with dandelion-like
flowers. Gr. *krepis*, a sandal; but why is not clear.
crepitans   [KREP-it-ans]
Rustling; crackling.
Crescentia   [kres-SEN-tia]
The Calabash tree, bearing the big fruits from which bowls
and dippers are made in hot countries. Named in honor of

Pietro Crescenzi (1230-1321), Italian author of a work on country living.

cretaceus, -a, -um [kret-AY-seus]
Pertaining to chalk; chalky.

creticus, -a, -um [KRET-ik-us]
From the island of Crete.

crinitus, -a, -um [kry-NY-tus]
Furnished with long, generally weak, hairs.

Crinodonna [kry-no-DON-na]
Genus name given to a hybrid cross between *Crinum* and *Amaryllis.*

Crinum [KRY-num]
Gr. *krynon,* a lily. Bulbous plants of the *Amaryllis* family.

crispatus, -a, -um [krisp-AY-tus]
crispus, -a, -um [KRISP-us]
Finely waved; closely curled.

cristagalli [kris-ta-GAL-ly]
A specific name meaning cock's comb.

cristatus, -a, -um [kris-TAY-tus]
Having tassel-like tips; crested.

crithmifolius, -a, -um [krith-mi-FO-lius]
With leaves like *Crithmum.*

Crithmum [KRITH-mum]
Samphire. Gr. *krithe,* barley; in allusion to the form of the seed of this perennial herb.

crocatus, -a, -um [kro-KAY-tus]
croceus, -a, -um [KRO-seus]
Saffron-colored; yellow.

crocosmaefforus, -a, -um [kro-kos-mee-FLOW-rus]
Crocosmia-flowered.

Crocosmia [kro-KOS-mia]
Gr. *krokos,* saffron; *osme,* a smell. The dried flowers in warm water have a strong smell of saffron.

Crocus [KRO-kus]
Gr. *krokos,* saffron. The genus includes both the common as well as the saffron crocus. The saffron crocus is widely grown in Mediterranean countries and elsewhere for the stigmas and part of the styles which are dried to produce a yellow dye, which was the royal color of ancient Greece. Saffron is also used in various types of cookery. It is an al-

most essential ingredient in bouillabaisse and also of Spanish rice to which it adds a pleasant flavor and color. It is fragrant and was once used on a considerable scale by Roman emperors to scatter in the streets when they went abroad. In some countries it is used in embalming.

Crossandra [kross-AND-ra]
Gr. *krossos,* a fringe; *aner,* male. The anthers of these evergreen flowering shrubs are fringed.

Crotalaria [kro-tal-AY-ria]
Rattle-box. Gr. *krotalon,* a rattle. The pods of these plants can be inflated to be used as rattles or castanets.

Croton [KRO-ton]
Greek for a tick, from the appearance of the seeds of these plants of solely economic interest. *C. tiglium* is the source of croton oil, a powerful cathartic.

crotonifolius, -a, -um [kro-to-ni-FO-lius]
With leaves like *Croton.*

Crucianella [kroo-si-an-ELL-a]
Crosswort. From the diminutive of L. *crux,* a cross; the leaves of these herbs being crosswise.

cruciatus, -a, -um [kroo-si-AY-tus]
In the form of a cross.

cruciferus, -a, -um [kroo-SIFF-er-us]
Bearing a cross.

cruentus, -a, -um [kroo-EN-tus]
The color of blood.

crus-galli [krus-GAL-ly]
A specific name meaning cock's spur.

crustatus, -a, -um [krus-TAY-tus]
Encrusted.

crux-andrae [krux-AND-ree]
Specific name meaning St. Andrew's cross.

crux-maltae [krux-MAWL-tae]
Specific name meaning Maltese cross.

Cryptantha [krip-TAN-tha]
From Gr. *krypto,* to hide; *anthos,* a flower. The flowers of these herbs are hidden.

Cryptanthus [kript-AN-thus]
From Gr. *krypto,* to hide; *anthos,* a flower. The flowers of these Brazilian plants are hidden among the bracts.

Cryptogramma [krip-toe-GRAM-ma]
Rockbrake. From Gr. *krypto*, to hide; *gramma*, writing. The spore cases are concealed in these ferns.

Cryptomeria [krip-to-MEER-ia]
Japanese cedar. Gr. *krypto*, to hide; *meris*, a part. All parts of the flower of this ornamental evergreen tree are concealed.

Cryptostegia [krip-to-STEE-jia]
Rubber vine. From Gr. *krypto*, to hide; *stego*, to cover. The scales in the throat of the flower cover the anthers.

Cryptostemma [krip-to-STEEM-ma]
Gr. *krypto*, to hide; *stemma*, a crown. The hairs of the seed cases cover the scales of the pappus in these hoary herbs.

crystallinus, -a, -um [kris-TAL-in-us]
Crystalline; transparent.

Ctenanthe [sten-AN-the]
From Gr. *kteis*, a comb; *anthos*, a flower; from the arrangement of the bracts of these Brazilian herbs.

ctenoides [sten-OY-deez]
Resembling a comb.

cubeba [kew-BEE-ba]
Specific name for *Piper cubeba* from the pre-Linnaean name for cubeb.

cucullaris, -is, -e [kew-kew-LAY-ris]
cucullatus, -a, -um [kew-kew-LAY-tus]
Hoodlike; having sides or apex curved inwards to resemble a hood.

cucumerifolius, -a, -um [kew-kew-mer-i-FO-lius]
Having leaves like cucumber.

cucumerinus, -a, -um [kew-kew-mer-EYE-nus]
Resembling cucumber.

Cucumis [KEW-kew-mis]
Cucumber. Melon. The ancient Latin name.

Cucurbita [kew-KERB-it-a]
Latin name for a gourd. The genus also includes such plants as squash and pumpkin.

cultorum [kult-OR-um]
Of gardeners.

cultratus, -a, -um [kul-TRAY-tus]
cultriformis, -is, -e [kul-tri-FORM-is]
Shaped like a knife blade.

Cuminum [KEW-min-um]
Cumin. The Greek name for this aromatic herb of ancient use.

cuneatus, -a, -um [kew-nee-AY-tus]
Wedge-shaped, generally with the narrow end down.

cuneifolius, -a, -um [kew-nee-i-FO-lius]
With wedge-shaped leaves.

cuneiformis, -is, -e [kew-nee-i-FORM-is]
In the form of a wedge.

Cunila [kew-NY-la]
Dittany. The Latin name for one of the mints.

Cunninghamia [kun-ing-HAM-ia]
Decorative coniferous evergreens named for James Cunning-
ham, East India Company surgeon at Amoy, China, who,
between the years 1698-1702, sent home large collections of
plants and superb plant drawings from Chusan.

Cupania [kew-PAY-nia]
Ornamental evergreen trees, resembling *Blighia*, named in
honor of Francesco Cupani, Italian monk and botanical
author.

Cuphea [KEW-pea]
Gr. *kyphos*, curved; from the shape of the seed capsule of
these herbs and sub-shrubs.

cupreatus, -a, -um [kew-pree-AY-tus]
cupreus, -a, -um [KEW-preus]
Coppery; copper-colored.

cupressifolius, -a, -um [kew-press-i-FO-lius]
With leaves like cypress.

cupressiformis, -is, -e [kew-press-i-FORM-is]
cupressinus, -a, -um [kew-press-EYE-nus]
cupressoides [kew-press-OY-deez]
Resembling cypress.

Cupressus [kew-PRESS-us]
Cypress. The Latin name for the Italian cypress tree (*C.
sempervirens*).

curassavicus, -a, -um [kew-rass-AV-ik-us]
From Curaçao.

Curculigo [ker-KEW-lig-o]
L. *curculio*, a weevil. The ovary of these palmlike foliage
plants is beaked like a weevil.

Curcuma [ker-KEW-ma]
Turmeric. The Latinized version of the Arabic name. The stout rootstocks are the source of turmeric which is both a dyestuff and a condiment. It is an important ingredient of curry to which it imparts its yellow color.

curtus, -a, -um [KER-tus]
Shortened.

curvatus, -a, -um [ker-VAY-tus]
Curved.

curvifolius, -a, -um [ker-i-FO-lius]
With curved leaves.

cuscutaeformis, -is, -e [kus-kew-tee-FORM-is]
Resembling *Cuscuta* or dodder.

cuspidatus, -a, -um [kus-pid-AY-tus]
With a sharp stiff point; cuspidate.

cuspidifolius, -a, -um [kus-pid-i-FO-lius]
With leaves with a sharp stiff point.

Cyananthus [sy-an-ANTH-us]
Gr. *kyanos*, blue; *anthos*, a flower; from the color of the flower of these herbaceous perennials.

cyananthus, -a, -um [sy-an-ANTH-us]
With blue flowers.

cyanocarpus, -a, -um [sy-an-o-KARP-us]
With blue fruit.

cyanophyllus, -a, -um [sy-an-o-FILL-us]
With blue leaves.

cyaneus, -a, -um [sy-AY-neus]
Blue.

Cyanotis [sy-an-o-tis]
Gr. *kyanos*, blue; *ous*, an ear; an allusion to the color and form of the petals of these *Tradescantia*-like herbs.

cyanis [sy-AN-us]
Old name and now the specific name for the cornflower, signifying blue.

Cyathea [sy-ATH-ea]
Tree fern. From Gr. *kyatheion*, a little cup; in allusion to the spore cases.

Cyathodes [sy-ath-o-deez]
From Gr. *kyathos*, a cup; *odous*, a tooth; in allusion to the cup-shaped, toothed disc of these evergreen shrubs.

cyatheoides [sy-ath-ee-OY-deez]
Resembling *Cyathea.*

Cycas [SY-kas]
Greek name for a kind of palm. Although palmlike these are not palms but conifers. Sago-palm is *C. revoluta.*

Cyclamen [SIK-lam-en]
Sowbread. The Greek name. They are regarded as a favorite food for swine in the South of France, Sicily, and Italy. It is claimed that a diet of cyclamen bulbs adds particular flavor to the pork products of the Perigord area.

cyclamineus, -a, -um [sik-lam-IN-eus]
Resembling *Cyclamen.*

Cyclanthera [sy-klan-THEER-a]
Gr. *kyklos,* a circle; *anthera,* anthers; from the arrangement of the anthers on these herbs.

Cyclanthus [sy-KLAN-thus]
Gr. *kyklos,* a circle; *anthos,* a flower; from the arrangement of the flowers on these herbs.

cyclocarpus, -a, -um [sy-klo-KARP-us]
With fruit arranged in a circle.

Cyclophorus [sy-KLOFF-or-us]
Japanese fern. From Gr. *kyklos,* a circle; *phoreo,* to bear; from the circular shape of the spore cases.

cyclops [SY-klops]
Gigantic.

Cydista [sy-DIS-ta]
From Gr. *kydistos,* most glorious; in reference to the spectacular flowers of these ornamental vines.

Cydonia [sy-DOE-nia]
Quince. The Latin name for this shrub or small tree, derived from the town of Cydon in Crete.

cylindraceus, -a, -um [sil-in-DRAY-seus]
 cylindricus, -a, -um [sil-in-DRIK-us]
Long and round, cylindrical.

cylindrostachyus, -a, -um [sil-in-dro-STAK-ius]
With a cylindrical spike.

Cymbalaria [sim-bal-AY-ria]
Ivy-leaved toadflax. Greek word meaning a cymbal. From the leaf shape of some of the species of these herbs.

Cymbidium [sim-BID-ium]

Gr. *kymbe,* a boat. There is a hollow recess in the lip of these orchids.

cymbiformis, -is, -e [sim-bi-FORM-is]

Boat-shaped.

Cymbopogon [sim-bo-PO-gon]

Gr. *kymbe,* a boat; *pogon,* a beard. A rather technical allusion to the form of the spikelets on these oil-producing grasses.

cymosus, -a, -um [sy-MO-sus]

Furnished with cymes or flower clusters in which the flower in the center opens first and then the remainder of the flowers open in succession outwards to the periphery (as in *Phlox*).

Cynanchum [sy-NAN-chum]

Gr. *kynos,* a dog; *ancho,* to strangle. Some of the species of these twining herbs and sub-shrubs are poisonous.

Cynara [SIN-a-ra]

Artichoke and cardoon. The Latin name for these herbs with spiny involucres.

cynaroides [sin-a-ROY-deez]

Resembling *Cynara.*

Cynodon [SY-no-don]

Bermuda grass. From Gr. *kynos,* a dog; *odus,* a tooth; in reference to the toothed sheath of the runners.

Cynoglossum [sy-no-GLOSS-um]

Hound's tongue. From Gr. *kynos,* a dog; *glossa,* a tongue; an allusion to the texture of the leaves of these weedy herbs.

Cypella [sy-PELL-a]

Gr. *kypellon,* a goblet; from the form of the flowers of these small bulbous plants.

Cyperus [sy-PEER-us]

Greek word meaning sedge. The genus includes Papyrus, from which the Egyptians made material to write on by cutting the pithlike tissues into strips, laying them crosswise and uniting them under pressure.

Cyphomandra [sy-fo-MAN-dra]

Gr. *kyphos,* a tumor; *aner,* male. The anthers of these shrubs and trees form a lump.

cypreus, -a, -um [SY-preus]

Like copper.

124

Cypripedium [sip-ri-PEE-dium]
Lady's slipper. From Gr. *Kypris*, Venus; *pedilon*, a slipper; from the shape of the flower.

Cyrilla [sy-RILL-a]
A shrub named in honor of Dominico Cyrillo (1734-1790), physician and Professor of Botany at Naples.

Cyrtomium [ser-TOE-mium]
Gr. *kyrtos*, arched; from the habit of growth of these ferns.

Cyrtopodium [ser-toe-PO-dium]
Gr. *kyrtos*, arched; *pous*, a foot; from the form of the lip of the flower of these terrestrial orchids.

Cyrtostachys [ser-TOS-tak-is]
Gr. *kyrtos*, arched; *stachys*, a spike. The flower spikes of these palms are curved.

Cystopteris [sis-TOP-ter-is]
Bladder fern. From Gr. *kystis*, a bladder; *pteris*, a fern.

cytherea [sith-EE-rea]
From the Greek Island of Kythera.

cytisoides [sit-is-OY-deez]
Resembling *Cytisus* or broom.

Cytisus [SIT-is-us]
Broom. Derivation of the name, which is Greek for a kind of clover, is uncertain in relation to these free-flowering shrubs.

D

Daboecia [dab-EE-shia]
St. Dabeoc's heath. Named after a rather obscure Irish saint.

dacrydioides [dak-rid-i-OY-deez]
Resembling *Dacrydium*.

Dacrydium [dak-RID-ium]
Gr. *dakrudion*, a small tear. The trees, called mountain pine in New Zealand, exude drops of resin.

dactyliferus, -a, -um [dak-till-IFF-er-us]
Fingerlike; furnished with fingers.

Dactylis [dak-TY-lis]
Cock's foot grass. From Gr. *dactylos*, a finger; of uncertain application here.

dactyloides [dak-til-OY-deez]
Resembling fingers.

Daemonorops [dee-MON-O-rops]
From Gr. *dema,* a cord; *rhops,* a shrub; in allusion to the stem of these climbing feather palms. Like cats, they climb by means of sharp recurved hooks on the main flower and leaf stalks.

Dahlia [DAH-lia, DAL-ia, DAY-lia]
Pronunciation is largely a matter of taste although the first is possibly the most correct. Herbaceous tuberous-rooted perennials from Mexico named in honor of Dr. Andreas Dahl, Swedish botanist and pupil of Linnaeus.

dahuricus, -a, -um [da-HEW-rik-us]
dauricus, -a, -um [DAW-rik-us]
davuricus, -a, -um [dav-YEW-rik-us]
From Siberia, classically known as Dahuria.

Dais [DAY-is]
Greek word meaning a torch; an allusion to the form of inflorescence or arrangement of the flowers of these shrubs in clusters.

Dalbergia [dal-BERJ-ia]
A genus of trees, shrubs, or climbers named for Nicholas Dalberg (1736-1820), Swedish botanist.

Dalea [DAY-lea]
Herbs and small shrubs named in honor of Dr. Samuel Dale (1659-1739), English botanist and author.

dalecarlicus, -a, -um [dayl-KAR-lik-us]
From the province of Dalecarlia, or Dalarna, in Sweden.

Dalechampia [dal-ie-SHAMP-ia]
Tropical shrubs named for Jacques Dalechamp (1513-1588), French physician and botanist.

Dalibardia [dal-i-BARD-ia]
An herbaceous perennial named in honor of Thomas François Dalibard (1703-1773), French botanist.

dalmaticus, -a, -um [dal-MAT-ik-us]
From Dalmatia.

damascenus, -a, -um [dam-ass-SEEN-us]
From Damascus.

Danaë [DAY-a-ee]
Alexandrian laurel. Named for the daughter of Acrisius, King

of Argos. Having been warned that she would bear a son who would eventually kill him, he shut her up in a brazen tower only to have Zeus descend in a shower of gold with the result that she gave birth to Perseus. Acrisius placed both in a wooden box and threw them into the sea. By one of those twists of fate which make up Greek tragic plots, Perseus grew up to kill his grandfather accidentally when practicing with the discus.

Daphne [DAFF-ne]
Greek name for the bay tree or laurel; some of the species resemble laurel. These ornamental woody plants with fragrant flowers are named after a nymph changed by the gods into a bay tree to save her from pursuit by Apollo.

Daphnephyllum [daff-ne-FILL-um]
Gr. *daphne*, laurel; *phyllon*, a leaf. The leaves of these evergreen shrubs and small trees resemble laurel.

daphnoides [daff-NOY-deez]
Resembling *Daphne*.

Darlingtonia [dar-ling-TO-nia]
An insectivorous herbaceous plant named in honor of Dr. William Darlington, early 19th-century Philadelphia physician and botanist who published the posthumous botanical work of his friend and fellow physician, William Baldwin, who died on an exploring trip up the Missouri River in 1819.

Darwinia [dar-WIN-ia]
Australian evergreen shrubs named in honor of Dr. Erasmus Darwin (1731-1802), man of science and writer of poems on scientific subjects, grandfather of Charles Darwin.

dasy- [das-i-]
A prefix in many compound words meaning thick, thus:

dasyacanthus	thick-spined
dasyanthus	shaggy-flowered
dasycarpus	with hairy fruit
dasycladus	shaggy-branched
dasyphyllus	shaggy-leaved
dasystemon	with hairy stamens

Dasylirion [das-i-LI-rion]
Gr. *dasys*, thick; *lirion*, lily; in allusion to the character of these succulents.

Datisca [dat-ISS-ka]

The derivation of the name of these herbaceous perennials is obscure.

Datura [da-TOOR-a]

Angel's trumpet. Thorn-apple. From an Oriental vernacular name. Some of the species are violently narcotic and poisonous, including Jimson weed (*D. stramonium*) when wilted. *D. tatula* is common in India and provides a convenient source of poison.

Daubentonia [daw-ben-TO-nia]

Herbs or shrubs named for a French naturalist, L. J. Daubenton.

daucifolius, -a, -um [daw-ki-FO-lius]

With leaves like carrot or *Daucus*.

daucoides [daw-KOY-deez]

Resembling carrot or *Daucus*.

Daucus. [DAW-kus]

Carrot. The Latin name.

Davallia [da-VAL-ia]

Hare's-foot fern. Named for Edmond Davall (1763-1798), Swiss botanist.

Davidia [Dav-ID-ia]

A handsome deciduous tree named in honor of Abbé Armand David (1826-1900), French missionary in China, 1862-1873, who collected many plants. He also discovered what is now known as Père David's deer in the Imperial Palace grounds in Pekin. It occurs only in captivity.

dawsonianus, -a, -um [daw-so-ni-AY-nus]

Species name for Jackson T. Dawson (1841-1916), first Superintendent of the Arnold Arboretum in Boston, Massachusetts.

dealbatus, -a, -um [dee-al-BAY-tus]

Whitened; covered with opaque white powder.

Deamia [DEEM-ia]

A cactus named for Charles C. Deam, American botanist.

debilis, -is, -e [DEB-ill-is]

Weak; frail.

Debregeasia [deb-reg-EE-sia]

A genus of shrubs or trees, named after Prosper Justin de Brègeas, French naval officer, who commanded the corvette

La Bonite on a voyage of exploration to the Far East (1836-1837).

Decaisnea [dek-AYS-nea]
Ornamental shrubs named in honor of Joseph Decaisne (1807-1882), Director of the Jardin des Plantes, Paris; eminent botanist and writer on plants.

decandrus, -a, -um [dek-AND-rus]
With ten stamens.

decapetalus, -a, -um [dek-a-PET-al-us]
With ten petals.

decaphyllus, -a, -um [dek-a-FILL-us]
With ten leaves.

deciduus, -a, -um [de-SID-yew-us]
Deciduous.

decipiens [de-SIP-iens]
Deceptive; not obvious.

declinatus, -a, -um [dek-lin-AY-tus]
Bent downwards.

Decodon [DEK-o-don]
Swamp loosestrife. Gr. *deka*, ten; *odous*, a tooth. The calyx of this shrubby perennial has ten teeth.

decolorans [dee-kol-OR-ans]
Discoloring; staining.

decompositus, -a, -um [dee-kom-POS-it-us]
More than once divided.

decorans [DEK-or-ans]
  decoratus, -a, -um [dek-or-AY-tus]
  decorus, -a, -um [dek-o-rus]
Decorative; becoming; comely.

decumanus, -a, -um [dek-yew-MAY-nus]
Very large; immense.

Decumaria [dek-yew-MAY-ria]
L. *decimus*, ten; from the number of parts of the flower of these ornamental climbing shrubs.

decumbens [dee-KUM-bens]
Trailing with tips upright; decumbent.

decurrens [dee-KERR-ens]
Running down the stem; decurrent; e.g., a leaf base that merges with the stalk below it.

Deeringia [deer-INJ-ia]
Climbing herbs or sub-shrubs named for Karl Deering

(d. 1749) who was born in Saxony and practiced medicine in London. He was the author of a catalogue of British plants.

deflexus, -a, -um [dee-FLEX-us]
Bent abruptly downward.

deformis, -is, -e [dee-FORM-is]
Misshapen; deformed.

dehiscens [dee-HISS-ens]
Dehiscent, namely the splitting or opening of a seed-pod for the release of seeds or the opening of an anther to discharge pollen. The function can sometimes be relatively violent and both visible and audible as in the popping of broom pods on a hot day. In the case of the castor-oil plant the seeds are thrown several feet and it is important to harvest in time.

dejectus, -a, -um [dee-JEK-tus]
Debased.

delectus, -a, -um [dee-LEK-tus]
Chosen.

delicatissimus, -a, -um [del-i-kay-TISS-im-us]
Most delicate.

delicatus, -a, -um [del-i-KAY-tus]
Delicate.

deliciosus, -a, -um [del-liss-i-o-sus]
Delicious.

Delonix [del-o-nix]
Royal poinciana, possibly the most gorgeous tree in cultivation. From Gr. *delos*, evident; *onux*, a claw; a reference to the form of the petals.

Delostoma [dee-LOS-to-ma]
Gr. *delos*, evident; *stoma*, a mouth. The flower of these Peruvian shrubs has a wide mouth.

delphinifolius, -a, -um [del-fin-i-FO-lius]
With leaves like *Delphinium*.

Delphinium [del-FIN-ium]
Larkspur. The Greek name, supposed to be derived from the word for a dolphin in allusion to the form of the flower as it was then known.

deltoides [del-TOY-deez]
deltoideus, -a, -um [del-TOY-deus]
Triangular.

Demazeria (incorrectly, **Desmazeria**) [Dee-maz-EER-ia]
A genus of grasses named after Jean Baptiste Joseph Henri Desmazières (1796-1862), French botanist.

demersus, -a, -um [dee-MER-sus]
Living under water; submerged.

demissus, -a, -um [dee-MISS-us]
Hanging down; weak.

dendricolus, -a, -um [den-dri-KO-lus]
Living on trees.

Dendrobium [den-DRO-bium]
Gr. *dendron,* a tree; *bios,* life. These tree-perching orchids are, next to the cattleyas, the most popular greenhouse orchids.

Dendrocalamus [den-dro-KAL-am-us]
Giant bamboo. From Gr. *dendron,* a tree; *calamus,* a reed. Some of the species go up as high as 100 feet. Among them is the male bamboo from which surf-casting and split-cane fishing rods are made.

Dendrochilum [den-dro-KY-lum]
Gr. *dendron,* a tree; *cheilos,* a lip. The flowers of these tree-perching orchids have lips.

dendroideus, -a, -um [den-DROY-deus]
Treelike.

Dendromecon [den-dro-MEE-kon]
Tree-poppy. From Gr. *dendron,* a tree; *mecon,* a poppy.

dendrophilus, -a, -um [den-DROFF-ill-us]
Tree-loving.

Dennstaedtia [den-STEET-ia]
Hayscented fern. In honor of August Wilhelm Dennstedt, German botanist of the early 19th century.

dens-canis [dens-KAY-nis]
Specific name meaning dog's tooth.

densiflorus, -a, -um [den-si-FLOW-rus]
Densely flowered.

densifolius, -a, -um [den-si-FO-lius]
Densely leaved.

densatus, -a, -um [den-SAY-tus]
densus, -a, -um [DEN-sus]
Compact; dense.

Dentaria [den-TAY-ria]
Toothwort. From L. *dens,* a tooth; in allusion to the toothlike

scales on the roots of this early-flowering herb which led to the supposition that it might be good for toothache.

dentatus, -a, -um [den-TAY-tus]
dentiferus, -a, -um [den-TIFF-er-us]
dentosus, -a, -um [dent-O-sus]
Toothed; furnished with teeth.

denticulatus, -a, -um [den-tik-ew-LAY-tus]
Slightly toothed.

denudatus, -a, -um [dee-new-DAY-tus]
Bare; naked.

deodara [dee-o-DAR-a]
Specific name from the North Indian name for the deodar (*Cedrus deodara*).

depauperatus, -a, -um [dee-paw-per-AY-tus]
Imperfectly developed; dwarfed.

dependens [dee-PEND-ens]
Hanging down.

depressus, -a, -um [dee-PRESS-us]
Flattened; pressed down.

Derris [DERR-is]
Gr., a leather covering; in allusion to the tough seed pods of these woody climbers. The insecticide, derris, is made from the powdered tuberous root. In the East Indies the powder is used to poison fish by stupefying them.

deserti [dee-SERT-ty]
Of the desert.

desertorum [dee-sert-OR-um]
Of the deserts.

Desfontainea [dez-fon-TAIN-ea]
A Chilean evergreen shrub named for R. L. Desfontaines (1752-1833), French botanist.

Desmanthus [dez-MAN-thus]
Gr. *desme*, a bundle; *anthos*, a flower. The flowers of these herbs or shrubs are collected together in spikes resembling bundles.

Desmodium [dez-MO-dium]
Tick-trefoil. From Gr. *desmos*, a band or chain. The stamens are joined together in these herbs and sub-shrubs.

desmoncoides [dez-mon-KOY-deez]
Resembling the genus *Desmoncus*.

Desmoncus [dez-MON-kus]
Gr. *desmos,* a band or chain; *onkos,* a hook. The ends of the leaves of these spiny feather palms are furnished with hook-like tips.

detonsus, -a, -um [dee-TON-sus]
Bare; shorn.

deustus, -a, -um [dee-YEW-stus]
Burned.

Deutzia [DEWT-zia, or DOIT-zia]
Very ornamental shrubs. After Johann van der Deutz (1743-1788), Dutch friend and patron of Carl Thunberg, Swedish botanist and pupil of Linnaeus.

diabolicus, -a, -um [dy-ab-OL-ik-us]
Devilish.

diacanthus, -a, -um [dy-ak-ANTH-us]
Furnished with two spines.

Diacrium [dy-AK-rium]
From Gr. *dia,* through; *akris,* a point. The stalks of these tree-perching orchids pass through a sheath.

diadema [dy-ad-EE-ma]
Crown; diadem.

diandrus, -a, -um [dy-AN-drus]
Furnished with two or twin stamens.

Dianella [dy-an-ELL-a]
Flax lily. Diminutive of Diana, goddess of the chase.

dianthiflorus, -a, -um [dy-anth-i-FLOW-rus]
Dianthus-flowered.

Dianthus [dy-AN-thus]
Pink. Carnation. From Gr. *Di,* of Zeus or Jove; *anthos,* flower. These small herbs have long been held in the highest esteem.

Diapensia [dy-a-PENS-ia]
Classical Greek plant name adopted by Linnaeus for these dwarf, evergreen, tufted perennials.

diaphanus, -a, -um [dy-AFF-an-us]
Transparent.

Diascia [dy-ASS-ia]
Gr. *di,* two; *askos,* a sac. The flowers of these herbs have two spurs.

Dicentra [dy-SEN-tra]
From Gr. *dis,* twice; *kentron,* a spur. The flowers of these

perennial plants, which include bleeding heart, have two spurs.

Dichorisandra [dy-kor-is-AND-ra]
Gr. *dis*, twice; *chorizo*, to divide; *aner*, male; all in allusion to a technicality in the character of the stamens of these ornamental-leaved perennial herbs.

dichotomus, -a, -um [dy-KOT-o-mus]
Forked in pairs; repeatedly dividing into two branches.

dichroanthus, -a, -um [dy-kro-ANTH-us]
With flowers of two distinct colors.

dichromus, -a, -um [dy-KRO-mus]
dichrous, -a, -um [DY-kro-us]
Of two distinct colors.

Dicksonia [dik-SO-nia]
Tree ferns named after James Dickson (1738-1822), British botanist, who founded a nursery which is still flourishing in England.

dicoccus, -a, -um [dy-KOK-us]
Furnished with two berries or nuts.

Dicranostigma [dy-kray-no-STIG-ma]
Glaucous herbs of the poppy family. From Gr. *dikranos*, two-branched; plus *stigma*.

Dictamnus [dik-TAM-nus]
Greek name for this perennial herb which is variously called dittany, gas plant, burning bush, and fraxinella. The leaves and stem, which have a strong odor, give out a volatile oil which, on a hot, still day, can be faintly ignited with a match.

dictyophyllus, -a, -um [dik-tio-FILL-us]
With leaves covered in a netlike pattern. Similarly, *dictyocarpus*, with netted fruit.

Dictyosperma [dik-tio-SPERM-a]
From Gr. *dictyon*, a net; *sperma*, seed; in a technical allusion to the seed of these *Areca*-like palms.

didymus, -a, -um [DID-im-us]
Twin or in pairs.

Dieffenbachia [dee-fen-BAK-ia]
Foliage plants named in honor of Dr. J. F. Dieffenbach, in charge of the gardens of the royal palace of Schönbrunn at Vienna around 1830.

Dierama [dy-er-AY-ma]
Wandflower. Greek, meaning a funnel; from the shape of the perianth of these South African cormous plants.

Diervilla [dy-er-VILL-a]
Bush honeysuckle. Named for M. Dierville, a French surgeon who traveled in Canada, 1699-1700, and who introduced *D. lonicera.*

difformis, -is, -e [dif-FORM-is]
Of unusual form in relation to the normal run of the genus.

diffusus, -a, -um [dif-FEW-sus]
Spreading; diffuse.

Digitalis [dij-it-AY-lis]
Foxglove. From L. *digitus,* a finger. The flowers of these herbaceous plants are like the fingers of a glove. *D. purpurea* is the source of the digitalis used in cardiac medicine.

digitatus, -a, -um [dij-it-AY-tus]
Shaped like an open hand; digitate.

dilatatus, -a, -um [dy-la-TAY-tus]
dilatus, -a, -um [dy-LAY-tus]
Spread out.

Dillenia [dill-EE-nia]
A genus of tall, tropical, evergreen trees named by Linnaeus for John James Dillenius (1684-1747), Professor of Botany at Oxford and one of the founders of the modern science. To quote Linnaeus, "Dillenia of all plants has the showiest flower and fruit, even as Dillenius made a brilliant show among botanists."

Dillwynia [dill-WIN-ia]
Evergreen flowering shrubs named in honor of Lewis Weston Dillwyn (1778-1855), a British natural historian and botanist.

dimidiatus -a, -um [dim-id-i-AY-tus]
Divided into two dissimilar or unequal parts.

Dimorphotheca [dy-mor-fo-THEE-ka]
Cape marigold. From Gr. *dis,* twice; *morphe,* a shape; *theka,* fruit; a technical reference to a characteristic of the fruit of these South African herbs and sub-shrubs.

dimorphus, -a, -um [dy-MORF-us]
Having two forms of leaf, flower, or fruit on the same plant.

diodon [DY-o-don]
Having two teeth.

dioicus, -a, -um [dy-o-ik-us]
Dioecious, i.e., having the male reproductive organs borne on one plant and the female on another.

Dionaea [dy-o-NEE-a]
Venus flytrap. One of the Greek names for Venus. Found only in North and South Carolina, the plant has leaves each divided into two hinged, valvelike segments, the inner faces of which have three sensitive "trigger" hairs. When an insect lands inside and touches any two of the hairs, the valves close like jaws, the interlocking stiff hairs around the outside edge of the leaves holding it. Once closed, the trap will reopen when the insect is digested.

Dioscorea [dy-os-kor-EE-a]
Yam. Named in honor of Pedanios Dioscorides, 1st-century Greek who laid the foundation of virtually all botanical knowledge—certainly until relatively modern times. He was the author of *Materia Medica* which dealt with medicinal herbs and which has gone into countless editions through the centuries.

Diosma [dy-os-ma]
Gr. *dios*, divine; *osme*, fragrance. The leaves of these heath-like shrubs when crushed are very fragrant.

diosmaefolius, -a, -um [dy-os-mee-FO-lius]
With leaves like *Diosma*.

Diospyros [dy-os-PY-ros]
Persimmon. Ebony. From Gr. *dios*, divine; *pyros*, wheat; in allusion to the edible fruits of this genus of trees and shrubs.

Diotis [dy-o-tis]
Cotton-weed. Gr. *dis*, two; *otos*, an ear. The lobes of the co-rolla of this perennial are shaped like ears.

Dipelta [dy-PEL-ta]
Gr. *dis*, two; *pelta*, a shield; referring to the form of the bracts on these ornamental deciduous shrubs.

dipetalus, -a, -um [dy-PET-al-us]
Having two petals.

Diphylleia [dy-fill-EE-a]
Gr. *dis*, two; *phyllon*, a leaf. The leaves on this perennial herb usually have two deep lobes.

diphyllus, -a, -um [dy-FILL-us]
Having two leaves.

Dipladenia [dip-la-DEE-nia]
Gr. *diploos,* double; *aden,* a gland. There are two glands on the ovary of these climbers.

Diplazium [dip-LAY-zium]
Gr. *diplazios,* double. The indusium, the covering over the spores, in these ferns is double.

Diploglottis [dip-lo-GLOT-is]
Gr. *diploos,* double; *glottis,* a tongue. The inner scale of the petals is double on this Australian tree.

diplostephioides [dip-lo-stee-fi-oy-deez]
Resembling *Diplostephium,* a genus of little garden interest.

dipsaceus, -a, -um [dip-SAY-shus]
Resembling the teasel or *Dipsacus.*

Dipsacus [DIP-sak-us]
Teasel. From Greek *dipsakos,* thirst; because a hollow in the leaf bases holds water. The plants are cultivated for the fruiting heads which are covered with stiff, hooked points. These heads are used in the woollen industry to raise the nap on cloth. So far, no man-made device has been found as effective.

dipterocarpus, -a, -um [dip-ter-o-KARP-us]
Having two-winged fruit.

Dipteronia [dip-ter-o-nia]
Gr. *dis,* two; *pteron,* a wing; in allusion to the winged fruit of this ornamental Chinese tree.

dipterus, -a, -um [DIP-ter-us]
Two-winged.

dipyrenus, -a, -um [dip-py-REEN-us]
Having two seeds or kernels.

Dirca [DER-ka]
Leatherwood. From Gr. *dirke,* a fountain. These early-blooming North American shrubs grow in moist places. The tough, flexible shoots can be used as tying material or for baskets, while rope can be made from the bark.

Disa [DY-sa]
Derivation of the name of these terrestrial orchids is obscure.

Discaria [dis-CA-ria]
Gr. *diskos,* a disk. The flower of these spiny shrubs has a large fleshy disk.

disciformis, -is, -e [disk-i-FORM-is]
In the shape of a disk.

Discocactus [dis-ko-KAK-tus]
Gr. *diskos,* a disk, and *Cactus.* From the shape of these plants which are globe-shaped or flattened endwise.

discoideus, -a, -um [disk-OY-deus]
Discoid; without rays.

discolor [DIS-kol-or]
Of two different and, usually, distinct colors.

dispar [DIS-par]
Unequal; dissimilar from the normal of the genus.

Disocactus [dis-o-KAK-tus]
From Gr. *dis,* twice; plus *Cactus.* These air plants are so called for rather technical reasons.

dispersus, -a, -um [dis-PER-sus]
Scattered.

Disporum [DIS-por-um]
Fairybells. From Gr. *dis,* two; *sporos,* seeds; in a technical allusion to the ovary of these small perennial herbs.

dissectus, -a, -um [dis-SEKT-us]
Deeply cut; divided into deep lobes or segments.

dissimilis, -is, -e [dis-SIM-ill-is]
Unlike the normal for the genus.

dissitiflorus, -a, -um [dis-sit-i-FLOW-rus]
The flowers in loose heads, not compact.

distachyus, -a, -um [dis-TAK-yus]
With two spikes.

distans [DIS-tans]
Widely separated.

distichophyllus, -a, -um [dis-tik-o-FILL-us]
With leaves arranged in two ranks.

distichus, -a, -um [DIS-tik-us]
In two ranks.

Distictis [DIS-tik-tis]
Gr. *dis,* twice; *stiktos,* spotted. The flattened seeds look like two rows of spots in the capsule of these climbing shrubs.

distortus, -a, -um [dis-TORT-us]
Misshapen; of grotesque form.

Distylium [dis-TY-lium]
Gr. *dis,* two; *stylos,* a style. These ornamental trees and shrubs have two styles.

distylus, -a, -um [dis-TY-lus]
Having two styles.

138

diurnus, -a, -um [dy-URN-us]
Day-flowering.
divaricatus, -a, -um [dy-va-rik-AY-tus]
Spreading; growing in a straggling manner.
divergens [dy-VERJ-ens]
Spreading out widely from the center.
diversicolor [dy-ver-SIK-ol-or]
Diversely colored. Also:

diversiflorus, -a, -um   diversely flowered
diversifolius, -a, -um   diversely leaved
diversiformis, -is, -e   of diverse forms

divisus, -a, -um [dy-VY-sus]
Divided.
divus, -a, -um [DY-vus]
Belonging to the gods.
dixanthus [dix-ANTH-us]
Of two shades of color.
Dizygotheca [di-zy-go-THEE-ka]
False aralia. From Gr. *dis*, twice; *zygos*, a yoke, *theka*, a case. The anthers of these ornamental trees and shrubs have twice the normal number of cells.
Docynia [do-SIN-ia]
Anagram of *Cydonia*. These trees are closely related to Cydonia or quince.
dodecandrus, -a, -um [do-dek-AND-rus]
Having twelve stamens.
Dodecatheon [do-dek-ATH-eon]
Shooting star, American cowslip. The derivation from Greek meaning twelve gods seems to have no particular significance in the naming of these North American herbs.
Dodonaea [do-don-EE-a]
A genus of trees and shrubs, chiefly Australian, named in honor of Rembert Dodoens (1518-1585), Dodonaeus, Dutch royal physician and a writer on plants.
dodonaeifolius, -a, -um [do-don-ee-i-FO-lius]
Dodonaea-leaved.
dolabratus, -a, -um [do-lab-RAY-tus]
  dolabriformis, -is, -e [do-lab-ri-FORM-is]
Hatchet-shaped.

Dolichandra [dol-ik-AND-ra]
Gr. *dolichos,* long; *aner,* male; in allusion to the form of the anthers of these climbing shrubs.

Dolichos [DOL-ik-os]
Greek word for long; in allusion to the long slender stems of these climbing plants closely related to beans.

Dolichothele [dol-ik-o-THEE-lee]
Gr. *dolichos,* long; *thele,* a nipple; an allusion to the elongated tubercles or small above-ground tubers of these cacti.

dolosus, -a, -um [dol-o-sus]
Deceitful; appearing like some other plant.

Dombeya [dom-BEE-a]
Ornamental evergreen trees or shrubs named in honor of Joseph Dombey, 18th-century French botanist, who traveled in Chile and Peru.

domesticus, -a, -um [do-MEST-ik-us]
Frequently used as a house plant; domesticated.

Doodia [DOO-dia]
Decorative ferns named in honor of Samuel Doody (1656-1706), London apothecary, Keeper of the Chelsea Botanic Garden, 1691.

Doritis [DOR-it-is]
From Gr. *doru,* a spear; the lip of these orchids being spear-shaped.

doronicoides [do-ron-ik-oy-deez]
Resembling *Doronicum.*

Doronicum [do-RON-ik-um]
Derivation obscure. Called leopard's bane, this genus of perennial herbs was considered useful in destroying and warding off wild beasts. *D. pardalianches,* meaning to strangle leopards, is reputedly poisonous.

Dorstenia [dor-STEEN-ia]
Herbs and small shrubs named for Theodore Dorsten (1492-1552), German botanist.

Doryanthes [do-ri-ANTH-ees]
Spear lily. From Gr. *dory,* a spear; *anthos,* a flower. The flower stem of this Australian desert plant is very long, sometimes as much as 20 feet.

Dorycnium [do-RIK-nium]
The ancient Greek name for these shrubby plants from the Mediterranean region.

Doryopteris [do-ri-OP-ter-is]
From Gr. *doru*, a spear; *pteris*, a fern; from the form of the fronds of these small ferns.

Douglasia [dug-LASS-ia]
Tufted perennial herbs, named for David Douglas (1798-1834), Scottish collector for the Royal Horticultural Society. He came to Oregon in 1825 for a two-year botanical exploration, returning in 1830. He was killed in Hawaii in a strange accident in which he fell into a wild-cattle trap where he was gored to death by a bull which had already been trapped.

douglasii [dug-LASS-i-eye]
The original specific name for douglas fir now generally described as *Pseudotsuga taxifolia* (See *Douglasia*).

Dovyalis [do-vi-AY-lis]
A tropical woody plant. Derivation obscure. Sometimes incorrectly spelled *Doryalis*.

Downingia [down-IN-jia]
Annual herbs, mostly Californian, named in honor of Andrew Jackson Downing (1815-1852), American landscape gardener and pomologist. He was the founder of a great tradition of American landscape design and his book *A Treatise on the Theory and Practice of Landscape Design* has run through many editions, with re-editing at least up to 1921. His ideas were free and naturalistic and they had great influence on subsequent practice.

Downing was also a notable pomologist. His book *The Fruits and Fruit Trees of America* was the standard work on the subject in America for at least sixty years. With his brother Charles he founded the Downing Nursery at Newburgh, New York.

Doxantha [dox-ANTH-a]
Cat's claw, North American climbing shrub. From Gr. *doxa*, glory; *anthos*, a flower.

Draba [DRAY-ba]
Whitlow-grass or nailwort. The classical Greek name for this spring-flowering tufted herb, which was supposed to have value in poulticing whitlows.

drabifolius, -a, -um [dray-bi-FO-lius]
Having leaves like *Draba* or whitlow-grass.

Dracaena [dra-SEE-na]
The accepted derivation of the name for these ornamental

treelike and shrublike plants is from Gr. *drakaina,* a female dragon. The color dragon's blood can be obtained from *D. draco,* the dragon tree. At least one authority (Pulteney), however, suggests that the genus was named by Clusius in honor of Sir Francis Drake, whom he met in 1581 and from whom he received some of his plant discoveries from the New World. Clusius, living in Flanders which was then occupied by the Spanish, and through the time of the Armada, would naturally have regarded Drake as someone worth commemorating.

A number of the plants popularly described and sold as *Dracaena* are in fact *Cordyline.*

dracaenoides [dra-see-NOY-deez]
Resembling *Dracaena.*

draco [DRAY-co]
Specific name meaning a dragon.

Dracocephalum [dray-ko-SEFF-al-um]
Dragonhead. From Gr. *draco,* a dragon; *cephale,* a head; from the shape of the flower of these herbaceous plants.

dracocephalus, -a, -um [dray-ko-SEFF-al-us]
Dragon-headed.

dracunculoides [drak-unk-ew-LOY-deez]
Resembling *Artemisia dracunculus* or tarragon.

Dracunculus [drak-UNK-ew-lus]
Dragon arum. Latin name for another plant, not this evil-smelling *Arum*-like plant.

dracunculus [drak-UNK-ew-lus]
Latin word meaning a small dragon; specific name for *Artemisia dracunculus* or tarragon.

drepanophyllus, -a, -um [dree-pan-o-FILL-us]
With sickle-shaped leaves.

Drimys [DRY-mis]
Greek word meaning acrid; from the taste of the bark of these evergreen trees and shrubs related to the magnolia family.

Drosera [DRO-ser-a]
Sundew. From Gr. *droseros,* dewy; in allusion to the gland-tipped hairs on the leaves which give a dewy appearance to these carnivorous plants.

drupaceus, -a, -um [droo-PAY-see-us]
drupiferus, -a, -um [droo-PIFF-er-us]
Bearing fleshy fruits or drupes such as peach, cherry, or plum.

Dryandra [dry-AND-ra]
Australian evergreen shrubs, named for Jonas Dryander
(1748-1810), Swedish botanist.

Dryas [DRY-as]
Mountain avens. From Gr. *dryades*, a wood nymph or dryad,
to whom the oak was sacred. The leaves of at least one species of these tufted evergreen plants, *D. octopetala*, resemble
oak leaves.

drymifolius, -a, -um [dry-mi-FO-lius]
With leaves like *Drimys*, a plant of little garden interest.

drynarioides [dry-na-ri-OY-deez]
Resembling *Drynaria*, a fern with fronds which look like
oak leaves.

Dryopteris [dry-op-TER-is]
American shield fern. Wood fern. From Gr. *dryades*, a wood
nymph; *pteris*, a fern.

dubius, -a, -um [DEW-bius]
Doubtful, in the sense of not following the genus pattern.

Duchesnea [doo-SHAYS-nea]
Indian or mock strawberry. Trailing herbs named in honor
of Antoine Michel Duchesne, a French expert on strawberries.

dulcamara [dul-ka-MAY-ra]
Latin for bittersweet. The species name for climbing nightshade (*Solanum dulcamara*).

dulcis, -is, -e [DUL-sis]
Sweet.

dumetorum [doo-met-OR-um]
Of hedges or of bushy places.

dumosus, -a, -um [doo-MO-sus]
Bushy, shrubby.

dunensis [doo-NEN-sis]
Of sand dunes.

duplex [DEW-plex]
duplicatus, -a, -um [dew-plik-AY-tus]
Double, duplicate.

durabilis, -is, -e [dew-RAY-bil-is]
Durable, lasting.

duracinus, -a, -um [dew-RAS-in-us]
With hard fruit or berries.

Duranta [dew-RAN-ta]
Tropical American woody plants named for Castor Duranta
(d. about 1590), physician and botanist in Rome.

Durio [DEW-rio]
From the Malayan name, durian, which is regarded by the
estoric as among the most delicious of fruits. The fruit,
which is larger than a coconut, has a spiky outside rind which
encloses an evil-smelling pith in which the pulp-covered
seeds are embedded. This pulp is the edible part. It is
creamy white, delicate, and sweet. The durian is a feature
of Eastern bazaars in June. It is popularly regarded as an
aphrodisiac with many earthy sayings attached to it.

duriusculus, -a, -um [du-ri-us-KEW-lus]
Somewhat hard.

durus, -a, -um [DU-rus]
Hard. Thus, *durior,* harder.

durra [DURR-a]
Native Egyptian name for a fodder sorghum, *Sorghum
vulgare* var. *durra,* fed to camels and other beasts.

Duvalia [dew-VAY-lia]
Dwarf succulent herbs named for H. A. Duval (1777-1814),
French botanical author.

Dyckia [DY-kia]
Succulent plants named for Prince Joseph Salm-Reiffer-
scheid-Dyck (1773-1861), author of outstanding books on
succulents.

Dyschoriste [dis-ko-RIS-tee]
Gr. *dys,* contrary to; *choriste,* divided. The stigma of these
tropical plants is almost entire.

Dysoxylum [dy-sox-ill-um]
Gr. *dusodes,* evil-smelling; *xylon,* wood. This genus of trees
has some species with a fetid odor.

E

ebenaceus, -a, -um [eb-en-AY-shus]
Resembling ebony.

Ebenus [EE-ben-us]
Greek name for another, leguminous plant, not this genus
of shrubs and sub-shrubs.

ebenus, -a, -um [EB-en-us]
Ebony-black.

ebracteatus, -a, -um [ee-brak-tee-AY-tus]
Without bracts.

eburneus, -a, -um [ee-BURN-eus]
Ivory-white.

Ecballium [ek-BAL-ium]
Gr. *ekballein*, to cast out. The seeds of this perennial trailer, called squirting cucumber, are violently dehisced or ejected.

Eccremocarpus [ek-rem-o-KARP-us]
Glory flower. From Gr. *ekkremes*, hanging from; *karpos*, fruit. The fruit is a slender, hanging pod.

Echeveria [esh-eve-EE-ria]
Succulent plants named for Atanasio Echeverria, Mexican-born botanical artist who accompanied the expedition under the Italian botanist Malaspina hunting plants in Mexico and Central America. He did the illustrations for *Flora Mexicana* (1858).

Echidnopsis [ee-kid-NOP-sis]
Gr. *echidne*, a viper, *opsis*, like; in allusion to the slender, somewhat prostrate stems of these succulents.

Echinacea [ek-in-AY-sea]
Cornflower (in the United States). Purple cone flower. From Gr. *echinos*, a hedgehog; in allusion to the prickly scales of the receptacle of these perennial herbs. The thick, black roots with a pungent flavor are edible.

echinatus, -a, -um [ek-in-AY-tus]
Covered with prickles like a hedgehog.

Echinocactus [ek-in-o-KAK-tus]
Gr. *echinos*, a hedgehog. These cacti are like hedgehogs in appearance.

echinocarpus, -a, -um [ek-in-o-KARP-us]
With prickly fruit like a hedgehog.

Echinocereus [ek-in-o-SEE-reus]
Gr. *echinos*, a hedgehog. This genus of cactus has spiny fruit which differentiates it from *Cereus*.

Echinocystis [ek-in-o-SIS-tus]
Prickly cucumber. Gr. *echinos*, a hedgehog; *kystis*, a bladder; from the prickly fruit.

Echinomastus [ek-in-o-MASS-tus]
Gr. *echinos,* a hedgehog; *mastos,* a breast. The tubercles of this cactus are spiny.

Echinopanax [ek-in-o-PAY-nax]
Gr. *echinos,* a hedgehog; *Panax,* the genus name for American ginseng. This ornamental shrub is densely covered with spines.

Echinops [EK-in-ops]
Globe thistle. From Gr. *echinos,* a hedgehog; *opsis,* like; in allusion to this herb's handsome spiny, globe-shaped flower heads of metallic blue.

Echinopsis [ek-in-OP-sis]
Sea-urchin cactus. From Gr. *echinos,* a sea-urchin (also hedgehog); *opsis,* like; from the resemblance of these round, spiny cacti to a sea-urchin.

echinosepalus, -a, -um [ek-in-o-SEP-al-us]
With prickly sepals.

echioides [ek-i-OY-deez]
Resembling viper's bugloss or *Echium.*

Echites [ek-KY-tees]
Gr. *echis,* a viper. This shrub is poisonous and of twining habit.

Echium [EK-ium]
Viper's bugloss. The Greek name. This genus of rough herbs and shrubs was supposed to discourage serpents, while the root drunk with wine was regarded both as good for snakebite and also as a continuing protection when bitten in the future.

ecornutus, -a, -um [ee-kor-NEW-tus]
Without horns.

Edgeworthia [ej-WORTH-ia]
Ornamental shrubs named in honor of M. P. Edgeworth (1812-1881) of the East India Company's Service and a botanist on the side.

Edraianthus [ed-ry-ANTH-us]
Gr. *edraios,* without a stalk; *anthos,* flower. The flowers of these perennials are in a cluster at the top of the main stalk.

edulis, -is, -e [ed-EW-lis]
Edible.

effusus, -a, -um [ef-FEW-sus]
Loosely spreading.

Ehretia [er-EESH-ia]

A genus of trees and shrubs named in honor of G. D. Ehret (1708-1770), German botanical artist, brother-in-law of Philip Miller, the English author of the great two-volume *Gardener's and Botanical Dictionary.*

Eichhornia [ike-HORN-ia]

Water-hyacinth. A genus of aquatic plants named for J. A. Eichhorn (1779-1856), Prussian patron of horticulture.

eichleri [IKE-ler-eye]

Of Wilhelm Eichler, a German who found *Tulipa eichleri* in the Caucasus.

eleagnifolius, -a, -um [el-ee-ag-ni-FO-lius]

With leaves resembling *Eleagnus.*

Eleagnus [el-ee-AG-nus]

A large genus of shrubs and trees. From Gr. *elaia,* an olive tree; *agnos,* the Greek name for *Vitex agnus-castus* or chaste-tree.

Elaeis [el-EE-is]

African oil palm. From Gr. *elaia,* an olive tree. Oil is obtained from the fruit of these feather palms as it is from olives. It is of great commercial importance in West Africa and other tropical areas. Palm-nut oil, less desirable but still valuable, is obtained from the kernels of the nuts within the fruits. Palm oil, locally called chop oil, is prized for cooking on the West African Coast.

Elaeocarpus [el-ee-o-KARP-us]

Gr. *elaia,* olive; *karpos,* fruit; from the appearance of the round fruit of these handsome evergreens which encloses a nut with a rough shell.

Elaeodendron [el-ee-o-DEN-dron]

Gr. *elaia,* olive; *dendron,* a tree. The fruit of these small trees or shrubs is like an olive with an oily seed.

Elaphoglossum [el-aff-o-GLOSS-um]

Elephant-ear fern. From Gr. *elaphos,* a stag; *glossa,* a tongue; an allusion to the appearance of the fronds.

elasticus, -a, -um [el-AS-tik-us]

Elastic.

elaterium [el-at-EER-ium]

Specific name of *Ecballium elaterium,* squirting cucumber. Both names have the implication of driving with force—an allusion to the way in which the seeds are thrown out.

elatior [el-AY-tior]
Taller.

elatus, -a, -um [el-AY-tus]
Tall.

elegans [EL-eg-ans]
elegantulus, -a, -um [el-eg-AN-tew-lus]
Elegant.

elegantissimus, -a, -um [el-eg-gan-TISS-im-us]
Very elegant.

elephantidens [el-eff-ANT-id-ens]
Large-toothed.

elephantipes [el-eff-ANT-ip-ees]
Like an elephant's foot.

elephantum [el-eff-ANT-um]
Of the elephants; monstrous, big.

Elettaria [el-et-AY-ria]
Cardamon. From the vernacular name in Malabar in south-western India. The cardamon of commerce is the seed of this perennial herb. In India and the East generally it is often chewed as a post-prandial carminative to aid digestion.

Eleusine [el-yew-SY-ne]
From the city of Eleusis in Greece where the temple of Ceres stood. The genus of coarse grasses includes various cereals such as African millet.

Elliottia [el-i-OT-ia]
A handsome shrub named after Stephen Elliott (1771-1830), American botanist.

ellipsoidalis, -is, -e [el-lip-soy-DAY-lis]
ellipticus, -a, -um [el-LIP-tik-us]
Elliptic; longer than wide, with rounded ends and sides.

Elodea [el-o-dea]
Waterweed or ditchmoss. From Gr. *elodes,* a marsh.

elongatus, -a, -um [ee-long-GAY-tus]
Lengthened; elongated.

Elsholtzia [el-SHOLT-zia]
Aromatic herbs and sub-shrubs named in honor of Johann Sigismund Elsholtz (1623-1688), Prussian naturalist and physician.

Elymus [EL-im-us]
Wild rye. From the Greek name for a kind of grass.

148

emarginatus, -a, -um [ee-mar-jin-AY-tus]
With a shallow notch at the end as though a piece had been removed.

Embothrium [em-BOTH-rium]
Gr. *en*, in; *bothrion*, a pit; an allusion to the position of the anthers on these evergreen shrubs or trees.

emeticus, -a, -um [ee-MET-ik-us]
Causing vomiting; emetic.

Emilia [ee-MILL-ia]
Tassel flower. Probably named for some individual but just who is commemorated in these flower-garden herbs is not known.

eminens [EM-in-ens]
Eminent; prominent.

Emmenanthe [em-en-ANTH-e]
California golden bells. Gr. *emmenos*, lasting; *anthos*, a flower. The corolla lasts for a long time on these bushy annuals.

Emmenopterys [em-en-OP-ter-is]
Gr. *emmenos*, enduring; *pterys*, a wing. The calyx lobes of this ornamental tree are large and winged.

empetrifolius, -a, -um [em-pet-ri-FO-lius]
With leaves like crowberry or *Empetrum*.

Empetrum [em-PET-rum]
Crowberry. From Gr. *en*, on; *petros, a rock;* a reference to the natural habitat of these Alpine plants.

Encelia [en-SEE-lia]
Gr. *enchelion*, a little eel; from the formation of the seeds of these herbs or sub-shrubs.

Encephalartos [en-seff-al-ART-os]
Gr. *en*, in; *cephale*, a head; *artos*, bread. The inner parts of the top of the trunks of these primitive palmlike trees are farinaceous and edible.

engelmannii [eng-gel-MAN-y-i]
Of Engelmann. Specific name of Englemann's spruce and oak (*Picea* and *Quercus engelmanni*) as well as of other less well-known plants. Named for Georg Engelmann (1809-1884), German-born St. Louis physician who had great knowledge of plants. He did some exploring but his greater contribution lay in his encouragement of others. He was first to call attention to the immunity of American grape

stocks to phylloxera. This virtually saved the European wine industry, for which we can all be deeply grateful.

Enkianthus [en-ki-ANTH-us]
Gr. *enknos,* pregnant; *anthos,* a flower. In some species of these shrubs the flower gives the appearance of being a flower within a flower.

enneacanthus, -a, -um [en-ne-ak-ANTH-us]
With nine spines.

enneaphyllus, -a, -um [en-ne-aff-ILL-us]
With nine leaves.

ensatus, -a, -um [en-SAY-tus]
Sword-shaped.

ensifolius, -a, -um [en-si-FO-lius]
With sword-shaped leaves.

ensiformis, -is, -e [en-si-FORM-is]
Quite straight and with a sharp point like a sword or the leaf of an iris.

Entelea [en-tel-EE-a]
Gr. *enteles,* perfect. The stamens of this shrub or small tree are all fertile.

entomophilus, -a, -um [ent-o-MOFF-ill-us]
Insect-loving. Applied as a specific name to certain plants that by means of color, odor, or nectar attract the insects which carry their pollen to other plants.

Eomecon [ee-o-MEE-kon]
Snow poppy. Gr. *heos,* Aurora or Eastern; *mekon,* a poppy; a Far Eastern species.

Epacris [EPP-ak-ris]
Gr. *epi,* upon; *akros,* a summit. Hill tops are the natural habitat of some of the species of these heathlike shrubs.

Ephedra [eff-EE-dra]
Greek name for the common mare's tail (*Hippuris*) which it resembles. Certain species of these low evergreen shrubs are the source of ephedrine which, as *ma-huang,* the Chinese have used in medicine for centuries.

Epidendrum [ep-i-DEN-drum]
Gr. *epi,* upon; *dendron,* a tree. These are epiphytic or tree-perching orchids.

Epigaea [ep-i-JEE-a]
Ground-laurel. Mayflower or trailing arbutus. From Gr. *epi,*

upon; *gaea,* the earth; a reference to the creeping habit of these evergreen woody-stemmed plants.

epigaeus, -a, -um [ep-i-JEE-us]
Growing close to the ground or, sometimes, growing on land and not in water.

Epilobium [ep-i-LO-bium]
Willow-herb. From Gr. *epi,* upon; *lobos,* a pod. The petals of these herbs surmount the podlike ovary.

Epimedium [ep-i-MEE-dium]
Barren-wort. The Greek name for these dainty herbs.

Epipactis [ep-i-PAK-tis]
Greek plant name adopted for this genus of terrestrial orchids.

Epiphronitis [ep-i-fron-EYE-tis]
Name applied to orchid hybrids resulting from crossing *Epidendrum* and *Sophronitis.*

Epiphyllum [ep-i-FILL-um]
Gr. *epi,* upon; *phyllon,* a leaf. It was originally thought that the flowers of these cacti were on the leaves which ultimately proved to be flattened stems.

Episcia [ep-ISS-ia]
From Gr. *episkios,* shaded; from the natural habitat of these herbaceous perennials.

Epithelantha [ep-i-thee-LANTH-a]
Gr. *epi,* upon; *thele,* a nipple; *anthos,* a flower. The flowers of these globular cacti are borne on tubercles.

equalis, -is, -e [ee-KWAY-lis]
Equal.

equestris, -is, -e [ee-KWEST-ris]
Pertaining to a horse or like the rider of a horse.

equinus, -a, -um [ee-KWY-nus]
Of horses.

equisetifolius, -a, -um [ee-kwi-see-ti-FO-lius]
With leaves like horsetail or *Equisetum.*

Equisetum [ek-kwi-SEE-tum]
Horsetail. L. *equus,* a horse; *seta,* a bristle. Of more historical than garden interest, the genus links modern plants with incredibly ancient orders of vegetation. In carboniferous period, the earth was covered with immense forests of gigantic *Equisetum* which today make up to a large extent our coal measures. It was called scouring rush in 17th-century New England because the presence of silica gave a fine finish in

scouring pewter. In modern times it is occasionally used to put a really fine finish on cabinet work.

Eragrostis [e-ra-GROS-tis]
Love-grass. From Gr. *eros*, love; *agrostis*, grass. The reason for the name is obscure.

Eranthemum [e-RAN-them-um]
Gr. *erranos*, lovely; *anthemon*, a flower. Some of these tropical shrubs and sub-shrubs are cultivated for their flowers.

Eranthis [er-ANTH-is]
Winter aconite. From Gr. *er*, spring; *anthos*, a flower. The plant is one of the earliest blooming of the spring flowers.

Ercilla [er-SILL-a]
A Peruvian twining shrub named for Alonso de Ercille (1533-1595) of Madrid.

erectus, -a, -um [ee-REK-tus]
Erect; upright.

Eremaea [er-em-EE-a]
Gr. *eremos*, solitary. The style is solitary.

Ermia [e-REE-mia]
Gr. *eremos*, solitary. There is but one seed in the cell of these heathlike shrubs.

Eremocitrus [e-ree-mo-SIT-rus]
Australian Desert kumquat. From Gr. *eremos*, solitary. There is but one species of this shrub or small tree.

Eremurus [e-ree-MEW-rus]
Desert-candle or foxtail lily. From Gr. *eremos*, solitary; *ouros*, a tail; from the appearance of the flower spike.

Eria [EE-ria]
Gr. *erion*, wool. The flowers and pedicels of these orchids are often woolly.

eri-
Prefix implying woolly. Thus:

eriacanthus   woolly-spined
eriantherus   with woolly anthers
erianthus   with woolly flowers

Erianthus [er-i-ANTH-us]
Plume-grass. From Gr. *erion*, wool; in allusion to the silvery woolly effect or the inflorescence.

Erica [E-rik-a, or e-RY-ka]
Heath. The Latin name. The Mediterranean *E. arborea* is

152

the source of brier (or briar) for tobacco pipes which are
turned from the roots which are sometimes very large and
solid. (French *bruyère,* heath.)

ericaefolius, -a, -um (also **ericifolius**)   [e-riss-ee-FO-lius]
With leaves like *Erica* or heath.

ericoides   [e-rik-OY-deez]
Resembling *Erica* or heath.

Erigenia   [e-rij-ee-NY-a]
Harbinger-of-spring. From Gr. *er,* spring; *genia,* born; a
reference to this small North American plant's early flowering.

Erigeron   [e-RIJ-er-on]
Fleabane. From Gr. *er,* spring; *geron,* an old man; from the
fact that some species of these aster-like herbs have a hoary,
downy covering early in the season.

erinaceus, -a, -um   [e-rin-AY-seus]
Resembling a hedgehog.

Erinus   [e-RY-nus]
Gr. *er,* spring; an allusion to their very early blooming habit
of this tufted perennial.

Eriobotrya   [e-rio-BOT-ria]
Gr. *erion,* wool; *botrys,* a cluster of grapes; from the woolly,
clustered panicles of this evergreen shrub or small tree.

eriobotryoides   [e-rio-bot-ri-OY-deez]
Resembling *Eriobotrya.*

eriocarpus, -a, -um   [e-rio-CARP-us]
Woolly-fruited. Also:

eriocephalus	woolly-headed
eriophorus	wool-bearing
eriospathus	with a woolly spathe
eriostachys	with a woolly spike
eriostemon	with a woolly stamen

Eriocephalus   [e-rio-SEFF-al-us]
Gr. *erion,* wool; *cephale,* a head. On these scented shrubs
the heads, after flowering, become woolly.

Eriogonum   [e-ri-OG-o-num]
Gr. *erion,* wool; *gonu,* a joint. The stems of these herbs or
sub-shrubs are downy at the nodes.

Eriophorum   [e-ri-OFF-or-um]
Cottongrass. From Gr. *erion,* wool; *phoreo,* to bear. The
heads of these sedgelike plants are cottony.

Eriophyllum [e-ri-o-FILL-um]
Gr. *erion,* wool; *phyllon,* a leaf. The leaves of these perennial herbs are woolly.

Eriopsis [e-ri-OP-sis]
Gr. resembling *Eria,* another genus of epiphytic or tree-perching orchids.

Eriostemon [e-ri-o-STEE-mon]
Gr. *erion,* wool; *stemon,* a stamen. The stamens of these evergreen shrubs are woolly.

Eritrichium [e-ri-TRIK-ium]
Gr. *erion,* wool; *trichos,* hair. These tufted perennial herbs
are woolly.

Erlangea [er-LAN-jee-a]
Shrubs or herbs, mostly African, named in honor of the University of Erlangen in Bavaria.

Erodium [er-o-dium]
Heron's bill. From Gr. *erodios,* a heron. The carpels of these
pretty plants resemble the head and beak of a heron.

erosus, -a, -um [ee-RO-sus]
Jagged, as if irregularly gnawed or bitten off.

erraticus, -a, -um [er-RAT-ik-us]
Unusual; sporadic; departing from the normal of the genus.

erubescens [e-roo-BESS-ens]
Blushing; becoming red.

Eruca [ee-ROO-ka]
Latin name for *Eruca sativa* or rocket-salad, grown for its
oil rich seed and sometimes for use as a salad plant.

erucastrum [e-roo-KAS-trum]
erucoides [e-roo-KOY-deez]
Resembling *Eruca* or rocket-salad.

Eryngium [e-RINJ-ium]
Sea-holly. Eryngo. The Greek name for these herbs. The
roots of sea-holly (*E. maritimum*) are sweet and aromatic
and once were well regarded for their supposed aphrodisiac
effect. They were candied and cookery books up to the 18th
century carried recipes for doing this.

Erysimum [e-RY-sim-um]
Blistercress. From Gr. *eryo,* to drag. Some species of these
herbs are said to produce blisters.

Erythea [e-ri-THEE-a]
These fan-palms are named for one of the three Hesperides

who lived far away in the West on the border of the ocean where the sun set, guarding the golden apples which Earth had given to Hera. They were sisters but no one quite knew who the parents were; some thought they were Erebus and Night, others Atlas and Hesperis.

Erythrina [e-rith-RY-na]
Coral tree. From Gr. *erythros*, red; an allusion to the color of the flower.

erythro-
As a prefix in compound words it signifies red. Thus:

erythrocarpus	having red fruit
erythrocephalus	red-headed
erythropodus	having a red foot or stem
erythropterus	with red wings
erythrosorus	having red spore cases

Erythronium [e-rith-RO-nium].
Dog's-tooth violet. Trout-lily. Adder's tongue. From Gr. *erythros*, red, the color of the flower in certain European species.

Erythroxylon [e-rith-ROX-ill-on]
From Gr. *erythros*, red; *xylon*, wood. Some species have red wood.

E. coca, the only source of cocaine, is a bush cultivated in the tropics for that product. Native in Bolivia and Peru, the inhabitants chew the leaves both for their euphoric effect and to sustain themselves in feats of endurance.

Escallonia [ess-kal-o-nia]
Shrubs and small trees named for Señor Escallon, a Spanish traveler in South America.

Eschscholtzia [esh-SHOLT-zia]
California poppy. Named in honor of Johann Friedrich Eschscholtz (1793-1831) of Dorpat in Russia, who accompanied Otto von Kotzebue on his expedition round the world (1815-1818). He wrote a number of botanical works.

Escobaria [es-ko-BAY-ria]
A genus of cacti named for two Mexicans, Romulo and Numa Escobar.

Escontria [es-KON-tria]
A treelike cactus named after Don Blas Escontria, a Mexican of distinction.

esculentus, -a, -um [es-kew-LEN-tus]
Related to eating; edible.
estriatus, -a, -um [es-tri-AY-tus]
Without stripes.
etruscus, -a, -um [ee-TRUS-kus]
From Tuscany, the classical Etruria, in Italy.
etuberosus, -a, -um [ee-tew-ber-o-sus]
Without tubers.
eucalyptoides [yew-kal-ip-TOY-deez]
Resembling *Eucalyptus.*
Eucalyptus [yew-kal-IP-tus]
Gum tree. Blue gum. From Gr. *eu,* well; *kalypto,* to cover, as with a lid; an allusion to the lidlike arrangement of the flowers. Among the largest trees in the world (highest recorded, 326 feet) they have very small and even minute seeds. The timber is durable and is much used in Australia for shipbuilding, engineering, and flooring.
Eucharidium [yew-kar-ID-ium]
Gr. *eucharis,* pleasing. These pretty annuals are sometimes referred to *Clarkia.*
Eucharis [YEW-ka-ris]
Amazon lily. Greek word meaning pleasing, charming; from the fragrant beauty of the flowers of these bulbous plants.
Euchlaenia [yew-KLEEN-ia]
Gr. *eu,* good; *chlaima,* wool. A technical reference to a characteristic of the stigmas of these grasses.
Eucomis [YEW-kom-is]
From Gr. *eu,* good, *kome,* hair; implying a beautiful head, from the tufted crown of the flower spike of these bulbous plants.
Eucommia [yew-KOM-ia]
Gr. *eu,* good; *kommi,* gum. Consisting of a single species (*E. ulmoides*) it is interesting as the only hardy rubber-producing tree. Extraction, however, is difficult and not commercially feasible, yet when the leaves are torn gently across, threads of rubber remain strong enough to support the torn portion.
Eucryphia [yew-KRIF-ia]
Gr. *eu,* well; *kryphios,* covered. The sepals of these white-flowered trees and shrubs, cohering at the tips, form a cap.

Eugenia [yew-JEEN-ia]
Clove tree. Rose apple. Ornamental trees and shrubs named in honor of Prince Eugene of Savoy (1663-1736). Most authorities suggest that he was a patron of botany, which is possible but not very probable in the light of his preoccupation with war. With him it was a passion which he pursued with energy, imagination, and resolution rare in the 18th century. Wounded thirteen times, in fifty years in the field, he did not spend two years together without fighting, almost invariably successfully. Among his best-known campaigns were those he fought as an ally of the Duke of Marlborough.

eugenioides [yew-jeen-i-OY-deez]
Resembling *Eugenia*.

Euonymus [yew-ON-im-us]
Spindle-tree. The ancient Greek name for these woody plants with handsome foliage and fruit.

eupatorioides [yew-pat-or-i-OY-deez]
Like *Eupatorium*.

Eupatorium [yew-pat-OR-ium]
Joe-Pye-weed. Thoroughwort. Boneset. The Greek name for these herbaceous and shrubby plants, commemorating Mithridates Eupator, King of Pontus, who is said to have discovered that one species was an antidote against poison. The English names indicate a traditional use in medicine.

Euphorbia [yew-FOR-bia]
Spurge. Classically supposed to have been named for one Euphorbus, physician to the king of Mauretania.

euphorbioides [yew-for-bi-OY-deez]
Resembling spurge or *Euphorbia*.

Euphoria [yew-FOR-ia]
Gr. *eu*, well; *phoreo*, to carry. The white, sweet, sub-acid fruits, natives of India, travel well. The vernacular name for these trees has been anglicized to Longan and Linkang.

Eupritchardia [yew-prich-ARD-ia]
Gr. *eu*, good; *Pritchardia*, another and related genus of ornamental Pacific palms which was named for W. T. Pritchard, author of *Polynesian Reminiscences*.

Euptelea [yew-PTEE-lea]
Gr. *eu*, good; *ptelea*, an elm; in reference to the edible fruit of these shrubs or small trees.

europaeus, -a, -um [eur-o-PEE-us]
European.

Eurotia [eur-o-tia]
Gr. *euros*, mold; in reference to the gray-white downy or moldy appearance of these herbs or sub-shrubs.

Eurya [EUR-ya]
Derivation of the name for these evergreen trees and shrubs is obscure.

Euryale [yew-RY-al-e]
Named after one of the three Gorgons, the monstrous daughters of the sea god, who had venomous snakes for hair and of whom Medusa was the only one who was mortal. The allusion here is to the very thorny, prickly character of these large and handsome water-lilies. The seeds are roasted and eaten in India.

Euscaphis [yew-SKAY-fis]
Gr. *eu*, good, *scaphis*, a vessel; from the character of the seed pod of this ornamental woody plant.

Eustoma [yew-STO-ma]
Prairie gentian. From Gr. *eu*, good; *stoma*, a mouth, or (less literally) a pretty face, in allusion to the showy flowers.

Eustrephus [YEW-streff-us]
Gr. *eu*, well; *strepho*, to twine, from the character of these Australian climbers.

Eutaxia [yew-TAX-ia]
Greek word meaning modesty; from the nature of these Australian flowering shrubs.

Euterpe [yew-TER-pe]
Named for one of the nine Muses, goddesses of the liberal arts. Euterpe had charge of lyric poetry. The genus includes the cabbage palm (*E. oleracea*), the terminal bud of which is eaten fresh as a salad or pickled.

evectus, -a, -um [ee-VEK-tus]
Extended.

everlasting
Immortelle—the term applied to a number of plants which retain their form and color when dry.

evertus, -a, -um [ee-VERT-us]
Turned inside out.

158

Evodia [ee-vo-dia]
Gr. *euodia,* a sweet scent. The leaves of these shrubs are fragrant.

Evolvus [ee-VOL-vus]
L. *evolvo,* to untwist or unravel. These plants of the convolvulus family do not twine.

Exacum [EX-ak-um]
The Latin name, from *exago,* to drive out. These herbs of the gentian family were supposed to have the power of driving out poisons.

exaltatus, -a, -um [ex-all-TAY-tus]
Very tall; lofty.

exaratus, -a, -um [ex-a-RAY-tus]
Engraved; furrowed.

exasperatus, -a, -um [ex-as-per-AY-tus]
Roughened.

excavatus, -a, -um [ex-cav-AY-tus]
Hollowed out.

excellens [ex-SELL-ens]
Excelling; excellent.

excelsus, -a, -um [ex-SELL-sus]
Tall.

excelsior [ex-SELL-sior]
Taller.

excisus, -a, -um [ex-SY-sus]
Cut-away; cut-out.

excorticatus, -a, -um [ex-kor-tik-AY-tus]
Without bark or cortex; stripped of bark.

exiguus, -a, -um [ex-IG-yew-us]
Very little; meager; poor.

eximius, -a, -um [ex-IM-ius]
Out of the ordinary; distinguished.

exitiosus, -a, -um [ex-it-i-o-sus]
Pernicious; destructive.

Exochorda [ex-o-KORD-a, or ex-OK-ord-a]
Pearl-bush. From Gr. *exo,* outside; *chorde,* a cord; referring to a technical characteristic of the flower. There are fibers outside the placenta.

exoletus, -a, -um [ex-o-LEE-tus]
Mature; dying away.

exoniensis, -is, -e [ex-o-ni-EN-sis]
From Exeter, England.
exoticus, -a, -um [ex-OT-ik-us]
From a foreign country.
expansus, -a, -um [ex-PAN-sus]
Expanded.
explodens [ex-PLO-dens]
Bursting suddenly; exploding.
exsculptus, -a, -um [ex-SKULP-tus]
Dug-out.
exsertus, -a, -um [ex-SERT-us]
Protruding.
exsurgens [ex-SUR-jens]
Rising up.
extensus, -a, -um [ex-TEN-sus]
Extended.
exudans [ex-YEW-dans]
Exuding.

F

Faba [FAY-ba]
Latin, the broad bean (*Vicia faba*), more appreciated in
Europe than in the United States, where the climate is
generally too hot and dry.
fabaceus, -a, -um [fab-AY-seus]
Resembling the broad bean.
Fabiana [fay-bi-AY-na]
False heath. Named in honor of Archbishop Francisco
Fabian y Fuero (1719-1801) of Valencia, Spain, a promoter
of botanical study.
Fagopyrum [fay-go-PY-rum]
Buckwheat. From Gr. *phago,* to eat; *pyros,* wheat.
Fagus [FAY-gus]
Beech. The Latin name.
falcatus, -a, -um [fal-KAY-tus]
falciformis, -is, -e [fal-si-FORM-is]
Sickle-shaped; falcate.
falcifolius, -a, -um [fal-si-FO-lius]
With sickle-shaped leaves.

falcinellus, -a, -um [fal-sin-ELL-us]
Resembling a small sickle.
fallax [FAL-ax]
Deceptive; false.
farinaceus, -a, -um [fa-rin-AY-seus]
Yielding starch; mealy, like flour.
farinosus, -a, -um [fa-rin-O-sus]
Mealy; powdery.
farleyensis, -is, -e [far-li-EN-sis]
From Farley Hill Gardens in Barbados, British West Indies.
farnesianus, -a, -um [far-nee-si-AY-nus]
From the gardens of the Farnese Palace, Rome.
farreri [fa-RER-ry, or FAR-er-ri]
Specific name of *Gentiana farreri* and other plants. In honor
of Reginald Farrer (1880-1902), English plant hunter and
botanist, who specialized in Alpines, particularly of Upper
Burma and the mountain regions of Kansu where he discovered this particular gentian among other good things. He
wrote several excellent books, possibly the best known
being *The English Rock Garden*.
fasciatus, -a, -um [fas-i-AY-tus]
Bound together.
fascicularis, -is, -e [fas-ik-ew-LAY-ris]
fasciculatus, -a, -um [fas-ik-ew-LAY-tus]
Clustered or grouped together in bundles.
fascinator [fas-in-AY-tor]
Fascinating.
fastigiatus, -a, -um [fas-tij-i-AY-tus]
Having branches close together and erect, often forming a
column; fastigiate.
fastosus, -a, -um [fast-O-sus]
Proud.
Fatsia [FAT-sia]
Latinized adaptation of the Japanese name for one of the
species of these shrubs or small trees.
fatuus, -a, -um [FAT-yew-us]
Simple or foolish but, in this relationship, insipid or, merely,
not good.
Faucaria [faw-KAY-ria]
L. *faux*, a gullet or throat. The growth of the leaves of these

succulents resembles a wide open mouth, hence the local South African name of tiger's chaps.

febrifugus, -a, -um [feb-RIFF-yew-jus]
Fever-dispelling.

Fedia [FEE-dia]
Meaning of the name for this valerian-like annual is obscure.

Feijoa [fy-JO-a]
A small tree or shrub with pineapple-flavored fruit. Named for Don de Silva Feijoa, 19th-century Brazilian botanist.

Felicia [fee-LISS-ia]
Blue daisy. After a German official, Felix, who died in 1846.

femina [FEM-in-a]
Female, but literally, a woman.

Ferocactus [fer-o-KAK-tus]
From L. *ferox*, ferocious, savage; in allusion to the horrible spines with which this cactus is armed.

Feronia [fer-o-nia]
Wood-apple. A spiny tree named in honor of the Roman nymph who presided over woods and groves.

Feroniella [fer-o-ni-ELL-a]
Diminutive of *Feronia* to which it is closely related.

fenestralis, -is, -e [fen-es-TRAY-lis]
Pierced with openings resembling windows.

ferox [FEE-rox]
Ferocious; very thorny.

ferreus, -a, -um [FER-reus]
Pertaining to iron or, sometimes, iron-hard.

ferrugineus, -a, -um [fer-roo-JIN-eus]
Rust-colored; rusty.

fertilis, -is, -e [fert-ILL-is]
Fruitful; producing numerous seeds.

Ferula [FER-yew-la]
Giant fennel. The classical Latin name. The word also means the rod used to chastise schoolboys and also slaves for minor offences. The giant fennel has tall sticklike stems.

ferulaefolius, -a, -um [fer-roo-lee-FO-lius]
With leaves resembling giant fennel or *Ferula*.

ferus, -a, -um [FER-us]
Wild.

festalis, -is, -e [fes-TAY-lis]
festinus, -a, -um [fes-TY-nus]

162

Festive; gay; bright.

Festuca [fes-TEW-ka]
Fescue. Latin word meaning a grass stalk.

fibrilosus, -a, -um [fib-ril-o-sus]
fibrosus, -a, -um [fy-BRO-sus]
Fibrous; composed of fibers.

ficifolius, -a, -um [fik-i-FO-lius]
With leaves like a fig.

ficoides [fik-OY-deez]
ficoideus, -a, -um [fik-OY-deus]
Resembling a fig or *Ficus*.

Ficus [FIK-us]
Latin name for *Ficus carica,* the edible fig. The genus includes some quite extraordinary species such as the banyan (*F. benghalensis*) of India which, starting from a single main trunk, sends down aerial roots which themselves become trunks, thus extending the original tree over areas which may be very large. *F. elastica* is possibly the most familiar in temperate climates. Naturally quite a large tree and once an important source of rubber, it is grown as the common household rubber plant and its latex-producing functions have been taken over by the genus *Hevea* and by synthetics. *F. carica,* a native of western Asia, has been widely grown for its fruit from remote antiquity. It was probably introduced early into Britain but was lost, as was the vine, possibly due to climatic changes. It was reintroduced by Cardinal Pole in 1525 and planted in the garden of the Archbishop at Lambeth. Another celebrated tree was brought from Aleppo in 1648 by Dr. Pocock, Regius Professor of Hebrew at Oxford and planted in the garden at Christ Church College where it survived, producing fine fruit, until 1833.

filamentosus, -a, -um [fil-a-ment-o-sus]
filarius, -a, -um [fil-AY-rius]
Furnished with filaments or threads.

filicatus, -a, -um [fil-i-KAY-tus]
filicinus, -a, -um [fil-i-SY-nus]
filicoides [fil-i-KOY-deez]
Resembling fern. From L. *filix,* a fern.

filicifolius, -a, -um [fil-iss-i-FO-lius]
With leaves resembling fern.

fili-

As a prefix, signifying threadlike. Thus:

filicaulis   With a threadlike stem
filiferus   Thread-bearing
filiformis   Threadlike
filipes   With threadlike stalks

Filipendula [fil-i-PEN-dew-la]
Meadow-sweet. L. *filium,* a thread; *pendulus,* hanging.
The root tubers in some species hang together with threads.

filipendulus, -a, -um [fil-i-PEN-dew-lus]
Resembling meadow-sweet or *Filipendula.*

fimbriatus, -a, -um [fim-bri-AY-tus]
Fringed.

fimbriatulus, -a, -um [fim-bri-AY-tew-lus]
With a small fringe.

firmatus, -a ,-um [firm-AY-tus]
firmus, -a, -um [FIRM-us]
Strong.

Firmiana [firm-i-AY-na]
Tropical trees named for Karl Josef von Firmian (1716-
1782), Governor of Lombardy when that province was part
of the Austrian Empire.

fissilis, -is, -e [FISS-ill-is]
fissus, -a, -um [FISS-us]
fissuratus, -a, -um [fis-yew-RAY-tus]
Cleft; split.

fistulosus, -a, -um [fis-tew-LO-sus]
Hollow, like a pipe.

Fittonia [fit-o-nia]
Ornamental-leaved perennials named in honor of Elizabeth and Mary Fitton, mid-19th-century authors of *Con-
versations on Botany.*

Fitzroya [fits-ROY-a]
Evergreen trees or shrubs named for Captain R. Fitzroy
(1805-1875), Royal Navy, who commanded the five-year
surveying expedition of H.M.S. *Beagle.* Charles Darwin was
aboard as official naturalist and, on the voyage, laid the
foundation for his life's work on the origin of species.

flabellatus, -a, -um [flab-ell-AY-tus]
Like an open fan.

flabellifer [flab-ELL-iff-er]
flabelliformis, -is, -e [flab-ell-if-FORM-is]
Fan-shaped.
flaccidus, -a, -um [FLAS-id-us]
Feeble; weak; soft.
Flacourtia [flay-KORT-ia]
Shrubs and small trees named for Etienne de Flacourt
(1607-1661), a director of the French East India Company.
flagellaris, -is, -e [flaj-ell-AY-ris]
flagellatus, -a, -um [flaj-ell-AY-tus]
flagelliformis, -is, -e [flaj-ell-i-FORM-is]
Whiplike; having long, thin, supple shoots like whips.
flagellum [flaj-ELL-um]
A whip or flail.
flammeus, -a, -um [flam-EE-us]
Flame-colored or flamelike.
flammula [FLAM-yew-la]
A small flame. The pre-Linnaean name for *Clematis flammula*.
flavens [FLAY-vens]
flaveolus, -a, -um [flav-ee-o-lus]
flavescens [flay-VESS-ens]
flavidus, -a, -um [FLAV-id-us]
Yellowish.
flavus, -a, -um [FLAY-vus]
Pure yellow. Also:

flavicomus   yellow-haired
flavispinus   yellow-spined

flavissimus, -a, -um [flay-VISS-im-us]
Deepest yellow.
Flemingia [flem-IN-jia]
Shrubs and sub-shrubs named in honor of John Fleming
(1747-1829), President of the Medical Board of Bengal,
East India Company.
flexicaulis, -is, -e [flex-i-KAW-lis]
Having a pliant stem.
flexilis, -is, -e [FLEX-ill-is]
Pliant; limber.
flexuosus, -a, -um [flex-yew-o-sus]
Tortuous; zigzag.

floccigerus, -a, -um [flok-IJ-er-us]
floccosus, -a, -um [flok-O-sus]
Woolly.

flocculosus, -a, -um [flok-yew-LO-sus]
Somewhat woolly.

flore-albo [flor-e-AL-bo]
With white flowers.

florentinus, -a, -um [flor-en-TY-nus]
From Florence, Italy.

flore-pleno [flor-e-PLEE-no]
With double flowers.

floribundus, -a, -um [flor-i-BUND-us]
floridus, -a, -um [FLOR-id-us]
floriferus, -a, -um [flor-IFF-er-us]
Free-flowering; producing abundant flowers.

floridanus, -a, -um [flor-id-AY-nus]
From Florida.

flos [floss]
Latin word meaning a flower, as in:

flos-cuculi   cuckoo flower (*Lychnis*)
flos-jovis   Jove's flower (*Lychnis*)

fluitans [FLEW-it-ans]
Floating.

fluminensis, -is, -e [flew-min-EN-sis]
fluvialis, -is, -e [flew-vi-AY-lis]
fluviatilis, -is, -e [flew-vi-AY-till-is]
Growing in a river or running water.

foemina [FEE-min-a]
Feminine.

foeniculaceus, -a, -um [fee-nik-yew-LAY-seus]
foeniculatus, -a, -um [fee-nik-yew-LAY-tus]
Resembling fennel or *Foeniculum*.

Foeniculum [fee-NIK-yew-lum]
Fennel. The Latin name for this traditional salad and potherb which, in Italian, is *finocchio*.

foetidus, -a, -um [FEE-tid-us]
Bad-smelling. Also *foetidissimus*, very bad-smelling.

foliaceus, -a, -um [fo-li-AY-seus]
Leaflike.

166

foliatus, -a, -um [fo-li-AY-tus]
  foliosus, -a, -um [fo-li-o-sus]
  Full of leaves; leafy.
foliolatus, -a, -um [fo-li-o-LAY-tus]
  foliolosus, -a, -um [fo-li-o-LO-sus]
  Furnished with leaflets.
follicularis, -is, -e [fol-ik-yew-LAY-ris]
  Bearing follicles. These are dry, one-chambered fruits splitting along only one seam, e.g., peony, milkweed.
Fontanesia [fon-tan-EE-sia]
  Named for René Louiches Desfontaines (1750-1833),
  author of *Flora Atlantica*.
fontanus, -a, -um [fon-TAY-nus]
  fontinalis, -is, -e [fon-tin-AY-lis]
  Pertaining to springs or fountains; growing in fast-running
  water.
Forestiera [for-es-STEER-a]
  Shrubs named for Charles Le Forestier, 18th-century French
  physician and naturalist.
formosanus, -a, -um [form-o-SAY-nus]
  From the island of Formosa.
formosus, -a, -um [form-o-sus]
  Handsome; beautiful. Also *formosissimus*, very handsome.
Forsythia [popularly, for-SITH-ia; preferably, for-SY-thia]
  Golden-bell. Ornamental shrubs named in honor of William
  Forsyth (1737-1804), Scottish superintendent of the Royal
  Gardens of Kensington Palace and author, among other
  works, of *A Treatise on the Culture and Management of
  Fruit Trees* which in its day was probably the most widely
  read work on the subject. From 1789 until his death Forsyth
  was a controversial figure in horticultural circles as a result
  of his claims for the concoction known as "Forsyth's plaister."
  This mixture, made up of lime, dung, wood-ashes, soap-
  suds, sand, urine, and so on, was not very different from
  others of the day designed to heal wounds in the bark of
  trees. Forsyth claimed that his "plaister" was capable "of
  curing defects in growing trees" and would restore oak trees
  "where nothing remained but the bark." As a result of these
  claims the British government, in urgent need of sound
  ship timber with which to pursue the wars with Napoleon,
  paid him the then generous gratuity of £1,500. Thomas A.

Knight, later President of the Royal Horticultural Society for many years, took active exception to statements made either by or on behalf of Forsyth, such as that holes in trees could be filled with the "plaister" and the trees themselves "brought to such a degree of soundness that no one can know the new wood from the old." In that gullible age, Forsyth found plenty of supporters including a well-known London physician, Dr. Lettson, one of the twenty-eight "original members" of the R. H. S., who, as a Quaker, chose to be insulted when Knight proposed a series of bets on the subject. Forsyth died before the argument was satisfactorily resolved, but in due course the "plaister" was thoroughly discredited.

Fortunella [for-tew-NELL-a]
Kumquat. Evergreen shrubs named for Robert Fortune (1812-1890), Scottish horticulturist and collector in China who ranks among the great plantsmen. With the exception of *Rhododendron fortunei* which he found wild and also one or two other less notable plants, most of his finds were in Chinese gardens and nurseries. In his day the difficulties of travel were such that he had small chance of going further afield. With a brief interval as curator of the Chelsea Physic Garden he was in China practically continuously from 1843 to 1861. He learned Chinese and earned the Chinese name of Sing Wah.

In 1846, he was engaged by the East India Company to bring tea plants to India. Despite the justifiable secretiveness of the Chinese, he was able to investigate the growing and manufacture of tea and eventually exported the plants, Chinese workers, and implements which established the industry, first in India and then in Ceylon. It has since, of course, grown to enormous commercial importance. In 1858, Fortune was employed by the United States government to bring tea plants to America for trial, with a view to the eventual establishment of an industry. Although there had been previous attempts—as early as 1772 in Georgia, between 1848 and 1852 by Junius Smith in the mountains of South Carolina and in Alabama and Florida with slave labor—all had failed. Within a couple of years, Fortune's plants, imported in Wardian cases, numbered some 35,000 growing under glass in the Propagation Garden in Washington, D. C. After several attempts, however, which lasted into the 1870's, the project of a United States tea industry was finally abandoned.

Fortune wrote several readable books on his adventures and, having started as a poor garden apprentice, he died reasonably well off as a result of his plant sales and of his flourishing business in curios.

fortunei [for-TEW-ne-eye]
Species name after Robert Fortune (see *Fortunella*).

Fothergilla [foth-er-GILL-a]
Dwarf alder. Ornamental shrubs named for Dr. John Fothergill (1712-1780), physician of Stratford, Essex, England, who specialized in growing American plants.

Fouquiera [foo-quee-EER-ia]
Candlewood. Small trees or shrubs named for Pierre Edouard Fouquier, 19th-century French physician.

fourcroides [foor-CROY-deez]
Resembling the genus *Furcraea*.

foveolatus, -a, -um [fo-vee-o-LAY-tus]
Slightly pitted.

Fragaria [frag-AY-ria]
Strawberry. From L. *fraga*, strawberry; deriving from *fragrans*, fragrant, in allusion to the perfume of the fruit.

fragarioides [frag-gay-ri-oy-deez]
Resembling strawberry or *Fragaria*.

fragilis, -is, -e [FRAG-il-is]
Brittle; easily broken; or, sometimes, wilting quickly.

fragrans [FRAY-grans]
Fragrant.

fragrantissimus, -a, -um [fray-gran-TISS-im-us]
Very fragrant.

Francoa [frank-O-a]
Chilean perennial herbs named in honor of Francisco Franco, 16th-century physician of Valencia, Spain.

Frankenia [frank-KEEN-ia]
Heathlike perennials and sub-shrubs named for John Frankenius (1590-1661), Professor of Botany at Uppsala, Sweden.

Frasera [FRAY-ser-a]
Glabrous herbs named for John Fraser (1750-1811), Scottish collector of North American plants who also kept a nursery

in Chelsea, England. He made several collecting expeditions from Newfoundland to the Carolinas. His close friend, Thomas Walter of South Carolina, named *Magnolia fraseri* in his honor.

fraseri [FRAY-ser-eye]
Of John Fraser (see *Frasera*).

fraxineus, -a, -um [frax-IN-eus]
Resembling ash or *Fraxinus*.

fraxinifolius, -a, -um [frax-in-i-FO-lius]
With leaves resembling ash or *Fraxinus*.

Fraxinus [frax-EYE-nus]
Ash. The classical Latin name.

Freesia [FREE-sia]
Bulbous plants with fragrant flowers named in honor of Friedrich Heinrich Theodor Freese (d. 1876), pupil of Ecklon, a German botanist who named the genus.

Fremontia [free-MONT-ia]
Flannel-bush. Discovered by and named in honor of Colonel John Charles Fremont who made four hazardous explorations in the far West between 1842 and 1848. He brought back many notable trees and shrubs to be studied and named by Torrey, Gray, and Darlington and in doing so made great contributions to both botany and horticulture. (See *Darlingtonia, Torreya.*)

Freycinetia [free-sin-EE-tia]
Climbing shrubs named for Admiral Louis Claude Desaulses de Freycinet (1779-1842), French navigator and a founder of the Paris Geographical Society. He made various exploring voyages to Australasia and the Pacific, returning with important collections.

frigidus, -a, -um [FRIJ-id-us]
Growing in cold regions.

Fritillaria [frit-ill-AY-ria]
Fritillary. From L. *fritillus*, a dicebox; from the spot markings on the flowers of some of the species.

Froelichia [free-LIK-ia]
American annuals named for Josef Albert Froelich (1796-1841), German physician and botanist.

frondosus, -a, -um [frond-o-sus]
Leafy.

fructescens [fruk-TESS-ens]
fructiferus, -a, -um [fruk-TIFF-er-us]
fructigenus, -a, -um [fruk-TIJ-en-us]
Fruit-bearing; fruitful.

frumentaceus, -a, -um [frew-men-TAY-seus]
Pertaining to grain; grain-bearing.

frutescens [frew-TESS-ens]
fruticans [FREW-tik-ans]
fruticosus, -a, um [frew-tik-o-sus]
Shrubby; bushy. From L. *frutex*, a shrub.

fruticicolus, -a, -um [frew-ti-sik-o-lus]
Growing in bushy places.

fruticulosus, -a, -um [frew-tik-yew-LO-sus]
Shrubby and dwarf.

fucatus, -a, -um [few-KAY-tus]
Painted; dyed.

Fuchsia [popularly, FEW-shia; correctly, FEWKS-ia]
Flowering shrubs and small trees named for Leonard Fuchs
(1501-1566), German botanist who published a book with
unusually beautiful woodcuts of plants.

fuchsioides [few-shi-OY-deez]
Resembling *Fuchsia*

fugax [FEW-gax]
Withering or falling off quickly; fleeting.

fulgens [FUL-jens]
fulgidus, -a, -um [ful-JY-dus]
Shining; glistening.

fuliginosus, -a, -um [few-li-jin-o-sus]
Dirty-brown; sooty.

fullonum [full-o-num]
Pertaining to fullers. Specific name of the fuller's teasel
(*Dipsacus fullonum*) used in the manufacture of woollen
cloth to raise the nap.

fulvescens [ful-VESS-ens]
fulvus, -a, -um [FUL-vus]
Tawny-orange; fulvous. Thus, *fulvidus*, slightly tawny.

Fumaria [few-MAY-ria]
Fumitory. From L. *fumus*, smoke; in allusion to the smoky
odor of some of the species. This old garden plant was once
very widely grown as a remedy for scurvy which was very

likely to show up in late winter and early spring after a prolonged diet lacking in fresh vegetables.

fumariaefolius, -a, -um [few-may-ri-ee-FO-lius]
With leaves resembling fumitory or *Fumaria*.

fumosus, -a, um [few-MO-sus]
Smoky.

funebris, -is, -e [FEW-neb-ris]
Funereal.

fungosus, -a, -um [fun-GO-sus]
Relating to or resembling fungus; spongy.

Funkia [FUNK-ia]
Plantain lily. Now classified under *Hosta* but originally named for a German botanist, Heinrich Funck.

funiculatus, -a, um [few-nik-yew-LAY-tus]
Resembling a thin cord or rope.

furcans [FER-kans]
furcatus, -a, -um [fer-KAY-tus]
Forked; furcate.

Furcraea [fer-KREE-a]
Succulent plants named for A. T. Fourcroy (1755-1809), French chemist and naturalist.

fufuraceus, -a, -um [few-few-RAY-seus]
Mealy; scurfy.

furiens [FEW-riens]
Exciting to madness.

fuscatus, -a, -um [fus-KAY-tus]
Brownish.

fuscifolius, -a, -um [fus-ki-FO-lius]
With dusky-brown leaves.

fusco-rubra [fus-ko-ROO-bra]
Brownish-red.

fuscus, -a, -um [FUS-kus]
Brown; dusky.

futilis, -is, -e [FEW-till-is]
Useless.

G

Gagea [GAY-jee-a]
Small bulbous plants named for Sir Thomas Gage (1761-1820), Hengrave Hall, Suffolk, who botanized in Ireland and

Portugal. The greengage plum, the English name for the Reine Claude, was named for his grandfather who introduced it from France.

Gaillardia [gay-LARD-ia]
Blanket-flower. Herbaceous plants named for a French patron of botany, Gaillard de Marentoneau.

galacifolius, -a, -um [gay-lass-i-FO-lius]
With leaves like *Galax.*

Galactites [gay-lak-TY-tees]
Gr. *gala*, milk. The veins of the leaves of these herbs are milky-white.

Galanthus [gay-LAN-thus]
Snowdrop. From Gr. *gala*, milk; *anthos*, flower; an allusion to the color of the flowers.

galanthus, -a, -um [gay-LAN-thus]
With milky-white flowers.

Galax [GAY-lax]
Wand plant. Gr. *gala*, milk; possibly an allusion to the white flowers of this evergreen perennial.

Galeandra [gal-ee-AND-ra]
Gr. *galea*, a helmet; *andros*, a stamen. One stamen in this orchid is helmet-shaped.

galeatus, -a, -um [gal-ee-AY-tus]
galericulatus, -a, -um [gal-er-rik-yew-LAY-tus]
Helmet-shaped

Galega [gal-EE-ga]
Goatsrue. From Gr. *gala*, milk. It was once thought that feeding these perennials would improve the milk flow.

galegifolius [gal-ee-gi-FO-lius]
With leaves resembling goatsrue or *Galega.*

galioides [gay-li-OY-deez]
Resembling *Galium* or bedstraw.

Galium [GAY-lium]
Bedstraw. Cleavers. From Gr. *gala*, milk. Yellow bedstraw (*G. verum*) can be used in cheese-making to curdle the milk.

gallicus, -a, -um [GAL-ik-us]
From France.

Galtonia [gawl-TOE-nia]
Spire lily. Giant summer hyacinth. Named in honor of Sir Francis Galton (1822-1911), primarily an anthropologist, who traveled widely in Africa. He was an early proponent

of fingerprinting for identification, laid the foundation of modern eugenic thinking, and wrote a distinguished book on meteorology in which he first stated the anti-cyclonic theory.

Gamolepis [gam-OLL-ep-is]
Gr. *gameo*, to marry; *lepis*, a scale. The bracts of the urn-shaped involucre are united on these South African herbs and shrubs.

gangeticus, -a, -um [gan-JET-ik-us]
From the region of the Ganges.

Garcinia [gar-SIN-ia]
Mangosteen. Named in honor of Laurent Garcin (1683-1751), French botanist, who traveled widely in India. The mangosteen (*G. mangostana*) is possibly the most delectable and one of the most local of all East Indian fruits. Native in Malaya, it does not do as well elsewhere. About the size of a tangerine, the leathery, russet skin conceals white- or rose-colored edible segments of delicious flavor and perfume. It is very wholesome and is a fruit that can be eaten harmlessly in bouts of malaria.

Gardenia [gar-DEE-nia]
Evergreen flowering shrubs or small trees named for Dr. Alexander Garden (1730-1791), friend of Linnaeus and a native of Charleston, South Carolina, educated at Edinburgh and for a time a professor at King's College, New York, now Columbia University. *G. jasminoides* is the species commonly offered by florists. It is often called Cape jasmine, but it is not a jasmine and it originated in China.

garganicus, -a, -um [gar-GAN-ik-us]
From the area of Monte di S. Angelo in southern Italy classically called Mount Garganus.

Garrya [GA-ria]
Silk-tassel bush. Named for Nicholas Garry, Secretary of the Hudson's Bay Company who, in about the decade 1820-1830, assisted David Douglas in his explorations of the Pacific Northwest.

Gasteria [gas-TEE-ria]
Gr. *gaster*, a belly. The base of the flower tube is swollen in these succulent plants.

Gastrochilus [gas-tro-KY-lus]
From Gr. *gaster*, a belly; *cheilos*, a lip. The lip of the flower on these herbs is swollen.

Gaultheria [gawl-THEE-ria]
Ornamental woody evergreen plants named for Dr. Gaultier, mid-18th-century French physician and botanist of Quebec. Perhaps the best-known member of the family is the wintergreen or checker-berry (*G. procumbens*) of the northeastern woods of America.

Gaura [GAW-ra]
Gr. *gauros*, superb; an allusion to the striking flowers of these herbs.

Gaylussacia [gay-loo-SAY-shia]
Huckleberry. Named in honor of Joseph Louis Gay-Lussac (1778-1850), celebrated French chemist who is best remembered for his law concerning the volume of gases. His work laid the foundation of the food-canning industry. Once he was very famous for his balloon ascents made in the interests of scientific investigation. In 1804 he ascended to 12,000 feet and then to 22,000 feet.

Gazania [gaz-AY-nia]
Treasure flower. Herbaceous plants named in honor of Theodore of Gaza (1398-1478), who translated the botanical works of Theophrastus from Greek into Latin.

Geitonoplesium [gyt-o-no-PLEE-sium]
Gr. *geiton*, a neighbor; *plesion*, near; from this twiner's close relationship to another Australian genus (*Eustrephus*).

gelidus, -a, -um [JEL-id-us]
From icy-cold regions.

Gelsemium [jel-SEEM-ium]
Latinized version of gelsomino, the Italian name for jasmine. *G. sempervirens* is called false jasmine.

gemmatus, -a, -um [jem-AY-tus]
Jeweled.

geminiflorus, -a, -um [jem-in-i-FLO-rus]
Having twin or several flowers. Also *geminispinus*, having twin or many spines.

gemmiferus, -a, -um [jem-IFF-er-us]
Bearing buds.

generalis, -is, -e [jen-er-AY-lis]
Prevailing; normal.

genevensis, -is, -e [jen-ee-VEN-sis]
From Geneva.

geniculatus, -a, -um [jen-ik-yew-LAY-tus]
Bent sharply like a knee.

Genipa [jen-NY-pa]
Latinized version of the Guiana vernacular name of one species, the Genipap tree, the juicy fruit of which is used to make a preserve locally called genipot.

Genista [jen-ISS-ta]
Broom. The Latin name from which the Plantagenet kings and queens of England took their name (*planta genista*). Dyer's greenweed (*G. tinctoria*) is now well established as an adventure wild flower in northeastern United States. It was first introduced for the yellow dye it yields by Governor John Endicott of Salem, Massachusetts, about 1630.

genistifolius, -a, -um [jen-iss-ti-FO-lius]
With leaves like broom or *Genista*.

Gentiana [jen-she-AY-na]
Gentian. Named for King Gentius of Illyria who was reputed to have discovered the medicinal virtues of the root of the yellow gentian or bitterwort (*G. lutea*) from which a tonic bitters is still made.

geocarpus, -a, -um [jee-o-KARP-us]
With fruit ripening in the earth.

geoides [jee-OY-deez]
Of the earth.

geometricus, -a, -um [jee-o-MET-rik-us]
geometrizans [jee--MET-ri-zans]
With markings arranged in a formal pattern.

geonomaeformis, -is, -e [jee-on-o-mee-FORM-is]
In the form of *Geonoma*.

Geonoma [jee-ON-o-ma]
Gr. *geonomos*, one skilled in agriculture. These feather palms send out buds from the apex of the stems which eventually grow into trees themselves.

georgianus, -a, -um [jorj-i-AY-nus]
From the state of Georgia, in the United States.

georgicus, -a, -um [JORJ-ik-us]
From Georgia in South Russia.

Geranium [jer-AY-nium]
Cranesbill. Herb-Robert. Geranion is the classical Greek

name for *geranos*, a crane; in allusion to the long beak of the carpels.

geranioides [jer-an-i-OY-deez]
Resembling *Geranium*.

Gerardia [jer-ARD-ia]
North American herbs named for John Gerard (1545-1612), garden superintendent to Lord Burghley, Minister to Queen Elizabeth I. He grew many exotic plants in his Hoxton garden but he is best known for his *Herball*, first published in 1597 with many subsequent editions. The first edition is very rare but later editions are fairly easily obtained. They are entertaining reading and have excellent illustrations.

The *Herball* is to a very great extent an adaptation and translation from Latin of the writings of Rembert Dodoens. The illustrations were mostly impressions from the wood blocks employed by Tabernaemontanus in his book published in Frankfurt seven years previously. In Gerard's day, however, plagiarism was generally accepted and widely practiced. It showed both learning and a proper appreciation of source material. The fact remains that the *Herball* is a great book. It was one of the first botanical books in English rather than Latin.

Gerbera (sometimes, incorrectly, **Gerberia**) [JER-ber-a]
Transvaal daisy. Perennial herbs named for Traugott Gerber, a German naturalist who traveled in Russia and who died in 1743.

germanicus, -a, -um [jer-MAN-ik-us]
From Germany.

Gesneria (sometimes, incorrectly, **Gesenera**) [jess-NEE-ria]
Herbaceous perennials named for Konrad von Gesner (1516-1565) of Zurich, the most celebrated naturalist of his day. He collected and described plants and animals, thus providing a starting point for the work of his successors. He is credited with having brought the tulip into repute in Western Europe after seeing a specimen growing in a garden in Augsberg in 1559. Within a dozen years, tulip-fancying had gripped Holland to culminate in the ruinous tulip mania of the 1630's. (See *Tulipa*.)

Geum [JEE-um]
Avens. Herb-bennet. The classical Latin name for these perennial herbs.

Gevuina [gev-yew-EYE-na]
The native name for this tree known as the Chilean hazel.

gibberosus, -a, -um [jib-er-O-sus]
Hunchbacked; humped on one side.

gibbiflorus, -a, -um [jibbi-FLO-rus]
Having flowers with a swelling or hump on one side.

gibbosus, -a, -um [jib-O-sus]
gibbus, -a, -um [JIB-us]
Swollen on one side.

gibraltaricus, -a, -um [jib-rawl-TAR-ik-us]
From Gibraltar.

giganteus, -a, -um [jy-gan-TEE-us]
Unusually tall or large.

gigas [JY-gas]
Of giants. Gigas were the sons of Terra who stormed the heavens but were killed by the lightning of Jove.

giganthes [jy-GAN-thees]
With giant flowers.

Gilia [GIL-ia or JIL-ia]
Herbs, probably named for Philipp Salvador Gil, a Spaniard, or possibly for Filippi Luigi Gillii, an Italian. Both are described as 18th-century botanists.

Gilibertia [gil-i-BERT-ia]
Tropical American shrubs named after J. E. Gilibert, a French physician and botanist.

Gillenia [gil-EE-nia]
Perennial herbs named for Arnold Gillenius, 17th-century German botanist.

Gingko [GING-ko]
Maidenhair tree. The Chinese name for this genus which consists of one species only and which is not known to exist in the wild state. Because it is dioecious, the male and female flowers are on separate trees. The female trees are undesirable because of the foul-smelling fruit. It is said that the kernel is edible but it would require a strong stomach to get that close to it

Ginseng.
See *Panax.*

glabellus, -a, -um [glab-ELL-us]
glabratus, -a, -um [glab-RAY-tus]
glabrescens [glab-RES-ens]

glabriusculus, -a, -um [glab-ri-us-KEW-lus]
Rather or somewhat smooth.

glaber, glabra, glabrum [GLAY-ber]
Smooth-skinned; without hairs; glabrous.
Also *glaberrimus*, very smooth-skinned.

glacialis, -is, -e [glay-si-AY-lis]
From icy-cold regions and especially from the neighborhood
of glaciers.

gladiatus, -a, -um [glad-i-AY-tus]
Swordlike.

Gladiolus [glad-EYE-o-lus, or glad-i-o-lus]
Latin for a small sword; in allusion to the shape of the leaves.
The plants are also sometimes called sword-lily. For some
reason, people generally make the plural Gladioli in a de-
parture from the normal custom of adding *s* to the singular
Latin name, as in antirrhinums, petunias, etc.

glandiformis, -is, -e [gland-i-FORM-is]
In the form of a gland or shaped like one. Also:

glanduliferus	gland-bearing
glanduliflorus	with glandular flowers
glandulosus	glandular

glaucescens [glaw-SESS-ens, or glaw-KESS-ens]
Having some bloom; somewhat blue or sea-green.

Glaucidium [glaw-SID-ium, or glaw-KID-ium]
Derivation obscure.

glaucifolius, -a, -um [glaw-ki-FO-lius]
glaucophyllus, -a, -um [glaw-ko-FILL-us]
Having gray- or bluish-green leaves; having bloom on the
leaves.

Glaucium [GLAW-sium, or GLAW-kium]
Horned poppy; sea poppy. From Gr. *glaukos*, grayish-green;
from the color of the leaves.

glaucoides [glaw-KOY-deez]
Appearing to be coated with bloom.

glaucus, -a, -um [GLAW-kus]
Having bloom, the fine, whitish, powdery coating which occurs on certain leaves (e.g., cabbage) and fruits (e.g., plum).

Gleditsia (also, incorrectly, **Gleditschia**) [gled-IT-sia, or
gled-IT-shia]
Honey locust. Ornamental trees named for Gottlieb Gled-

itsch (d. 1786), Director of the Botanical Gardens, Berlin.

Gliricidia [gli-ris-ID-ia]
L. *glis*, a dormouse; *cida*, a killer. Some of the species of these woody plants are poisonous.

globosus, -a, -um [glo-BO-sus]
Round; spherical.

globiferus, -a, -um [glo-BIFF-er-us]
Bearing globe-shaped or spherical clusters.

Globularia [glob-yew-LAY-ria]
Globe daisy. L. *globulus*, a small round ball; from the form of the flower heads of these herbs and shrubs.

globularis, -is, -e [glob-yew-LAY-ris]
Pertaining to a small sphere or ball.

globuliferus, -a, -um [glob-yew-LIFF-er-us]
Bearing clusters in the form of small globes or spheres.

globuligemma [glob-yew-li-JEM-ma]
Having round buds.

globulosus, -a, -um [glob-yew-LO-sus]
Small and globular.

glomeratus, -a, -um [glo-mer-AY-tus]
Clustered into more or less rounded heads. Also *glomeruliferus*, having small rounded heads or clusters.

glomeruliflorus, -a, -um [glo-mer-roo-li-FLOW-rus]
Having flowers in glomerules. A glomerule is an inflorescence consisting of a cyme (a group or cluster of flowers opening from the center outwards as in sweet cherry) growing at the end of its own stalk.

Gloriosa [glow-ri-o-sa]
Glory-lily. From L. *gloriosus*, glorious.

gloriosus, -a, -um [glow-ri-o-sus]
Superb; glorious.

Glottiphyllum [glot-ti-FILL-um]
Gr. *glottis*, a tongue; *phyllon*, a leaf. The leaves of these succulent plants are very thick, soft, and fleshy, and shaped like tongues. They are brittle and easily snapped.

Gloxinia [glox-IN-ia]
What is usually called Gloxinia by florists is, in fact, *Sinningia*. The true *Gloxinia*, much less common, is named for Benjamin Peter Gloxin, a late 18th-century botanical writer.

gloxinioides [glox-in-i-OY-deez]
Resembling *Gloxinia*.

glumaceus, -a, -um [gloo-MAY-seus]
Having glumes, the chaffy bracts enclosing the flowers of grasses or sedges.

glutinosus, -a, -um [gloo-tin-o-sus]
Sticky; gluey; glutinous.

Glyceria [gly-SEE-ria]
Manna grass. From Gr. *glykys*, sweet. The roots and leaves of some species are sweet.

Glycine [gly-SY-ne]
Soybean. From Gr. *glykys*, sweet; in allusion to the sweetness of the roots and leaves of some species, none of which begins to compare in importance with the soybean. Quick to mature, drought-resistant and easy to grow, this plant has been in cultivation for at least five thousand years. It yields oil, meal, cheese, curds, and cake as well as milk, which in some places is delivered daily as we do cow's milk. About two-thirds of the world's crop is grown in Manchuria where it has caused wars as well as political and commercial maneuvering. It is imported by Western countries for use in soap, paint, synthetic-rubber manufacture, etc., as well as for food, both for humans and cattle.

glycinioides [gly-sin-i-OY-deez]
Resembling soybean or *Glycine*.

Glycosmis [gly-KOS-mis]
Gr. *glykys*, sweet; *osme,* smell. Both the flowers and the leaves of these shrubs and small trees are fragrant.

Glycyrrhiza [gly-ki-RY-za]
Licorice. From Gr. *glykys*, sweet; *rhiza*, a root. The root of *G. glabra,* the only species of any interest, provides the licorice of commerce of which the Catalonian is the most highly regarded.

Glyptostrobus [glib-TOSS-tro-bus]
From Gr. *glypto*, to carve; *stropos*, a cone; an allusion to the markings on the cones of these deciduous but cypresslike trees.

Gmelina [mel-LY-na]
Trees and shrubs named for Johann Gottlieb Gmelin (1709-1755), German traveler and naturalist.

Gnaphalium [naff-AY-lium]
Cudweed. From Gr. *gnaphalon*, soft down. Most species of these herbs and sub-shrubs have woolly leaves.

gnaphaloides [naff-al-OY-deez]
Resembling cudweed or *Gnaphalium.*

Godetia [go-DEE-shia]
Showy annuals named for C. H. Godet (1797-1879), Swiss botanist.

Gomesa [go-MEE-sa]
Epiphytic orchids named for Bernardino Gomez, Portuguese Naval surgeon, who published a book on the plants of Brazil in 1803.

Gomphocarpus [gom-fo-KARP-us]
Milkweed. Gr. *gomphos,* a club; *karpos,* fruit. Recently reclassified under *Asclepias.*

gomphocephalus [gom-fo-SEFF-al-us]
Club-headed.

gomphococcus, -a, -um [gom-fo-KOK-us]
With berries resembling clubs.

Gompholobium [gom-fo-LO-bium]
Gr. *gomphos,* a club, *lobos,* a pod; from the appearance of the pod on these Australian evergreen flowering shrubs.

Gomphrena [gom-FREE-na]
Globe amaranth. Latin name for a kind of amaranth, possibly this one; usually grown as an "everlasting."

Gongora [gon-GO-ra, also GON-go-ra]
Epiphytic orchids named for Don Antonio Cabellero y Gongora, 18th-century Spanish Viceroy of New Granada, now Colombia, and patron of José Celestino Mutis (1732-1818), naturalist and plant explorer, who was responsible for the Bogotá Observatory which became a renowned center of scholarship and research.

gongylodes [gon-gil-o-deez]
Swollen; roundish.

goniatus, -a, -um [go-ni-AY-tus]
With corners or angles.

goniocalyx [go-ni-o-KAY-lix]
The calyx having corners or angles.

Goodia [GOOD-ia]
Shrubs named for Peter Good (d. 1803), botanical collector in Australia.

Goodyera [good-YER-a]
Rattlesnake plantain. A terrestrial orchid named in honor

of John Goodyer (1592-1664) who assisted Johnson in his edition of Gerard's *Herball*.

Gordonia [gord-o-nia]
Ornamental evergreen or deciduous shrubs and trees with white flowers named for James Gordon (d. 1781), correspondent of Linnaeus and nurseryman of Mile End, London. *Franklinia* is often placed in this genus.

Gormania [gor-MAY-nia]
Plants now included in *Sedum* named for M. W. Gorman of Portland, Oregon, collector of plants of the Pacific Northwest.

gossypinus, -a, -um [go-SIP-in-us]
Resembling cotton or *Gossypium*.

Gossypium [go-SIP-ium]
Cotton. The Latin name. The English name derives ultimately from Arabic. Cotton has been cultivated since prehistoric times in the Old World and was found already in use in the New when the Spanish arrived. The most important of vegetable fibers, it is said to supply about 90 per cent of the clothing used in the world.

Gourliea [gor-li-EE-a]
Shrubs and small trees named for Robert Gourlie (d. 1832), Scottish botanist in Chile.

Grabowskia [grab-ow-skia]
Spiny shrubs named for H. Grabowsky (1792-1842), German botanist.

gracilentus, -a, -um [gras-ill-ENT-us]
gracilis, -is, -e [GRAS-ill-is]
Graceful; slender. Also:

graciliflorus	With slender or graceful flowers
gracilior	More graceful
gracilipes	With a slender stalk
gracilistylus	With a slender style
gracillimus	Most graceful

graecus, -a, -um [GREEK-us]
Greek; Grecian.

gramineus, -a, -um [gram-IN-eus]
graminis, -is, -e [GRAM-in-is]
Resembling grass.

graminifolius, -a, -um [gram-in-i-FO-lius]
With leaves resembling grass.

Grammatophyllum [gram-at-o-FILL-um]

From Gr. *grammata,* letters; *phyllon,* a leaf; an allusion to the markings on the flowers of these orchids.

grammopetalus, -a, -um [gram-o-PET-al-us]

With striped petals.

grandis, -is, -e [GRAND-is]

Big; showy. Also:

grandiceps	large-headed
grandicuspis	having big points
grandidentatus	having big teeth
grandiflorus	large flowered
grandifolius	with big leaves
grandiformis	on a large scale
grandipunctatus	having large spots

graniticus, -a, -um [gran-IT-ik-us]

Growing on or in crevices of granite or other hard quartz rocks.

granulatus, -a, -um [gran-yew-LAY-tus]

granulosus, -a, -um [gran-yew-LO-sus]

Composed of minute grains or appearing as though covered with them.

Graptopetalum [grap-to-PET-al-um]

Gr. *grapho,* to write; *petalon,* a petal; from the variegated markings on the petals of these sedums.

Graptophyllum [grap-to-FILL-um]

Gr. *grapho,* to write; *phyllon,* a leaf; from the variegated markings on the leaves of these shrubs.

Gratiola [grat-i-o-la]

L. *gratia,* agreeableness or pleasantness; in allusion to the medical uses of these herbs.

gratissimus, -a, -um [grat-ISS-im-us]

Very pleasing or agreeable.

gratus, -a, -um [GRAY-tus]

Pleasing.

graveolens [grav-ee-o-lens]

Heavily scented.

Greigia [GRY-gia]

Large showy herbs named for Major-General Samuel Alexei-vich Greig (1827-1887), President of the Russian Horticultural Society.

Grevillea [grev-ILL-ea]
Evergreen trees and shrubs named for Charles Francis Greville (1749-1809), a founder of the Royal Horticultural Society and a Vice President of the Royal Society.

Grewia [GROO-ya]
A genus of trees and shrubs named for Nehemiah Grew (1641-1712), English botanist.

Greyia [GRAY-ya]
A small tree from Natal named for Sir George Grey (1812-1898), notable colonial governor who ultimately became the elected Prime Minister of New Zealand where he initiated great reforms.

Grindelia [grin-DEE-lia]
Gumplant. Named for David Hieronymus Grindel (1766-1836), German Professor of Botany at Riga.

Griselinia [gris-el-IN-ia]
Evergreen shrubs and trees named for Franc Griselini (1717-1783), Venetian botanist.

griseus, -a, -um [GRIZ-eus]
Grey.

groenlandicus, -a, -um [green-LAND-ik-us]
From Greenland.

gronovii [gron-o-vi-eye]
Species name in honor of J. Gronovius (1690-1760) of Leyden; one of the celebrated scholars of his day.

grosse-serratus, -a, -um [GRO-ser-ray-tus]
With large saw teeth.

grossus, -a, -um [GRO-sus]
Very large.

gruinus, -a, -um [groo-EYE-nus]
Resembling a crane.

Guaiacum [GWY-ak-um]
From the South American vernacular word guaiac, the name for lignum vitae (*G. officinale*), meaning wood of life, so named because of its high repute in medicine. Guaiacum resin is used for a number of acute and chronic conditions, as well as in certain tests for blood. The wood of these trees is hard, dense, and virtually unsplittable. It is used for such things as mallets, ships' blocks and, formerly, for propeller shaft bearings. Lignum vitae was used in the lock gate hinges on the Erie Canal where they lasted for a century.

Guilielma [gwy-li-EL-ma]
Palms named for Queen Frederica Guilielma Carolina of Bavaria.

Guizotia [gy-zo-tia]
Annuals named for Father P. G. Guizot (1787-1874), French botanist.

gummifer, gummifera, gummiferum [GUM-iff-er]
Producing gum.

gummosus, -a, -um [gum-o-sus]
Gummy.

Gunnera [GUN-er-ra]
Perennial herbs. Named in honor of Ernest Gunner (1718-1773), Swedish bishop and botanist. Of all foliage plants one of the most handsome and impressive. The leaves of *G. manicata* may be six feet across and the crown as large as a man's body.

gunneraefolius [gun-ner-ee-FO-lius]
With leaves like *Gunnera*.

guttatus, -a, -um [gut-AY-tus]
Spotted; speckled with small dots.

Guzmania [guz-MAY-nia]
Herbaceous perennials. Named for a Spanish naturalist, A. Guzman.

Gymnocalycium [jim-no-kal-ISS-ium]
Gr. *gymnos*, naked; *kalyx*, a bud; because the flower buds of these succulent plants are naked.

gymnocarpus, -a, -um [jim-no-KARP-us]
Having naked fruit.

Gymnocladus [jim-NOK-lay-dus]
From Gr. *gymnos*, naked; *klados*, a branch. The branches are bare of twigs in winter. One species, the Kentucky coffee-tree (*G. dioica*), has seeds which the pioneers used as a coffee substitute.

Gynandropsis [jy-nan-DROP-sis]
Gr. *gyne*, female; *andros*, male; *opsis*, appearance; from the manner in which the stamens appear to be inverted on the top of the ovary on these annuals.

Gynerium [jy-NER-ium]
Gr. *gyne*, female; *erion*, wool; a reference to the hairy spikelets of the female plants of these grasses.

Gynura [jy-NOOR-ra]
Gr. *gyne*, female; *oura*, a tail; from the long, rough stigma on these foliage plants.

Gypsophila [jip-SOFF-ill-a]
Baby's breath. Gr. *gypsos*, gypsum; *philos*, a friend. Some species of these small-flowered plants of the *stitchwort* family are lime-loving.

gyrans [JY-rans]
Going around in circles.

H

haageanum [hah-gi-AY-num]
In honor of J. N. Haage (1826-1878), seed grower of Erfurt, Germany.

Habenaria [hab-en-AY-ria]
Fringed orchis. Rein orchis. From Gr. *habena*, a rein. In some species the spur is long and shaped like a strap.

Haberlea [hab-ER-lee-a]
Tufted herbs named for Karl Konstantin Haberle (1764-1832), Professor of Botany at Budapest.

Hacquetia [hak-EE-sha]
Herbaceous perennial named for Balthasar Hacquet (1740-1815), Austrian writer on Alpine plants.

hadriaticus, -a, -um [hay-dri-AT-ik-us]
From the shores of the Adriatic.

Haemanthus [hee-MAN-thus]
Red Cape tulip. Blood-lily. From Gr. *haema*, blood; *anthos*, a flower.

haemanthus, -a, -um [hee-MAN-thus]
With blood-red flowers. Also:

haemastomus	with mouth a blood-red
haematocalyx	with blood-red calyx
haematochilus	with blood-red lip
haematodes	blood-red

Haematoxylum [hee-mat-ox-eye-lum]
Logwood. From Gr. *haema*, blood; *xylon*, wood. Since the 16th century it has been a very valuable export from Central America and the West Indies for the sake of the brilliant

red dye produced from the heart wood which synthetic chemistry has never been able to match. *H. campechianum* is known by several other names, such as bloodwood-tree and campeachy-wood.

Hakea [HAY-kea]
Australian evergreen shrubs named for Baron von Hake 1745-1818), German patron of botany.

hakeoides [hay-ke-OY-deez]
Resembling *Hakea.*

Halesia [hal-EE-sia]
Silver bell. Flowering trees and shrubs named in honor of the Reverend Stephen Hales (1677-1761), curate of Teddington, near London, physiologist, chemist, and inventor whose wide-ranging curiosity resulted in important and far-reaching experiments in plant physiology as well as, possibly, the first measurement of blood pressure. It was performed one Sunday on a white mare, thrown and tied to a gate, whose blood, transferred through a goose's windpipe (an efficient medium before the invention of rubber tubing), rose in a glass tube to a height of 8 feet 3 inches.

He also invented an effective method of ventilating prisons to control jail fever, and ships to prevent dry rot; a "sea gauge" for taking soundings, and a method of fumigating wheat with brimstone to preserve it from weevils.

halimifolius, -a, -um [hal-im-i-FO-lius]
With leaves like *Halimium,* a *Cistus*-like plant of no particular garden interest.

Halimodendron [hal-im-o-DEN-dron]
Salt tree. From Gr. *halimures,* maritime; *dendron,* a tree. A salt-tolerant shrub from Central Asia.

halophilus, -a, -um [hal-OFF-il-us]
Salt-loving.

Hamamelis [ham-am-EE-lis, also sometimes ham-am-ELL-is]
Witch-hazel. The Greek name for a plant with a pear-shaped fruit, possibly the medlar. The bark and twigs of *H. virginiana* supply the witch-hazel of pharmacy. The twigs are also a favorite choice of dowsers or water-diviners.

Hamatocactus [ham-at-o-KAK-tus]
L. *hamatus,* hooked, plus *cactus;* a mistaken allusion, for the spines of this genus are straight.

hamatus, -a, -um [ham-AY-tus]
ham-o-sus, -a, um [ham-o-sus]
Hooked.

Hamelia [ham-EE-lia]
Handsome shrubs named in honor of Henri Louis de Hamel du Monceau (1700-1782), celebrated French botanical writer.

Harbouria [har-BOR-ia]
Herbaceous plants named for J. P. Harbour, collector of Rocky Mountain plants.

Hardenbergia [har-den-BER-jia]
Australian sarsaparilla. Evergreen twiners named in honor of Franziska, Countess von Hardenberg, sister of Baron Karl von Hügel (1794-1870) who traveled widely in the Philippines.

harpophyllus, -a, -um [har-po-FILL-us]
With leaves shaped like sickles.

Harrisia [har-ISS-ia]
Cacti named for William Harris (1860-1920), Superintendent of the Public Gardens, Jamaica.

Hartwegia [hart-WEE-jia]
Epiphytic orchids named for Theodor Hartweg (1812-1871), Royal Horticultural Society collector in California and Mexico.

hastatus, -a, -um [has-TAY-tus]
Spear-shaped. Also:

hastiferus	bearing a spear
hastilabium	with a spear-shaped lip
hastilis	of a spear
hastulatus	somewhat spear-shaped

Hatiora [hati-i-o-ra]
Anagram of *Hariota*, a genus of cacti; which was renamed when it was reclassified. Originally named in honor of Thomas Hariot, a 16th-century botanist.

Haworthia [ha-WORTH-ia]
Succulent plants named for Adrian Haworth (1768-1833), English authority on succulent plants.

Hebe [HEE-bee]
New Zealand evergreen shrubs named in honor of the cup-bearer to the gods who later married Hercules when he as-

cended to Olympus. Some authorities classify in *Veronica* but Bailey states specifically that they are separate and that *Hebe* forms a genus in its own right.

hebecarpus, -a, -um [hee-bee-KAR-pus]
With fruit covered in down.

hebephyllus, -a, -um [hee-bee-FILL-us]
Downy-leaved.

Hebenstreitia [hee-ben-STREE-shia]
A genus of shrubs, sub-shrubs, and annuals named for Johann Ernst Hebestreit (1702-1757), Professor of Botany at Leipzig.

Hechtia [HEK-tia]
Mexican succulents named for J. H. G. Hecht (d. 1837), a counselor to the King of Prussia.

Hedeoma [hed-e-o-ma]
American pennyroyal. Gr. *hedys*, sweet; *aroma*, a spice or sweet herb; from the aromatic foliage.

Hedera [HED-er-a]
Ivy. The Latin name. Ivy was held sacred to Bacchus, the god of wine, and was intimately connected with his revels.

hederaceus, -a, -um [hed-er-AY-seus]
Resembling ivy.

Hedychium [hed-IK-ium]
Ginger-lily. From Gr. *hedys*, sweet; *chion*, snow. The flower of one species is white and fragrant.

Hedysarum [hed-iss-A-rum]
Greek name *hedys*, sweet, plus *Arum*. This genus of ornamental herbs or sub-shrubs includes the handsome and fragrant French-honeysuckle (*H. coronarium*).

Hedyscepe [hed-i-SEEP-e]
Umbrella palm. From Gr. *hedys*, sweet; *scepe*, a covering; from the manner in which the flowers of this feather palm are produced, in a dense cluster from the leaf crown.

Heimia [HY-mia]
Shrubs named for Geheimrat Dr. Heim (d. 1834), of Berlin.

Helenium [hel-EE-nium]
Sneezeweed. From the Greek name for another plant named for Helen of Troy.

Heliamphora [hee-li-AM-fo-ra]
Gr. *helios*, the sun; *amphora*, a jar. From the habit and form of these insectivorous pitcher plants.

Helianthella [hee-li-an-THELL-a]
Diminutive of *Helianthus* to which they are closely related.

Helianthemum [hee-li-AN-them-um]
Sunrose. From Gr. *helios,* the sun; *anthemon,* a flower.

helianthoides [hee-li-an-THOY-deez]
Resembling *Helianthus.*

Helianthus [hee-li-AN-thus]
Sunflower. From Gr. *helios,* the sun; *anthos,* a flower. *H. tuberosus* is the "Jerusalem artichoke."

Helichrysum [hee-li-KRY-sum]
Everlasting. Immortelle. From Gr. *helios,* the sun; *chrysos,* golden.

Helicodiceros [hel-ik-o-DISS-er-os]
Dragon's mouth. Twist-arum. From Gr. *helix,* a spiral; *dis,* twice; *keras,* a horn. The basal divisions of the leaves are twisted and stand erect like horns.

Heliconia [hel-ik-o-nia]
After Mount Helicon in Greece where is was supposed that the Muses lived. A member of the family Musaceae.

Heliocereus [hee-li-o-SEE-reus]
Gr. *helios,* the sun; *cereus,* cactus; because of the desert habitat of these procumbent Mexican plants.

Heliophila [he-li-o-FILL-a]
Gr. *helios,* the sun; *philein,* to love. From the habitat of these South African plants.

Heliopsis [he-li-OP-sis]
Gr. *helios,* the sun; *opsis,* resembling. In allusion to the rayed yellow flower heads of these American perennials.

Heliotropium [he-li-o-TRO-pium]
Heliotrope. Cherry-pie. From Gr. *helios,* the sun; *trope,* a turning; in allusion to an old disproved idea that the flower heads turned with the sun. The leaves and flowers of many plants do this and are known as heliotropic.

Helipterum [hell-IP-ter-um]
Everlasting. From Gr. *helios,* the sun; *pteron,* a wing; a technical reference to the plumed pappus.

helix [properly HELL-ix, often HE-lix]
Greek (and Latin) for a twining plant.

Helleborus [hell-LEB-or-us]
Classical Greek name of the Christmas-rose (*H. niger*).

The roots of some species yield a violent poison once used in the treatment of insanity.

hellenicus, -a, -um [hell-EEN-ik-us]
Of Greece.

helodes [hell-o-deez]
Of bogs.

helodoxa [hell-o-DOX-a]
Glory of the marsh.

Helonias [hell-o-nias]
Stud flower. Swamp pink. From Gr. *helos,* a marsh; the natural habitat of these bulbous plants.

helveticus, -a, -um [hell-VET-ik-us]
Of Switzerland.

helvolus, -a, -um [hell-vo-lus]
Reddish-yellow.

helvus, -a, -um [HELL-vus]
Honey-colored.

Helwingia [hell-WING-ia]
Deciduous shrubs named after Georg A. Helwing (1666-1748), German botanist.

Helxine [hell-ZY-nee]
Baby's tears. A creeping herb with a classical name for a related plant (pellitory or *Parietaria*).

Hemerocallis [heem-er-o-KAL-is]
Day-lily. Gr. *hemera,* day; *kallos,* beauty. Each flower lasts but one day.

Hemiandra [hem-i-AN-dra]
Gr. *hemi,* half; *andros,* male. Only one of the normally two anther lobes to each stamen is developed in this genus.

Hemigraphis [hem-i-GRAFF-is]
Gr. *hemi,* half; *grapho,* to write. Apparently a meaningless application to these Asian herbs.

Hemionitis [hem-i-o-NY-tis]
Gr. *hemionos,* a mule; because these ferns were once regarded as sterile.

hemiphloeus, -a, -um [hem-i-FLEE-us]
Half-barked.

Hemiptelea [hem-ip-TELL-ea]
Gr. *hemi,* half; *ptilon,* a wing; in allusion to the winged fruits of this spiny tree.

hemisphaericus, -a, -um [hem-i-SFEER-ik-us]
Hemispherical; in the shape of half a ball.

Hepatica [hee-PAT-ik-a]
Liverwort. From Gr. *hepar*, the liver. This is a double allusion to the color and shape of the leaves as well as to the long-held thought that, in consequence, they would be good for complaints of the liver.

hepaticaefolius, -a, -um [hee-pat-i-see-FO-lius]
With leaves like *Hepatica*.

hepta-
In compound words signifying seven. Thus *heptaphyllus*, seven-leaved.

heracleaefolius, -a, -um [her-ak-lee-ee-FO-lius]
With leaves like *Heracleum* or cow-parsnip.

Heracleum [her-ak-LEE-um]
Cow-parsnip. Greek name for these herbs in honor of Hercules (Gr. *Herakles*).

herbaceus, -a, -um [her-BAY-see-us]
Not woody; herbaceous.

Herniaria [her-ni-AIR-ia]
Herniary, rupturewort, burstwort. From Gr. *hernia*, a rupture; for which the plant was once supposed to be effective.

Hesperaloe [hes-per-AL-o]
Gr. *hesperos*, western. The plants are New World with aspects of the Old World *Aloe*.

Hesperis [HES-per-is]
Sweet rocket. Dame's violet. From Gr. *hesperos*, the evening. The plants have a marked fragrance as the sun goes down.

Hesperoyucca [hes-per-o-YUK-a]
From Gr. *hesperos*, western, and Yucca. The habitat is California.

hesperus, -a, -um [HES-per-us]
Of the West.

heter-, hetero-
In compound words signifying various, diverse, thus:

heteracanthus	diversely spined
heteranthus	diversely flowered
heterocarpus	diversely fruited
heterodon	diversely toothed
heterodoxus	differing from the genus type
heteroglossus	diversely tongued

heterolepsis	diversely scaled
heteromorphus	differing in form
heteropetalus	diversely petaled
heterophyllus	diversely leaved
heteropodus	diversely stalked

Heterocentron [het-er-o-SEN-tron]
Gr. *heteros,* varying; *kentron,* a spur. The anthers of these herbs or shrubs are of unequal length.

Heteromeles [het-er-o-MEE-leez]
Toyon, Christmas-berry. From Gr. *heteros,* different; *mele,* apple. The fruit of this evergreen shrub or tree differs from that of related genera with applelike fruit.

Heterospathe [het-er-o-SPAY-thee]
Gr. *heteros,* differing. The spathes of this palm are of unequal length.

Heuchera [hew-KER-a]
Alum-root. In honor of Johann Heinrich von Heucher (1677-1747), Professor of Medicine at Wittenberg University.

Hevea [HEV-ee-a]
Latinized form of the Brazilian name for the Para rubber tree (*H. braziliensis*), the most important source of natural rubber.

Following discovery of the secret of vulcanization (Hancock in England, 1834; Goodyear in the United States, 1839) demand soon exceeded the Amazon supplies. The Director of Kew, Sir Joseph Hooker, determined in the 1870's to collect seed. Difficulties in transporting it in fertile condition were solved by Wickham who chartered a special steamship to carry his prepared baskets of 70,000 seeds. Hothouses at Kew were summarily emptied and within two weeks there were over 2,000 seedlings, most of which went to Ceylon. Thus was started the great rubber-growing industry in Southeast Asia which by 1910 eclipsed the Amazon.

hexa-
In compound words signifying six, thus:

hexagonopterus	six-angled wings
hexagonus	six-angled
hexandrus	with six stamens
hexapetalus	six-petaled
hexaphyllus	six-leaved

hians [HY-ans]
Gaping.
Hibbertia [hib-BER-shia]
Evergreen shrubs named in honor of George Hibbert (1757-1837), English patron of botany.
hibernalis, -is, -e [hy-ber-NAY-lis]
Pertaining to winter.
hibernicus, -a, -um [hy-BERN-ik-us]
Irish.
hibernus, -a, -um [hy-BERN-us]
Winter-flowering or winter-green.
hibiscifolius, -a, -um [hy-bis-ki-FO-lius]
With leaves resembling *Hibiscus.*
Hibiscus [hy-BISK-us]
Rose-mallow. The Greek name for mallow. *H. rosa-sinensis* is what is generally called *Hibiscus.* This magnificent shrub is widely grown in frost-free areas and in greenhouses. It is said that the blooms are worn by the ladies of Tahiti and other Pacific islands in conventional fashions to indicate freedom or otherwise from commitments to the opposite sex. In some places it is also known as the shoe-black-plant because the petals can be used to put a polish on shoes. The genus also includes rose-mallow (*H. moscheutos*), rose-of-Sharon (*H. syriacus*), the confederate rose (*H. mutabilis*) and roselle (*H. sabdariffa*).
Hidalgoa [hy-DAL-goa]
Climbing dahlia. In honor of Hidalgo, a Mexican naturalist.
hiemalis, -is, -e [hy-em-MAY-lis]
Of the winter; winter-flowering.
Hieracium [hy-er-RAY-sium]
Hawkweed. The classical name for another plant.
Hierochloë [hy-er-ROK-lo-ee]
Gr. *hieros,* sacred; *chloa,* grass. In some parts of northern Europe these fragrant grasses are strewn before church doors on saints' days.
hierochuntica [hy-er-o-CHUN-tik-a]
Specific name of rose-of-Jericho or resurrection plant. From the classical name of the town of Jericho.
himalaicus, -a, -um [him-a-LAY-ik-us]
himalayensis, -is, -e [him-a-lay-EN-sis]
Of the Himalayas.

Hippeastrum [hip-e-AST-rum]
Gr. *hippeos;* a mounted man; *astron,* a star; but there is no known reason for the allusion. These bulbous plants are popularly known as *Amaryllis.*

hippocastanum [hip-o-KAS-tan-um]
Latin name for the horse-chestnut. There is a clearly marked horseshoe under the leaf axils.

Hippocrepis [hip-o-KREE-pis]
Horseshoe vetch. Gr. *hippos,* a horse; *krepis,* a shoe; from the shape of the pod of this trailing herb.

Hippophäe [hip-OFF-ay-ee]
Sea-buckthorn. The classical Greek name for another plant, probably prickly spurge.

hircynus, -a, -um [her-SY-nus]
Smelling of goat or goatlike.

hirsutus, -a, -um [her-SU-tus]
Hairy, thus:

hirsutissimus	very hairy
hirsutulus	somewhat hairy
hirtellus	rather hairy
hirtiflorus	hairy flowered
hirtipes	hairy stemmed
hirtus	hairy

hispanicus, -a, -um [his-PAN-ik-us]
Spanish.

hispidus, -a, um [HISS-pid-us]
Bristly.

Hoffmania [hoff-MAN-ia]
Herbs or shrubs named in honor of Georg Franz Hoffmann (1761-1826), Professor of Botany, Göttingen.

Hoheria [Ho-HEER-ia]
Latinized version of the New Zealand Maori name for these small trees and shrubs.

Holcus [HOL-kus]
Sorghum. Greek name for some other kind of grass.

hollandicus, -a, -um [ho-LAND-ik-us]
Of Holland.

Holmskioldia [holm-ski-OLD-ia]
Shrubs named in honor of Thodor Holmskiold (1732-1794), Danish botanist.

holo-
In compound words signifying completely, thus:

holocarpus	whole-fruited
holochrysus	completely golden
hololeucus	wholly white
holosericeus	covered all over with silky hairs

Holodiscus [ho-lo-DISK-us]
Gr. *holos*, entire; *diskos*, a disk. An allusion to the disk of the flower of these ornamental shrubs.

holostea [ho-LOSS-tea]
Species name for *Stellaria*, starwort. From the Greek for a chickweed-like plant.

Homalanthus [ho-mal-ANTH-us]
Gr. *homalos*, smooth; *anthos*, a flower; from the appearance of the flower of these tropical trees.

Homalocephala [ho-mal-o-SEFF-al-a]
Gr. *homalos*, flat; *hephale*, a head; referring to the flat top of the flower on these plants of the Cactus family.

Homalomena [ho-mal-o-MEE-na]
Derivation of the name of these foliage plants is uncertain.

homolepis [ho-MO-lep-is]
Having structurally similar scales.

Hordeum [HOR-deum]
Wild barley. Latin name for barley (*H. vulgare*). Squirreltail grass is *H. jubatum*.

horizontalis, -is, -e [ho-riz-on-TAY-lis]
Flat to the ground; horizontal.

Horminum [hor-MY-num]
Greek name for Sage to which this genus is related.

horridus, -a, -um [HO-rid-us]
Very prickly.

hortensis, -is, -e [hor-TEN-sis]
    hortorum [hor-TOR-um]
    hortulanus, -a, -um [hor-tew-LAY-nus]
    hortulatis, -is, -e [hor-tew-LAY-tis]
    hortulorum [hor-tew-LOR-um]
Of or pertaining to gardens.

Hosackia [ho-SAK-ia]
Herbaceous plants named in honor of David Hosack (1769-1835), Professor of Botany and Materia Medica at Colum-

bia College. In 1801 he purchased land, part of which is now occupied by Rockefeller Center, to form the Elgin Botanic Garden which he maintained at his own cost. Nine years later the Garden was transferred to the state of New York under control of the College of Physicians and Surgeons which, in 1814, became part of Columbia University.

Hosta [HOS-ta]
Plantain lily. Named for Nicholaus Thomas Host (1761-1834), physician to the Emperor of Austria.

Houlletia [hoo-LET-ia]
Epiphytic orchids. Named for M. Houllet (1811-1890), Assistant Curator at the Jardin des Plantes, Paris.

Houstonia [hoo-STO-nia]
Bluet. Named for Dr. William Houston (1695-1733), botanist, who collected and wrote of plants in Mexico and the West Indies.

Houttuynia [hoo-TOO-nia]
An aquatic perennial named for Martin Houttuya (1720-1794), Dutch naturalist.

Hovea [HO-vea]
Evergreen flowering shrubs named in honor of A. P. Hove, mid-19th-century Polish botanist and collector for Kew Gardens.

Hovenia [ho-VEE-nia]
Japanese raisin tree. Named for David Hoven, 18th-century Dutch senator.

Howea [HOW-ee-a]
From Lord Howe Island, east of Australia, where alone this genus of palms is found.

Hoya [HOY-ya]
Wax-flower. Climbing flowering evergreen plants named for Thomas Hoy, 18th-century head gardener to the Duke of Northumberland at Sion House on the outskirts of London.

Hudsonia [hud-so-nia]
Beach heather. Named for William Hudson (1730-1793), author of *Flora Anglica*.

Huernia [HER-nia]
Succulent dwarf perennials named in honor of Justin Heurnius (1587-1652), Dutch missionary and the first collector of Cape of Good Hope plants. The genus was named by

Robert Brown who sailed to Australia with Flinders and who originated the misspelling.

hugonis [hew-GO-nis]
Specific name for *Rosa hugonis* in honor of Father Hugh Scallon, missionary in West China, 1890-1900.

Humata [hew-MAY-ta]
From L. *humus,* soil; in allusion to the creeping habit of these ferns.

Humea [HEW-mea]
Herbs and shrubs named for Lady Hume of Wormelybury, Hertfordshire, c. 1800.

humifusus, -a, -um [hew-mi-FEW-sus]
Sprawling on the ground.

humilis, -is, -e [HEW-mil-is]
Low-growing; dwarfer than most of its kindred.

Humulus [HEW-mew-lus]
Hop. L. *humus,* the soil; from the plant's prostrate habit when not supported. There are two species widely grown commercially—*H. americanus* and *H. lupulus,* the European hop (*lupulus,* meaning a small wolf, an allusion to the plant's habit of smothering the trees over which it grows). The principal use is in brewing, the ripe flower heads or cones being dried and used to supply aroma and the bitter flavor as well as to assist in the technical processes of brewing. Dried hops can be used to raise bread and are particularly useful when yeast is not available.

hungaricus, -a, -um [hun-GAIR-ik-us]
Hungarian.

Hunnemannia [hun-em-MAN-ia]
A Mexican perennial named for John Hunneman, English botanist and introducer of plants who died in 1839.

hunnewellianus, -a, -um [hun-e-well-i-AY-nus]
For the Hunnewell family of Wellesley, Massachusetts, founders of the Hunnewell Arboretum.

hupehensis, -is, -e [hew-pay-EN-sis]
From Hupeh, China.

Hura [HEW-ra]
Sand-box tree. Monkey-dinnerbell. Latin version of the South American name for these curious and ornamental trees.

Hutchinsia [hutch-IN-sia]
Low herbs named in honor of Ellen Hutchins (1785-1815) of Bantry, Ireland, accomplished in cryptogamic (flowerless plant) botany.

hyacinthinus, -a, -um [hy-a-sin-THY-nus]
hyacinthus, -a, -um [hy-a-SIN-thus]
Dark purplish-blue; hyacinthine.

Hyacinthus [hy-a-SIN-thus]
Greek name for hyacinth. Named in honor of Hyakinthos, a youth of great beauty, who, it is said, was accidentally killed by Apollo when teaching him to throw the discus. From his blood sprang the hyacinth which is thought by some not to have been our hyacinth but the fritillary, the petals of which are marked with the mournful exclamation "ai ai" (alas, alas).

hyalinus, -a, -um [hy-al-LY-nus]
Transparent or nearly so.

hybridus, -a, -um [HY-brid-us]
Mixed; hybrid.

Hydrangea [hy-DRAN-jia]
Gr. *hudor*, water; *aggos*, a jar. The fruit of these shrubs is cup-shaped.

hydrangeoides [hy-dran-jee-OY-deez]
Resembling *Hydrangea*.

Hydrastis [hy-DRAS-tis]
Golden seal. Orange root. Derivation of the name for these showy perennials is unknown.

Hydriastele [hy-dri-ass-TEE-lee]
Gr. *hudor*, water; *stele*, a column. In the wild the trees are often near springs.

Hydrocharis [hy-DROK-a-ris]
Gr. *hudor*, water; *charis*, grace. They are pretty water plants.

Hydrocleys [hy-DROK-lees]
Water poppy. Gr. *hudor*, water; *kleis*, a key. There is no clear reason for the allusion.

Hydrocotyle [hy-dro-KOT-ill-e]
Water pennywort. Gr. *hudor*, water; *kotyle*, a small cup; from the form of the leaves.

Hydrolea [hy-dro-LEE-a, or hy-DRO-lea]
Gr. *hudor*, water; *elaia*, olive oil; from the habitat near water

and a characteristic of one species of these herbs or sub-shrubs which appears oily.

Hydrophyllum [hy-dro-FILL-um]
Water-leaf. There seems to be no reason for either name; the plants are not aquatic.

Hydrosme [hy-DROS-mee]
Gr. *hudor,* water; *osme,* stink. These evil-smelling plants like water.

hyemalis, -is, -e [hy-em-AY-lis]
Of winter; flowering in winter. Sometimes spelled *hiemalis.*

Hylocereus [hy-lo-SEE-reus]
Gr. *hule,* a wood; *cereus,* cactus. These ephiphytes prefer some shade.

hylophilus, -a, um [hy-LOFF-ill-us]
Woods-loving.

Hymenaea [hy-men-EE-a]
After Hymen, the Greek god of marriage, in allusion to the twin leaflets on these tropical evergreen trees.

Hymenanthera [hy-men-ANTH-er-a]
Gr. *hymen,* a membrane; the anthers are terminated by a membrane on these shrubs or small trees.

hymen-
In compound words signifying membranous, thus:

hymenanthus	with flowers bearing a membrane
hymenodes	resembling a membrane
hymenorrhizus	membranous rooted
hymenosepalus	with sepals membranous

Hymenocallis [hy-men-o-KAL-is]
Spider lily. Gr. *hymen,* a membrane; *kallos,* beauty; in allusion to the membrane uniting the stamens.

Hymenosporum [hy-men-o-SPOR-um]
Gr. *hymen,* a membrane; *sporus,* a seed. The seeds on this ornamental evergreen have a membranous wing.

Hyophorbe [hy-o-FOR-bee]
Pignut palm. Gr. *hys,* a pig; *phorbe,* food. The fleshy fruits are eaten by pigs.

Hyoscyamus [hy-o-SY-am-us]
Henbane. The Greek name meaning pigbean. Highly poisonous, the plant yields hyoscamine which has certain medical applications as a narcotic.

hyperboreus, -a, -um [hy-per-BOR-eus]
Far-northern.

hypericifolius, -a, -um [hy-per-iss-i-FO-lius]
With leaves like *Hypericum*.

hypericoides [hy-per-i-KOY-deez]
Resembling *Hypericum*.

Hypericum [hy-PER-ik-um]
St. John's wort. The Greek name. The plant is in bloom
around the 24th of June, St. John's Day.

Hyphaene [hy-FEE-nee]
Gr. *hyphaino,* to entwine; in allusion to the fibers of the
fruit on these palms.

hypnoides [hip-NOY-deez]
Mosslike.

Hypocalymma [hy-po-kal-IM-a]
Gr. *hypo,* under; *kalymma,* a veil. The calyx falls off like a
veil or cape on these evergreen shrubs.

Hypochoeris [hy-po-KEER-is]
Cat's ear. Perennial herbs with dandelion-like flowers. Of
uncertain derivation.

hypochondriacus, -a, -um [hy-po-kon-DRY-ak-us]
Of melancholy appearance; with somber-colored flowers.

hypogaeus, -a, -um [hy-po-JEE-us]
Underground; developing underground.

hypo-
In compound words signifying under, thus:

hypoglaucus	smooth beneath
hypoleucus	white beneath
hypophyllus	under the leaf

hypoglottis, -is, -e [hy-po-GLOT-is]
With a swollen tongue.

Hypolepis [hy-PO-lep-is]
Gr. *hypo,* under; *lepis,* a scale; from the position of the
sori on these ferns.

Hypoxis [hy-POX-is]
Star grass. Yellow star grass. Gr. *hypo,* under; *oxys,* sharp;
in allusion to the form of the base of the seed capsule.

hyrcanium [her-KAY-nium]
From the Caspian area.

hyssopifolius, -a, -um [his-sop-i-FO-lius]
With leaves like hyssop.

Hyssopus [hiss-O-pus]
Hyssop. The classical name for this sweet herb. It is almost certainly not the hyssop of the Bible, for *Hyssopus* is not indigenous in Palestine. The biblical hyssop is generally thought to be *Origanum maru.*

hystrix [HISS-trix]
Bristly; porcupine-like.

I

ianthinus, -a, -um [eye-AN-thin-us]
Violet-blue.

ibericus, -a, -um [eye-BER-ik-us]
Of Iberia, i.e., Spain and Portugal.

iberideus, -a, -um [eye-ber-ID-eus]
Resembling *Iberis.*

iberidifolius, -a, -um [eye-ber-id-i-FO-lius]
Iberis-leaved.

Iberis [eye-BER-is]
Candytuft. From Iberia, classical name for Spain, where many species grow wild.

Iboza [eye-BO-za]
Latin version of the Kaffir name for this showy shrub.

icaco [ik-AK-o]
Spanish name for the cocaplum (*Chrysobalanus icaco*).

icosandrus, -a, -um [eye-ko-SAND-rus]
Having twenty stamens (*icos-* in compound words signifies twenty).

idaeus, -a, -um [eye-DEE-us]
Of Mount Ida of ancient Greece.

ida-maia [eye-da-MAY-a]
Species name of *Brevoortia* (*q.v.*) after Ida May Burke, daughter of a California stagecoach driver, for whom the plant was named c. 1867.

Idesia [eye-DEE-sia]
A flowering tree with heart-shaped leaves, named for Eberhard Ysbrant Ides, Dutch traveler in China c. 1720.

ignescens [ig-NESS-ens]
igneus, -a, -um [IG-nee-us]
Fiery red.
Ilex [EYE-lex]
Holly. From the Latin name for the holm oak (*Quercus ilex*).
ilicifolius, -a, -um [eye-liss-i-FO-lius]
Ilex or holly-leaved.
illicebrosus, -a, -um [ill-liss-ee-BRO-sus]
Enticing, charming.
Illicium [ill-ISS-ium]
Allurement; from the enticing aromatic odor of these small trees and shrubs.
illinitus, -a, -um [ill-in-EYE-tus]
Smeared; smirched.
illustratus, -a, -um [ill-us-TRAY-tus]
Pictured.
illustris, -is, -e [ill-US-tris]
Brilliant, lustrous.
illyricus, -a, -um [ill-LI-rik-us]
Of Illyria, on the Yugoslavian shores of the Adriatic.
imberbis, -is, -e [im-BER-bis]
Without spines or beard.
imbricans [IM-brik-ans]
imbricatus, -a, -um [im-brick-AY-tus]
Overlapping in regular order like tiles, e.g., scales.
immaculatus, -a, -um [im-mak-ew-LAY-tus]
Spotless.
immersus, -a, -um [im-MER-sus]
Under water.
Impatiens [im-PAT-iens]
Touch-me-not. Balsam. Latin, impatient, in allusion to the violent discharge of the seeds from the pods when ripe.
impatiens [im-PAT-iens]
Impatient; with seed capsules dehiscing as soon as ripe.
imperati [im-per-AY-teye]
After Ferrante Imperato (1550-1625), an apothecary of Naples.
imperator [im-per-AY-tor]
Showy; commanding.

204

imperatricis [imper-ay-TRY-sis]
Of the Empress Josephine, who, as ex-wife of Napoleon, established an outstanding horticultural project at Malmaison and gathered round her some of the best gardeners of the day.

imperialis, -is, -e [im-peer-i-AY-lis]
Fine; showy.

implexus, -a, -um [im-PLEX-us]
Tangled.

impressus, -a, -um [im-PRESS-us]
Sunken or impressed, as veins may be.

inaequalis, -is, -e [in-ee-KWAY-lis]
Unequal; in compound words, *inaequi-*.

incanus, -a, -um [in-KAY-nus]
Hoary; quite gray.

incarnatus, -a, -um [in-kar-NAY-tus]
Flesh-colored.

Incarvillea [in-kar-VILL-ea]
Showy herbs named after Fr. Pierre d'Incarville (1706-1757), French missionary in China and botanical correspondent of the great botanist Bernard de Jussieu.

incertus, -a, -um [in-SERT-us]
Doubtful; uncertain.

incissifolius, -a, -um [in-sis-i-FO-lius]
With cut leaves.

incisus, -a, -um [in-SY-sus]
Incised; deeply and irregularly cut.

inclaudens [in-KLAU-dens]
Never closing.

inclinatus, -a, -um [in-kly-NAY-tus]
Bent down.

incomparabilis [in-kom-par-AY-bil-is]
Incomparable.

incomptus, -a, -um [in-KOMP-tus]
Unadorned.

inconspicuus, -a, -um [in-kon-SPIK-yew-us]
Inconspicuous.

incrassatus, -a, -um [in-kras-AY-tus]
Thickened.

incurvatus, -a, -um [in-ker-VAY-tus]

incurvus, -a, -um [in-KER-vus]
Bent inward, as in the rays of some chrysanthemums.

indicus, -a, -um [in-DIK-us]
Literally of India but also applied to plants originating throughout the East Indies and from as far away as China. *Rosa indica,* for instance, came from near Canton. It seems as if any plant that came home in an Indiaman might be given this species name without further ado—to the confusion of future generations.

Indigofera [in-dig-OFF-er-a]
Indigo. From indigo plus L. *fero,* to bear. An important crop before the advent of aniline dyes, the first indigo was planted in the British colonies in North America in 1747 by 17-year-old Eliza Lucas of Charleston, South Carolina, from seed sent by her father, Colonel George Lucas, Governor of Antigua. She married Colonel Charles Pinckney. Eliza died in 1793, by which time well over a million pounds of indigo was being produced in the United States annually. George Washington was one of her pallbearers.

indivisus, -a, -um [in-div-EYE-sus]
Undivided.

induratus, -a, -um [ind-yor-AY-tus]
Hard.

inebrians [in-EE-bri-ans]
Intoxicating.

inermis, -is, -e [in-ERM-is]
Unarmed; without prickles.

infaustus, -a, -um [in-FAW-stus]
Unfortunate.

infectorius, -a, -um [in-fect-OR-ius]
Dyed; colored.

infestus, -a, -um [in-FEST-us]
Dangerous; troublesome.

inflatus, -a, -um [in-FLAY-tus]
Swollen up.

infortunatus, -a, -um [in-for-tew-NAY-tus]
Poisonous.

infractus, -a, -um [in-FRACT-us]
Curving inward.

infundibuliformis, -is, -e [in-fun-dib-yew-li-FORM-is]
Funnel- or trumpet-shaped.

infundibulum [in-fun-DIB-yew-lum]
A funnel.

Inga [ING-ga]
The Latinized West Indian name for these acacia-like trees
and shrubs.

ingens [IN-jenz]
Enormous.

inodorus, -a, -um [in-o-DOR-us]
Unscented.

inornatus, -a, -um [in-or-NAY-tus]
Without ornament; unadorned.

inquinans [IN-kwin-ans]
Filthy; defiled.

inscriptus, -a, -um [in-SKRIP-tus]
Inscribed; marked with what might seem to be letters.

insignis, -is, -e [in-SIG-nis]
Distinguished; remarkable.

insititius, -a, -um [in-sit-ISH-us]
Grafted.

insulans [INS-yew-lans]
  insularis, -is, -e [ins-yew-LAY-ris]
Pertaining to an island.

intactus, -a, -um [in-TAK-tus]
Untouched; intact.

integer, integra, integrum [IN-tej-er]
Entire.

integrifolius, -a, -um [in-teg-ri-FO-lius]
With entire or uncut leaves.

intermedius, -a, -um [in-ter-MEE-dius]
Intermediate in color, form, or habit.

interruptus, -a, -um [in-ter-RUPT-us]
Interrupted; not continuous, as with scattered leaves or
flowers.

intertextus, -a, -um [in-ter-TEXT-us]
Intertwined.

intortus, -a, -um [in-TORT-us]
Twisted.

intricatus, -a, -um [in-trik-KAY-tus]
Tangled.

introrsus, -a, -um [in-TROR-sus]
Turned inward toward the axis.

intumescens [in-tew-MESS-ens]
Swollen.

intybus [IN-tib-us]
Species name for chicory; of uncertain application.

Inula [IN-yew-la]
The Latin name for these herbaceous perennials. *I. Helenium* is elecampane.

inutilis, -is, -e [in-YEW-til-is]
Useless.

inversus, -a, -um [in-VER-sus]
Turned over.

invisus, -a, -um [in-VY-sus]
Unseen; not visible.

involucratus, -a, -um [in-vol-lew-KRAY-tus]
Provided with an involucre, a ring of bracts surrounding several flowers.

involutus, -a, -um [in-vol-LEW-tus]
Rolled inward, as leaves in a bud.

Iochroma [eye-o-KRO-ma]
Gr. *ion,* violet; *chroma,* color; from the color of the flowers of these shrubs or small trees.

ioensis, -is, -e [eye-o-EN-sis]
From Iowa.

ionanthus, -a, -um [eye-o-NAN-thus]
With violet-colored flowers.

Ionidium [eye-o-NID-ium]
Gr. *ion,* violet; *eidos,* a resemblance. The flowers resemble violets.

ionopsidium [eye-o-nop-SID-ium]
Gr. *ion,* violet; *opsis,* like. There is a resemblance to some tufted violets.

ionopterus, -a, -um [eye-o-NOP-ter-us]
Violet-winged.

Ipomoea [eye-po-MEE-a]
Morning-glory. From Gr. *ips,* bind-weed; *homoios,* similar to.

Iresine [eye-res-EYE-ne]
Gr. *eiros,* woolly; the flowers of these herbaceous plants with brilliantly, colored leaves are woolly.

iridescens [i-rid-ESS-ens]
Iridescent.

iridiflorus, -a, -um [eye-rid-i-FLO-rus]
Iris-flowered. Also:

iridifolius   iris-leaved
iridoides   resembling iris

Iris [EYE-ris]
Rhizomatous and bulbous rooted perennials named for the Greek goddess of the rainbow.

irregularis, -is, -e [i-reg-yew-LAY-ris]
With parts of dissimilar size.

irriguus, -a, -um [i-RIG-yew-us]
Watered.

irritans [i-rit-ANS]
Causing discomfort.

isandrus, -a, -um [eye-SAND-rus]
With equal stamens.

Isatis [EYE-sat-is]
Woad. The classical Greek name. *I. tinctoria* provided the blue dye used by ancient Britons to stain their bodies. It is still cultivated in Britain as one of the best of the blue vegetable dyes.

Isertia [iss-ERT-ia]
South American shrubs and trees named for P. E. Isert, a German surgeon, c. 1820.

Isoloma [iss-o-LO-ma]
Gr. *isos*, equal; *loma*, a border. The lobes of the corolla are equal on these tropical herbaceous plants.

Isoplexis [iss-o-PLEX-is]
Gr. *isos*, equal; *pleko*, to plait or braid. Application to these shrubs related to foxgloves is not clear.

isophyllus, -a, -um [iss-o-FILL-us]
With equal-sized leaves.

Isopogon [iss-o-PO-gon]
Gr. *isos*, equal; *pogon*, a beard. The inflorescence of these Australian evergreen shrubs has a beardlike fringe.

Isopyrum [iss-o-PY-rum]
Gr. *isos*, equal; *pyros*, wheat. Application to these low perennial herbs is not clear.

Isotoma [iss-OT-o-ma]
Gr. *isos*, equal; *toma*, a section. The segments of the corolla are equal in these *Lobelia*-like herbs.

istriacus, -a, -um [iss-tri-AY-kus]
Of Istria.

italicus, -a, -um [eye-TAL-ik-us]
Of Italy

Itea [IT-ee-a]
Greek name for the willow applied to these trees and shrubs.

Ixia [IX-ia]
Gr. *ixia*, bird-lime; from the sticky sap of these South African plants.

ixioides [ix-i-OY-deez]
Ixia-like.

Ixiolirion [ix-i-o-LI-rion]
Ixia plus *lirion*, a lily; in allusion to the similarity to *Ixia*.

ixocarpus, -a, -um [ix-o-CARP-us]
With sticky or glutinous fruit.

Ixora [ix-o-ra]
Latinized name of the Malabar deity to whom the flame-of-the-forest tree (*I. coccinea*) is sacred.

J

Jacaranda [jak-a-RAND-a]
The Latinized Brazilian name for these flowering trees and shrubs.

jackmanii [JAK-man-i-eye]
Species name of *Clematis*. Named after G. Jackman of Woking, Surrey, c. 1865.

jacobaeus, -a, -um [jak-o-BEE-us]
Specific name applied to various plants, possibly in honor of St. James (Jacobus).

jackii [JAK-i-eye]
Specific name honoring John George Jack (1861-1949), Canadian dendrologist at the Arnold Arboretum, Boston, Massachusetts.

Jacobinia [jak-o-BIN-ia]
Tubular-flowered plants named for the town of Jacobina near Bahia, Brazil.

Jacquemontia [jak-MONT-ia]
Herbs or sub-shrubs with flowers like *Convolvulus* named for Victor Jacquemont (1801-1832), French naturalist and traveler in the East Indies.

jalapa [JAL-ap-a]
Latin form of Xalapa, a town in Mexico. Specific name for
four-o'clock (*Mirabilis jalapa*) from which the drug jalap
was once supposed to be derived. (It comes, in fact, from
Exogonium jalapa.)

jamaicensis, -is, -e [jam-ay-KEN-sis]
From Jamaica.

Jamesia [JAYMS-ia]
A white-flowering shrub named in honor of Dr. Edwin James
(1797-1861), American botanical explorer of the Rocky
Mountain area.

japonicus, -a, -um [jap-ON-ik-us]
Japanese. Japonica is a common name for both Camellia and
Japanese quince.

Jasione [jass-ee-o-nee]
Sheep's-bit scabious. Greek name for another plant.

jasmineus, -a, -um [jas-MIN-eus]
jasminioides [jas-min-i-OY-deez]
Resembling jasmine. Also jasminiflorus—jasmine flowered.

Jasminum [JAS-min-um]
Jasmine (sometimes called jessamine). The Latin version of
the Persian name for these sweet-scented shrubs and climbers.

Jatropha [JAT-ro-fa]
Gr. *iatros*, a physician; *trophe*, food. Some species of these
herbs, shrubs, or trees have medicinal value.

javanicus, -a, -um [ja-VAN-ik-us]
From Java.

Jeffersonia [jeff-er-so-nia]
Twin leaf. Attractive small herbs named in honor of Thomas
Jefferson (1743-1826), President of the United States, 1801-
1809. A truly great man of many parts, he was an outstanding plantsman and patron of botany with deep interest in
horticulture and farming.

Jovellana [jo-vell-AY-na]
Herbs or sub-shrubs named for Caspari Melchior de Jovel-
lanos, mid-19th-century student of the flora of Peru.

Juania [Joo-AY-nia]
A palm. From Juan Fernandez, a rocky archipelago some
400 miles west of Valparaiso, Chile.

Jubaea [joo-BEE-a]
A palm named for King Juba of Numidia, who committed suicide in 46 B.C. when his ancient kingdom in North Africa was absorbed as a province by the Romans.

jubatus, -a, -um [joo-BAY-tus]
With awns; crested.

jucundus, -a, -um [joo-KUN-dus]
Agreeable; pleasing.

jugalis, -is, -e [joo-GAY-lis]
jugosus, -a, -um [joo-GO-sus]
Yoked.

Juglans [JOO-glans]
Walnut. The Latin name. From *jovis,* of Jupiter; *glans,* an acorn.

junceus, -a, -um [JUN-see-us]
Rushlike.

Juncus [JUN-kus]
Rush. The classical Latin name for the bulrush.

juniperifolius, -a, -um [joo-nip-er-i-FO-lius]
Juniper-leaved.

juniperinus, -a, -um [joo-nip-er-EYE-nus]
Juniper-like; bluish-brown like juniper berries.

Juniperus [joo-NIP-er-us]
Latin name for the juniper. Apart from ornament, a principal use of juniper is as the source of the berries which flavor gin.

Jussiaea [jus-si-EE-a]
Primrose willow. Tropical herbs or shrubs or small trees named for Bernard de Jussieu (1699-1777), French botanist, who laid the foundation for the natural system of plant classification.

Justicia [jus-TISS-ia]
Showy herbs named for James Justice, celebrated 18th-century Scottish horticulturist.

K

Kadsura [kad-soo-ra]
The Japanese name for this evergreen twining shrub.

Kaempferia [kamp-FER-ia]
Tuberous of fleshy-rooted plants named for Engelbert

Kaempfer (1651-1716), German physician, who traveled widely throughout the East, lived for two years in Japan, and wrote a book about Japanese plants.

kaempferi [KAMP-fer-eye]
Varietal name of the Azalea, *Rhododendron obtusum* (see *Kaempferia*).

Kalanchoë [kal-an-KO-ee]
From the Chinese name of one species of these succulent herbs or sub-shrubs.

Kalmia [KAL-mia]
Laurel—mountain, sheep, swamp, etc. Calico bush. Named in honor of Pehr Kalm (1715-1779), Finnish pupil of Linnaeus who was sent by the Swedish government in 1748 to report on the natural resources of North America. His descriptions of the domestic economy and natural history are both interesting and trustworthy.

kalmiaeflorus, -a, -um [kal-mi-ee-FLO-rus]
With flowers like *Kalmia*.

kamtschaticus, -a, -um [kam-CHAT-ik-us]
From Kamchatka.

kashmirianus, -a, -um [kash-meer-i-AY-nus]
Of Kashmir.

Kelseyia [KEL-si-a]
A small blooming sub-shrub with densely imbricated leaves named for Harlan P. Kelsey (1872-1958), nurseryman of Boxford, Massachusetts.

Kennedia [ken-ED-ia]
Trailing or climbing perennials named for L. Kennedy (1775-1818), an original partner of Lee and Kennedy, nurserymen of Hammersmith, London.

Kernera [ker-NEE-ra]
Perennial herbs named for Johann Simon von Kerner (1755-1830), Professor of Botany at Stuttgart.

Kerria [KUR-ria]
A showy flowering shrub named for William Kerr (d. 1814) of Kew, who collected in China.

Keteleeria [ket-el-EE-ria]
Chinese evergreen trees named in honor of J. B. Keteeler (b. 1813), horticulturist of Brussels.

kewensis, -is, -e [kew-EN-sis]
Of Kew Gardens.

Kickxia [KIX-ia]
Annual creeping herbs named for Jean Kickx (1775-1831), apothecary of Brussels and writer on cryptogamic (flowerless) plants.

Kigelia [ky-GEE-lia]
Sausage-tree. The Latin version of the African vernacular name.

Kirengeshoma [ky-reng-esh-o-ma]
A tall Japanese perennial with the Japanese name for another plant, yellow *Anemopsis*.

kirkii [KIR-ki-eye]
Specific name in honor of Sir John Kirk (1832-1922), for many years British Consul at Zanzibar, ardent botanist and father of Colonel J. W. C. Kirk, author of *A British Garden Flora*—required reading for botanically minded gardeners.

Knightia [NY-tia]
Trees and shrubs named for Thomas A. Knight (1759-1838), a president of the Royal Horticultural Society and a well-known pomologist.

Kniphofia [ny-FO-fia]
Red-hot poker. Named for Johann Hieronymus Kniphof (1704-1763), Professor of Medicine at Erfurt and author of a folio of colored illustrations of plants (1747).

Kochia [KO-kia, also KO-shia]
Summer cypress. A large genus of herbs and sub-shrubs which includes Belvedere, an annual grown for its autumn foliage; named for Wilhelm Daniel Josef Koch (1771-1849), Professor of Botany, Erlangen.

Koelreuteria [kol-roo-TEE-ria]
Deciduous flowering trees named for Josef G. Koelreuter (1773-1806), Professor of Natural History at Karlsruhe.

Kolkwitzia [kolk-WITZ-ia]
Beauty bush. A deciduous flowering shrub named for R. Kolkwitz, Professor of Botany, Berlin c. 1900.

koreanus, -a, -um (also **korianus**) [ko-ree-AY-nus]
koriaensis, -is, -e [ko-ree-ee-EN-sis]
Of Korea.

kousa [KOW-sa]
Japanese name for *Cornus kousa*.

Korthalsia [kor-TAL-sia]
Climbing palms named for Peter Wilhelm Korthals (1807-1892), Dutch botanist.

Kosteletzkya [kos-tel-ETS-kia]
Perennial herbs or shrubs related to *Hibiscus,* named in honor of Vincenz Franz Kosteletzky of Prague, writer on medical botany, 1830-1840.

Krameria [kram-EE-ria]
Woody plants and perennial herbs named for the Kramers, father and son, Austrian botanists in the first half of the 19th century.

Krigia [KRIG-ia]
Dwarf dandelion. Named for David Krieg, German physician who collected in Maryland.

Kuhnia [KOO-nia]
Small perennial herbs named for Adam Kuhn, American botanist, c. 1820.

Kunzea [KUN-zia]
Evergreen shrubs or small trees named for Gustav Kunze (1793-1851), Professor of Botany at Leipzig.

L

labiatus, -a, -um [lab-i-AY-tus]
labiosus, -a, -um [lab-i-o-sus]
Lipped.

labilis, -is, -e [LAB-ill-is]
Slippery; unstable.

laburnifolius, -a, -um [lab-urn-i-FO-lius]
Laburnum-leaved.

Laburnum [lab-URN-um]
Latin name for these shrubs, all parts of which are poisonous.

lacerus, -a, -um [LAS-er-us]
laciniatus, -a, -um [las-in-i-AY-tus]
Torn or cut into fringelike segments.

Lachenalia [lak-en-AY-lia]
Cape cowslip. Named for Werner de la Chenal (1736-1800), Professor of Botany at Basel.

Lachnanthes [lak-NAN-thees]

Gr. *lachne,* down; *anthos,* a flower; an allusion to the woolly flowers of this eastern United States aquatic perennial.

lacryma-jobi [lak-rim-a-JO-by]

Job's tears. Specific name under the genus *Coix.* The edible seeds form a dirty white beadlike structure. ("My face is foul with weeping, and on my eyelids is the shadow of death." Job 16:16.)

lacrimans [LAK-rim-ans]

Weeping.

lactatus, -a, -um [lak-TAY-tus]

Milky. Thus:

lacteus	milk-white
lactescens	containing milky sap
lacticolor	milk-white
lactiferus	producing milky sap
lactiflorus	milk-white flowers

Lactuca [lak-TEW-ka]

Lettuce. L. *lac,* milk; from the milky sap.

lacunosus, -a, -um [lak-yew-NO-sus]

With deep holes or pits.

lacustris, -is, -e [lak-US-tris]

Pertaining to lakes.

ladaniferus, -a, -um [lad-an-IFF-er-us]

ladanifer [lad-an-IFF-er]

Bearing ladanum (occasionally labdanum), a fragrant resinous juice used in medicine. This is the myrrh of the Bible.

Laelia [LEE-lia]

A genus of epiphytic orchids named after one of the Vestal virgins.

Laeliocattleya [lee-li-o-KAT-lia]

Laelia plus *Cattleya* for these hybrid orchids.

laetus, -a, -um [LEE-tus]

Bright; vivid. Also: *laetiflorus,* bright flowered; *laetevirens,* vivid green.

laevigatus, -a, -um [lee-vig-AY-tus]

laevis, -is, -e [LEE-vis]

Smooth.

laevicaulis, -is, -e [lee-vik-AW-lis]

Smooth-stemmed.

Lagenaria [laj-en-AY-ria]
Bottle-gourd. Gr. *lagenos,* a bottle.
Lagerstroemia [lay-ger-STREEM-ia]
Showy flowering trees and shrubs named for Magnus von
Lagerström (1691-1759) of Göteborg by his friend Lin-
naeus.
lagodechianus, -a, -um [lay-go-dech-i-AY-nus]
From Lake Lagodechi in the Caucasus.
Lagunaria [lag-yew-NAY-ria]
A handsome flowering tree named for Andrea de Laguna
(1494-1560), Spanish botanist.
Lagurus [lag-YEW-rus]
Hare's-tail grass. From Gr. *lagos,* a hare; *oura,* a tail.
Lallemantia [lal-em-ANT-ia]
After J. E. Lallemant, an official of the Botanic Garden,
Leningrad.
Lamarckia [lam-ARK-ia]
Ornamental annual grass. Named for the Chevalier de la
Marck (1744-1829), distinguished French naturalist whose
work on evolution was an important forerunner to Darwin's.
Lambertia [lam-BER-shia]
Australian shrubs named for Aylmer Bourke Lambert (1761-
1842), English author of *The Genus Pinus* (1804).
Lamium [LAY-mium]
Dead-nettle. The Greek name.
lanatus, -a, -um [lan-AY-tus]
Woolly.
lanceolatus, -a, -um [lan-see-o-LAY-tus]
lanceus, -a, -um [LAN-see-us]
Spear-shaped. Thus: *lancifolius,* lance-leaved.
lanigerus, -a, um [lan-IJ-er-us]
lanosus, -a, -um [lan-O-sus]
lanuginosus, -a, -um [lan-u-gin-O-sus]
Woolly.
Lantana [lan-TAY-na]
Latin name for *Viburnum.* Mostly Western Hemisphere
shrubs. Since introduction into India and elsewhere as or-
namentals they have established themselves as difficult
weeds in tea gardens and other cultivated areas.
Lapageria [lap-aj-ER-ria]
An evergreen twining shrub with bell-shaped flowers named

after La Pagerie, the family estate on which the Empress Josephine lived as a girl in Martinique.

Lapeyrousia [la-pay-ROO-sia]
Bulbous flowering plants named after Jean François de Galoup, Comte de la Pérouse (1741-1788), French admiral and explorer. Following active service in the Seven Years and American Revolutionary wars, he sailed in 1785 with two ships to continue Cook's exploration of the Pacific. As was normal he carried with him a full complement of scientists. He disappeared in 1788, the wrecks of his ships being found in 1826 off the Santa Cruz Islands.

lappa [LAP-pa]
A bur.

lapponicum [lap-ON-ik-um]
lapponum [lap-o-num]
Of Lapland.

Lardizabala [lar-diz-a-BAY-la]
Evergreen flowering climbers named for M. Lardizabalay, Spanish naturalist c. 1830.

laricinus, -a, -um [la-riss-SY-nus]
Resembling larch. Also *laricifolius*, larch-leaved.

Larix [LAY-rix]
Larch. The classical name for the tree highly valued for centuries for its tough, strong wood, particularly useful in underwater work.

Larrea [LA-rea]
Creosote bush. Evergreen shrubs named for Juan Antonio de Larrea, Spanish patron of science, c. 1810.

Laserpitium [la-ser-PIT-ium]
The classical Latin name for these perennial herbs.

lasi-
In compound words signifying woolly. Thus:

lasiandrus	woolly-stamened
lasicanthus	woolly-spined
lasicarpus	woolly-fruited
lasiflorus	woolly-flowered
lasiodontus	woolly-toothed
lasioglossus	having a rough or hairy tongue
lasipetalus	woolly-petaled

Lasthenia [las-THEE-nia]

Yellow-flowered glabrous herbs from California, given the name of the girl who attended Plato's classes dressed as a boy. Remarkable as an aberration in ancient Greece, transvestitism causes no remark in female higher education today.

Latania [la-TAN-ia]

From the Mauritius vernacular name for these palms.

latabrosus, -a, -um [la-ta-BRO-sus]

Pertaining to dark or shady places.

lateralis, -is, -e [lat-er-AY-lis]

On the side. In compound words *lateri-*, as in *lateripes*, (with stalk on the side).

lateritius, -a, -um [lat-er-EYE-shus]

Brick-red.

Lathyrus [LATH-i-rus]

Sweet pea. Beach pea. Everlasting pea. The Greek name for pea or pulse. Sweet pea is *L. odoratus*. The edible garden pea comes under *Pisum* (*P. sativum*).

latus [LAT-us]

Broad; wide. In compound words *lati-*, thus:

latiflorus	broad-flowered
latifolius	broad-leaved
latifrons	with broad fronds
latilabrus	wide-lipped
latilobus	wide-lobed
latimaculatus	with broad spots
latipes	with a broad stalk
latispinus	with wide thorns
latisquamus	with wide scales

laudatus, -a, -um [law-DAY-tus]

Praiseworthy.

Laurelia [law-REE-lia]

Bay-tree. *L. laurus;* from a similarity in the fragrance of the leaves.

laurifolius, -a, -um [law-ri-FO-lius]

Bay-leaved.

laurinus [law-RY-nus]

Resembling *Laurus*, true laurel, or bay-tree.

Laurocerasus [law-ro-SER-ay-sus]

Cherry-laurel. From L. *laurus*, laurel; *cerasus*, a cherry.

Laurus [LAW-rus]
Latin name for the laurel or bay. The laurel crown was of bay leaves. The sweet bay provides the leaves so essential in good cookery.

Lavandula [lav-AN-dew-la]
Lavender. From L. *lavo*, to wash; from its use in soaps and toiletries of various kinds.

lavandulaceus, -a, -um [lav-an-dew-LAY-shus]
lavandulifolius, -a, -um [lav-an-dew-li-FO-lius]
Lavender-like or with lavender-like leaves.

Lavatera [lav-at-TEE-ra]
Tree-mallow. Named for two 18th-century brothers Lavater, both physician naturalists of Zurich.

lavateroides [lav-at-er-OY-deez]
Resembling *Lavatera*.

Lawsonia [law-SO-nia]
Henna. Named by Linnaeus to honor his friend Dr. Isaac Lawson, who wrote *Travels in North Carolina* (1709). He appears to have been the brother of John Lawson, surveyor-general and author of *A History of North Carolina*. The latter was taken by Indians in 1714 and tortured to death by having fat pine splinters stuck in his skin and being set on fire.

laxus, -a, -um [LAX-us]
Loose or open. Thus, *laxiflorus, laxifolius*, loose-flowered and loose-leaved.

Layia [LAY-ia]
Annual herbs with yellow or white flowers, named for George Tradescant Lay, naturalist on the voyage of exploration made in 1825 by Frederick William Beechey (British) to the Pacific Northwest and the Bering Straits.

ledifolius, -a, -um [led-i-FO-lius]
With leaves resembling *Ledum*.

Ledum [LEE-dum]
Labrador tea, wild rosemary, etc. From Gr. *ledon*, Cistus.

Leea [LEE-a]
Tropical small trees or shrubs named for James Lee (1715-1795), nurseryman of Hammersmith, London.

leianthus, -a, -um [ly-ANTH-us]
Smooth-flowered. Also:

leiocarpus   smooth-fruited
leiogynus   with a smooth pistil
leiophyllus   with smooth leaves

leichtlinii [lykt-LIN-i-eye]
For Max Leichtlin (1831-1910) of Baden, who introduced many plants.

Leiophyllum [ly-o-FILL-um]
Sand-myrtle. From Gr. *leios*, smooth; *phyllon*, a leaf; from the glossy foliage.

Lemaireocereus [lem-air-o-SEE-reus]
Named for Charles Lemaire (1801-1871), French specialist in cacti.

Lemna [LEM-na]
Duckweed. The Greek name for some water weed.

Lemoinei [lem-OY-ni-eye]
For Victor Lemoine (b. 1823), nurseryman of Nancy, France, who introduced many new lilacs.

Lens [lens]
Lentil. The classical name for this ancient pulse, the original habitat for which is not known. Esau sold Jacob his birthright for a red-lentil pottage.

lenticularis, -is, -e [len-tik-yew-LAY-ris]
lentiformis, -is, -e [len-ti-FORM-is]
Shaped like a lens.

lentiginosus, -a, -um [len-tig-in-o-sus]
Freckled.

lentus, -a, -um [LEN-tus]
Tough but pliant.

leonis [lee-o-nis]
Colored or toothed like a lion.

leontoglossus, -a, -um [lee-ont-o-GLOSS-us]
With a throat or tongue like a lion.

Leonotis [lee-on-o-tis]
Gr. *leon*, a lion; *ous*, an ear. The corolla of these annual and perennial herbs might be imagined to look like a lion's ear.

Leontopodium [lee-ont-o-PO-dium]
Edelweiss. The classical name meaning lion's foot, from some fancied resemblance in the flower heads.

leonurus, -a, -um [lee-on-YEW-rus]
Like a lion's tail.

Leonurus [lee-on-YEW-rus]
Motherwort or lion's-tail. From Gr. *leon,* a lion; *ouros,* a tail.

leopardinus, -a, -um [lee-o-pard-EYE-nus]
Conspicuously spotted like a leopard.

Lepachys [LEP-ak-is]
Cone-flower. From Gr. *lepis,* scale; *pachys,* thick; from the thickened tips of the chaff.

Lepidium [lep-ID-ium]
Garden cress, pepper-grass. The classical name.

lepidus, -a, -um [LEP-id-us]
Graceful; elegant.

leporellus [lep-or-EL-us]
A little hare.

lept-
In compound words, signifies thin or slender. Thus:

leptanthus	slender-flowered
leptocaulis	thin-stemmed
leptocladus	thin-branched
leptolepis	thin-scaled
leptopetalus	thin-petaled
leptophyllus	thin-leaved
leptosepalus	thin-sepaled
leptopus	thin-stalked
leptostachys	slender-spiked

Leptodermis [lept-o-DER-mis]
Gr. *leptos,* thin; *derma,* skin; from the thin inner wall of the fruits of these deciduous shrubs.

Leptopteris [lep-TOP-ter-is]
Gr. *leptos,* slender; *pteris,* a fern.

Leptopyrum [lept-o-PY-rum]
Gr. *leptos,* slender; *pyrus,* wheat; from the form of the fruits of these perennial herbs.

Leptospermum [lept-o-SPERM-um]
Gr. *leptos,* thin; *sperma,* seed. From the nature of the seed of these evergreen shrubs.

lepturus, -a, -um [lep-TEW-rus]
lepturoides [lep-tew-ROY-deez]
Like a hare's tail.

Leschenaultia [lesh-en-AWL-tia]
Ornamental heathlike Australian plants named for L. T.

Leschenault de la Tour (1773-1826), French botanist and traveler.

Lespedeza [les-ped-EE-za]
Bush clover. Named by the French botanist Michaux who collected widely in North America to honor the Spanish governor of Florida, Lespedez, c. 1790.

Lesquerella [les-kwer-ELL-a]
A genus of hairy herbs named in honor of Leo Lesquereux, foremost authority on American fossil botany in the latter part of the 19th century.

Lettsomia [let-so-mia]
Climbing, somewhat hairy shrubs named for John Coakley Lettsom (1744-1815), London physician and botanist as well as an original member of the Royal Horticultural Society. He became ardently involved in the dispute surrounding Forsyth's plaister (see *Forsythia*). He took refuge in being a Quaker to avoid backing his views with a substantial sum of money and thereby earned a certain amount of ridicule.

Leucadendron [lew-kad-END-ron]
Silver tree. From Gr. *leukos,* white; *dendron,* a tree. An allusion to the foliage.

leucanthemifolius [lew-kan-them-i-FO-lius]
With leaves like *Leucanthemum,* a group often placed in the genus *Chrysanthemum,* the best known being *C. leucanthemum,* the ox-eyed daisy.

leuc-
In compound words signifies white. Thus:

leucanthus	white-flowered
leucocaulis	white-stemmed
leucocephalus	white-headed
leucochilus	white-lipped
leucodermis	white-skinned
leuconeurus	white-nerved
leucophaeus	dusky-white
leucophyllus	white-leaved
leucorhizus	white-rooted
leucostachys	white-spiked
leucotriche	white-haired
leucoxanthus	whitish-yellow
leucoxylon	white-wooded

Leucaena [lew-SEE-na]
Gr. *leukos*, white; in allusion to the flowers of these *Acacia*-like trees and shrubs.

Leuceria (incorrectly, **Leucheria**) [lew-SEE-ria]
Gr. *leucheres*, white. Some species of these South American herbs are white and woolly.

Leucocrinum [lew-ko-KRIN-um]
Sand lily. Gr. *leukos*, white; *crinum*, a lily. A small early-blooming bulbous plant.

Leucojum [lew-KO-jum]
Snowflake. St. Agnes' flower. The Greek name for spring-snowflake (*L. vernum*).

Leucothoë [lew-KO-tho-ee]
Ornamental shrubs named in honor of Leucothoë, one of the many loves of Apollo.

Leuzia [LEW-zia]
Herbaceous perennials named for a friend of de Candolle, Joseph Philippe François Deluze (1753-1835) of Avignon and Paris.

Levisticum [lev-ISS-tik-um]
Lovage. Said to be a corruption of *Ligusticum*.

Lewisia [lew-ISS-ia]
Bitterwort. Small showy herbaceous perennials from the Rocky Mountains. In honor of Captain Meriwether Lewis (1774-1809), senior leader of the Lewis and Clark expedition, the first coast-to-coast crossing.

Leycesteria [ly-sess-TEE-ria]
Deciduous shrubs with whorled flowers. Named for William Leycester, Chief Justice of Bengal c. 1820.

Liatris [ly-AY-tris]
Unknown derivation. This genus of North American perennial herbs includes plants under many English names: prairie-button, snakeroot, Kansas gay-feather, blue blazing star, etc.

libani [lib-AY-ny]
libanoticus, -a, -um [lib-an-o-tik-us]
Of Mount Lebanon.

libericus, -a, -um [ly-BEER-ik-us]
From Liberia.

Libertia [lib-BER-shia]
Perennial herbs in the iris family, named for Marie A.

Libert (1782-1863), Belgian botanist who wrote on liver-worts.

Libocedrus [lib-o-SEE-drus]
Incense cedar. From Greek *libanos*, incense; *cedrus*, cedar. In allusion to the fragrant wood.

liburnicus, -a, -um [ly-BERN-ik-us]
From Croatia (Liburnia) on the shores of the Adriatic.

Licuala [liss-yew-AY-la]
From the native Moluccan name for these palms.

lignosus, -a, -um [lig-NO-sus]
Woody.

Ligularia [lig-yew-LAY-ria]
L. *ligula*, a strap; from the strap shape of the ray florets of these handsome herbaceous perennials of the daisy family.

ligularis, -is, -e [lig-yew-LAY-ris]
ligulatus, -a, -um [lig-yew-LAY-tus]
Straplike.

Ligusticum [ly-GUS-tik-um]
Lovage. Named for Liguria, the Italian province in which is the city of Genoa, where the plant abounds.

ligusticus, -a, -um [ly-GUS-tik-us]
Of Liguria (see *Ligusticum*).

ligusticifolius, -a, -um [ly-gus-tik-i-FO-lius]
Lovage-leaved.

ligustrifolius, -a, -um [ly-gus-tri-FO-lius]
Privet-leaved.

ligustrinus, -a, -um [ly-gus-TRY-nus]
Privetlike.

Ligustrum [ly-GUS-trum]
Latin for privet.

lilacinus, -a, -um [ly-las-SY-nus]
Lilac—either color or form.

lili-
In compound words signifying lily. Thus:

liliaceus	lilylike
liliflorus	lily-flowered
lilifolius	lily-leaved

Lilium [LIL-ium]
Lily. The Latin name akin to Gr. *leirion*, the madonna-lily.

limbatus, -a, -um [lim-BAY-tus]
Bordered.

limeanus, -a, -um [ly-mee-AY-nus]
limensis, -is, -e [ly-MEN-sis]
From Lima, Peru.

Limnanthes [lim-NAN-thees]
Meadow foam. Gr. *limne,* a marsh; *anthos,* a flower. From the habitat of these American annuals.

Limnocharis [lim-NOK-a-ris]
Gr. *limne,* a marsh; *charis,* beauty. From the habitat and beauty of the flowers of these aquatic perennials.

limnophilus, -a, -um [lim-no-FILL-us]
Swamp-loving.

limonifolius [lim-o-ni-FO-lius]
Lemon-leaved.

Limonium [ly-MO-nium]
Sea-lavender, sea-pink. From Gr. *leimon,* a meadow; in allusion to the common habitat in salt meadows.

limosus, -a, -um [lim-o-sus]
Of marshy or muddy places.

Linanthus [ly-NAN-thus]
Gr. *linum,* flax; *anthos,* a flower. Now often classified under *Gilia.*

Linaria [lin-AY-ria]
Toadflax. Butter-and-eggs. From Gr. *linum,* flax; from the flaxlike leaves.

linariifolius, -a, -um [ly-nay-ri-i-FO-lius]
Linaria-leaved.

Lindelofia [lin-del-o-fia]
Herbaceous perennials named for Friedrich von Lindelof, patron of botany of Darmstadt c. 1840.

Lindera [LIN-der-a]
Feverbush. Benjamin bush. Benzoin. Deciduous and evergreen shrubs and trees with aromatic bark named after Johann Linder, a Swedish botanist and physician (1676-1723).

linearis, -is, -e [lin-e-AY-ris]
Narrow, with sides nearly parallel.

lineatus, -a, -um [lin-ee-AY-tus]
With lines or stripes.

lingua [LING-wa]
A tongue or tonguelike.
lingueformis, -is, -e [lingue-FOR-mis]
Tongue-shaped.
lingulatus, -a, -um [ling-u-LAY-tus]
Tongue-shaped.
liniflorus, -a, -um [lin-i-FLO-rus]
Flax-flowered.
linifolius, -a, -um [lin-i-FO-lius]
Flax-leaved.
Linnaea [lin-EE-a]
Twin-flower. Named by Carl von Linné, universally known
as Linnaeus (1707-1778), and described by him as "a
plant of Lappland, lowly, insignificant, disregarded, flowering but for a brief space—from Linnaeus who resembles it."
Born in Sweden, Linnaeus was trained as a physician but
soon concentrated on botany. His *Genera Plantarum* must be
regarded as the starting point of modern systematic botany
by which chaos was reduced to order.
Later, he applied the same systematic approach to the
animal and mineral worlds. He was a teacher without peer.
His pupils, such as Pehr Kalm (see *Kalmia*), became botanic
leaders in their own right. He was a prodigious writer and
his published works total more than 180 titles. His garden
at Uppsala still attracts pilgrims from all over the world.
It was inevitable that his system based on genital structure
should become modified over the intervening two hundred
years, but this does not in any way detract from his essential
genius.
His "herborising lectures" while he walked through lanes
and fields at the head of two or three hundred students were
social events of the Swedish summer. Attended by a band
of trumpets and French horns, his pupils were divided into
detached companies to be called together by music when
he wished to discourse on any particular subject.
His weakness, if it can be called that, was a curious obsession with certain aspects of sex. "The genitalia of plants,"
he said, "we regard with delight; of animals with abomina-
tion, and of ourselves with strange thoughts." He made a
close study of what he called "floral nuptials" and collected

records of men who had deceived their wives and had, in turn, been deceived by them. The petals of flowers he regarded as "bridal beds which the Creator has so gloriously arranged, adorned with such noble bed-curtains and perfumed with so many sweet scents that the bride-groom may celebrate his nuptials with his bride with all the greater solemnity." The great Linnaean collections are now at Burlington House in London, having been purchased by Sir James Smith for one thousand guineas in 1784. Their sale to an Englishman very nearly caused an international incident, although it is not true that the Swedish government sent a warship after the brig *Appearance* to retrieve them.

The epitaph on Linnaeus' tomb in the cathedral at Uppsala describes him simply as "Princeps Botanicorum," which is possibly as close to the truth as need be.

linneanus, -a, -um [lin-ee-AY-nus]
In honor of Linnaeus.

Linum [LY-num]
Flax. The Latin name. Until cotton came into supply in the 18th century, flax was by far the most important vegetable fiber, at least as far as Western man was concerned. Indeed, for Western prehistoric man it was the only fiber and, as far as can be determined, the principles of manufacture have remained unchanged. Flax is also the source of linseed.

Liparis [LIP-a-ris]
Twayblade. From Gr. *liparos*, oily or smooth; in allusion to the character of the leaves.

Lippia [LIP-pia]
Lemon verbena. Named for Augustus Lippi (1678-1701), Italian naturalist and botanist. He was killed in Abyssinia.

Liquidambar [lik-wid-AMB-ar]
Sweetgum. From L. *liquidus*, liquid; *ambar*, amber. A fragrant resin called liquid storax is prepared from the inner bark of one species (*L. orientalis*).

Liriodendron [li-ri-o-DEND-ron]
Tulip tree. From Gr. *leirion*, a lily; *dendron*, a tree.

Liriope [li-ri-o-pe]
A perennial herb named in honor of a Greek woodland nymph of that name.

228

Listeria [lis-TEE-ra]
Small terrestrial orchids named for Martin Lister (1638-1712), British botanist. This is called twayblade in Britain.

Litchi [LY-chee]
From the Chinese name for the handsome tree producing the well-known fruits which are popularly called nuts and spelled in any one of a half-dozen different ways.

Lithocarpus [lith-o-KARP-us]
Tanbark or chestnut-oak. From Gr. *lithos, a* stone; *karpos,* fruit. In allusion to the hard acorns.

Lithophragma [lith-o-FRAG-ma]
Californian perennial herbs. From Gr. *lithos,* a stone; *phragma,* a fence; in allusion to the rocky habitat.

lithophilus, -a, -um [lith-OFF-il-us]
Rock-loving.

Lithops [lith-ops]
Pebble plants. From Gr. *lithos,* a stone; *ops,* like; from the resemblance of these South African succulents to small stones.

Lithospermum [lith-o-SPERM-um]
Gromwell. The classical name. The plant has been reported as having been used by North American Indians as an oral contraceptive, a fact which has been investigated by modern science.

lithospermus, -a, -um [lith-o-SPERM-us]
With very hard stonelike seeds.

Lithraea [lith-REE-a]
From the Chilean vernacular name for these evergreen shrubs or small trees.

Litsea [LIT-see-a]
The Japanese name for these trees and shrubs.

littoralis, -is, -e [lit-or-AY-lis]
littoreus, -a, -um [lit-OR-eus]
Of the seashore.

lividus, -a, -um [LIV-id-us]
Lead-colored; bluish-gray.

Livistona [live-ist-o-na]
A genus of tall palms, named by Robert Brown for Patrick Murray of Livistone near Edinburgh c. 1820.

Loasa [lo-AY-sa]
The native Chilean name for these plants with showy flowers and stinging foliage.

lobatus, -a, -um [lo-BAY-tus]
lobularis, -is, -e [lob-yew-LAY-ris]
Lobed. Also:

lobocarpus with lobed seeds
lobophyllus with lobed leaves
lobulatus with small lobes

Lobelia [lo-BEE-lia]
A large genus of herbs and sub-shrubs. Named for Mathias de l'Obel (1538-1616), Flemish botanist and physician to James I of England. Cardinal flower is *L. cardinalis*.
lobelioides [lo-bel-i-OY-deez]
Resembling *Lobelia*.
Lobivia [lo-BIV-ia]
Anagram of Bolivia where these cacti are found.
Lobularia [lob-yew-LAY-ria]
Sweet alyssum. From L. *lobulus*, the diminutive of *lobus*, a lobe. In allusion to the small lobelike fruit.
Lockhartia [lok-HART-ia]
Epiphytic orchids named for David Lockhart (d. 1846) of Trinidad.
Lodoicea [lo-DOY-see-a]
Double coconut. Coco-de-mer. Named for Louis XV of France (1710-1774). Louis is Loderwijk in Dutch.
Loeselia [lo-SEE-lia]
Central American herbs named for Johann Loesel (1607-1657), German botanical writer.
Logania [lo-GAY-nia]
New Zealand and Australian herbs and sub-shrubs named for James Logan (1674-1751), Governor of Pennsylvania and a botanical writer. Contemporary and friend of John Bartram, his principal work was devoted to Indian corn.
Loiseleuria [loy-sel-YEW-ria]
A trailing evergreen flowering shrub named for Loiseleur, whose full name was Jean Louis Auguste Loiseleur-Deslongchamps (1774-1849), one of the great company of botanist-physicians.
loliaceus, -a, -um [lo-li-AY-shus]
Like *Lolium*.
Lolium [LO-lium]
Rye-grass. The classical name for one species.

Lomatia [lo-MAY-shia]
Gr. *loma,* an edge; a reference to the winged edges of the seeds of these evergreen shrubs or trees.
Lonas [LO-nas]
African daisy. The derivation of the genus name is unknown.
Lonchocarpus [lon-ko-KARP-us]
Gr. *lonche,* a lance; *karpos,* fruit. An allusion to the shape of the pods of these trees or climbing shrubs.
longus, -a, -um [LONG-gus]
Long. In compound words signifying long. Thus:

longebracteatus	with long bracts
longepedunculatus	with a long peduncle
longicaulis	long-stalked
longicomus	long-haired
longicuspis	long-pointed
longiflorus	long-flowered
longifolius	long-leaved
longihamatus	with long hooks
longilabris	long-lipped
longilobus	with long lobes
longimucronatus	ending in a long sharp point
longipes	long-stalked
longipetalus	with long petals
longipinnatus	having leaflets arranged on each side of a long common stalk; long-pinnate
longiracemosus	with long racemes
longirostris	long-beaked
longiscapus	with a long scape
longisepalus	with long sepals
longispathus	with long spathes
longispinus	long-thorned
longistylus	with a long style
Also: longissimus	very long.

Lonicera [lon-ISS-er-a]
Honeysuckle. Named for Adam Lonicer (1528-1586), German botanist.
Lopezia [lo-PEE-zia]
Mexican herbs and sub-shrubs named for Tomas Lopez,

Spanish botanist, who wrote on the plants of South America
c. 1540.

lophanthus, -a, -um [lo-FAN-thus]
Having crested flowers.

Lophophora [lo-FO-for-a]
Gr. *lophis,* a crest; *phoreo,* to bear; from the tufts of hairs
borne on the equivalent of leaf axils of these cacti.

lorifolius [lo-ri-FO-lius]
With strap-shaped leaves.

Loropetalum [lo-ro-PET-al-um]
Gr. *loron,* a strap; *petalon,* petals. The petals are long and
narrow on these evergreen flowering shrubs.

lotifolius, -a, -um [lo-ti-FO-lius]
Lotus-leaved.

Lotus [LO-tus]
Lotos. The classical Greek name.

louisianus, -a, -um [loo-iss-i-AY-nus]
From Louisiana.

lucens [LOO-sens]
lucidus, -a, -um [LOO-sid-us]
Bright; shining; clear.

Luculia [loo-KEW-lia]
From the East Indian vernacular name for these evergreen
flowering shrubs.

ludovicianus, -a, -um [loo-do-vik-i-AY-nus]
Of Louisiana.

Luffa [LUF-fa, also LOO-fa]
Dish-cloth gourd. Vegetable sponge. From the Arabic name.
L. cylindrica produces the curious fruit, the dried fibrous
interior of which is sold in drugstores to be used as a bath
sponge.

Lunaria [loo-NAY-ria]
Honesty. Satin-flower. Moonwort. L. *luna,* the moon; from
the form of the seed vessel.

lunatus, -a, -um [lew-NAY-tus]
lunulatus, -a, -m [lew-new-LAY-tus]
Shaped like a crescent moon.

Lupinus [loo-PY-nus]
Lupin or lupine. The classical name. Supposed to be derived from *lupinus,* a wolf, because of the superstition that
these plants destroyed the fertility of the soil. Today they

are a favorite crop for plowing-in as green manure, since, like other leguminous plants, they are able to fix nitrogen and thus increase the fertility of soil. The seeds are eaten in eastern Mediterranean countries.

lupulinus, -a, -um [loo-pew-LY-nus]
Hoplike.

lupulus [LOO-pew-lus]
Specific name of hop (*Humulus lupulus*). Literally, lupulus means a small wolf, the vine once having been locally called willow-wolf from its persistent habit of climbing over willow trees.

luridus, -a, -um [LEW-rid-us]
Pale yellow; sallow; wan.

lusitanicus, -a, -um [lew-sit-AN-ik-us]
From Portugal (Lusitania).

luteolus, -a, -um [lew-tee-o-lus]
Yellowish.

lutetianus, -a, -um [lew-tee-she-AY-nus]
Of Paris.

luteus, -a, -um [LEW-teus]
Yellow. Also in compound words, *luteo-*.

luxurians [lux-UR-ians]
Luxuriant.

Lycaste [ly-KAS-te]
Derivation of the name for these orchids is unknown.

lychnidifolius, -a, -um [like-nid-i-FO-lius]
Lychnis-leaved.

Lychnis [LIK-nis]
Catchfly. Maltese cross. Evening campion. The classical name, said to be derived from Gr. *lychnos*, a lamp; in allusion to the flame-colored flowers.

Lycium [LIS-sium]
Matrimony vine or box-thorn. From the Greek name for another plant.

lycoctonum [ly-KOK-to-num]
Specific name for *Aconitum lycoctonum* or wolf's-bane, one of the more poisonous species of monkshood.

Lycopersicon [ly-ko-PER-sik-on]
Tomato. Gr. *lykos*, a wolf; *persicon*, a peach; probably in allusion to the inferior fruit.

lycopodioides [ly-ko-po-di-oy-deez]
Resembling *Lycopodium* or club-moss.

Lycopodium [ly-ko-po-dium]
Ground pine. Club-moss. From Gr. *lykos*, a wolf; *pous*, a foot; from some fancied resemblance to a wolf's foot.

Lycopus [LY-ko-pus]
Water hoarhound. Gr. *lykos*, wolf; *pous*, a foot; from some fancied resemblance of these herbaceous perennials to a wolf's foot.

Lycoris [LY-ko-ris]
Golden spider lily. Named in honor of a lovely Roman actress of that name, the mistress of Marc Antony.

lydius, -a, -um [LID-ius]
From Lydia in Asia Minor.

Lygodium [ly-GO-dium]
Climbing-fern. From Gr. *lygodes*, twining; in allusion to the climbing habit.

Lyonia [ly-o-nia]
Ornamental shrubs named for John Lyon, a Scottish gardener and botanist of great skill. He was associated with Frederick Pursh in developing William Hamilton's beautiful garden at Woodlands, Philadelphia. He achieved enthusiastic notice from Captain Mayne Reid and died on an exploring expedition in Tennessee betwen 1814 and 1818.

Lyonothamnus [ly-o-no-THAM-nus]
An ornamental woody plant named for W. S. Lyon, an American collector who sent plants to Asa Gray c. 1880. The second half of the name is from Gr. *thamnos*, a shrub.

Lysichitum [ly-sik-IT-um]
Gr. *lysis*, a loosening; *chiton*, a cloak. The spathe is cast off on this almost stemless swamp herb.

Lysimachia [ly-sim-AK-ia]
Loosestrife. So named by Dioscorides after King Lysimachus of Thracia.

lysimachioides [ly-sim-ak-i-oy-deez]
Lysimachia-like.

Lythrum [LY-thrum]
Gr. *lythron*, blood; from the color of the flowers on these herbs or sub-shrubs. Purple loosestrife, the willow-herb, is *Lythrum salicaria*.

234

M

Maackia [MAK-ia]
Flowering trees and shrubs named for Richard Maack (1825-1886), Russian naturalist.

Maba [MAY-ba]
Vernacular name in the Tonga Islands for these ebonylike trees and shrubs.

macedonicus, -a, -um [mas-sed-ON-ik-us]
From Macedonia.

Machaerocereus [mak-ee-ro-SEE-reus]
Gr. *machaira*, a dagger; *cereus*, cactus. A reference to the spines.

macilentis, -is, -e [mas-il-EN-tis]
Thin; lean.

Macleaya [mak-LAY-ya]
Handsome herbaceous perennials named for Alexander Macleay (1767-1848), Colonial Secretary for New South Wales and once Secretary of the Linnean Society (London). Plume poppy is *Macleaya cordata*, syn. *Bocconia cordata*.

Maclura [mak-LURE-a]
Osage orange. Named for W. Maclure (d. 1840), American geologist.

Macradenia [mak-rad-EE-nia]
Gr. *makros*, long; *aden*, a gland; an allusion to the length of the pollen bundles on these epiphytic orchids.

macro-
In compound words signifying either long or big. Thus:

macracanthus	with large spines
macradenus	with large glands
macrandrus	with long anthers
macranthus	with large flowers
macrobotrys	with large grapelike clusters
macrocarpus	large-fruited
macrocephalus	large-headed
macromeris	with many parts
macrophyllus	with long or large leaves
macropodus	stout-stalked
macrorrhiza	with large roots or root stocks
macrospermus	with large seeds
macrostachyus	with long or large spikes

Macrozamia [mak-ro-ZAY-mia]
Gr. *makros*, large; plus *Zamia*, a related genus. These Australian plants are highly poisonous to sheep.

maculatus, -a, -um [mak-yew-LAY-tus]
maculosus, -a, -um [mak-yew-LO-sus]
Spotted.

Maddenia [mad-EE-nia]
Trees and shrubs, natives of India and China, named for Colonel Edward Madden (d. 1856), who collected in India.

Madia [MAY-dia]
Tarweed. From the native Chilean name.

Maesa [MEE-sa]
From the Arabic name for these shrubs.

maesiacus, -a, -um [mee-SY-ak-us]
Of Moesia—the Balkans generally.

magellanicus, -a, -um [maj-el-AN-ik-us]
From the area of the Straits of Magellan.

magnificus, -a, -um [mag-NIF-ik-us]
Showy.

Magnolia [mag-NO-lia]
Sweet bay. Deciduous and evergreen flowering trees and shrubs named for Pierre Magnol (1638-1751), Director of the Botanic Garden, Montpellier, France.

magnus, -a, -um [MAG-nus]
Great; big.

Mahernia [ma-HERN-ia]
Honey-bell. Anagram of *Hermannia*, a genus related to these herbs and evergreen sub-shrubs.

Mahonia [ma-HO-nia]
Handsome evergreen flowering shrubs named for Bernard M'Mahon (1775-1816), American horticulturist and author of *The American Gardener's Calendar* (1807).

Maianthemum [my-ANTH-e-mum]
Wild lily-of-the-valley. From Gr. *maios*, May; *anthemon*, blossom.

majalis, -is, -e [ma-JAY-lis]
May-flowering.

majesticus, -a, -um [ma-JEST-ik-us]
Majestic.

major [MAY-jor]
majus, -a, -um [MAY-jus]
Bigger; larger.
Majorana [maj-or-AY-na]
Sweet marjoram. Derivation uncertain but, in any case, now often considered as *Origanum majorana*.
malabaricus, -a, -um [mal-a-BAR-ik-us]
From the Malabar coast of India.
Malachra [mal-AK-ra]
Greek name for a Persian tree, now applied to these hairy herbs.
Malacocarpus [mal-ak-o-KAR-pos]
Gr. *malakos*, soft; *karpos*, fruit. From the fleshy fruit of this South American cactus.
malacoides [mal-ak-OY-deez]
Soft; mucilaginous; like mallow.
malacospermus, -a, -um [mal-ak-o-SPERM-us]
With soft seeds.
Malcomia [mal-KO-mia]
Virginia-stock. Named for William Malcolm, London nurseryman, who published a catalogue of greenhouse plants in 1778 and for his son, also William (1769-1835).
maliformis, -is, -e [mal-i-FORM-is]
Apple-shaped.
Mallotus [mal-LO-tus]
Kamila tree. Gr. *mallotos*, woolly. The fruit in some species has white spines.
Malope [MAL-o-pe]
Greek for a kind of mallow to which family these annual herbs belong.
Malpighia [mal-PIG-ia]
Barbados-cherry, named for Marcello Malpighi (1628-1694), Italian anatomist and professor at Bologna.
Malus [MAY-lus]
Latin name for apple. For derivations of some named varieties of *Malus pumila*, the cultivated apple, see *Apple*.
Malva [MAL-va]
Mallow. The classical name for these ornamental herbs.
malvaceus, -a, -um [mal-VAY-shus]
Like mallow.

malvaeflorus, -a, -um [mal-vee-FLO-rus]
Mallow-flowered.

Malvastrum [mal-VAS-trum]
False mallow. L. *malva*, mallow; plus *aster*. From a similarity
to *Malva*.

Malvaviscus [mal-va-VISK-us]
L. *malva*, mallow; *viscus*, glue. Some species produce plen-
tiful mucilage.

malvinus, -a, -um [mal-VY-nus]
Mauve.

mammaeformis, -is, -e [mam-ee-FORM-is]
Nipplelike.

mammillatus, -a, -um [mam-il-LAY-tus]
  mammilaris, -is, -e [mam-il-LAY-ris]
  mammosus, -a, -um [mam-O-sus]
Furnished with nipples or breasts.

mammilosus, -a, -um [mam-il-O-sus]
With small nipples.

Mammea [MAM-ee-a]
Mammee-apple. From the West Indian name.

Mammilaria [mam-il-LAY-ria]
L. *mammilla*, a nipple; from the form of this cactus.

Mandevilla [man-dev-ILL-a]
Climbing milky-juiced shrubs named for H. J. Mandeville,
British Minister in Buenos Aires c. 1837.

Mandragora [man-DRAG-or-a]
Mandrake. The Greek name. Long known for its poisonous
and narcotic properties and used in classical times to deaden
pain in surgical operations, it has also been much esteemed
as an aphrodisiac and in love potions, presumably because
of the shape of the root. It was supposed that the plant
shrieked when touched ("And shrieks like mandrake torn out
of the earth that mortals, hearing them, run mad." *Romeo
and Juliet.*) In the East the plant was supposed to facilitate
pregnancy. The mandrake of North America is the May-
apple. (*Podophyllum peltatum*).

mandshuricus, -a, -um [mand-SHU-rik-us]
Of Manchuria.

manicatus, -a, -um [man-ik-AY-tus]
With long sleeves.

Manettia [man-ET-tia]
Ornamental twining plants named for Xavier Manetti, mid-18th-century Prefect of the Botanic Gardens in Florence.

Mangifera [man-JIFF-er-a]
Mango. The vernacular name plus L. *fero*, to bear. The Bombay Alfonso, at its best, is probably the most delectable of the many varieties.

Manihot [MAN-i-hot]
Cassava or tapioca. From the Brazilian name, *manioc*. The tuberous roots in their natural state are very poisonous and become edible only after steeping in water.

Manulea [man-ew-LEE-a]
L. *manus*, a hand; from the fingerlike divisions of the corolla on these South African herbs and sub-shrubs.

manzanilla [man-zan-ILL-a]
Specific name of *Arctostaphylos*. From the Spanish word meaning a small apple.

Maranta [mar-ANT-a]
Arrowroot. Named for Bartolommeo Maranti, Venetian botanist c. 1559.

Marattia [ma-RAT-tia]
Evergreen ferns named for J. F. Maratti (d. 1777), Italian botanist and writer.

margaritus, -a, -um [mar-gar-RY-tus]
margaritaceus, -a, -um [mar-gar-it-AY-shus]
Pertaining to pearls.

margaritiferus, -a, -um [mar-gar-it-IFF-er-us]
Pearl-bearing.

marginalis, -is, -e [mar-jin-AY-lis]
marginatus, -a, -um [mar-jin-AY-tus]
Margined; striped.

marginellus, -a, -um [mar-jin-EL-us]
With a narrow margin.

Margyricarpus [marj-ji-ri-KARP-us]
Gr. *margaron*, a pearl; *karpos*, fruit; from the white fruit of these South American sub-shrubs.

marianus, -a, -um [mair-ri-AY-nus]
Specific name of various plants with white-mottled leaves, notably Our Lady's or blessed thistle (*Silybum marianum*). The spots were supposed to have resulted from drops of Her milk falling on the leaves.

marilandicus, -a, -um (also **marylandicus**) [mair-i-LAND-ik-us]
Of Maryland.

maritimus, -a, -um [mair-IT-im-us]
Pertaining to the sea.

marmoratus, -a, -um [mar-more-AY-tus]
marmoreus, -a, -um [mar-MOR-eus]
Marbled; mottled.

maroccanus, -a, -um [ma-rok-AY-nus]
With marbled leaves.

maroccans, -a, -um [ma-rok-AY-nus]
Of Morocco.

Marrubium [ma-ROO-bium]
Hoarhound. The classical name for this familiar cough remedy.

Marsdenia [mars-DEE-nia]
Tropical twining shrubs named for William Marsden (1754-1836), Fellow of the Royal Society, traveler and author.

Marshallia [mar-SHAL-ia]
Perennial North American herbs named for Humphrey Marshall (1722-1801), a relative of John Bartram, who wrote *The American Grove*, the first American book on trees.

Marsilea [mar-SIL-ee-a]
Aquatic flowerless plants named for Giovanni Marsili (d. 1804), botanist of Bologna.

Martinezia [mar-tin-EE-zia]
Ornamental palms named for Archbishop Balthassar Martinez, Companon of Peru c. 1840.

mas [mas]
masculatus, -a, -um [mas-kew-LAY-tus]
masculus, -a, -um [MAS-kew-lus]
Male; masculine.

Mascarenhasia [mas-ka-reen-HAY-sia]
Small trees or shrubs named for the Mascarene Islands in the southwest Indian Ocean.

Masdevallia [mas-dev-AL-ia]
Tufted epiphytic orchids named for José Masdevall (d. 1801), Spanish botanist and physician.

Matthiola (also, incorrectly, **Mathiola**) [mat-i-o-la]
Stock. Named for Piersandrea Mattioli (1500-1577), Italian physician and botanist.

Matricaria [mat-ri-KAY-ria]

Mayweed. L. *mater*, mother; *caries*, decay; because of its one-time medical use in affections of the uterus.

matronalis, -is, -e [may-tron-AY-lis]

Pertaining to March 1st which was the Roman festival of the matrons.

Maurandia [mor-AND-ia]

Showy perennial herbs, some climbing. Named for Catherine Pancratia Maurandy, student of botany at Cartagena c. 1797.

mauritanicus, -a, -um [mor-it-AN-ik-us]

From North Africa, particularly Morocco.

Maxillaria [max-ill-AY-ria]

L. *maxilla*, the jaw. The flowers of these epiphytic orchids resemble the jaws of an insect.

maxillaris, -is, -e [max-ill-AY-ris]

Pertaining to the jaws.

maximus, -a, -um [MAX-im-us]

Largest.

Maytenus [may-TEE-nus]

From the Chilean name for these evergreen shrubs or trees.

Mazus [MAY-zus]

Gr. *mazos*, a teat; from the tubercles closing the mouth of the corolla of these low-growing herbs.

meadia [MEED-ia]

Specific name for shooting star (*Dodecatheon meadia*). Named for Richard Mead (1673-1754), English physician.

Meconopsis [mek-on-OP-sis]

Indian poppy. Blue poppy. Gr. *mekon*, a poppy; *opsis*, like.

Medeola [med-e-o-la]

Indian cucumber root. Named for the sorceress Medea because of its medicinal properties.

Medicago [med-ik-AY-go]

Alfalfa. Lucerne. The classical name for some grass.

medicus, -a, -um [MED-ik-us]

Medicinal.

Medinilla [med-in-IL-la]

Handsome tropical shrubs named for J. de Medinilla of Pineda, Governor of the Marianna Islands, c. 1820.

Mediocactus [mee-dio-KAK-tus]

L. *medius*, middle; plus *Cactus*. This genus is intermediate between two others.

mediopictus [mee-dio-PIK-tus]
Striped or colored down the middle.

mediterraneus, -a, -um [med-it-er-AY-nee-us]
Mediterranean.

medius, -a, -um [ME-dius]
Intermediate; middle.

medullaris, -is, -e [med-ul-LAY-ris]
medullus, -a, -um [med-UL-lus]
Pithy.

mega-
In compound words signifies big. Thus:

megacanthus	with big spines
megacarpus	big-fruited
megalanthus	big-flowered
megalophyllus	with big leaves
megapotamicus	of the big river (generally the Amazon)
megarrhizus	big-rooted
megaspermus	with big seeds
megastachyus	with a big spike
megastigmus	with a big stigma

meiacanthus, -a, -um [my-ak-ANTH-us]
Small-flowered.

Melaleuca [mel-a-LEW-ka]
Bottlebrush. From Gr. *melas*, black; *leukos*, white. Often the trees have a black trunk and white branches.

melancholicus, -a, -um [mel-an-KOL-lik-us]
Drooping; sad-looking.

Melanthium [mel-ANTH-ium]
Bunchflower. From Gr. *melas*, black; *anthos*, a flower. The flower segments are persistent and become dark after flowering.

Melasphaerula [mee-las-FEE-rew-la]
Gr. *melas*, black; *sphaerula*, a small ball. In allusion to the small black bulbs of this pretty South African plant.

Melastoma [mel-AS-tom-a]
Gr. *melas*, black; *stoma*, a mouth. Eating the berries of these tropical shrubs and trees stains the mouth black.

meleagris, -is, -e [mel-ee-AY-gris]
Spotted like the guinea fowl.

Melia [MEE-lia]
Bead-tree. Chinaberry. Greek name for the ash tree in allusion to the similarity of the leaves.

Melianthus [mel-i-ANTH-us]
Honeybush. From Gr. *meli*, honey; *anthos*, a flower. The flowers are very sweet with honey.

Melica [MEE-lik-a]
Melic grass. Greek name for a sweet grass.

Melicocca [mel-i-KOK-a]
Honeyberry. From Gr. *meli*, honey; *kokkos*, a berry. An allusion to the sweetness of the fruit.

Melicytus [mel-i-SY-tus]
Derivation of the name for these berry-bearing shrubs is obscure.

Melilotus [mel-il-LO-tus]
Sweet clover. From Gr. *meli*, honey; *lotus*, Lotus. The foliage is fragrant, bees enjoy the flowers, and the genus is similar to *Lotus*.

Meliosma [mel-i-OS-ma]
Gr. *meli*, honey; *osma*, fragrance. The flowers of these trees and shrubs are honey-scented.

Melissa [mel-ISS-a]
Balm. From Gr. *melissa*, a honeybee. The flowers of these herbaceous perennials are liked by them.

Melittis [mel-LIT-tis]
Bastard balm. From Gr. *melissa*, a honeybee. Bees enjoy the flowers.

melleus, -a, -um [MEL-leus]
Pertaining to honey.

mellitus, -a, -um [mel-LY-tus]
Honey-sweet. Also: *melliferus*, honey-bearing; *melliodorus*, honey-scented.

meloformis, -is, -e [mee-lo-FORM-is]
Melon-shaped.

Melothria [mel-o-thria]
The Greek name for another plant, probably *Bryonia*. These are climbing herbs of the cucumber family.

membranaceus, -a, -um [mem-bran-AY-shus]
Skinlike; membranous.

meniscifolius, -a, -um [men-iss-i-FO-lius]
With crescent-shaped leaves.

Menispermum [men-iss-PERM-um]
Moonseed. Gr. *mene,* the crescent moon; *sperma,* a seed; from the shape of the seed.

Mentha [MEN-tha]
Mint. The Latin name.

Mentzelia [ment-ZEE-lia]
Prairie lily, blazing star. A genus of showy-flowered plants named for Christian Mentzel (1622-1701), German botanist.

Menyanthes [men-YAN-thees]
Bogbean, buckbean. Of uncertain derivation.

Menziesia [men-ZEES-ia]
Low deciduous flowering shrubs named for Archibald Menzies (1754-1842), British naval surgeon and botanist who accompanied Vancouver on his voyage of Northwest Pacific exploration, 1790-1795. David Douglas almost literally followed in his footsteps.

menziesii [men-ZEE-si-eye]
Specific name of *Arbutus.* See *Menziesia.*

Meratia [mer-RAY-tia]
Ornamental shrubs with fragrant flowers named for François Victo Merat (1780-1851), French physician and botanist.

Mercurialis [mer-kyur-ri-AY-lis]
Herb-Mercury. Named in honor of the messenger of the gods. The source of a blue dye.

meridianus, -a, -um [mer-rid-i-AY-nus]
meridionalis, -is, -e [mer-rid-i-on-AY-lis]
Of noonday; blooming at noontime.

Mertensia [mer-TEN-sia]
Bluebell (in the United States), Virginia cowslip. Named for Francis Carl Mertens (1764-1831), Professor of Botany at Bremen.

Meryta [MER-it-a]
Derivation of the name for these glabrous small trees is uncertain.

Mesembryanthemum [mez-em-bri-ANTH-em-um]
Fig marigold.
Here is one of the etymological tangles which taxonomic botanists appear to relish. Originally the spelling was *mesembrianthemum,* derived from Gr. *mesembria,* midday; *anthemon,* flower; in allusion to the fact that the only species then known all bloomed at noon. When species of other habits became known, the genus was renamed *mesembryanthemum*

—a change of sense but not of sound. As now spelled, the derivation is *mesos*, middle; *embryon*, fruit; *anthemon*, flower; which all seems to the amateur rather farfetched and hardly worthwhile, even for so huge a genus which has become a kind of botanical catch-all.

Mespilus [MEZ-pill-us]
Medlar. The Latin name for this fruit, which is pleasant when frosted or rotten and which goes well with wine.

metallicus, -a, -um [met-AL-ik-us]
Metallic.

Metrosideros [met-ro-sid-EE-ros]
Iron tree. From Gr. *metra*, middle; *sideros*, iron; from the hardness of the heart-wood.

Meum [MEE-um]
Baldmoney. The Greek name for this perennial aromatic herb.

mexicanus, -a, -um [mex-ik-KAY-nus]
Mexican.

micans [MY-kans]
Glittering.

Michauxia [mish-o-ya]
Biennial herbs named for André Michaux (1746-1803), French collector, explorer, and plantsman who in ten years in North America carried out remarkable journeys and sent back a very complete dried herbarium. When he himself returned to France, he took with him forty boxes of seeds in addition to the 60,000 living plants he had at various times already dispatched.

michauxioides [mish-o-i-OY-deez]
Resembling *Michauxia*.

Michelia [mich-EE-lia]
Evergreen flowering trees and shrubs named for Pietro Antonio Micheli (1679-1737), Florentine botanist.

Miconia [my-KO-nia]
Tropical American trees and shrubs with showy foliage, named for Francisco Mico (b. 1528), Spanish physician and botanist.

micro-
In compound words signifying small. Thus:

micracanthus	small thorns
micranthus	small-flowered

microcarpus	small-fruited
microcephalus	with a small head
microchilum	small-lipped
microdasys	small and shaggy
microdon	small-toothed
microglossus	small-tongued
microlepis	small-scaled
micromeris	with a small number of parts
micropetalus	small-petaled
microphyllus	small-leaved
micropterus	small-winged
microsepalus	with small sepals
microthele	with small nipples

Microcitrus [my-kro-SIT-rus]
Finger lime. Gr. *mikros,* small; *citrus,* a lemon.

Microglossa [my-kro-GLOSS-a]
Gr. *mikros,* small; *glossa,* a tongue; in reference to the short ray florets of these Asian and African shrubs.

Microlepia [my-kro-LEE-pia]
Gr. *mikros,* small; *lepis,* a scale; a reference to the small indusia on these ferns.

Micromeria [my-kro-MEER-ia]
Yerba buena. Gr. *mikros,* small; *meris,* a part. The flowers of these low-growing herbs and sub-shrubs are very small.

Microstylis [my-KROSS-ty-lis]
Gr. *mikros,* small; *stylus,* a column. These orchids have small columns.

Mikania [my-KAY-nia]
Climbing hempweed. Shrubs and twining herbs, named in honor of Joseph G. Mikan (1743-1814), Professor of Botany at Prague.

miliaceus, -a, -um [mil-i-AY-seus]
Pertaining to millet.

militaris, -is, -e [mil-it-AY-ris]
Pertaining to soldiers; like a soldier.

Milla [MIL-la]
A bulbous plant with scented waxy white blossoms named for Juliani Milla, 18th-century gardener to the king of Spain.

millefoliatus, -a, -um [mil-li-fo-li-AY-tus]
millefolius, -a, -um [mil-li-FO-lius]
Many-leaved; literally, with a thousand leaves.

Miltonia [milt-o-nia]
Epiphytic orchids named for Viscount Milton, later Lord Fitzwilliam (1748-1833), patron of gardening.

Mimosa [mim-o-sa]
Gr. *mimos*, a mimic. A reference to the sensitive collapse, when touched, of the leaves of some species of these feathery-foliaged trees, shrubs, and herbs.

mimosoides [mim-o-SOY-deez]
Like *Mimosa*.

Mimulus [MIM-yew-lus]
Monkey-flower. Latin diminutive of *mimus*, a mimic. The corolla looks like the face of a monkey.

Mimusops [MIM-yew-sops]
L. *mimus*, a mimic. Gr. *opsis*, like; from the appearance of the corolla of these milky-juiced tropical trees.

minax [MY-nax]
Threatening; forbidding.

miniatus, -a, -um [min-i-AY-tus]
Cinnabar-red.

minimus, -a, -um [MIN-im-us]
Smallest.

minor [MY-nor]
minus, -a, -um [MY-nus]
Smaller.

minutus, -a, -um [my-NEW-tus]
Very small. Also:

minutiflorus	minute-flowered
minutifolius	minute-leaved
minutissimus	most minute

Mirabilis [my-RAB-il-is]
Four-o'clock. Tuberous-rooted perennials. Latin word meaning wonderful.

mirabilis, -is, -e [my-RAB-il-is]
Wonderful; remarkable.

Miscanthus [mis-KAN-thus]
Gr. *miskos*, a stem; *anthos*, a flower; an allusion to the stalked spikelets of these handsome perennial grasses.

Mitchella [mich-ELL-a]
Partridge berry. An evergreen trailing herb named for Dr. John Mitchell (1680-1768), physician of Virginia who,

coming from England in 1700, was a correspondent of Linnaeus and the probable author of an anonymous book, *American Husbandry*, published in London in 1775.

Mitella [my-TELL-a]
Bishop's cap. Mitrewort. Diminutive of Gr. *mitra*, a cap; in allusion to the form of the young fruit of this perennial herb.

mitis, -is, -e [MY-tis]
Mild; gentle; without spines.

Mitraria [my-TRAY-ria]
Gr. *mitra*, a mitre or cap; from the shape of the seed pod on this evergreen flowering shrub.

mitratus, -a, -um [my-TRAY-tus]
Turbaned; mitred.

mitriformis, -is, -e [my-tri-FORM-is]
Caplike.

mixtus, -a, um [MIX-tus]
Mixed.

modestus, -a, -um [mo-DESS-tus]
Modest.

moesiacus, -a, -um [mee-si-AY-kus]
From Moesia—the Balkans.

moldavicus, -a, -um [mol-DAV-ik-us]
From the Danube basin.

Molinia [mo-LIN-ia]
Perennial grasses named for Juan Ignacio Molina (1740-1829), writer on the natural history of Chile.

mollis, -is, -e [MOLL-is]
Soft; with soft hairs.

mollissimus, -a, -um [moll-ISS-im-us]
Very soft.

mollugo [moll-YEW-go]
Specific name, derived from the genus *Mollugo* which has no garden interest except as a pernicious carpetweed.

Molospermum [mo-lo-SPERM-um]
Gr. *molops*, a stripe; *sperma*, a seed. The fruit of this handsome-foliaged perennial appears to be striped.

Moltkia [MOLT-kia]
Perennial herbs named for Count Joachim Gadske Moltke (1746-1818), Danish statesman.

moluccanus, -a, -um [mo-luk-KAY-nus]
From the Maluccas or Spice Islands of the Malay Archipelago.

Molucella [mo-lew-SELL-a]
Shell-flower. Derivation of the name for these Mediterranean herbs is uncertain.

Momordica [mo-MORD-ik-a]
L. *mordeo*, to bite. The seeds of these tropical climbers appear bitten.

monacanthus, -a, -um [mo-nak-ANTH-us]
One-spined.

monandrus, -a, -um [mo-NAND-rus]
With one stamen.

Monanthes [mo-NAN-thees]
Gr. *mono*, one; *anthos*, a flower. The flowers of these fleshy herbs were once thought to be solitary.

Monarda [mo-NARD-da]
Bee-balm. Bergamot. Horse-mint. Named for Nicholas Monardes (1493-1588), physician and botanist of Seville who wrote a book in 1571 on American products. The genus includes bee-balm, lemon mint, wild bergamot.

Monardella [mo-nar-DELL-a]
Diminutive of *Monarda* which this genus of aromatic herbs resembles.

mondo [MON-do]
Japanese name used as a specific.

Moneses [mo-NEE-seez]
One-flowered pyrola. Gr. *monos*, single; *esis*, delight. These dwarf perennial herbs have pretty solitary flowers.

mongolicus, -a, -um [mon-GO-lik-us]
Mongolian.

moniliferus, -a, -um [mo-nil-IFF-er-us]
Having a necklace.

moniliformis, -is, -e [mo-nil-i-FORM-is]
In the form of a necklace with alternate swellings and constrictions.

mono-
In compound words signifying single, thus:

| monocephalus | with one head |
| monogynus | with one pistil |

monopetalus	single-petaled
monophyllus	one-leafed
monopterus	with a single wing
monopyrenus	with one stone or pyrene
monosepalus	one-sepalled
monostachyus	one-spiked

Monotropa [mon-OT-ro-pa]
Indian pipe. Gr. *monos,* single; *tropos,* a turn. The top of the stem of these saprophytic herbs is turned to one side.

monspessulanus, -a, -um [mons-pess-yew-LAY-nus]
Of Montpellier in southern France.

Monstera [mon-STEER-a]
Derivation obscure.

monstrosus, -a, -um [mons-TRO-sus]
Abnormal.

Montanoa [mon-tan-o-a]
Shrubs named for Luis Montana, supposed to have been a mid-19th-century Mexican politician.

montanus, -a, -um [mon-TAY-nus]
Pertaining to mountains.

Montbretia [mon-BREE-sha]
Now often under *Tritonia.* Cormous plants named for Antoine Francois Ernest Conquebert de Montbret (1781-1801), official botanist to Napoleon's invasion of Egypt (1798).

montensis, -is, -e [mon-TEN-sis]
monticolus, -a, -um [mon-tik-o-lus]
Growing on mountains.

montigenus, -a, -um [mon-ti-JEN-us]
Mountain-born.

Moraea (Morea) [mor-EE-a]
Butterfly iris. Named by Linnaeus for his father-in-law, Dr. Johann Moraeus.

morifolius, -a, -um [mor-i-FO-lius]
Mulberry-leaved.

Morina [mo-RY-na]
Whorl flower. Perennial herbs named for Louis Morin (1636-1715), French botanist.

Morinda [mo-RIN-da]
Indian mulberry. L. *morus,* a mulberry; *indicus,* Indian.

250

Moringa [mo-RING-ga]
Latin version of the Malay name. The seeds of these trees yield ben-oil used in perfumery and for lubricating watches and other fine mechanisms.

Morus [MO-rus]
Mulberry. The Latin name. The tree is widely cultivated as food for silk-worms, most species being useful for this purpose. The best and sweetest fruit is borne by *M. nigra.*

mosaicus, -a, -um [mos-SAY-ik-us]
Parti-colored in a pattern.

Moscharia [mos-KAY-ria]
Gr. *moschos,* in allusion to the fragrance. A Chilean annual.

moschatus [mos-KAY-tus]
Musky.

mucosus, -a, -um [mew-KO-sus]
Slimy.

mucronatus, -a, -um [mew-kron-AY-tus]
Pointed; mucronate.

mucronulatus, -a, -um [mew-kron-yew-LAY-tus]
Having a short hard point.

Mucuna [mew-KEW-na]
From the Brazilian name for these beanlike vines.

Muehlenbeckia [mew-len-BEK-ia]
Semi-woody shrubs named for H. G. Muehlenbeck (1798-1845), Swiss physician.

multi-
In compound words signifies many. Thus:

multibracteatus	with many bracts
multicaulis	many-stemmed
multicavus	with many hollows
multiceps	with many heads
multicolor	many-colored
multicostatus	many-ribbed
multifidus	many times divided—generally of much-torn leaves
multiflorus	many-flowered
multifurcatus	much-forked
multijugus	many yoked together
multilineatus	many-lined

multinervis	many-nerved
multiplex	much-folded
multiradiatus	with many rays
multisectus	much-cut

mundulus, -a, -um [MUN-dew-lus]
Trim; neat.

muralis, -is, -e [mew-RAY-lis]
Growing on walls.

muricatus, -a, -um [mew-rik-KAY-tus]
Roughened, with hard points.

Murraya (also incorrectly **Murraea**) [MUR-ri-a]
Curry-leaf. Orange jessamine. Satinwood tree. Named for Johann Andreas Murray (1740-1791), Swedish popil of Linnaeus and Professor of Medicine and Botany, Göttingen.

Musa [MEW-sa]
Banana. Named for Antonius Musa (63-14 B.C.), physician to the first Roman emperor, Octavius Augustus. The genus is of Old World origin but quite early was established in the New. Next to the coconut it is probably the most important tropical plant for food, fiber, and many other purposes. *M. paradisiaca,* in one of its many sub-species provides most of the edible fruits—var. *sapientum* being the one most commonly exported to the Western world. The first commercial shipments of bananas reached New York about the year 1865.

musaicus, -a, -um [mew-SAY-ik-us]
Resembling banana.

muscaetoxicus, -a, -um [mus-kee-TOX-ik-us]
Poisonous to flies.

Muscari [mus-KAY-ri]
Grape-hyacinth. From Gr. *moschus,* musk; an allusion to the sweet scent of some species.

muscipulus, -a, -um [mus-ki-PULL-us]
Fly-catching.

muscivorus, -a, -um [mus-KIV-or-us]
Fly-eating.

muscoides [mus-KOY-deez]
muscosus, -a, -um [mus-KO-sus]
Resembling moss.

mussini [mew-SY-nee]
Species name of *Nepeta*. Named for the Russian Count Mussin-Puschkin (d. 1815), a keen student of Caucasian plants.

mutabilis, -is, -e [mew-TAY-bill-is]
mutatus, -a, -um [mew-TAY-tus]
Changeable, especially as to color.

muticus, -a, -um [MEW-tik-us]
Blunt; without a point.

mutilatus, -a, -um [mew-til-AY-tus]
Divided as though torn, as with some leaves.

Mutisia [mew-TIS-ia]
Flowering shrubs, many of them climbers, named for José C. Mutis (1732-1809), physician of Cadiz and student of South American plants.

myoporoides [my-o-po-ROY-deez]
Like *Myoporum*.

Myoporum [my-OP-or-um]
Gr. *myo*, to shut; *poros*, a pore; referring to the transparent spots on the leaves of these evergreen trees and shrubs.

myosotidiflorus, -a, -um [my-o-sot-id-i-FLO-rus]
With flowers like *Myosotidium*.

Myosotidium [my-o-so-TID-ium]
Antarctic forget-me-not. From *Myosotis* (forget-me-not), the two genera being related.

Myosotis [my-o-SO-tis]
Forget-me-not. The classical Greek name.

myri-
In compound words signifying very many. Thus:

myriacanthus	with very many thorns
myriocarpus	many-fruited
myriocladus	many-branched
myriophyllus	many-leaved
myriostigmus	with many stigmas

Myrica [mi-RY-ka]
Gale. Bog myrtle. Bayberry. Wax myrtle. Derived from the Greek name for tamarisk. These shrubs provide the aromatic tallow, the greasy covering of the fruit, from which bayberry candles are made.

Myricaria [mi-ri-KAY-ria]
False tamarisk. From Gr. *myricä,* the tamarisk, to which this genus is related.

Myriocephalus [mi-riо-SEFF-al-us]
Gr. *myrios,* many; *kephale,* a head. The flower heads of these Australian herbs are very numerous.

Myriophyllum [mi-ro-FILL-um]
Water milfoil. Gr. *myrios,* many; *phyllon,* a leaf. The leaves of these aquatics are much divided.

Myristica [mir-IS-tik-a]
Nutmeg. Gr. *myristicos,* fit for anointing. A large genus of tropical trees. The fruit of *M. fragrans* is the source of nutmeg.

myrmecophilus, -a, -um [mer-mee-KOFF-ill-us]
Literally, ant-loving—a specific applied to plants much frequented by ants as providing them with either food or shelter, as in the case of certain plants with hollow pseudobulbs.

Myroxylon [mi-ROX-sy-lon]
Gr. *myron,* a sweet-smelling oil; *xylon,* wood. The heartwood of these trees is resinous and fragrant.

Myrrhis [MI-ris]
Myrrh. Sweet cicely. The Greek name for this plant as well as for the true myrrh. This genus is an herbaceous plant of the carrot family once grown as a salad plant. True myrrh of the Bible is a fragrant gum resin once very highly esteemed for ceremonial, religious, and embalming purposes. It comes from *Commiphora myrrha,* a small East African and Arabian tree.

Myrsine [MIR-sin-e, or mir-SINE-e]
From a Greek name for myrtle; not these trees and shrubs.

myrsinifolius, -a, -um [mir-sin-i-FO-lius]
Myrsine-leaved.

myrsinoides [mir-sin-OY-deez]
Resembling *Myrsine.*

myrtifolius, -a, -um [mir-ti-FO-lius]
Myrtle-leaved.

Myrtillocactus [mir-till-o-KAK-tus]
L. *myrtillus,* a small myrtle. The allusion is to the small myrtlelike fruits, not unlike blueberries, of these cacti.

254

Myrtus [MIR-tús]

Myrtle. The Greek name. The Greeks held the plant sacred to Aphrodite (the Roman Venus) and in Christian religious painting it became one of the plants associated with the Virgin. In ancient Rome there were two old myrtles, one called the Patrician and the other the Plebian. The political fortunes of the nobles as against those of the plebians could be judged as each plant flourished or languished.

N

Naegelia [nay-GEL-ia]

Herbaceous perennials with velvety leaves named for Karl von Naegeli, Professor of Botany in Munich in the 19th century.

Nandina [nan-DY-na]

Japanese name for these shrubs.

nanellus, -a, -um [nan-ELL-us]

Very dwarf.

Nannorhops [NAN-o-rups]

A small tufted palm. Gr. *nannos*, a dwarf; *rhops*, a bush.

nankinensis, -is, -e [nan-kin-EN-sis]

From Nanking, China.

nanus, -a, -um [NAY-nus]

Dwarf.

napiformis, -is, -e [nap-i-FORM-is]

Turnip-shaped; in the shape of a flattened sphere.

napobrassica [nap-o-BRAS-ik-a]

Specific name for rutabaga—literally, "turnip-cabbage."

narcissiflorus, -a, -um [nar-sis-i-FLO-rus]

Narcissus-flowered.

Narcissus [nar-SIS-us]

Daffodil. Classical Greek name in honor of a beautiful youth who became so entranced with his own reflection that the gods turned him into a flower.

narinosus, -a, -um [nar-in-o-sus]

Broad-nosed.

nasturtium [nass-TER-shium]

In Latin, *nasi tortium*, a twisted nose, due to the plant's pungent qualities. Specific name of water-cress (*Rorippa*

nasturtium-aquaticum). The plant familiarly known as nasturtium is *Tropaeolum* (q.v).

nasutus, -a, -um [nas-YEW-tus]
Large-nosed.

natalensis, -is, -e [nat-al-EN-sis]
From Natal, South Africa.

natans [NAY-tans]
Floating.

nauseosus, -a, -um [naw-see-O-sus]
Nauseating.

navicularis, -is, -e [nav-ik-yew-LAY-ris]
Boat-shaped.

neapolitanus, -a, -um [nee-ap-pol-it-AY-nus]
From Naples.

nebulosus, -a, -um [neb-yew-LO-sus]
Cloudlike.

neglectus, -a, -um [neg-LEK-tus]
A plant hitherto overlooked.

Neillia [NEEL-ia]
Nine bark. Ornamental shrubs named for Patrick Neill
(1776-1851), printer, of Edinburgh. Secretary of the Cale-
donian Horticultural Society.

nelumbifolius, -a, -um [nell-um-bi-FO-lius]
With leaves like *Nelumbium* or lotus.

Nelumbium [nell-UM-bium]
Lotus. From the Cingalese name for these bold aquatics.

Nemastylis [nee-MAS-ty-lis]
Gr. *nema*, a thread; *stylos*, a column, from the slender style
of these blue-flowering bulbs.

Nemesia [nem-EE-sia]
The Greek name for a plant similar to these attractive herbs.

Nemopanthus [nee-mo-PANTH-us]
Mountain holly. Gr. *nema*, a thread; *anthos*, a flower. The
peduncle is very slender on this North American shrub.

Nemophila [nem-OFF-ill-a]
Gr. *nemos*, a grove; *phileo*, to love; in allusion to the habitat
of some species of these spreading North American annuals.

nemoralis, -is, -e [nem-o-RAY-lis]
nemorosus, -a, -um [nem-o-RO-sus]
Growing in shady places.

Neobesseya [nee-o-BESS-ia]
Cactus. Named for Dr. Charles Bessey (1845-1915), Professor of Botany, University of Nebraska.

Neolloydia [nee-o-LOY-dia]
Cactus. Named for Professor Francis E. Lloyd, American collector and student of cacti.

Nepenthes [nep-EN-theez]
Pitcherplants. From the name of a plant in Greek literature which could assuage grief and, classically, any plant capable of producing euphoria. Used here in connection with its supposed medical qualities.

Nepeta [NEP-et-a]
Ground-ivy. Latin name for these herbaceous plants which include catnip.

nepetoides [nep-et-OY-deez]
Like *Nepeta*.

Nephrolepis [neff-ROL-ep-is]
Sword fern. Gr. *nephros*, a kidney; *lepis*, a scale; an allusion to the form of the indusium.

nephrolepis, -is, -e [neff-ROL-ep-is]
With kidney-shaped scales.

neriifolius, -a, -um [ner-i-eye-FO-lius]
Oleander-leaved.

Nerine [ne-RY-ne]
Bulbous plants named for the water nymph of that name.

Nerium [NEE-rium]
Oleander. Rose bay. The classical Greek name. Although Neriums are very poisonous, these flowering shrubs are very popular where climate is suitable.

Nertera [NER-ter-a]
Gr. *nerteros*, lowly; from the habit of growth of these creeping herbs.

nervis, -is, -e [NER-vis]
nervosus, -a, -um [ner-VO-sus]
With evident nerves.

Neviusa [nev-i-YEW-sa]
Snow wreath. An ornamental shrub named for the Rev. D. R. Nevius (1827-1913), of Alabama, who discovered it there.

Nicandra [ny-KAN-dra]
Apple-of-Peru. An annual herb named for Nikander of Colo-

phon, a poet who wrote of plants and their medical uses, c. 100 B.C.

Nicotiana [nik-o-shee-AY-na]
Tobacco. Named for Jean Nicot (1530-1600), French ambassador to Lisbon who introduced tobacco into France.

nictitans [NIK-ti-tans]
Blinking; moving.

Nidularium [Nid-yew-LAY-rium]
L. *nidus*, a nest. A reference to the position and appearance of the flower heads of these epiphytes.

nidus [NY-dus]
A nest.

Nierembergia [neer-em-BERJ-ia]
Cup-flower. Creeping perennial herbs named for Father John Eusebius Nieremberg (1595-1658), Spanish Jesuit and author of a book on the marvels of nature.

Nigella [ny-JELL-a]
Love-in-a-mist. Fennel-flower. From the diminutive of L. *niger*, black; in allusion to the color of the seeds of these annuals.

niger, nigra, nigrum [NY-jer]
nigricans [NY-grik-ans]
Black.

nigratus, -a, -um [ny-GRAY-tus]
nigrescens [ny-GRESS-ens]
Blackish.

nilocticus, -a, -um [ny-LO-tik-us]
From the valley of the Nile.

Nipa [NY-pa]
From the Moluccan name for this palm.

nipponicus, -a, -um [nip-ON-ik-us]
Japanese.

nitens [NY-tens]
nitidus, -a, -um [NIT-id-us]
Shining.

nivalis, -is, -e [niv-AY-lis]
niveus, -a, -um [NIV-eus]
nivosus, -a, -um [niv-O-sus]
Snow-white; growing near snow.

nobilis, -is, -e [NO-bil-is]
Noble; famous or renowned.

noctiflorus, -a, -um [nok-ti-FLO-rus]
nocturnus, -a, -um [nok-TERN-us]
Night-flowering.

nodiflorus, -a, -um [no-di-FLO-rus]
Flowering at the nodes.

nodosus, -a, -um [no-DO-sus]
Having conspicuous joints or nodes.

nodulosus, -a, -um [nod-yew-LO-sus]
With small nodes.

Nolana [no-LAY-na]
Chilean bellflower. L. *nola,* a small bell; from the form of
the corolla of these prostrate herbs.

noli-tangere [no-li-TANG-er-e]
Touch-me-not. Specific name of *Impatiens.*

Nolina [no-LY-na]
Bear-grass. Short-trunked desert plants named for P. C.
Nolin, French agricultural writer c. 1755.

Noltea [NOLL-tee-a]
Soap-bush. South African shrubs named for E. F. Nolte,
mid-19th-century professor of natural history at Kiel.

nonscriptus, -a, -um [non-SKRIP-tus]
Without markings.

Nopalea [no-PAY-lea]
From the Mexican name for these cacti, upon a species of
which the cochineal insect is cultivated.

Nopalxochia [no-pal-XOK-ia]
Reportedly from the Aztec name for these epiphytic cacti.

norvegicus, -a, -um [nor-VEE-jik-us]
Norwegian.

notatus, -a, -um [no-TAY-tus]
Spotted; marked.

Nothofagus [no-tho-FAY-gus]
Southern beech. Gr. *nothos,* false or Gr. *notos,* southern; L.
fagus, beech. Closely related to beech and from the southern
hemisphere.

Nothopanax [no-tho-PAY-nax]
Gr. *nothos,* false; *panax,* ginseng. Evergreen shrubs with
palmate leaves, they resemble true *Panax.*

Nothoscordum [no-tho-SKORD-um]
Gr. *nothos,* false; *skordon,* garlic. These bulbous herbs resemble garlic in appearance but without the flavor and odor.

novae-angliae [no-vee-ANG-li-ee]
Of New England.
novaeboracensis, -is, -e [no-vee-bor-ass-EN-sis]
  novibelgii [no-vy-BEL-gi-eye]
From New York.
novaecaesareae [no-vee-see-sar-REE-ee]
Of New Jersey.
novaezealandiae [no-vee-zee-LAND-i-ee]
Of New Zealand.
nubicolis, -is, -e [new-BIK-o-lis]
Growing among the clouds.
nubigenus, -a, -um [new-bi-JEN-us]
Born among the clouds.
nuciferus, -a, -um [new-SIFF-er-us]
Bearing nuts.
nudatus, -a, -um [new-DAY-tus]
  nudus, -a, -um [NEW-dus]
Naked; bare. Also:

nudicaulis   bare-stemmed
nudiflorus   with flowers coming before the leaves

numidicus, -a, -um [new-MID-ik-us]
From Algeria.
numismatus, -a, -um [new-MIS-mat-us]
  nummularius, -a, -um [num-yew-LAY-rius]
Resembling coins.
Nuphar [NEW-far]
Spatter-dock. Yellow water-lily. From the Arabic name.
nutans [NEW-tans]
Nodding.
nyctagineus, -a, -um [nik-ta-JIN-eus]
  nycticalis, -is, -e [nik-ti-KAY-lis]
Night-blooming.
Nyctanthes [nik-TAN-theez]
Gr. *nyktos*, night; *anthos*, a flower. The flowers of this small
Indian tree or shrub open at nightfall and drop at dawn.
Nyctocereus [nik-to-SEE-reus]
Gr. *nyktos*, night; *cereus*, cactus. They are night-blooming.
Nymphaea [nim-FEE-a]
Water-lily. Named for Nymphe, one of the water nymphs.

Nymphoides [nim-FOY-deez]
Resembling *Nymphaea*, a genus of ornamental aquatic herbs.

Nyssa [NIS-sa]
Tupelo, sour gum. A great favorite of bees. Named for Nyssa, one of the water nymphs. The cotton gum, *Nyssa aquatica*, grows in swamps.

O

obconicus, -a, -um [ob-KON-ik-us]
Shaped like an inverted cone.

obesus, -a, -um [o-BEE-sus]
Fat.

obfuscatus, -a, -um [ob-fuss-KAY-tus]
Confused; clouded.

oblatus, -a, -um [ob-LAY-tus]
Flattened at the ends.

obliquus, -a, -um [ob-LY-kwus]
Lopsided.

obliteratus, -a, -um [ob-lit-er-AY-tus]
Erased.

oblongatus, -a, -um [ob-long-GAY-tus]
Oblong.

oblongifolius, -a, -um [ob-long-gi-FO-lius]
With oblong leaves.

oblongus, -a, -um [ob-LONG-gus]
Elliptical with blunt ends.

obovatus, -a, -um [ob-o-VAY-tus]
Inverted ovate.

obscurus, -a, -um [ob-SKEW-rus]
Hidden.

obsoletus, -a, -um [ob-so-LEE-tus]
Rudimentary.

obtusatus, -a, -um [ob-tew-SAY-tus]
obtusus, -a, -um [ob-TEW-sus]
Blunt.

obtusifolius, -a, -um [ob-tew-si-FO-lius]
Blunt-leaved.

obtusior [ob-TEW-si-or]
Blunter.

obvallatus, -a, -um [ob-val-LAY-tus]
Walled-up.
occidentalis, -is -e [ox-id-ent-TAY-lis]
Western.
oceanus, -a, -um [o-see-AY-nus]
Growing near the sea; of the sea.
ocellatus, -a, -um [o-sell-LAY-tus]
With an eye; having a spot enclosed by another spot of a
different color.
Ochna [OK-na]
Tropical trees or shrubs. Greek name for the wild pear to
which the foliage of this genus has some resemblance.
ochraceus, -a, -um [o-KRAY-seus]
Ochre-colored.
ochroleucus, -a, -um [o-kro-LEW-kus]
Yellowish-white.
Ocimum [o-SY-mum]
Basil. From the Greek name for an aromatic herb, possibly
this one.
octandrus, -a, -um [ok-TAN-drus]
Having eight stamens.
Octomeria [ok-to-MEE-ria]
Gr. *okto*, eight; *meris*, a part; in allusion to the eight pollen-
bearing masses.
octopetalus, -a, -um [ok-to-PET-al-us]
Having eight petals.
oculatus, -a, -um [ok-yew-LAY-tus]
Eyed.
oculiroseus, -a, -um, [ok-yew-li-RO-seus]
With a rose-colored eye.
ocymoides [o-sy-MOY-deez]
Resembling basil (*Ocymum*).
odessanus, -a, -um [o-dess-AY-nus]
From Odessa.
odontochilus, -a, -um [o-don-to-KY-lus]
Having a toothed lip.
Odontoglossum [o-don-to-GLOSS-um]
Gr. *odous*, a tooth; *glossa*, a tongue. The lip of these epi-
phytic orchids is toothed.
Odontonema [o-don-to-NEE-ma]
Gr. *odous*, a tooth; *nema*, a thread. The stamen of these
herbs or shrubs has toothed filaments.

Odontosoria [o-don-to-so-ria]
Gr. *odous,* a tooth; *sorus,* a spore case. These ferns have toothed frond segments.

odoratus, -a, -um [o-do-RAY-tus]
odoriferus, -a, -um [o-do-RIFF-er-us]
odorus, -a, -um [o-DO-rus]
Fragrant. Also, *odoratissimus,* very fragrant.

Oenothera [ee-noth-EE-ra or ee-NOTH-er-a]
Evening primrose. The Greek name, which is supposed to derive from *oinos,* wine; *thera,* booty. The root when eaten was supposed to increase one's capacity for wine.

officinalis, -is, -e [o-fiss-in-AY-lis]
Sold in shops; applies to edible, medicinal, and otherwise useful plants.

officinarum [o-fiss-in-AY-rum]
Of shops, generally apothecaries.

Olea [o-lee-a]
Olive. The classical name for this most long-lived and beautiful of fruit trees which from antiquity has been a symbol of peace and good will.

oleaefolius, -a, -um [o-le-ee-FO-lius]
oleifolius, -a, -um [o-le-eye-FO-lius]
With leaves like the olive.

Olearia [o-lee-AY-ria]
Tree aster. Daisy bush. Derivation of the name for these Australasian and New Zealand shrubs is obscure.

oleiferus, -a, -um [o-lee-IFF-er-us]
Oil-bearing.

oleoides [o-lee-OY-deez]
Resembling olive.

oleraceus, -a, -um [o-lee-RAY-seus]
Of the vegetable garden; a potherb used in cooking.

oliganthus, -a, -um [o-lig-ANTH-us]
With few flowers. Also:

oligocarpus	with few fruits
oligophyllus	with few leaves
oligospermus	with few seeds

olitorius, -a, -um [o-lit-o-rius]
Pertaining to culinary herbs.

olivaceus, -a, -um [o-live-AY-seus]
Greenish-brown; olive-colored.

Oliveranthus [o-liv-er-ANTH-us]
Named for G. W. Oliver, United States Department of Agriculture.

olympicus, -a, -um [o-LIM-pik-us]
Of Mount Olympus.

omorika [o-MO-rik-a]
Local name of the Serbian spruce, of which this is the specific.

Omphalodes [om-fal-o-deez]
Gr. *omphalos*, a navel. The nutlet of these herbs resembles the human navel.

Oncidium [on-SID-ium]
Gr. *onkos*, a tumor. The crest at the base of the lip of these epiphytic orchids is swollen.

Oncoba [ONK-o-ba]
From the Arabic name for these shrubs or small trees.

Onobrychis [on-OB-ry-kis; also on-o-BRY-kis]
Sainfoin. From Gr. *onos*, an ass; *brycho*, to bray. Asses are said to bray for it.
The English name means holy clover (sometimes saintfoin) because it was said to have been the hay in Christ's manger.

Onoclea [on-ok-KLEE-a]
Greek name for another plant, possibly borage, but applied here because of its meaning: *onos*, a vessel; *kleio,* to close; refers to the closely rolled fertile fronds of these ferns.

Ononis [on-o-nis]
Rest-harrow. The classical Greek name for these plants.

Onopordum [on-o-POR-dum]
Scotch thistle. The Greek name for these thistlelike herbs.

Onosma [on-os-ma]
Golden drop. Gr. *onos*, an ass, *osme*, a smell; but it is uncertain whether these bristly herbs and sub-shrubs are supposed to smell like an ass or whether asses are fond of it.

Onosmodium [on-os-MO-dium]
False gromwell. Greek name. Resembles *Onosma* (*q.v.*) to which it is closely related.

Onychium [o-NIK-ium]
Gr. *onyx*, a claw; in allusion to the shape of the frond lobes on these ferns.

ophioglossifolius, -a, -um [of-fi-o-gloss-i-FO-lius]
With leaves like adder's tongue fern.

Ophioglossum [o-fi-o-GLOSS-um]
Adder's tongue fern. Gr. *ophis,* a snake; *glossa,* a tongue; from the shape of the fronds.

Ophrys [o-fris]
The Greek name for these terrestrial orchids.

Oplismenus [op-LISS-me-nus]
Gr. *oplismenos,* equipped. The spikelets of these grasses have awns.

Opopanax [o-po-PAY-nax]
Gr. *opos,* a milky juice; *panax,* a remedy. The sap of these perennial herbs was once used medicinally. Today, gum opopanax is obtained from the root for use in perfumery.

oppositifolius, -a, -um [op-po-sit-i-FO-lius]
With leaves growing opposite to each other on each side of a stem.

opuloides [op-yew-LOY-deez]
Resembling the guelder-rose, *Viburnum opulus.* Also: *opuliflorus* and *opulifolius* with flowers and leaves, respectively, like the guelder-rose.

Opuntia [o-PUN-tia]
Prickly pear. Greek name for a different plant which grew around Opuntium in ancient Greece.

orbicularis, -is, -e [or-bik-yew-LAY-ris]
orbiculatus, -a, -um [or-bik-yew-LAY-tus]
Round and flat; disk-shaped.

orchideus, -a, -um [or-KID-eus]
orchioides [or-ki-OY-deez]
orchoides [or-KOY-deez]
Orchid-like.

orchidiflorus [or-kid-i-FLO-rus]
With orchid-like flowers.

Orchis [OR-kis]
Classical Greek name, from *orchis,* a testicle; from the root-form of some species. For that reason, *Orchis* has been regarded since antiquity as an aphrodisiac.

oreganus, -a, -um [o-reg-GAY-nus]
From Oregon.

Oreopanax [o-ree-o-pay-nax, or o-ree-o-PAY-nax]
Gr. *oreos,* a mountain; plus *Panax.* These shrubs and trees are found in mountains.

oreophilus, -a, -um [o-ree-OFF-il-us]
Mountain-loving.

orgyalis, -is, -e [or-jee-AY-lis]
The length of the arms extended, i.e., about six feet.

orientalis, -is, -e [o-ree-en-TAY-lis]
From the Orient; Eastern.

origanifolius, -a, -um [o-rig-gan-i-FO-lius]
With leaves like marjoram or *Origanum.*

origanoides [o-rig-gan-OY-deez]
Resembling marjoram.

Origanum [o-RIG-an-um]
Marjoram. The classical Greek name for these aromatic herbs.

Orixa [o-RIX-a]
From the Japanese name for this shrub.

Ormosia [or-MO-sia]
Gr. *hormos,* a necklace. The scarlet seeds of *O. coccinea* are strung as beads in Guiana where the tree is indigenous.

ornans [OR-nans]
ornatus, -a, -um [or-NAY-tus]
Ornamental; showy.

ornatissimus, -a, -um [or-nay-TISS-im-us]
Very showy.

Ornithidium [or-nith-ID-ium]
Gr. *ornis,* a bird; *eidos,* a shape. The upper lip of the stigma is beaklike in these epiphytic orchids.

Ornithochilus [or-nith-o-KY-lus]
Gr. *ornis,* a bird; *cheilos,* a lip; in allusion to the shape of the lip of these epiphytic orchids.

ornithocephalus, -a, -um [or-nith-o-SEFF-al-us]
Bird-headed.

Ornithogalum [or-nith-OG-al-um]
Gr. *ornis,* a bird; *galos,* milk. The flowers of these bulbous plants are white. The bulbs of star-of-Bethlehem (*O. umbellatum*) are supposed by some to have been the "dove's dung" of the Bible of which a "cab" measure was sold for a shekel during the Babylonian siege of Jerusalem.

ornithopus, -a, -um [or-nith-o-pus]
ornithopodus, -a, -um [or-nith-o-PO-dus]
Resembling a bird's foot.

Orontium [o-RON-tium]
Golden club. The name of this North American aquatic perennial is of uncertain derivation.

Oroxylon [o-ROX-il-lon]
Gr. *oros*, a mountain; *xylon*, wood. Application obscure; the tree grows also on plains.

ortho-
In compound words signifying upright or straight. Thus:

orthobotrys	with upright clusters
orthocarpus	with upright fruit
orthochilus	with a straight lip
orthoglossus	with a straight tongue
orthopterus	straight-winged
orthosepalus	straight-sepaled

Orthocarpus [or-tho-KARP-us]
Gr. *orthos*, upright; *karpos*, fruit; from the small upright pods on these herbs.

Oryza [o-RY-za]
Rice, from the Arabic name. Rice (*O. sativa*) is one of the staple cereals, world production being of the order of 100 million tons annually. It originated as a wild grass in India but is now grown throughout the tropical and warm temperature regions, wherever conditions are suitable. With the exception of the so-called "hill rice" which is grown on dry land, all varieties need water conditions for part of their development.

Osmanthus [os-MAN-thus]
Sweet olive. Gr. *osme*, fragrance; *anthos*, a flower. All the species of these ornamental shrubs and small trees are very fragrant.

osmanthus, -a, -um [os-MAN-thus]
With fragrant flowers.

Osmaronia [os-ma-RO-nia]
Osoberry. Gr. *osme*, fragrance; *Aronia*, choke-cherry. Resembles choke-cherry and is very fragrant.

Osmunda [os-MUN-da]
Said to be named for Osmundus or Asmund c. 1025, a Scandinavian writer of runes who helped prepare the way for the Swedish acceptance of Christianity. It is uncertain why this individual should be perpetuated in the royal, the

cinnamon, and the interrupted ferns. Osmunder is the Scandinavian name for Thor.

Osteomeles [os-tee-OM-ee-lees]
Gr. *osteon*, a bone; *meles*, an apple; an allusion to the fruit of these evergreen shrubs.

Ostrowskia [os-TRO-skia]
Giant bellflower. Named for Michael Nicholazewitsch von Ostrowsky, Russian Minister of Imperial Domains c. 1884 and a patron of botany.

Ostrya [os-tria]
Hop-hornbeam. From the Greek name for some other hard-wood tree.

Othonna [o-THON-na]
Greek name for a different plant than this genus of daisy family, some of which are succulent.

Ourisia [ow-RIS-ia]
Small herbs, named for Governor Ouris of the Falkland Islands c. 1860.

ovalis, -is, -e [o-VAY-lis]
Oval.

ovatus, -a, -um [o-VAY-tus]
Ovate; egg-shaped, with the broad end down.

oviferus, -a, -um [o-VIFF-er-us]
ovigerus, -a, -um [o-VIJ-er-us]
Bearing ovules.

ovinus, -a, -um [o-VY-nus]
Relating to sheep; woolly; sheep fodder.

Oxalis [ox-AY-lis]
Wood-sorrel. Gr. *oxys*, acid. *O. acetellosa*, wood-sorrel, is one of the several plants called shamrock. The delicious sorrel soup of France is made from *Rumex acetosa*.

Oxera [ox-EE-ra]
Gr. *oxys*, acid. The sap of the shrub is sour.

oxyacanthus, -a, -um [ox-i-ak-ANTH-us]
Sharp-spined.

Oxydendrum [ox-i-DEN-drum]
Sour-wood. Gr. *oxys*, sour; *dendron*, a tree. The foliage is acid.

oxygonus, -a, -um [ox-i-GO-nus]
With sharp angles.

oxyphyllus, -a, -um [ox-i-FILL-us]
With sharp-pointed leaves.

Oxytropis [ox-IT-ro-pis, or ox-i-TROP-is]
Gr. *oxys*, sharp; *tropis*, a keel; an allusion to the form of the flower on these perennial herbs and shrubs.

P

pabularius, -a, -um [pab-yew-LAY-rius]
Providing pasture or fodder.

Pachira [pak-KY-ra]
From the native Guiana name for these trees.

Pachistima [pak-ISS-tim-a]
Ornamental evergreen woody plants. From Gr. *pachys*, thick; *stigma*, a stigma.

Pachycereus [pak-i-SEE-reus]
Gr. *pachys*, thick; *cereus*, cactus. These cacti have very stout stems.

Pachyphytum [pak-IFF-it-um]
Gr. *pachys*, thick; *phyton*, a plant. Both stems and leaves are thickened on these succulent plants.

Pachyrrhizus [pak-i-RY-zus]
Gr. *pachys*, thick; *rhyza*, a root. The roots of these twining herbs are thick and tuberous.

Pachysandra [pak-iss-AND-ra]
Mountain spurge. Gr. *pachys*, thick; *aner*, a stamen. The stamens of these herbs and sub-shrubs are thick.

Pachystachys [pak-ISS-tak-iss]
Gr. *pachys*, thick; *stachys*, a spike; in allusion to the dense flower clusters on this tropical ornamental perennial.

pachy-
In compound words signifies thick. Thus:

pachyanthus	thick-flowered
pachycarpus	with a thick pericarp
pachyphloeus	with thick bark
pachyphyllus	thick-leaved
pachypterus	with thick wings

pacificus, -a, -um [pass-IFF-ik-us]
Of the Pacific Ocean.

Paeonia [pee-o-nia]
Peony. The classical Greek name said to be derived from the name of the Greek physician Paeon who is supposed to have been the first to use the plants medicinally.

palestinus, -a, -um [pal-es-TY-nus]
From Palestine.

Palaquium [pal-AY-quium]
Latin version of the Philippine name for these trees.

Palisota [pal-iss-O-ta]
Perennial herbs named for J. Palisot de Beauvais (1752-1820), French botanist and traveler.

Paliurus [pal-i-YEW-rus]
The ancient Greek name for these ornamental shrubs or small trees.

pallens [PAL-ens]
pallidus, -a, -um [PAL-id-us]
Pale. Also *pallescens*, rather pale.

palliatus, -a, -um [pal-i-AY-tus]
Shrouded.

palmaris, -is, -e [pal-MAY-ris]
palmatus, -a, -um [pal-MAY-tus]
Palmate.

palmifolius, -a, -um [pal-mi-FO-lius]
Palm-leaved.

paludosus, -a, -um [pal-yew-DO-sus]
palustris, -is, -e [pal-US-tris]
Marsh-loving.

Panax [PAY-nax]
Ginseng. From Gr. *panakes*, all-healing, a panacea. In allusion to the obsessive value placed on it by the Chinese for medicinal purposes, especially aphrodisiac. American ginseng is very closely related to the Chinese (*P. Schinseng* from which the English name derives), and the appearance is the same, with the result that it was an important item of trade with Canton during the palmy days of the China trade (c. 1810-40).

Pancratium [pan-KRAY-tium]
Mediterranean lily. Sea daffodil. Greek name for a bulbous plant.

Pandanus [pan-DAY-nus]
Screw-pine. The Latin version of the Malayan name.

Pandorea [pan-DO-rea]
Ornamental twiners. Named for Pandora. In Greek mythology she was the first woman sent to earth by Zeus in subtle revenge for the theft of fire by Prometheus. The gods

endowed her with their choicest gifts, while Zeus himself gave her a box which was not to be opened. Eventually curiosity got the better of her, with the result that she released all evils and managed to retain only Hope.

panduratus, -a, -um [pan-dew-RAY-tus]
Fiddle-shaped.

paniculatus, -a, -um [pan-ik-yew-LAY-tus]
With flowers arranged in panicles.

Panicum [PAN-ik-um]
Millet. The Latin name.

pannonicus, -a, -um [pan-o-nik-us]
From Central Europe—Hungary and Yugoslavia.

pannosus, -a, -um [pan-o-sus]
Tattered.

Papaver [pap-AY-ver]
Poppy. The Latin name.

papaveraceus, -a, -um [pap-ay-ver-AY-shus]
Poppy-like.

papilio [pap-ILL-io]
Latin word for butterfly. Specific name for the butterfly orchid (*Oncidium papilio*).

papilligerus, -a, -um [pap-ill-IJ-er-us]
papillosus, -a, -um [pap-ill-o-sus]
Having papillae, soft protuberances on a surface.

papyraceus, -a, -um [pap-py-RAY-shus]
Papery.

papyriferus, -a, -um [pap-py-RIFF-er-us]
Paper-bearing.

Paradisea [pa-rad-IZ-ea]
St. Bruno's lily. Named for Count Giovanni Paradisi (1760-1826) of Modena.

paradisi [pa-rad-DY-si]
paradisiacus, -a, -um [pa-rad-is-si-AK-us]
Of parks or gardens.

Parietaria [par-eet-AIR-ia]
Pellitory. The name derives from the Latin, *paries*, a wall, where the plant likes to grow, as Pliny knew when he described it.

Paris [PA-ris]
Herb-Paris. L. *par*, equal; alluding to the regularity of the parts of this small rhizomatous perennial.

Parkinsonia [park-in-so-nia]

Tropical trees or shrubs named for John Parkinson (1567-1650), apothecary of London and author of two important books, *Theatrum Botanicum* (relating to botanical descriptions of known plants) and *Paradisi in Sole, Paradisus Terrestris*. Having perpetrated a gross pun in the title of the latter (it translates as "Park in sun's earthly paradise"), he proceeds to extol the joys of a garden in one of the first books to do so.

paradoxus, -a, -um [pa-rad-OX-us]

Strange; unexpected in that genus.

parasiticus, -a, -um [pa-ra-SIT-ik-us]

Parasitic.

pardalinus, -a, -um [par-dal-LY-nus]

pardinus, -a, -um [par-DY-nus]

Spotted like a leopard.

Parmentiera [par-men-ti-EE-ra]

Panama candle-tree. Named for Antoine Augustin Parmentier (1737-1813), French agricultural economist who promoted cultivation of the potato in France. Potage Parmentier (potato soup) is named for him.

Parnassia [par-NASS-ia]

Grass-of-Parnassus. From Mount Parnassus in Greece. Low moisture-loving herbs.

parnassifolius, -a, -um [par-nass-i-FO-lius]

With leaves like *Parnassia*.

Parochetus [pa-ROK-et-us]

Blue oxalis. Gr. *para*, near; *ochetus*, a brook; from the normal habitat in moist places of this trailing perennial.

Paronychia [pa-ro-NIK-ia]

Whitlow-wort. Gr. *paronychia*, a whitlow; for which these little herbs were thought to be a cure.

Parrotia [pa-ROT-ia]

Ornamental shrubs and trees named for F. W. Parrot (1792-1841), German naturalist who climbed Mount Ararat in 1829.

Parthenium [par-THEE-nium]

American feverfew. Greek name for some plant with white ray flowers.

parthenium [par-THEE-nium]

Specific name for *Chrysanthemum* (see *Parthenium*).

Parthenocissus [par-thee-no-SISS-us]
Boston ivy, Virginia creeper, woodbine, etc.
parthenos, a virgin; *kissos,* ivy. P. *quinquefolia,*
creeper, is often listed under *Ampelopsis.*

partitus, -a, -um [par-TY-tus]
Parted.

parvus, -a, -um [PAR-vus]
Small. In compound words *parvi-,* as in *parviflorus,* with
small flowers; also *parvissimus,* very small.

Paspalum [PAS-pal-um]
Millet. The Greek name.

Passiflora [pass-i-FLO-ra]
Passion-flower. L. *passio,* passion; *flos,* a flower. The name
was given by the early missionaries in South America who
thought they saw in the parts of the flower various aspects
of Christ's crucifixion. The corona became the crown of
thorns, other parts represented the nails and the wounds,
while the five sepals and five petals were ten of the apostles
(omitting Peter who denied and Judas who betrayed).

Pastinaca [pas-tin-AY-ka]
Parsnip. From L. *pastus,* food; in allusion to the edible root.
Nowadays often classified under *Peucedanum.*

patagonicus, -a, -um [pat-a-GON-ik-us]
From Patagonia.

patavinus, -a, -um [pat-a-VY-nus]
From the neighborhood of Padua.

patellaris, -is, -e [pat-ell-AY-ris]
patelliformis, -is, -e [pat-ell-i-FORM-is]
Disk-shaped; circular.

patens [PAY-tens]
patulus, -a, -um [PAT-yew-lus]
Spreading.

paucus, -a, -um [PAW-kus]
Few. In compound words *pauci-.* Thus:

pauciflorus	with few flowers
paucifolius	with sparse leaves
paucinervus	with few nerves

Paullinia [paul-LIN-ia]
Twining shrubs named for Simon Paulli (1603-1680) and
his son Christian Francis (1643-1742), Danish botanists.

nia]

...ind Japanese trees named for Princess ...795-1865), daughter of Czar Paul I of

...a [paw-PER-kew-lus]

...]
...shrubs named for José Pavon (d. 1844),
Spanish botanical author in Peru.

pavoninus, -a, -um [pav-o-NY-nus]
Peacock-blue.

paxtonii [pax-TO-ni-eye]
In honor of Sir Joseph Paxton (1801-1865), gardener and architect. Starting as a poor apprentice at the Chiswick arboretum, he became head gardener to the Duke of Devonshire at Chatsworth, manager of the Duke's princely estates and general *homme de confiance*. Having designed and built the huge Chatsworth conservatory of nearly 300 feet in length, he used it as a model for the great Crystal Palace for the Great Exhibition of 1851. Later he designed many other important buildings, became a company director and a member of Parliament. In gardening, he dispatched collectors to many parts of the world and introduced a number of new plants, including the great water lily, *Victoria regia*, which he brought into bloom at Chatsworth.

Pear
With very few exceptions, pears in cultivation are varieties of *Pyrus communis*. Centuries of breeding and tests of seedlings have resulted in much the same conditions that govern apples and for the same reasons (see *Apple*). The range of the pear, however, is much more limited than the apple. Pears cannot be grown, except on a very limited scale, much north of Zone Four in the United States, and only the warmer southern parts of England are really suitable for good growth of fine varieties. Pears can be, and are, grown in less favored climates but they need special treatment and, generally, sheltered locations.

Few pears ripen well on the tree. Production of the best-quality fruit needs very special attention in picking in just the right stage and in ripening in cool, dark, dry quarters.

For these reasons the finest pears seldom find their way into the markets and then only as speciality items. Indeed, even in private orchards, few people are prepared to take the trouble necessary to put really fine fruit on the table. At least, this is the case in the United States. It may well be different in France and Belgium where most of the very best sorts originated. This is demonstrated in the many French or Flemish names in the best sorts and the recurrence of the terms *beurré* (Beurré Bosc) and *doyenné* (Doyenné de Comice). The first means juicy and melting in the mouth; the second, melting and sugary.

The Romans thought highly of pears and it was they who introduced them into England. At least two fine varieties are thought to antedate the Christian era. Both make small demands on the skill and patience of the grower and will ripen fairly satisfactorily on the tree. Jargonelle is one and is about the earliest of all. The other is Bon Chrétien, called Williams Bon Chrétien, or just Williams in England and Bartlett in the United States.

The latter arrived in England some time in the latter part of the 18th century and acquired the name of Williams who was the great pear breeder of the day. About 1820, Enoch Bartlett of Dorchester, Massachusetts, released it in America under his own name. By the time that it was identified it was too late to change the name.

The finest American contribution to pear growing is the highly flavored Seckel. This was found on the Seckel farm near Philadelphia by a character called "Dutch Jacob," a cattle dealer and sportsman, who brought back the pear from one of his expeditions. He kept the source secret but was finally forced to protect his find by buying the piece of land on which the tree stood. It was sent to London in 1819 where the Royal Horticultural Society awarded its approval. The great period of pear growing in America was in the fifty years after 1820, interest centering in eastern Massachusetts and, particularly, the Massachusetts Horticultural Society. In the middle of the period Robert Manning of Salem was offering about 1,000 varieties and other growers' lists were in the many hundreds. Specialty shows with as many as 300 varieties shown continued into the 1900's.

pectinaceus, -a, -um [pek-tin-AY-shus]
pectinatus, -a, -um [pek-tin-AY-tus]
Comblike.

pectoniferus, -a, -um [pek-ton-IFF-er-us]
Having a comb.

pectoralis, -is, -e [pek-to-RAY-lis]
Shaped like a breastbone.

pedalis, -is, -e [pee-DAY-lis]
About one foot long.

pedatifidus, -a, -um [pee-day-TIFF-id-us]
Cut like a bird's foot.

pedatus, -a, -um [pee-DAY-tus]
Like a bird's foot, especially of leaves palmately cut with side divisions.

pedemontanus, -a, -um [pee-dee-mon-TAY-nus]
Of Piedmont, Italy.

Pedicularis [pee-dik-yew-LAY-ris]
Louse-wort, wood-betony. From L. *pediculus,* a louse. The presence of the plant in fields was supposed to produce lice in sheep.

pedicularius, -a, -um [pee-dik-yew-LAY-rius]
Lousy.

Pedilanthus [pee-dill-ANTH-us]
Slipper-flower. Gr. *pedos,* a shoe; *anthos,* a flower; from the appearance of the flowers on this succulent shrub.

Pediocactus [pee-di-o-KAK-tus]
Gr. *pedios,* a plain; plus *cactus;* from its habitat on the Great Plains.

peduncularis, -is, -e [pee-dunk-yew-LAY-ris]
pedunculatus, -a, -um [pee-dunk-yew-LAY-tus]
With a flower stalk.

pedunculosus, -a, -um [pee-dunk-yew-LO-sus]
With many flower stems.

Pelargonium [pel-ar-GO-nium]
The geranium of the florists. From Gr. *pelargos,* a stork. The fruit has a beak not unlike that of a stork. Sometimes called stork's-bill.

Pelecyphora [pel-e-SIFF-or-a]
Gr. *pelekos,* a hatchet; *phoreo,* to bear. The flattened tubercles of this cactus are thought to be hatched-shaped.

Pellaea [pell-EE-a]
Cliff-brake. From Gr. *pelloos*, dark; in allusion to the stalks of this fern's fronds which are generally dark.

Pellionia [pell-i-o-nia]
Creeping foliage plants named for Alphonse Pellion who accompanied the French navigator Freycinet on his voyage around the world (1800-1805).

Peltandra [pel-TAN-dra]
Arrow-arum. Gr. *pelta*, a shield; *aner*, a stamen; from the character of the male flowers.

Peltaria [pel-TAY-ria]
Shield-wort. Gr. *pelta*, a shield; from the form of the leaf of this garlic-scented herb.

peltatus, -a, -um [pel-TAY-tus]
Shield-shaped.

Peltiphyllum [pel-ti-FILL-um]
Umbrella plant. Gr. *pelta*, a shield, *phyllon*, a leaf; from the form of the leaves of this waterside perennial.

Peltophorum [pel-TOFF-or-um]
Gr. *pelta*, a shield; *phoreo*, to bear; from the form of the stigma of these tropical trees.

pelviformis, -is, -e [pel-vi-FORM-is]
Forming a shallow cup.

pendulus, -a, -um [PEN-dew-lus]
Hanging.

penicillatus, -a, -um [pen-iss-ill-LAY-tus]
penicillius, -a, -um [pen-i-SILL-ius]
Covered with tufts of hair.

peninsularis, -is, -e [pen-in-su-LAY-ris]
Relating to peninsulas.

Peniocereus [pen-i-o-SEE-reus]
Gr. *penios*, a thread; *cereus*, cactus. The stems are very slender.

pennatus, -a, -um [pen-AY-tus]
Feathered.

pennigerus, -a, -um [pen-IJ-er-us]
Bearing feathers, as featherlike leaves.

Pennisetum [pen-i-SEE-tum]
Gr. *penna*, a feather; *seta*, a bristle. The flower of these grasses has long, feathery bristles.

pennsylvanicus, -a, -um [pen-sil-VAY-nik-us]
From Pennsylvania.
pensilis, -is, -e [PEN-sil-is]
Hanging
Penstemon (also, incorrectly, **Pentstemon**) [pen-STEE-mon]
Beard-tongue. Gr. *pente*, five; *stemon*, a stamen. The plants
have five stamens, one of them sterile.
penta-
In compound words signifying five. Thus:

pentadenius	five-toothed
pentagonus	five-angled
pentagynus	with five pistils
pentandrus	with five stamens
pentapetaloides	resembling five petals
pentaphyllus	with five leaves
pentapterus	five-winged

Pentapterygium [pen-tap-ter-RIJ-ium]
Gr. *pente*, five; *pterygion*, a small wing. The calyx has five
small wings on this epiphytic shrub.
Peperomia [pep-er-o-mia]
Gr. *peperi*, pepper; *homos*, resembling. The plants resemble
and are closely related to true pepper.
perbellus, -a, -um [per-BELL-us]
Very beautiful.
percussus, -a, -um [per-KUS-us]
Perforated, or apparently so.
peregrinus, -a, -um [per-eg-GRY-nus]
Exotic; immigrant.
perennaeus, -a, -um [per-ENN-eus]
perennis, -is, -e [per-ENN-is]
Perennial.
Pereskia [per-ESK-ia]
Barbados gooseberry. Leafy cacti named for Nicholas Claude
Fabry de Peiresc (1580-1637), French naturalist.
Pereskiopsis [per-esk-i-OP-sis]
Pereskia (*q.v.*) plus Gr. *opsis*, like. The two genera re-
semble each other.
Perezia [per-EE-zia]
American herbs named for Lazarus Perez, 16th-century
Spanish apothecary, author of a history of drugs.

perfoliatus, -a, -um [per-fo-li-AY-tus]
 perfossus, -a, -um [per-FOSS-us]
With the leaf surrounding or embracing the stem; perfoliate.
perforatus, -a, -um [per-for-AY-tus]
Having small holes or appearing to.
pergracilis, -is, -e [per-GRAS-ill-is]
Very slender.
Perilla [per-ILL-a]
Beefsteak plant. Derivation obscure; possibly from the native oriental name for these annuals.
Periploca [per-i-PLO-ka]
Silk vine. Gr. *peri,* around; *ploke,* twining. Some species intertwine.
Peristeria [per-iss-TEE-ria]
Gr. *peristera,* a dove. The column has a dovelike appearance.
Peristrophe [per-iss-tro-fee]
Gr. *peri,* around; *strophe,* a belt; an allusion to the form of the bracts beneath the flowers of these tropical herbs.
permixtus, -a, -um [per-MIX-tus]
Much-mixed.
Pernettya (originally **Pernettia**) [per-NET-ia]
Ornamental shrubs of the heath family named for Antoine Joseph Pernetty (1716-1801), who sailed with Bougainville and wrote the story of his voyage to the South Pacific (1766-1769).
Perovskia [per-ov-skia]
Semi-woody plants named for V. A. Perovski, Governor of a Russian Central Asian province, c. 1890.
Persea [PER-see-a]
Avocado or alligator pear. From the Greek name for an Egyptian tree.
persicaefolius, -a, -um [per-sik-ee-FO-lius]
 persicifolius, -a, -um [per-sik-eye-FO-lius]
With leaves like a peach.
persicus, -a, -um [PER-sik-us]
Persian.
persistus, -a, -um [per-SIS-tus]
Persistent.
Persoonia [per-SOO-nia]
European shrubs or small trees named for Christian

Hendrick Persoon (1761-1836), South African botanist, who worked and died in Paris.

persolutus, -a, -um [per-so-LEW-tus]
Garland-like.

perspicuus, -a, -um [per-SPIK-yew-us]
Transparent.

pertusus, -a, -um [per-TEW-sus]
Perforated; thrust through.

perulatus, -a, -um [per-yew-LAY-tus]
Like a pocket.

peruvianus, -a, -um [per-yew-vi-AY-nus]
Peruvian.

petaloideus, -a, -um [pet-al-OY-deus]
Petal-like.

Petalostemum [pet-al-o-STEE-mum]
Prairie-clover. Gr. *petalon*, a petal; *stemon*, a stamen. Petals and stamens are joined.

Petasites [pet-a-SY-tees]
Butter-bur. The Greek name, from *petasos*, a hat with a broad brim, with reference to the large leaves of this herb.

petiolaris, -is, -e [pet-i-o-LAY-ris]
petiolatus, -a, -um [pet-i-o-LAY-tus]
Furnished with a leaf stalk.

Petiveria [pet-i-VEE-ria]
Shrubby herbs named for James Petiver (1665-1718), apothecary of London.

petraeus, -a, -um [pet-REE-us]
Rock-loving.

Petrea [PET-rea]
Tropical American woody plants named for Lord Petre (1713-1743), patron of botany, called "the Phoenix of this age" by Collinson.

Petrocallis [pet-ro-KAL-is]
Gr. *petros*, a rock; *kallis*, beauty; from the habitat and the beauty of the flowers.

petrocallis, -is, -e [pet-ro-KAL-is]
Rock beauty.

Petrocoptis [pet-ro-KOP-tis]
Gr. *petros*, a rock; *kopto*, to break. These dwarf plants grow in cracks and broken crevices of rock.

Petrophila [pet-ROFF-ill-a]

Gr. *petros,* a rock; *phileo,* to love; from the habitat of these Australian shrubs.

Petrophytum [pet-ROFF-fy-tum]

Gr. *petros,* a rock; *phyton,* a plant. These prostrate shrubs inhabit stony places.

Petroselinum [pet-ro-sel-LY-num]

Parsley. Gr. *petros,* a rock; L. *selinum,* parsley. It is not clear why the name was not left as *Selinum.*

Petteria [pet-EE-ria]

A yellow-flowered shrub named for Franz Petter (1798-1853), Austrian professor at Spalato who wrote on the botany of Dalmatia.

Petunia [pet-YEW-nia]

The Latinized Brazilian name for these popular annuals.

Peucedanum [pew-SEE-dan-um]

The Greek name for parsnip. See *Pastinacea.*

Peumus [pee-YEW-mus]

Chilean boldo tree. The Chilean name latinized.

Phacelia [fass-EE-lia]

California-bluebell. Gr. *phakelos,* a bundle; from the arrangement of the flowers.

Phaedranthus [fee-DRAN-thus]

Gr. *phaidros,* joyous; *anthos,* a flower. The flowers of this Mexican climber are showy.

phaeocarpus, -a, -um [fee-o-KARP-us]

With dark fruit.

phaeus, -a, -um [FEE-us]

Dusky.

Phaius [FY-us]

Gr. *phaios,* dusky. The flowers of most species of these orchids are dark-colored.

Phalaenopsis [fal-ee-NOP-sis]

Moth orchid. Gr. *phalaina,* a moth; *opsis,* like.

Phalaris [FAL-a-ris]

Greek name for a grass, but not this one, which is sometimes grown for bird feed.

Phaseolus [fass-EE-o-lus]

Greek name for bean. Known from antiquity and cultivated all over the world, this genus includes the French or string bean, limas, and scarlet runners. Other beans are included under *Vicia* (the broad or horse bean) and *Glycine* (soybean.

Phebalium   [fee-BAY-lium]
Gr. *phibale,* myrtle; from the similarity of the plants.

Phellodendron   [fell-o-DEN-dron]
Cork-tree. Gr. *phellos,* cork; *dendron,* a tree; from the corky bark. This is not the cork-producing cork-oak (*Quercus suber*).

Phellosperma   [fell-o-SPERM-a]
Gr. *phellos,* cork; *sperma,* a seed; because of the corky base of the seed of these cacti.

philadelphicus, -a, -um   [fill-a-DEL-fik-us]
Of Philadelphia.

Philadelphus   [fill-a-DEL-fus]
Mock-orange. The Greek name meaning brotherly. In some parts of England the flowers were often used to take the place of orange blossoms in the country bride's wedding bouquet. It is sometimes (wrongly) called syringa as a vernacular name.

Philesia   [fill-EE-sia]
Gr. *phileo,* to love; from the beauty of the flowers of this Chilean shrub.

Phillyrea   [fill-LI-rea]
The classical Greek name for these ornamental evergreen shrubs and small trees.

Philodendron   [fill-o-DEN-dron]
Gr. *phileo,* to love; *dendron,* a tree; from the tree-climbing habits of these ornamental plants.

phleioides   [fly-OY-deez]
Phleum-like or resembling a reed.

Phleum   [FLEE-um]
Timothy. The name for these perennial grasses comes from Gr. *phleos,* a kind of rush or reed.

phlogiflorus, -a, -um   [flog-i-FLO-rus]
With flame-colored flowers; with flowers like *Phlox.*

phlogifolius, -a, -um   [flog-i-FO-lius]
With leaves like *Phlox.*

Phlomis   [FLO-mis]
Jerusalem sage. Greek name for some plant without application here to these herbs and shrubs.

Phlox [flox]
Gr. *phlox,* a flame. Also the Greek name for some plant with flame-colored flowers.

phoeniceus, -a, -um [fee-NISH-us]
Purple-red.

phoenicolasius, -a, -um [fee-ni-lo-LASS-ius]
With purple hairs.

Phoenix [FEE-nix]
Date palm. The Greek name.

Pholidota [fo-lid-O-ta]
Rattlesnake orchid. Gr. *pholidos,* a scale; *ous,* an ear. The allusion is to the scaly earlike bracts on these epiphytic orchids.

Phormium [FORM-ium]
New Zealand flax. Gr. *phormos,* a basket. The plant provides a fiber which can be woven. It is an important cordage plant in New Zealand.

Photinia [fo-TIN-ia]
Gr. *photizo,* to illuminate; from the shining leaves on these shrubs and trees.

Phragmites [frag-MY-teez]
Gr. *phragma,* a fence or screen; from the habit of these large grasses of hedgelike growth along ditches.

Phygelius [fy-JEE-lius]
Gr. *phyga,* flight; *helios,* the sun. These small South African shrubs are said to do best in shade.

phrygius, -a, -um [FRIJ-ius]
From Phrygia in the western part of Asia Minor.

Phylica [FILL-iss-a]
Gr. *phyllikos,* leafy; in allusion to these shrubs' abundant foliage.

Phyllagathis [fill-AG-ath-is]
Gr. *phyllon,* a leaf; *agathos,* divine. The foliage is beautiful on these herbaceous shrubs.

Phyllanthus [fill-ANTH-us]
Gr. *phyllon,* a leaf; *anthos,* a flower. In some species the flowers are produced on the edges of the leaflike branches of these herbs, shrubs, and trees.

Phyllitis [fill-LY-tis]
Hart's-tongue fern. Gr. *phyllon,* a leaf; the fronds of these ferns are simple.

Phyllocladus [fill-OK-lay-dus]

Gr. *phyllon,* a leaf; *klados,* a branch. The branches of these evergreen trees and shrubs are flattened like leaves.

Phyllodoce [fill-ODD-o-see]

Heathlike shrubs named for a sea-nymph, attendant of Cyrene, a local North African sea goddess.

phyllomaniacus, -a, -um [fill-o-man-EYE-ak-us]

Running wildly to leaves.

Phyllostachys [fill-os-tak-is]

Gr. *phyllon,* a leaf; *stachys,* a spike; referring to the leafy inflorescence of these bamboos.

Physalis [FY-sal-is]

Cape gooseberry. Ground-cherry. Gr. *physa,* a bladder; from the inflated calyx of these herbs.

Physocarpus [fy-so-KARP-us]

Nine bark. Gr. *physa,* a bladder; *karpos,* fruit; from the inflated follicles of these deciduous shrubs.

Physosiphon [fy-so-SY-fon]

Gr. *physa,* a bladder; *siphon,* a tube. The tube of the flower is inflated.

Physostegia [fy-so-STEE-jia]

Obedient plant. False dragon-head. Gr. *physa,* a bladder; *stege,* a covering. The fruits of these herbaceous perennials are covered by an inflated calyx.

Phytelephas [fy-TELL-eff-as]

Ivory-nut palm. Gr. *phyton,* a plant; *elephas,* ivory. The nut of this palm is vegetable ivory which in some ways resembles true ivory. It can be carved into various articles as large as billiard balls.

Phyteuma [fy-TEW-ma]

Rampion. The Greek name for some aphrodisiac plant. Rampion was once supposed to have the same property.

Phytolacca [fy-to-LAK-a]

Pokeweed, pokeberry, inkberry. Gr. *phyton,* a plant; L. *lacca,* the lac insect from which a dark dye can be extracted. The allusion is to the staining qualities of the fruit of these herbs, shrubs, or trees.

Picea [PY-see-a or PISS-ee-a]

Spruce. Gr. *pix,* pitch; in allusion to the exuded resin of these trees.

picturatus, -a, -um [pik-tew-RAY-tus]
With variegated leaves.

pictus, -a, -um [PIK-tus]
Painted; brightly colored.

Pieris [py-EE-ris]
Andromeda. Handsome shrubs named for the Pierides, the generic name of the Muses.

Pilea [PILL-ea, also PY-lea]
Gr. *pilos*, a cap; from the shape of the flowers of these herbs.

pileatus, -a, -um [pill-ee-AY-tus]
Furnished with a cap.

piliferus, -a, -um [py-LIFF-er-us]
With soft short hairs.

pilosus, -a, -um [py-LO-sus]
Covered with long soft hairs.

Pilularis, -is, -e [pil-yew-LAY-ris]
piluliferus, -a, -um [pil-yew-LIFF-er-us]
With globular fruit.

Pimelea [pim-ELL-ea]
Rice-flower. Gr. *pimele*, fat; from the oily, fleshy seeds of these shrubs.

pimeleoides [pim-ell-e-OY-deez]
Like *Pimelea.*

Pimenta [pim-EN-ta]
Allspice. From Spanish *pimento*. Not to be confused with pimiento (*Capsicum*).

Pimpinella [pim-pin-ELL-a]
Anise. Derivation of these herbs' name is uncertain. The fruit of one species yields oil of anise with a strong, aromatic flavor. Most of the oil of commerce used by liqueur makers is derived from the star-anise of China (*Illicium verum*).

pimpinellifolius, -a, -um [pim-pin-ell-i-FO-lius]
With leaves like *Pimpinella.*

Pinanga [pin-ANG-ga]
From the Malayan name for these palms.

pinetorum [py-nee-TOW-rum]
Of pine forests.

pineus, -a, -um [PY-neus]
Relating to the pine.

Pinguicula [pink-GWIK-yew-la]
Butterwort. L. *pinguis,* fat; an allusion to the greasy appearance of the leaves of these insectivorous herbs.
pinguifolius -a, -um [pin-gwi-FO-lius]
With fat leaves.
pinifolius, -a, -um [py-ni-FO-lius]
With leaves like pine.
pinnatus -a, -um [pin-NAY-tus]
Featherlike; having leaflets arranged on each side of a common stalk. Also:

pinnatifidus	cut in feather form
pinnatifolius	with leaves like feathers
pinnatifrons	with featherlike fronds
pinnatinervis	with nerves like feathers

Pinus [PY-nus]
Pine. The Latin name.
P. strobus, the magnificent white pine of North America and one of the most beautiful species, is often called Weymouth pine in England from the name of the ship which brought in the first cargo from 17th-century New England. The arbitrary marking by the Crown of all pines over 24 inches diameter as Crown property for mast timber was one of the causes of discontent which helped feed the fires of the Revolution. As a consequence too it is very seldom possible to find pine boards in old New England houses in excess of 23 inches width because anything wider would automatically have been taken from a Crown mast-tree.
Mast timbers were shipped in large quantity from northern New England ports in special mast ships loaded through bow ports which were closed and battened down for the voyage home.
Piper [PY-per]
Pepper. The Latin name. Black pepper is made from the whole fruit of *Piper nigrum,* a vinelike climbing plant. For the more expensive white pepper, the external coat is removed and with it much of the flavor.
piperascens [py-per-ASS-ens]
Like pepper.
piperitus, -a, -um [py-per-RY-tus]
Like the pepper vine; pepperlike.

Piptadenia [pip-ta-DEEN-ia]
Gr. *pipto*, to fall; *aden*, a gland; with reference to the falling glands on the stamens of these tropical trees and shrubs.

Piptanthus [pip-TAN-thus]
Gr. *pipto*, to fall; *anthos*, a flower. The blooms are not long-lived on these ornamental Asian shrubs.

Piqueria [py-KWEE-ria]
Fragrant perennial herbs and shrubs named for A. Piquer, 18th-century Spanish author.

pisiferus, -a, -um [py-SIFF-er-us]
Pea-bearing.

pisocarpus, -a, -um [py-SO-KARP-us]
With pealike fruit.

Pistacia [pis-TAY-shia]
Pistachio. From *pistake*, the Greek name for the nut.

Pistia [PIS-tia]
Water-lettuce. Gr. *pistos*, water; in allusion to the watery habitat of this herb.

Pisum [PY-sum]
Pea. The Latin name. Peas, known since prehistoric times, have been found in Swiss lake dwellings of the Bronze Age.

Pitcairnia [pit-KAIRN-ia]
Low herbs and shrubs with showy flowers named tor W. Pitcairn (1711-1791), London physician.

Pithecellobium (also, **Pithecolobium**) [pith-ee-sell-o-bium]
Gr. *pithekos*, a monkey; *lobos*, an ear. The native name for these tropical trees and shrubs means monkey's ear.

Pittosporum [pit-os-por-um]
Parchment bark. Australian laurel. Gr. *pitta*, pitch; *speros*, seed. The seed of these evergreen woody plants has a resinous coating.

Pityrogramma [pit-ty-ro-GRAM-ma]
Gold fern, silver fern. Gr. *pituron*, chaff; *gramma*, writing; from the powder on the fonds.

placatus, -a, -um [plak-AY-tus]
Quiet; calm.

Plagianthus [plaj-i-ANTH-us]
Ribbon wood. Gr. *plagios*, oblique; *anthos*, a flower. The petals have unequal sides on these trees or shrubs.

MEANINGS AND ORIGINS OF NAMES

Planera [plan-EE-ra]
Water-elm. Named for J. J. Planer (1743-1789), German botanist.

Plantago [plan-TAY-go]
Plantain. The Latin name for these herbs and sub-shrubs.

planus, -a, -um [PLAY-nus]
Flat. Also:

planiflorus with flat flowers
planifolius with flat leaves
planipes with a flat stalk

platanifolius, -a, -um [plat-an-i-FO-lius]
With leaves like the plane tree (*Platanus*).

platanoides [plat-an-OY-deez]
Resembling a plane tree (*Platanus*).

Platanus [plat-TAY-nus]
Plane tree. The Greek name.
The London plane (*P. acerifolius*) is the most widely planted city tree in London, Paris, New York, and other northern cities. It stands almost every kind of abuse, atmospheric and otherwise. It was originally a cross (*P. occidentalis* × *orientalis*), first raised, it is said, in Oxford prior to 1700. Handel's too well-known "Largo" is an ode to a plane tree.

platy-
In compound words signifies flat or broad. Thus:

platanthus with flat flowers
platycanthus with flat spines
platycarpus flat-fruited
platycaulis with a flat stem
platycentrus with a flat center
platycladus flat-branched
platyglossus flat-tongued
platypetalus with flat petals
platyphyllus flat-leaved
platypodus flat-stalked
platyspathus with a flat spathe
platyspermus flat-seeded

Platycarya [plat-i-KAY-ria]
Gr. *platys*, broad; *karya*, a nut, from the form of the fruit of this deciduous Chinese tree.

Platycerium   [plat-i-SEE-rium]
Staghorn fern. Gr. *platys*, broad; *keras*, a horn; in allusion to the form of the fronds.

Platycodon   [plat-i-KO-don]
Balloon flower. Japanese bellflower. Gr. *platys*, broad; *kodon*, a bell; from the form of the bellflowers.

Platystemon   [plat-i-STEE-mon]
Gr. *platys*, broad; *stemon*, a stamen. The stamens are broad on these low annual herbs.

Pleione   [ply-o-nee]
Indian crocus. Indian mountain orchids named for the mother of the seven Pleiades.

pleionervis, -is, -e   [ply-o-NERV-is]
With many nerves.

Pleiospilos   [ply-o-SPY-los]
Gr. *pleios*, many; *spilos*, a spot. The leaves of these succulent plants are conspicuously spotted.

pleniflorus, -a, -um   [plee-ni-FLO-rus]
With double flowers.

plenissimus, -a, -um   [plee-NISS-im-us]
Very double.

plenus, -a, -um   [PLEE-nus]
Double or full.

pleurostachys   [plew-ro-STAK-is]
With spikes on the side.

Pleurothallis   [plew-ro-THAL-is]
Gr. *pleuron*, a side; *thallo*, to blossom; an allusion to the position of the flowers at the junction of the leaf stalks to the stems of these epiphytic orchids.

plicatus, -a, -um   [ply-KAY-tus]
Plaited.

plumarius, -a, -um   [ploo-MAY-rius]
plumatus, -a, -um   [ploo-MAY-tus]
Plumed; feathered.

plumbaginioides   [plum-bay-jin-i-OY-deez]
Like *Plumbago*.

Plumbago   [plum-BAY-go]
Leadwort. The Latin name derived from *plumbum*, lead; possibly because the plant was used in the treatment of lead poisoning.

plumbeus, -a, -um [PLUM-beus]
Relating to lead.

Plumeria (also, incorrectly, **Plumiera**) [ploo-MEE-ria]
Frangipani. Tropical trees named for Charles Plumier (1646-1704), French traveler and author.

plumosus, -a, -um [ploo-MO-sus]
Feathery.

pluriflorus, -a, -um [plur-i-FLO-rus]
Many-flowered.

Poa [PO-a]
Gr. *poa*, grass. The genus comprises a variety of useful lawn and fodder grasses including Kentucky and Canada blue grass.

poculiformis, is, -e [po-kew-li-FORM-is]
Cup-shaped.

Podachaenium [po-da-CHEE-nium]
Gr. *pous*, a foot; *achene*, an achene or dry, one-seeded fruit. The allusion is to a technical aspect of the achenes on these tall shrubs.

Podalyria [po-da-LI-ria]
South African shrubs named for Podalyrius, son of Aesculapius.

Podocarpus [po-do-KAR-pus]
Gr. *pous*, a foot; *karpos*, a fruit. The fruits of these evergreen trees related to yew are borne on a fleshy stalk.

Podolepis [po-do-LEP-is]
Gr. *pous*, a foot; *lepis*, a scale. The pedicels of these Australian herbs are scaly.

podolicus, -a, -um [po-DO-lik-us]
From the Ukraine in southwestern Russia (Podolia).

Podophyllum [pod-o-FILL-um]
May-apple. Gr. *pous*, a foot; *phyllon*, a leaf; the reasoning is obscure.
The roots of these herbs have medicinal properties as a cathartic.

podophyllus, -a, -um [pod-o-FILL-us]
With stout-stalked leaves.

poeticus, -a, -um [po-ET-ik-us]
Pertaining to poets.

Pogonia [po-GO-nia]
Adder's mouth. Gr. *pogonias,* bearded. The lip in most species of these terrestrial orchids is fringed.

Poinciana [poin-si-AY-na]
Flamboyant. Showy-flowered trees named for M. de Poinci, 17th-century French Governor of Martinique.

Poinsettia [poin-SETT-ia]
Although now included under *Euphorbia* it will probably remain popularly *Poinsettia* indefinitely. It was named for Joel R. Poinsette (1775-1851), gardener, botanist, and diplomat of South Carolina. The first American Ambassador to Mexico in 1824, he introduced the plant to Charleston friends in 1833. He was bitterly opposed to Secession and for that reason his name is often held in small account in the South.

Polemonium [po-lee-MO-nium]
The Greek name for these herbaceous perennials. Jacob's ladder is *P. coeruleum.*

Polianthes [po-li-ANTH-eez]
Tuberose. Gr. *polios,* white; *anthos,* a flower.

polifolius, -a, -um [po-li-FO-lius]
Having white leaves.

Poliothyrsis [po-li-o-THER-sis]
Gr. *polios,* white, *thyrsos,* a panicle; in allusion to the white panicles of this tree.

politus, -a, -um [po-LY-tus]
Elegant; polished.

poly-
In compound words signifies many. Thus:

polyacanthus	with many thorns
polyandrus	with many stamens
polyanthemos	with many flowers
polyanthus	with many flowers
polybotryus	with many clusters
polybulbon	with many bulbs
polycarpus	many-fruited
polycephalus	many-headed
polychromus	of many colors
polylepis	with many scales

polymorphus	of many forms; variable
polypetalus	with many petals
polyphyllus	with many leaves
polyrrhizus	many-rooted
polysepalus	with many sepals
polystachyus	many-spiked
polystictus	many-spotted

Polygala [po-LIG-gal-a]
Milkwort. The Greek name, from *polys*, much; *gala*, milk. These herbs and shrubs were reputed to aid the secretion of milk.

polygaloides [po-lig-gal-OY-deez]
Resembling *Polygala*.

Polygonatum [po-lig-o-NA-tum]
Solomon's seal. The Greek name. From *polys*, many; *gonu*, the knee-joint; in allusion to the many joints of the rhizomes. Once reputed to have value in healing bruises.

Polygonum [po-LIG-on-um]
Smart or knotweed. Gr. *polys*, many; *gonu*, a knee-joint; from the many joints in the stems.

Polypodium [po-lip-PO-dium]
Polypody fern. Gr. *polys*, many; *pous*, a foot. The rhizomes are much branched and spread widely.

Polypteris [po-LIP-ter-is]
Gr. *polys*, many; *pteron*, a wing; in allusion to the form of the pappus on these North American herbs.

Polyscias [po-LISS-ias]
Gr. *polys*, many; *skias*, shade; because of the abundant foliage on these ornamental shrubs and trees.

Polystachya [po-liss-TAK-ia]
Gr. *polys*, many; *stachys*, a spike. The reference is to the form of the inflorescence of many species of these epiphytic orchids.

Polystichum [po-LISS-tik-um]
Christmas fern. Gr. *polys*, many; *stichos*, a row. The sori of these ferns are in many rows.

pomaceus, -a, -um [po-MAY-shus]
Applelike.

Pomaderris [po-ma-DER-ris]
Gr. *poma*, a lid; *derris*, a leathern covering; from the membranous covering of the capsule on these flowering shrubs.

pomeridianus, -a, -um [po-mer-rid-i-AY-nus]
Of the afternoon.

pomiferus, -a, -um [po-MIFF-er-us]
Apple-bearing.

pomponius, -a, -um [pom-PO-nius]
With a tuft or topknot.

Poncirus [pon-SY-rus]
Hardy orange. Fr. *Poncire,* a kind of fragrant citron. This shrub can be used as a root-stock for citrus fruits.

ponderosus, -a, -um [pon-der-o-sus]
Heavy.

Pongamia [pong-GAY-mia]
From the Malabar name for this tree or shrub.

Pontederia [pon-te-DEE-ria]
Aquatic perennials named for G. Pontedera (1688-1757), Professor of Botany at Padua. *P. cordata* is pickerel-weed.

ponticus, -a, -um [PON-tik-us]
From the south shore of the Black Sea.

populifolius, -a, -um [pop-yew-li-FO-lius]
Poplar-leaved.

populneus, -a, -um [pop-ULL-neus]
Relating to poplar.

Populus [POP-yew-lus]
Poplar. The Latin name. Includes aspen, cottonwood, popple, and so on.

Porana [po-RAY-na]
From the East Indian name for these twining herbs or shrubs.

porcinus, -a, -um [por-SY-nus]
Relating to pigs; pig-food.

porophyllus, -a, -um [po-ro-FILL-us]
Having holes in the leaves or seeming to.

porrifolius, -a, -um [po-ri-FO-lius]
With leaves like leek. L. *porrum,* meaning leek, is now the specific name.

porphyreus, -a, -um [por-FY-reus]
Warm reddish color.

Portlandia [port-LAND-ia]
Ornamental trees and shrubs named for the Duchess of Portland (1715-1785), bluestocking friend and correspondent of Jean Jacques Rousseau.

Portulaca [por-tew-LAY-ka]
Purslane. From the Latin name, *portilaca*, for these fleshy herbs.

Portulacaria [por-tew-lak-KAY-ria]
Closely related to *Portulaca*.

portulaceus, -a, -um [por-tew-LAY-shus]
Portulaca-like.

Posoqueria [po-so-KWEE-ria]
From the native Guiana name for these shrubs or small trees.

potamophilus, -a, -um [pot-am-OFF-ill-us]
Loving rivers or wet places.

potatorum [po-tat-OR-rum]
Relating to drinkers.

Potentilla [po-ten-TILL-a]
Cinquefoil. L. *potens*, powerful; from the reputed medicinal properties.

Poterium [pot-EE-rium]
Greek name for another plant (burnet), not these herbs and shrubs.

Pothos [PO-thos]
From the Cingalese name for these climbers.

praealtus, -a, -um [pree-ALT-us]
Very tall.

praecox [pree-kox]
Very early.

praemorsus, -a, -um [pree-MOR-sus]
Appearing to be bitten off at the end.

praestans [PREE-stans]
Distinguished; excelling.

praetextus, -a, -um [pree-TEX-tus]
Bordered.

prasinatus, -a, -um [pras-in-NAY-tus]
Greenish.

prasinus, -a, -um [pras-SY-nus]
Grass-green.

pratensis, -is, -e [prat-ENS-is]
Of the meadows.

Pratia [PRAY-tia]
Low-growing herbs named for a French naval officer, Prat-Bernon, who sailed with Freycinet on his voyage to the

South Pacific in 1817 but who died within a few days of the expedition's setting out.

pravissimus, -a, -um [prav-ISS-im-us]
Very crooked.

precatorius, -a, -um [prek-at-O-rius]
Relating to prayer.

Premna [PREM-na]
Gr. *premnon,* the stump of a tree. Most of these trees and shrubs are low growing.

prenans [PREE-nans]
Drooping.

Prenanthes [pree-NAN-theez]
Rattlesnake root. Gr. *prenes,* face downwards; *anthos,* a flower. The flower heads droop on these perennial herbs.

Primula [PRIM-yew-la]
Primrose. Diminutive of L. *primus,* first; implying that the flowers are first in spring.

primulaefolius, -a, -um [prim-yew-lee-FO-lius]
primulifolius, -a, -um [prim-yew-li-FO-lius]
Primrose-leaved.

primulinus, -a, -um [prim-yew-LY-nus]
primuloides [prim-yew-LOY-deez]
Resembling primrose.

princeps [PRIN-seps]
Distinguished.

Prinsepia [prin-SEE-pia]
Asian shrubs named for James Prinsep (1799-1840), Secretary of the Asiatic Society of Bengal.

prismaticus, -a, -um [pris-MAT-ik-us]
Shaped like a prism.

Pritchardia [prich-ARD-ia]
Fan palms named for W. T. Pritchard, 19th-century British official in Polynesia.

proboscideus, -a, -um [pro-bos-SID-eus]
Snoutlike.

procerus, -a, -um [pro-SEE-rus]
Tall.

procumbens [pro-KUM-bens]
Prostrate.

procurrens [pro-KUR-ens]
Spreading out under ground.

MEANINGS AND ORIGINS OF NAMES

productus, -a, -um [pro-DUK-tus]
Lengthened.
profusus, -a, -um [pro-FEW-sus]
Abundant.
proliferus, -a, -um [pro-LIFF-er-us]
Producing side shoots in order to increase.
prolificus, -a, -um [pro-LIFF-ik-us]
Very fruitful.
Promenaea [pro-men-EE-a]
Small orchids named after a Greek prophetess of that name.
propens [pro-PENS]
Hanging down.
propinquus, -a, -um [pro-PIN-kwus]
Related.
Prosopis [pro-SO-pis]
Mesquite. The Greek name for the butter-bur, but why it was allotted here is obscure.
The tree is of great economic value. The pods are eagerly eaten by stock and also by humans.
Prostanthera [pro-stan-THEE-ra]
Mint-bush. Gr. *prostithemi,* to append or add to; *anthera,* anthers. The allusion is to a somewhat technical character-istic of the anthers.
prostratus, -a, -um [pro-STRAY-tus]
Flat to the ground.
Protea [PRO-tee-a]
Cape-of-Good-Hope shrubs, trees, and perennials named for Proteus, a potent Greek sea-god.
protrusus, -a, -um [pro-TREW-sus]
Protruding.
provincialis, -is, -e [pro-vin-si-AY-lis]
From Provence in France.
pruinatus, -a, -um [prew-in-AY-tus]
pruinosus, -a, -um [prew-in-o-sus]
Glistening as though frosted over.
Prunella [proo-NELL-a]
Self-heal. Probably from the German, meaning quinsy which these herbs were supposed to cure.
prunelloides [proo-nell-OY-deez]
Resembling *Prunella.*

prunifolius, -a, -um [proo-ni-FO-lius]
With leaves like plum.

Prunus [PROO-nus]
Plum. Cherry. The Latin name.

pruriens [PROO-riens]
Itching.

Pseuderanthemum [soo-der-ANTH-em-um]
Gr. *pseudo*, false, plus *Eranthemum*. These showy shrubs
are related to *Eranthemum*.

Pseudolarix [soo-do-LAY-rix]
Golden larch. Gr. *pseudo*, false; *Larix,* larch, which it resembles.

Pseudopanax [soo-do-PAY-nax]
Gr. *pseudo*, false; *Panax*, which this genus of shrubs and
trees resembles.

Pseudophoenix [soo-do-FEE-nix]
Gr. *pseudo*, false; *Phoenix*, the date palm, to which this
palm bears a general resemblance.

Pseudotsuga [soo-do-TSOO-ga]
Douglas fir. Gr. *pseudo;* false; *Tsuga,* hemlock. There is
some resemblance.

Psidium [SID-ium]
Guava. Gr. *psidion*, a pomegranate. These evergreen shrubs
and trees have edible fruit.

psittacinus, -a, -um [sit-ta-SY-nus]
Parrotlike.

psittacorum [sit-ta-KOR-um]
Of parrots.

Psophocarpus [so-fo-KAR-pus]
Gr. *psophos*, a noise. The seed capsules of these twiners
explode noisily when ripe.

Psoralea [so-RAY-lea]
Scurfy pea. Gr. *psoraleos,* scabby. These herbs and shrubs
are covered with spots.

Psychotria [sy-KO-tria]
Wild coffee. Gr. *psyche*, life. The plant was supposed to
have potent medicinal properties.

psycodes [sy-KO-deez]
Fragrant.

Ptelea [TEE-lee-a]
Greek name for an elm tree, but the application here is
obscure.

pteranthus, -a, -um [ter-ANTH-us]
  With winged flowers.
Pteridium [ter-ID-ium]
  Bracken. Brake. Gr. *pteron,* a wing; from the form of the
  fronds of these ferns. Commonly known as *Pteris.*
pteridoides [ter-id-OY-deez]
  Resembling *Pteris.*
Pteris [TEE-ris]
  Gr. *pteron,* a wing; from the feathery fronds. (See *Pterid-
  ium.*)
Pterocarya [ter-o-KAY-ria]
  Gr. *pteron,* a wing; *karya,* a nut. These ornamental trees
  are called wing-nut.
Pterocephalus [ter-o-SEFF-al-us]
  Gr. *pteron,* a wing; *kephale,* a head. The fruiting head of
  these herbs and shrubs appears to be covered with feathers.
pteroneurus, -a, -um [ter-o-NEW-rus]
  With winged nerves.
Pterospermum [ter-o-SPERM-um]
  Gr. *pteron,* a wing; *sperma,* a seed. The seeds of these
  trees or shrubs are winged.
Pterostyrax [ter-os-ty-rax]
  Gr. *pteron,* a wing; plus *Styrax.* The seeds of one species
  of these *Halesia*-like trees and shrubs have winged seeds
  like *Styrax.*
Ptychosperma [ty-ko-SPER-ma]
  Gr. *ptyche,* a fold; *sperma,* a seed; in allusion to a technical
  characteristic of the seed of these palms.
pubens [PEW-bens]
  pubescens [pew-BESS-ens]
  Downy.
pudicus, -a, -um [PEW-dik-us]
  Bashful.
Pueraria [pew-er-RAY-ria]
  Herbs and shrubs. Climbers and twiners, named for M. N.
  Puerari (1765-1845), Danish botanist.
pugioniformis, -is, -e [pew-ji-o-ni-FORM-is]
  Dagger-shaped.
pulchellus, -a, -um [pul-KEL-us]
  pulcher, pulchra, pulchrum [PUL-ker]
  Pretty.

pullus, -a, -um [PULL-us]
Dark-colored.

Pulmonaria [pul-mo-NAY-ria]
Lungwort. L. *pulmo*, the lung. The plant was considered to be an effective remedy for diseases of the lung for the reason that the spotted leaves were supposed to resemble diseased lungs.

Pultenaea [pul-ten-EE-a]
Shrubs named for Dr. Richard Pulteney (1730-1801), English botanist.

pulverulentus, -a, -um [pul-ver-rew-LENT-us]
Powdered as with dust.

pulvinatus, -a, -um [pul-vin-NAY-tus]
Cushionlike.

pumilus, -a, -um [PEW-mill-us]
Dwarf.

punctatus, -a, -um [punk-TAY-tus]
Spotted.

pungens [PUN-jens]
Sharp-pointed.

Punica [PEW-nik-a-]
Pomegranate. The Latin name.

puniceus, -a, -um [pew-NISS-eus]
Reddish-purple.

purgans [PER-gans]
Purgative.

purpuraceus, -a, -um [per-per-AY-seus]
purpuratus, -a, -um [per-per-AY-tus]
purpureus, -a, -um [per-PER-eus]
Purple. Also *purpurascens*, tending to purple.

Purshia [PER-sha]
A spreading shrub named for Frederick Traugott Pursh (1774-1820), German explorer, collector, horticulturist, author, who made distinguished contributions to America in all his fields during the twenty-one years he resided there.

Puschkinia [push-KIN-ia]
Striped squill. Bulbous plants named for the Russian Count Mussin-Puschkin (d. 1805), who collected in the Caucasus.

pusillus, -a, -um [pew-SILL-us]
Very small.

pustulatus, -a, -um [pus-tew-LAY-tus]
Appearing as though blistered.

Puya [PEW-ya]
The Chilean vernacular name for these herbaceous or woody plants.

Pycnanthemum [pik-NAN-the-mum]
Mountain mint. Gr. *pyknos*, dense; *anthos*, a flower. The flowers of these North American perennial herbs are densely arranged.

Pychnostachys [pik-NOSS-tak-is]
Gr. *pychnos*, dense; *stachys*, a spike. These perennial herbs have dense flower spikes.

pygmaeus, -a, -um [pig-MEE-us]
Pygmy.

Pyracantha [py-ra-KAN-tha]
Fire-thorn. Gr. *pyr*, fire; *acanthos*, a thorn; in allusion to the thorny branches and the showy crimson fruit of these shrubs.

pyramidalis, -is, -e [py-ram-id-DAY-lis]
Pyramid-shaped.

pyrenaeus, -a, -um [pi-ren-EE-us]
pyrenaicus, -a,-um [pi-ren-NY-kus]
From the Pyrenees.

Pyrethrum [py-REE-thrum]
Feverfew. Gr. *pyr*, fire; in allusion to the bitter roots which were regarded as a remedy for fevers. Now classified under *Chrysanthemum*, but the older name remains in familiar use. The dried heads of one species (C. *cinerariaefolium*) provide an effective insecticide, and the plant is grown as a crop for that purpose.

pyrifolius, -a, -um [py-ri-FO-lius]
Pear-leaved.

pyriformis, -is, -e [py-ri-FORM-is]
Pear-shaped.

Pyrola [PYR-o-la]
Shinleaf. The Latin diminutive of *Pyrus*, pear, from the pear-shaped leaves of these low perennial herbs.

Pyrostegia [py-ro-STEE-jia]
Gr. *pyr*, fire; *stegia*, a roof; from the color and form of the upperlip of the flowers on these ornamental vines.

Pyrus [PY-rus]
Pear. The Latin name.

pyxidatus, -a, -um [pix-id-DAY-tus]
Boxlike.

Pyxidanthera [pix-id-anth-EE-ra]
Flowering moss. Gr. *pyxis*, a small box; *anthera*, anthers.
The anthers of this evergreen creeping plant open like the
lid of a box.

Q

quadratus, -a, -um [kwad-RAY-tus]
In fours or in four. Thus:

quadrangularis	with four angles
quadrangulatus	with four angles
quadriauritus	with four ears
quadricolor	four-colored
quadridentatus	four-toothed
quadrifidus	cut into four
quadrifolius	four-leaved
quadripartitus	parted four ways
quadrivalvis	with four valves
quadrivulnerus	with four marks

Quamoclit [KWAM-ok-lit]
Derivation of the name of these vines is obscure. Possibly
Gr. *kuamos*, bean.

Quassia [KWASH-ia]
Name given by Linnaeus to honor Graman Quasi, a Negro,
who used the bark of this tree of Surinam as a remedy for
fever. It is used today in medicine as a bitter tonic and
a vermifuge.

quercifolius, -a, -um [kwer-si-FO-lius]
With leaves like *Quercus* or oak.

quercinus, -a, -um [kwer-SY-nus]
Relating to the oak.

Quercus [KWER-kus]
Oak. The Latin name. The oak has long been considered
a symbol of strength and is celebrated in legend and mythology in many lands. It was sacred to Jupiter and Thor,

while Druids thought that it inspired prophecy, and built their altars under its branches. The timber of most species is valuable, the bark of some is used in tanning, while the acorn is used both for animal and human food. In southern France pigs are fattened on acorns, the lard to be used in making certain delicate flower perfumes.

Quillaja [kwill-AY-ja]
Soap-bark tree. The Chilean name for these evergreen trees and shrubs.

quinatus, -a, -um [kwin-AY-tus]
In fives. Thus:

quinquecolor	of five colors
quinqueflorus	with five flowers
quinquefolius	five-leaved
quinquenervis	five-nerved
quinquepunctatus	five-spotted
quinquevulnerus	with five marks

Quisqualis [kwis-KWAY-lis]
L. *quis*, who? *qualis*, what? Originally there was uncertainty as to the family and relationship of this genus of rambling shrubs.

R

racemiflorus, -a, -um [ras-seem-i-FLO-rus]
racemosus, -a, -um [ras-see-MO-sus]
With flowers in racemes, i.e., bearing flowers on short stems from a longer stem, as in lily-of-the-valley.

radians [RAY-dians]
Radiating outward.

radiatus, -a, -um [ray-di-AY-tus]
With rays.

radicans [RAD-ik-ans]
Having rooting stems. Also:

radicatus	having conspicuous roots
radicosus	with many roots
radicum	of roots

radiosus, -a, -um [ray-di-o-sus]
Having many rays.

radula [RAD-yew-la]
Rough.
ramiflorus, -a, -um [ram-i-FLO-rus]
With a branching inflorescence.
Ramonda [ram-ON-da]
Stemless herbs named for L. F. Ramond (d. 1827), French botanist and traveler.
ramondioides [ram-on-di-OY-deez]
Resembling *Ramonda.*
ramosus, -a, -um [ram-o-sus]
Branches. Also, *ramulosus,* twiggy.
Ranevea [ran-EE-vea]
A dwarf palm named for Louis Ranevé, horticulturist of Berlin, c. 1870.
ranunculoides [ran-un-kew-LOY-deez]
Resembling *Ranunculus.*
Ranunculus [ran-UN-kew-lus]
Buttercup. Crowfoot. The Latin name from the diminutive of *rana,* a frog, because many species grow in damp places.
Raoulia [ray-oo-lia]
Creeping perennial herbs named for Edouard Raoul (1815-1852), French naval surgeon who collected in New Zealand and wrote a book about it.
rapaceus [ra-PAY-seus]
Relating to turnips.
Raphanus [RAFF-ay-nus]
Radish. The Greek name for this vegetable which has been known from antiquity.
Raphia [RAFF-ia]
Raffia—the source of the almost indispensable garden tying fiber. From Gr. *raphis,* a needle; in allusion to the beaked fruit of these palms.
Raphiolepis [raf-i-OLL-ep-is]
India hawthorn. Gr. *raphis,* a needle; *lepis,* a scale; from the needlelike bracts on these evergreen shrubs.
rapunculoides [rap-unk-yew-LOY-deez]
Species name, resembling *Rapunculus,* the now obsolete name for a genus of bellflowers.
rariflorus, -a, -um [ray-ri-FLO-us]
With scattered flowers.

rarus, -a, -um [RAIR-us]
Rare; uncommon.

Rathbunia [rath-BUN-ia]
Cacti named for Dr. Richard Rathbun (1852-1918), Assistant Secretary of the Smithsonian Institute, Washington, D. C.

raucus, -a, -um [RAW-kus]
Hoarse; raw.

Rauwolfia [raw-WOLFF-ia]
Trees and shrubs named for Leonhard Rauwolf, German physician and traveler c. 1750. Long familiar to Oriental medicine, certain species have now achieved respectability by their acceptance in Western medicine, especially in the treatment of nervous disorders.

Ravenala [ray-ven-AY-la]
Traveler's tree. From the native name in Madagascar.

Rebutia [reb-BEW-tia]
Cacti named for P. Rebut, French dealer in cacti, c. 1900.

reclinatus, -a, -um [rek-lin-AY-tus]
Bent backward.

rectus, -a, -um [REK-tus]
Upright.

recurvatus, -a, -um [ree-ker-VAY-tus]
recurvus, -a, -um [ree-KER-vus]
Curved backward.

redivivus, -a, -um [red-iv-VY-vus]
Brought back to life.

reflexus, -a, -um [ree-FLEX-us]
refractus, -a, -um [ree-FRACT-us]
Bent sharply backward.

refulgens [ree-FUL-jens]
Shining brightly.

regalis, -is, -e [ree-GAY-lis]
Of outstanding merit; regal.

reginae [rej-JY-nee]
Of the queen. As a specific in *Tradescantia* honoring Queen Marie of the Belgians, wife of Leopold II.

regius, -a, -um [REE-jius]
Royal.

Rehmannia [ree-MANN-ia]
Perennial herbs named for Joseph Rehmann (1799-1831), physician of St. Petersburg.

304

Reineckia [ry-NEK-ia]
A perennial herb named for J. Reinecke, German gardener who, c. 1900, was very successful with tropicals.

Reinwardtia [ryn-WARD-tia]
A North Indian flowering shrub named for K. G. K. Reinwardt (1733-1822), Director of the Leyden Botanical Gardens.

religiosus, -a, -um [ree-lij-i-o-sus]
Used for religious ceremonies; sacred.

remotus, -a, -um [ree-MO-tus]
Scattered.

Renanthera [ree-nan-THEE-ra]
Gr. *renes*, a kidney; *anthera*, anthers; in reference to the shape of the anthers of these epiphytic orchids.

reniformis, -is, -e [ree-ni-FORM-is]
Kidney-shaped.

repandens [ree-PAN-dens]
With wavy margins.

repens [REE-pens]
reptans [REP-tans]
Creeping.

replicatus, -a, -um [rep-lik-KAY-tus]
Doubled back; folded.

resectus, -a, -um [ree-SEK-tus]
Cut off sharply.

Reseda [ree-SEE-da]
Mignonette. The Latin name derived from *resedo*, to heal, the plant having once been used as a remedy for bruises.

resiniferus, -a, -um [res-in-IFF-er-us]
resinosus, -a, -um [res-in-o-sus]
Resinous.

reticulatus, -a, -um [ree-tik-yew-LAY-tus]
Netted.

retroflexus, -a, -um [ree-tro-FLEX-us]
retortus, -a, -um [ree-TORT-us]
retrofractus, -a, -um [ree-tro-FRAK-tus]
Twisted back.

retusus, -a, -um [ree-TEW-sus]
With a rounded, slightly notched tip.

reversus, -a, -um [ree-VER-sus]
Reversed; turned around.

revolutus, -a, -um [ree-vo-LEW-tus]
Rolled backward, as some leaves are at the edges.

Rhabdothamnus [rab-do-THAM-nus]
Gr. *rhabdos*, a rod; *thamnos*, a bush. A New Zealand shrub with a twiggy habit.

Rhagodia [rag-o-dia]
Salt-bush. Gr. *rhagos*, a berry; in reference to the fruit. Sheep delight in this drought-resistant Australian bush and grow very fat on it. Few plants, however, could appear less inviting.

rhamnifolius, -a, -um [ram-ni-FO-lius]
With leaves like *Rhamnus*.

rhamnoides [ram-NOY-deez]
Resembling *Rhamnus*.

Rhamnus [RAM-nus]
Buckthorn. The Greek name. Many of the species have medicinal value, the dried bark of *R. purshiana* being the source of cascara sagrada.

Rhaphithamnus [raff-i-THAM-nus]
Gr. *rhaphis*, a needle, *thamnos*, a shrub. These small evergreen trees are spiny.

Rhapidophyllum [rap-id-o-FILL-um]
Blue palmetto. Needle palmetto. A genus of dwarf fan palms, with a resemblance to *Rhapis* in producing suckers freely.

Rhapis [RAPP-is]
Ground rattan. Gr. *rhapis*, a needle; with reference to the needlelike leaf segments of these sucker-producing palms.

Rhektophyllum [rek-to-FILL-um]
Gr. *rhakoeis*, tattered; *phyllon*, a leaf. The leaves of these African climbers are cut and perforated.

Rheum [REE-um]
Rhubarb. The Greek name was *rha*. Like it or not, for most of us rhubarb means the first truly fresh dessert of spring. Many species, however, have considerable medicinal value. In the palmy days of the China trade (1800-1850), the best medicinal rhubarb was exported from Canton. In fact, the Chinese Imperial government of the day staked much on the theory that Westerners could not do without it.

Rhexia [REX-ia]
Meadow-beauty. Deer-grass. Gr. *rhexio*, to rupture; possibly in reference to supposed healing properties.

Rhipogonum [rip-POG-o-num]

Gr. *rhips,* wicker-work; *gonu,* a knee; from the many, jointed stalks on these climbing shrubs.

Rhipsalis [RIP-sal-is]

Gr. *rhips,* wicker-work; from the pliant interlacing twigs on these epiphytic cacti.

rhizophyllus, -a, -um [ry-zo-FILL-us]

With rooting leaves.

rhodanthus, -a, -um [ro-DAN-thus]

With roselike flowers.

Rhodochiton [ro-DOK-it-on]

Gr. *rhodo,* red; *chiton,* a cloak; the calyx is large and rose-colored on this flowering vine.

Rhododendron [ro-do-DEN-dron]

Gr. *rhodon,* a rose; *dendron,* a tree. These handsome woody plants are highly ornamental.

Rhodomyrtus [ro-do-MER-tus]

Gr. *rhodon,* a rose, *myrtos,* myrtle; from the rose-colored, myrtle-like flowers of these shrubs.

Rhodothamnus [ro-do-THAM-nus]

Gr. *rhodon,* a rose; *thamnos,* a shrub; from the shrub's rosy flowers.

Rhodotypus [ro-DO-tip-us]

Gr. *rhodon,* a rose; *typos,* a type. From the resemblance of this shrub's flowers to a rose.

Rhoeo [REE-o]

Derivation of this herb's name is unknown.

rhombicus, -a, -um [ROM-bik-us]

rhomboideus, -a, -um [rom-BOY-deus]

Diamond-shaped; rhomboidal.

Rhopalostylis [ro-pal-os-ty-lis]

Gr. *rhopalon,* a club; *stylos,* a pillar; from the club-shaped spadix of these palms.

Rhus [Russ]

Sumach. The Greek name for one species. *R. typhina,* staghorn sumach, was also known to the early colonists as dyer's sumach from the yellow dye which could be made from it. This genus of shrubs also includes *R. toxicodendron,* poison-oak, and poison-ivy (*R. radicans*).

Rhynchosia [rin-ко-sia]

Gr. *rhynchos,* a beak; from the beaked shape of the keel on these herbs and shrubs.

Rhynchostylis [rin-ко s-ty-lis]

Gr. *rhynchos,* a beak; *stylos,* a pillar; in allusion to the shape of the column on these epiphytic orchids.

Rhyticocus [ry-ti-ко-kus]

Gr. *rhytis,* a wrinkle; *Cocos,* coconut. Closely related to *Cocos,* the name derives from a technical characteristic in the seed of these palms.

rhytidophyllus, -a, -um [ry-tid-o-FILL-us]

With wrinkled leaves.

Ribes [RY-beez]

Currant, gooseberry, etc. A large and useful genus, the name of which derives from the Arabic name of some shrub with acid fruit.

Ricinus [RISS-in-us]

Castor bean. L. *ricinus,* a tick; from the resemblance of the seeds. Possibly best known for its medicinal properties, the greatest commercial use of castor oil is in the manufacture of soap, margarine, and lubricants. Large quantities are widely grown for these purposes. Not many years back it had considerable value as an ingredient in high-altitude lubricants for airplanes. The seeds themselves are very poisonous. They must be harvested with care because as soon as the capsules are ripe they dehisce audibly, shooting the seeds many feet, to the loss of the crop.

ricinifolus, -a, -um [ris-sin-i-FO-lius]

With leaves like *Ricinus.*

ricinoides [ris-sin-OY-deez]

Resembling *Ricinus.*

Ricotia [rik-ко-shia]

These herbs are named for Ricot, a little-known French botanist.

rigens [RY-jens]
rigidus, -a, -um [RIJ-id-us]

Rigid; stiff.

ringens [RIN-jens]

Gaping, e.g., the mouth of an open two-lipped corolla.

riparius, -a, -um [ry-PAY-rius]

Of the banks of rivers.

rivalis, -is, -e [ry-VAY-lis]
Growing by streams.
Rivina [riv-VY-na]
Rouge plant. Herbs with attractive berries named for A. Q.
Rivinus (1652-1722), Professor of Botany, Leipzig.
rivularis, -is, -e [riv-yew-LAY-ris]
Brook-loving.
Robinia [ro-BIN-ia]
Yellow locust. False acacia. Trees and shrubs named for
Jean Robin (d. 1629), herbalist to Henri IV of France.
robur [RO-bur]
Latin word for oak-wood, also strength. Specific name of
English oak (*Quercus robur*).
robustispinus, -a, -um [ro-bus-ti-SPY-nus]
With strong spines.
robustus, -a, -um [ro-BUS-tus]
Stout; strong in growth.
Rochea [RO-kea]
Succulents named for Francois de la Roche (d. 1813),
French botanical writer.
Rodgersia [ro-JER-sia]
Herbaceous perennials named for Admiral John Rodgers
(1812-1882), distinguished American naval officer who
saw considerable service in the Far East during which the
first species of this genus was discovered.
Rodriguezia [rod-ree-GAY-zia]
Epiphytic orchids named for Emanuel Rodriguez, 18th-
century Spanish physician and botanist.
Roemeria [ree-MEE-ria]
Annuals named for Johann Jakob Roemer (1763-1819),
Professor of Botany, Zurich.
Rohdea [RO-dea]
A foliage plant named for Michael Rohde, 18th-century
physician of Bremen.
romanus, -a, -um [ro-MAY-nus]
Roman.
Romanzoffia [ro-man-ZOFF-ia]
Perennial herbs named for Prince Nicholas Romanzoff, who
financed a round-the-world expedition, 1816-1817.
Rondeletia [ron-del-LEE-shia]
Evergreen shrubs and trees named for Guilleume Rondelet

(1507-1566), chancellor of the University of Montpellier, France, and one of the early masters of botany.

Rosa [RO-sa]
Rose. The Latin name. See *Rose*.

rosaceus, -a, -um [ro-ZAY-eus]
Roselike.

Rorippa (or, incorrectly, **Roripa**) [RO-rip-a]
Water-cress. The precise derivation is uncertain but possibly from L. *roro*, to be moist; *ripa*, a riverbank.

Roscheria [rose-CHEE-ria]
Derivation of this palm's name is obscure.

Rose
No flower of the Western world has had such great significance for so long as the rose. As a symbol it recurs constantly in religion, art, literature, and heraldry. Identification of the old roses, however, was only approximate until the researches of Dr. C. C. Hurst, rose genealogist, at the Cambridge University Botanic Gardens, between the two world wars. Using his studies of rose genes one can now be fairly positive as to species and varieties, and also trace the parentage of modern roses with accuracy.

Prior to the latter part of the 16th century, only four species of rose were known to the Western world. These were *Rosa rubra*, the highly scented Apothecary's rose, or the rose of Provins; *Rosa phoenicia*, the Damask or Crusaders' rose; *Rosa moschata*, the musk rose; and *Rosa canina*, the dog rose. All these roses bloomed but once a year, except *Rosa bifera*, the so-called Virgil's rose of Paestum, which bloomed twice. All these roses were red or white or pink.

Sometime in the 16th century a Persian yellow rose arrived on the scene which became known as the Austrian brier rose and is a parent of all the 19th-century Pernet hybrids. In the 16th century also, the Dutch triumphed in producing *Rosa centifolia*, the cabbage rose, which is a hybrid of all the four then-known species. The sentimentally popular little moss rose is a sport of this rose.

The revolution in rose breeding came about the year 1800 with the introduction of fine China rose species which had been in cultivation in Chinese and Indian gardens for many centuries. There were four recognized China stud roses: Slater's Crimson; Parson's Pink; Hume's Blush; and Park's

Yellow, all ever-blooming and tea-scented. Here began today's great groups of garden roses—the teas, the hybrid teas; the hybrid perpetuals, etc. Roses of high scent and fine color with excellent growth habits could now be produced to bloom all summer long.

The advent of the China roses marked the beginning of a vogue for rose breeding which soon reached very large proportions. Within a space of a dozen years the nurseryman and breeder, Vibert, achieved some fame by saving no fewer than ten thousand seedlings, in pots, in face of the victorious armies advancing from Waterloo. The movement was greatly stimulated by the ex-Empress Josephine, to whom Napolean had given La Malmaison as a kind of toy. It was an expensive one with millions poured into the development of house and garden.

Among other things, Josephine was determined to possess the greatest collection of roses in the world. To this end, she employed the best gardeners to be found, including an Englishman who continued in her service, quietly breeding roses, war or no war. Also, in the first year or two of the century, John Champney, a wealthy rice planter of Charleston, South Carolina, achieved his Champney's Pink Cluster with a skillful cross of the musk rose and Parson's Pink China. Noisette, a French nurseryman in Charleston, sent seedlings to his brother in Paris, who gave them his own name, by which they are still known. The Noisette rose appears in the parentage of such famous roses as Marechal Niel, Gloire de Dijon, and Reve d'Or. It is also a progenitor of the rose named for the great American rose fancier, William Allen Richardson. The introduction of Parson's Pink China into the Ile de Bourbon (Reunion) resulted in a natural cross with the only other rose then growing on the island, Pink Autumn Damask. This marked the beginning of the group of Bourbon roses from which stem all of today's hybrid perpetuals.

The Chinese and Japanese multiflora roses which became available about mid-century were responsible for polyantha roses, in the development of which the name of the Danish breeder, Poulsen, is probably the best known.

rosea [RO-see-a]

Rose color. As a feminine noun used as a specific it does not have to agree with the gender of the genus, e.g., *Sedum rosea*. This use is a hangover from the old herbalists.

roseus, -a, -um [RO-see-us]
Rose-colored.

rosmarinifolius, -a, -um [rose-ma-ry-ni-FO-lius]
With leaves like rosemary.

Rosmarinus [rose-ma-RY-nus]
Rosemary. The Latin name for this aromatic shrub, derived from *ros*, dew; *marinus*, the sea. It is found wild on sea cliffs in southern Europe.

rostratus, -a, -um [ros-TRAY-tus]
Beaked.

rosularis, -is, -e [ros-yew-LAY-ris]
Having rosettes.

rotatus, -a, -um [ro-TAY-tus]
Wheel-shaped.

rotundatus, -a, -um [ro-tun-DAY-tus]
  rotundus, -a, -um [ro-TUN-dus]
Rounded.

rotundifolius, -a, -um [ro-tun-di-FO-lius]
With round leaves.

Roupala [ROO-pal-a]
From the native Guiana name for these ornamental trees and shrubs.

Royena [roy-EE-na]
Evergreen trees and shrubs named for Adrian van Royen (d. 1779), Professor of Botany, Leyden.

Roystonea [roy-STO-nea]
Palms named for General Roy Stone (1836-1905), American army engineer in Puerto Rico.

rubellinus, -a, -um [roo-bel-LY-nus]
  rubellus, -a, -um [roo-BEL-us]
  rubescens [roo-BESS-ens]
Reddish-colored.

rubens [ROO-bens]
  ruber, rubra, rubrum [ROO-ber]
Red. In compound words, *rubri-*.

Rubia [ROO-bia]
Madder. L. *ruber*, red; in allusion to the reddish dye obtained from the roots of these herbs.

rubiginosus, -a, -um [roo-bij-in-o-sus]
Rusty.

rubioides [roo-bi-oy-deez]
Resembling *Rubia*.

Rubus [ROO-bus]
Blackberry. Bramble. Raspberry. The Latin name.

Rudbeckia [rood-BEK-ia]
Cone-flower. Black-eyed Susan. Named for Olaf Rudbeck
(1660-1740), Professor of Botany at Uppsala and a teacher
of Linnaeus.

rudis, -is, -e [ROO-dis]
Wild.

Ruellia [roo-ELL-ia]
Herbs and shrubs named for Jean de la Ruelle (1474-1537),
herbalist to François I of France.

rufus, -a, -um [ROO-fus]
Red.

rugosus, -a, -um [roo-GO-sus]
Wrinkled.

Rumex [ROO-mex]
Sorrel. Dock. The Latin name. R. *acetosa* is a plant un-
fortunately more used for vegetable greens in France than
in America; it forms the basis of one of the more delectable
soups.

rupestris, -is, -e [roo-PESS-tris]
Rock-loving.

rupicolus, -a, -um [roo-pik-o-lus]
Growing in cliffs and ledges.

rupifragus, -a, -um [roo-pi-FRAY-gus]
Growing in clefts of the rock.

ruscifolius, -a, -um [rus-ki-FO-lius]
Having leaves like butcher's broom or *Ruscus*.

Ruscus [RUS-kus]
Butcher's broom. The Latin name.

russatus, -a, -um [russ-AY-tus]
Russet.

Russelia [russ-EE-lia]
Shrubs named for Dr. Alexander Russell who traveled in
the Near East in the middle of the 18th century.

rusticanus, -a, -um [rus-tik-AY-nus]
rusticus, -a, -um [RUS-tik-us]
Pertaining to the country.
Ruta [ROO-ta]
Rue. The Latin word. As in English, the same word means
bitterness or unpleasantness. The leaves of these perennial
herbs have a bitter taste.
ruthenicus, -a, -um [roo-THEEN-ik-us]
From Ruthenia in Czechoslovakia.
rutilans [ROO-til-ans]
Reddish.

S

Sabal [SAY-bal]
Palmetto. Possibly from the South American name for these
spineless palms.
Sabbatia [sab-BAY-shia]
Rose pink. American centaury. Showy herbs named for an
Italian botanist and author, L. Sabbati, of the middle of
the 18th-century.
saccatus, -a, -um [sak-KAY-tus]
Resembling a bag.
saccharatus, -a, -um [sak-ka-RAY-tus]
saccharinus, -a, -um [sak-ka-RY-nus]
Sweet.
Saccharum [SAK-ka-rum]
Sugarcane. Gr. saccharon, a sweet juice. Sugarcane has
been known since antiquity in Asia whence it passed to
Africa. It was introduced into Sicily around A.D. 800 and
by the Moors into Spain before A.D. 1000. The cane was
taken by Columbus to the New World on his second voyage
where it quickly became widely cultivated. Manufactured
sugar was imported into Europe from very early times.
In the Middle Ages it was handled by apothecaries as a
medicine. It became cheap and readily available to all with
the advent of steam navigation and manufacturing machin-
ery.
It is cultivated throughout the tropical and semitropical
regions of the world.
sacciferus, -a, -um [sak-IFF-er-us]
Bag-bearing.

sacchariferus, -a, -um [sak-ka-RIFF-er-us]
sacchiferus, -a, -um [sak-IFF-er-us]
Sugar-producing.
saccharoides [sak-ka-ROY-deez]
Resembling sugarcane.
sacrorum [sak-RO-rum]
Of sacred places.
Sadleria [sad-LEE-ria]
Tree ferns named for Joseph Sadler (1791-1841), Professor of Botany, Budapest.
Sagina [sa-JY-na]
Pearlwort. L. *sagina,* fodder; from the fattening qualities of spurrey (*Spergula sativa*) on which sheep quickly gain condition and which was once classified in this genus of tufted herbs.
sagittalis, -is, -e [saj-it-TAY-lis]
sagittatus, -a, -um [saj-it-TAY-tus]
Arrow-shaped.
Sagittaria [saj-it-TAY-ria]
Arrowhead. L. *sagitta,* an arrow; from the form of the leaves of these perennial aquatic herbs.
sagittifolius, -a, -um [saj-jit-ti-FO-lius]
Arrow-leaved.
Saintpaulia [saynt-PAW-lia]
African violet. Named for a German, Baron Walter von Saint Paul-Illaire (1860-1910), who discovered the African violet (*S. ionantha*) in East Africa.
salicariaefolius, -a, -um [sal-iss-ay-ri-ee-FO-lius]
salicifolius, -a, -um [sal-iss-i-FO-lius]
Willow-leaved.
salicinus, -a, -um [sal-iss-SY-nus]
Willow-like.
Salicornia [sal-ik-KORN-ia]
Glasswort. Marsh samphire. L. *sal,* salt; *cornu,* a horn; from the hornlike branches of this genus of salt-marsh herbs.
salicornioides [sal-ik-korn-i-OY-deez]
Resembling *Salicornia.*
salignus, -a, -um [sal-IG-nus]
Resembling willow.
salinus, -a, -um [sal-LY-nus]
Growing in salty places.

Salix [SAY-lix]

Willow. The Latin name.

Willow bark was, until the early part of this century, the sole source of salicylic acid which has great medicinal value, especially in the treatment of rheumatism. Synthesis of the acid was a German discovery when it became the principal ingredient of aspirin, originally a trade name closely covered by patents held by the Bayer interests. Their monopoly was broken as a result of World War I when aspirin came into wide general use at modest prices.

The discovery of the value of salicylic acid for the treatment of rheumatism came about from application of the once widely held theory that any endemic ill had its remedy close by. Rheumatism being endemic in damp places, it was natural to seek the remedy close at hand.

In many country places in England, pussy willows are eagerly sought by children for the silky catkin-bearing twigs called "palms" to be used for church decoration on Palm Sunday. Similarly, in northern Russia in more civilized times the week before Palm Sunday was called "willow week." The "palms," tied with bright ribbons, were sold for Palm Sunday.

Salpichroa [sal-pik-RO-a]

Gr. *salpinx*, a trumpet; *chroos*, a skin; from the shape and texture of the flowers of these shrubs and sub-shrubs.

Salpiglossis [sal-pi-GLOSS-is]

Gr. *salpinx*, a trumpet; *glossa*, a tongue. The style is like a tongue at the mouth of the trumpet-shaped corolla on these attractive herbs.

Salsola [SAL-so-la]

Russian thistle. L. *sal*, salt. They are generally salt-soil plants, not true thistles.

salsuginosus, -a, -um [sal-soo-jin-o-sus]

Growing in salt marshes.

Salvia [SAL-via]

Sage. The Latin name, itself derived from *salveo*, to heal; from the supposed medicinal values of the plants. S. *sclarea*, clary or clear-eye, was particularly valued for affections of the eye, hence the English name.

316

salviaefolius, -a, -um [sal-vi-ee-FO-lius]
salvifolius, -a, -um [sal-vi-FO-lius]
Salvia-leaved.

Salvinia [sal-VIN-ia]
A floating plant named for Antonio Maria Salvini (1633-1729), Professor of Greek at Florence.

Samanea [sam-an-EE-a]
Rain-tree or monkey-pod. From the native South American name. It is called rain-tree because the leaflets fold up in cloudy weather and at night.

sambucifolius, -a, -um [sam-bew-si-FO-lius]
With leaves like elder or *Sambucus*.

sambucinus, -a, -um [sam-bew-SY-nus]
Resembling *Sambucus* or elder.

Sambucus [sam-BEW-kus]
Elder. The Latin name, from *sambuca*, a kind of harp made of elder wood.

Samolus [SAM-o-lus]
The Latin name for these herbs of the primrose family.

Samuela [sam-yew-EE-la]
Date-yucca. Named for Samuel F. Trelease, American botanist. Both flowers and fruit of these large plants are eaten locally in Mexico.

Sanchezia [san-CHEE-zia]
Handsome shrubs and herbs named for José Sanchez, a 19th-century Professor of Botany at Cadiz.

sanctus, -a, -um [SANK-tus]
Holy.

Sanguinaria [sang-gwin-AY-ria]
Bloodroot. L. *sanguis*, blood. All parts of these low perennials have copious yellowish-red sap.

sanguineus, -a, -um [sang-GWIN-eus]
Blood-red.

Sanguisorba [sang-gwi-SOR-ba]
Burnet. L. *sanguis*, blood; *sorbeo*, to soak up. This herb was supposed to have styptic qualities.

Sansevieria [san-sev-EE-ria]
Bow-string hemp and, in the florists shops, snake plant or leopard lily. Named for Raimond de Sansgrio, Prince of Sanseviero (1710-1771).

Santalum [SAN-tal-um]

Sandalwood. From the Persian name. For most of us sandalwood means the fragrant, carved boxes and fans from India. The wood, however, is employed in funeral and religious rites wherever Buddhism prevails. Also, ground to a paste, it is one of the pigments used by Brahmans in making their caste marks.

Santolina [san-to-LY-na]

Lavender cotton. L. *sanctum linum,* holy flax, an old name for one of the species of these shrubby herbs, *S. virens.*

Sanvitalia [san-vit-TAY-lia]

Yellow-flowered herbs named for the Sicilian Sanvitali family.

sapidus, -a, -um [SAP-id-us]

Pleasant to taste.

sapientum [sap-i-EN-tum]

Pertaining to wise men.

Sapindus [sap-IND-us]

Soap-berry. L. *sapo,* soap; *indicus,* Indian. The pulp of these trees and shrubs lathers like soap and was used as such by North American Indians.

Sapium [SAY-pium]

Latin name for a resinous pine. The stems of these trees, which are not pines, exude a sticky sap. *S. sebiferum,* the Chinese tallow tree, has seeds with a waxy covering which can be used for soap and candles.

saponaceus, -a, -um [sap-o-NAY-seus]

Soapy.

Saponaria [sap-o-NAY-ria]

Soapwort. Bouncing Bet. L. *sapo,* soap. The leaves of *S. officinalis* will lather and remove soil.

Sapota [sap-o-ta]

Sapodilla. From the native South American name for this tree. The one species, *S. achras,* has a delicious fruit but commercially it is most important as the source of chicle which is the basis of chewing gum.

Saraca [sa-RAY-ka]

From the East Indian name for these trees.

Sarcanthus [sar-KAN-thus]

Gr. *sarkos,* flesh; *anthos,* a flower. The flowers of these orchids are fleshy.

Sarcochilus [sar-ko-KY-lus]
Gr. *sarkos*, flesh; *cheilos*, a lip. The flower lip of these epiphytic orchids is fleshy.

Sarcococca [sar-ko-KOK-a]
Sweet box. Gr. *sarkos*, flesh; *kokkos*, a berry; in allusion to the fleshy fruits of these ornamental shrubs.

sarcodes [sar-KO-deez]
Fleshlike.

sarmaticus, -a, -um [sar-MAT-ik-us]
From south Russia.

sarmentosus, -a, -um [sar-ment-o-sus]
Having or bearing runners.

Sarracenia [sar-rass-EE-nia]
Pitcherplant. Named for Dr. D. Sarrasin, 17th-century French physician and botanist of Quebec who sent the first of these carnivorous plants to Europe.

Sasa [SAY-sa]
The Japanese name for these bamboos.

Sassafras [SASS-a-fras]
Derivation of the name for these handsome trees is dubious. The roots and bark are aromatic and are the source of oil of sassafras which is used in perfumery. During the 17th and 18th centuries sassafras was an important export from the New World, ranking second only to gold among the commodities which ships' captains sailing for America were called on to seek. Oil of sassafras was used in medicine and at one time was regarded as the sure cure for syphilis which had spread explosively throughout Europe in particularly virulent form following the entry of Charles VIII of France into Naples in 1495. Syphilis was clinically unknown before 1493 and was supposed to have been brought from Haiti by Columbus' sailors, several of whom are known to have taken part in the French-Neapolitan war.
The tree grows to considerable size under the proper conditions. The wood is white, strong, close-grained, and elastic.

sativus, -a, -um [sat-TY-vus]
Cultivated.

saturatus, -a, -um [sat-yew-RAY-tus]
Saturated.

Satureja (also at one time, **Satureia**) [sat-yew-REE-ia]
Savory. The Latin name for this herb which was well known
to the ancients. It is an excellent bee plant and is recom-
mended for planting around hives by Virgil in the *Georgics*.

saurocephalus [saw-ro-SEFF-al-us]
Lizard-headed.

Sauromatum [saw-ROM-at-um]
Gr. *sauros*, a lizard. The inside of the spathe is spotted like
a lizard on these perennial herbs.

Saururus [saw-REW-rus]
Gr. *sauros*, a lizard; *ouros*, a tail; from the form of the inflorescence on these perennial marsh herbs.

Saussurea [saw-SUE-rea]
Perennial herbs named for Horace Bénédict de Saussure
(1740-1799), Swiss philosopher.

saxatilis, -is, -e [sax-AT-ill-is]
Found among rocks.

Saxegothaea [sax-go-THEE-a]
Prince Albert's yew. A Chilean evergreen conifer named for
Prince Albert of Saxe-Coburg-Gotha, Prince Consort of
Queen Victoria, (1819-1861).

saxicolus, -a, -um [sax-IK-o-lus]
Growing in rocks.

Saxifraga [sax-IFF-rag-a]
Saxifrage. L. *saxum*, a rock; *frango*, to break. Growing in
rock crevices this herb was supposed to be capable of
breaking rocks. Hence, by deduction, it was accorded a
medicinal quality of breaking up stone in the bladder.

saxosus, -a, -um [sax-o-sus]
Full of rocks.

scaber, scabra, scabrum [SKAY-ber]
Rough.

Scabiosa [skab-i-o-sa]
Mourning bride. Pincushion flower. Scabious. L. *scabies*,
the itch, which by the analogy of the roughness of the leaves,
the plant was supposed to cure.

scabiosaefolius, -a, -um [skab-i-os-ee-FO-lius]
With leaves like *Scabiosa*.

scandens [SKAN-dens]
Climbing.

scaposus, -a, -um [skap-o-sus]
With scapes.

scariosus, -a, -um [skay-ri-o-sus]
Shriveled.

sceptrum [SEP-trum]
A scepter.

Schaueria [sho-EE-ria]
Shrubby herbs with ornamental foliage named for John
Conrad Schauer (1813-1848), Professor at Greifswald.

Scheelea [SHEE-lia]
Palms named for Karl Wilhelm Scheele (1742-1786), German chemist.

Schefflera [sheff-LEE-ra]
Trees or shrubs named for J. C. Scheffler, 19th-century
botanist of Danzig.

schidigerus, -a, -um [shid-IJ-er-us]
Spine-bearing.

Schima [SKY-ma]
From the Arabic name for these evergreen trees and shrubs.

schinseng [SHIN-seng]
Chinese word for ginseng for which this is the specific
(*Panax schinseng*).

Schinus [SKY-nus]
Pepper-tree. Gr. *schinos*, the mastic tree, which this genus
resembles in that the trees are resinous and yield a mastic-
like juice.

Schisandra (also, incorrectly, **Schizandra**) [sky-ZAN-dra]
Gr. *schizo*, to divide; *aner*, male; in allusion to the cleft
anthers of these aromatic shrubs.

Schismatoglottis [skis-mat-o-GLOT-is]
Gr. *schismatos*, deciduous; *glotta*, a tongue. The spathe
drops quickly on these herbs.

Schivereckia [shiv-er-REK-ia]
Dwarf perennials named for S. B. Schivereck (1782-1815)
of Innsbruck.

Schizaea [skiz-EE-a]
Comb or rush fern. Gr. *schizo*, to divide. The fronds are
divided into a fan shape.

Schizanthus [sky-ZAN-thus]
Butterfly or fringe flower. Gr. *schizo*, to divide; *anthos*, a

flower; in allusion to the deeply cut corolla on these annual herbs.

Schizocentron [sky-zo-SEN-tron]
Gr. *schizo*, to divide; *kentron*, a spur. From the form of the flower on these trailing plants.

Schizocodon [sky-zo-KO-don]
Gr. *schizo*, to divide; *kodon*, a bell. The bell-shaped corolla of these glabrous herbs has a fringe.

Schizolobium [sky-zo-LO-bium]
Gr. *schizo*, to divide; *lobos*, a lobe; from the cut lobes of these tropical trees.

Schizopetalon [sky-zo-PET-al-on]
Gr. *schizo*, to divide; *petalon*, a petal. The petals of these annual herbs are deeply cut.

schizopetalus, -a, -um [sky-zo-PET-al-us]
With cut petals.

Schizophragma [sky-zo-FRAG-ma]
Gr. *schizo*, to divide; *phragma*, a fence or screen. Parts of the vase-shaped fruits on these climbing, flowering shrubs fall away, leaving them skeletonized.

schizophyllus, -a, -um [sky-zo-FILL-us]
With cut leaves.

Schizostylis [sky-zos-til-is]
Kaffir lily. Gr. *schizo*, to divide; *stylos*, a column. The style of these South African herbs is divided into three parts.

Schlumbergera [schlum-ber-JEE-ra]
Cacti named for Frederick Schlumberger, Belgian horticulturist, c. 1900.

scholaris, -is, -e [sko-LAY-ris]
Relating to school.

Schomburgkia [shom-BURK-ia]
Epiphytic orchids named for Sir Robert Schomburgk (1804-1865), German-born, naturalized British, explorer who found the *Victoria regia* water-lily in Guiana. He was a compulsive surveyor and map-maker, who also had Siamese deer named for him.

Schotia [SHO-tia]
Small trees and shrubs named for Richard van der Schot (d. 1819), head gardener at the Austrian palace at Schönbrunn.

Schrankia [SHRANK-ia]
Perennial herbs and shrubs named for Franz von Paula von Schrank (1747-1835), German botanist.
Sciadopitys [sy-a-DOP-it-is]
Umbrella pine. Gr. *skia*, a shade; *pitys*, a fir tree. The spreading whorls of needles resemble the ribs of an umbrella (for which there is no word in Greek).
Scilla [SILL-a]
Squill. The Greek name for these bulbous plants. The English bluebell used be to named S. *nutans*, but is now classified in the genus *Endymion*.
scilloides [sill-OY-deez]
Resembling *Scilla*.
Scindapsus [sin-DAP-sus]
Ivy arum. From the Greek name for a plant resembling ivy applied to these climbing perennials.
Scirpus [SKER-pus]
Bulrush. The Latin name. The biblical bulrush was the related *Cyperus papyrus*.
Sclerocactus [sklee-ro-KAK-tus]
Gr. *scleros*, cruel, plus *Cactus;* in allusion to the wicked spines.
sclerocarpus, -a, -um [sklee-ro-KARP-us]
With hard fruits.
Scolymus [SKOL-im-us]
Latin name for Spanish oyster-plant. This biennial plant is edible and closely related to salsify.
scoparius, -a, -um [sko-PAY-rius]
Broomlike.
scopulorum [skop-yew-LO-rum]
Of the rocks.
scorpioides [skor-pi-OY-deez]
Resembling a scorpion.
Scorpiurus [skor-pi-YEW-rus]
Gr. *skorpios*, a scorpion; *urus*, a tail; from the form of the pods on these herbs.
Scorzonera [skor-zo-NEE-ra]
Black salsify. From Old French *scorzon*, a snake. The root of this herb was once regarded as a cure for snakebite.
scoticus, -a, -um [SKO-tik-us]
Scottish.

sculptus, -a, -um [SKULP-tus]
Carved.

scutatus, -a, -um [skew-TAY-tus]
scutellaris, -is, -e [skew-tell-AY-ris]
scutellatus, -a, -um [skew-tell-AY-tus]
Dish- or shield-shaped.

scutum [SKEW-tum]
A shield.

Scrophularia [skroff-yew-LAY-ria]
Fig-wort. L. *scrofula*, which it was supposed to cure. The roots of some species of these herbs look like scrofulous tumors.

Scutellaria [skew-tel-AY-ria]
Skullcap. L. *scutella*, a small shield; from the form of the fruiting calyx of these herbs.

Scuticaria [skew-ti-KAY-ria]
L. *scutica;* a whip; from the shape of the leaves of these orchids.

sebiferus, -a, -um [seb-IFF-er-us]
Tallow-bearing.

sebosus, -a, -um [seb-O-sus]
Full of grease or tallow.

Secale [seek-KAY-le]
Rye. Latin name for some cereal grain, perhaps rye.

sechellarum [see-shell-AY-rum]
Of the Seychelle Islands in the Indian Ocean.

Sechium [SEE-kium]
From the West Indian name for this tuberous-rooted climbing herb.

seclusus, -a, -um [see-KLOO-sus]
Hidden.

secundatus, -a, -um [sek-kun-DAY-tus]
secundiflorus, -a, -um [sek-kun-di-FLO-rus]
secundus, -a, -um [sek-KUN-dus]
One-sided, secund. Applied to leaves or flowers arranged on one side of a stalk only.

Securidaca [sek-yew-RID-ass-a]
L. *securis*, an ax; from the shape of the wing at the end of the pods of these tropical shrubs, often climbers.

Securigera [see-kew-RIJ-er-a]
Hatchet vetch. L. *securis*, an ax; *gero*, to bear; from the shape of the pods.

324

securigerus, -a, -um [see-kew-RIJ-er-us]
Ax-bearing.
Sedum [SEE-dum]
Stonecrop. Wall-pepper. L. *sedo*, to sit; from the manner in which some species of these herbs attach themselves to rocks and walls.
segetalis, -is, -e [sej-et-TAY-lis]
segetum [sej-ET-um]
Of cornfields.
Selaginella [sel-aj-in-ELL-a]
Club-moss. Diminutive of *Selago*, the name of another moss-like plant.
selaginoides [sel-aj-in-OY-deez]
Resembling club-moss.
Selenicereus [see-lee-ni-SEE-reus]
Night-blooming cereus. Gr. *selene*, the moon, plus *Cereus*. The flowers of these cacti are mostly nocturnal.
Semele [SEE-mel-ee]
A climbing shrub named for the daughter of Kadmos and mother of Dionysus, the Roman Bacchus.
semperflorens [sem-per-FLO-rens]
Ever-blooming.
sempervirens [sem-per-VY-rens]
Evergreen.
sempervivoides [sem-per-viv-OY-deez]
Resembling *Sempervivum*.
Sempervivum [sem-per-VY-vum]
House-leek. L. *semper*, always; *vivo*, to live. Hen-and-chickens, *S. tectorum* (of roofs), was regarded as effective against lightning and for that reason this fleshy herb was planted on roofs.
Senecio [sen-EE-sio]
Groundsel. Ragwort. L. *senex*, an old man; from the hoary pappus of these herbs.
senecioides [sen-ess-i-OY-deez]
Resembling *Senecio*.
senilis, -is, -e [see-NY-lis]
White-haired.
sensibilis, -is, -e [sen-SIB-ill-is]
sensitivus, -a, -um [sen-sit-TY-vus]
Sensitive; responding quickly to touch, changes in light, etc.

sepiarius, -a, -um [see-pi-AY-rius]
sepium [SEE-pium]
Growing along hedges.
sept-
In compound words signifying seven. Thus:

septangularis	seven-angled
septemfidus	with seven cuts
septemlobus	with seven lobes
septempunctatus	seven-spotted

septentrionalis, -is, -e [sep-ten-tri-o-NAY-lis]
Northern.
sepultus, -a, -um [see-PUL-tus]
Buried.
Sequoia [see-KWOY-a]
Redwood. The name is probably of American Indian origin.
Sequoiadendron [se-kwoy-a-DEN-dron]
Big tree. *Sequoia* plus Gr. *dendros,* tree. In England Wellingtonia is the commonly accepted synonym of *S. gigantea.* This
is sometimes claimed as the biggest and oldest living thing
known to man. The first seeds seem to have been collected
in the early 1850's by G. H. Woodruff, a New Yorker and
down-and-out gold miner in California, who found himself
in a shower of seeds dropped by squirrels feeding on the
cones. He filled his snuff-box and sent the seeds by pony
express at a cost of $25 to the nursery of Ellwanger and
Barry of Rochester, New York. They obtained about 4,000
seedlings, of which 400 went to England to be eagerly
snapped up there. Europeans were soon taking all they
could lay their hands on, for every great house and botanic
garden wanted an avenue. Woodruff's share of the profits
came to $1,030.60. The tree was originally listed as "Wash-
ingtonia gigantea, . . . Wellingtonia of the English and
Sequoia of the French."
Serenoa [ser-en-o-a]
Palms named for Sereno Watson (1826-1892), distinguished
American botanist.
sericanthus, -a, -um [ser-ik-ANTH-us]
With silky flowers.
sericeus, -a, -um [ser-ISS-eus]
Silky.

sericiferus, -a, -um [ser-iss-IFF-er-us]
sericoferus, -a, -um [ser-i-KOFF-er-us]
Silk-bearing.
Sericocarpus [ser-iss-o-KARP-us]
Gr. *serikos*, silk; *karpos*, fruit. The dry fruits of these aster-like herbs are covered with silky hairs.
Serissa [ser-ISS-a]
From the East Indian name for this shrub.
serotinus, -a, -um [ser-ROT-in-us]
Late in flowering or ripening.
serpens [SER-pens]
Creeping.
serpentinus, -a, -um [ser-pen-TY-nus]
Serpentine; relating to snakes, or to certain soils called serpentine.
serpyllifolius, -a, -um [ser-pill-i-FO-lius]
With leaves like *Thymus serpyllum*.
serratifolius, -a, -um [ser-rat-i-FO-lius]
With serrated or saw-toothed leaves.
Serratula [ser-RAT-yew-la]
L. *serrula*, a small saw; from the serrated leaves of these thistlelike perennials.
serratus, -a, -um [ser-RAY-tus]
Saw-toothed.
Sesamum [SES-am-um]
Sesame. The Greek name for this important oil plant some-times commercially called gingelly.
Sesbania [ses-BAY-nia]
From the Arabic name for these herbs and shrubs.
sesquipedalis, -is, -e [ses-qui-pee-DAY-lis]
One and one-half feet in length or height, applied to a species of *Angraecum* because of the length of this orchid's spur.
sessilis, -is, -e [SESS-il-is]
Stalkless; sessile. In compound words *sessi-*
setaceus, -a, -um [set-AY-seus]
Bristled.
Setaria [see-TAY-ria]
Foxtail millet. L. *seta*, a bristle; from the bristly awns of these grasses.

seti-

In compound words signifies bristled. Thus:

setifolius with bristly leaves
setigerus bearing bristles
setiger   bearing bristles
setispinus with bristly spines
setosus   full of bristles
setulosus full of small bristles

Severinia [sev-er-IN-ia]
A shrub or small tree related to the orange, named for M.
A. Severino (1580-1656), Professor of Anatomy at Naples.
sexangularis, -is, -e [sex-ang-gew-LAY-ris]
With six angles.
Shepherdia [shep-PER-dia]
Ornamental shrubs or small trees named for John Shepherd
(1764-1836), curator of the Botanical Gardens, Liverpool.
Shortia [SHORT-ia]
Evergreen stemless herbs named for Dr. Charles W. Short
(1794-1863), Kentucky botanist. There are two species, the
American S. *galacifolia*, sometimes called Oconee bells, and
the Japanese, S. *uniflora*, Nippon bells. The former was
found by Asa Gray in its dried state when he went to Paris
to organize Michaux's North American collection made some
fifty years before but which, owing to wars and other
troubles, had never been put in order.
Gray had never before seen the plant and was much struck
by it. All he could be sure of was that it was North American. When the Japanese species was described, Gray had a
clue as to its possible habitat in the odd affinity between the
flora of the Appalachian region and of Japan. S. *galacifolia*
was eventually found, growing in the area in which Gray ex-
pected it to be. It would be pleasant to record that it had
been named after him.
siameus, -a, -um [sy-AM-eus]
Of Siam (Thailand).
Sibiraea [sib-i-REE-a]
From the Siberian habitat of one species of these spiraea-like
shrubs.
Sibthorpia [sib-THORP-ia]
Perennial herbs named for Humphrey Sibthorp (1713-

1797), English botanist and father of John Sibthorp (1758-1796), Professor of Botany, Oxford.

Sicana [sy-KAY-na]
From the Peruvian name for these vines of the cucumber family.

siculiformis, -is, -e [sik-yew-li-FORM-is]
Dagger-shaped.

siculus, -a, -um [SIK-yew-lus]
Of Sicily.

Sicyos [SIK-yos]
Bur-cucumber. Greek for cucumber, to which this is closely related.

Sidalcea [sy-DAL-sea]
False mallow. From *Sida* and *Alcea*, both related genera.

Sideritis [sy-der-RY-tis]
The Greek name, from *sideros*, iron. These herbs and shrubs were supposed to heal wounds caused by swords and other iron weapons.

siderophloius, -a, -um [sy-der-o-FLOY-us]
Iron-barked.

Sideroxylon [sy-der-ox-il-on]
Miraculous berry of West Africa. From Gr. *sideros*, iron; *xylon*, wood; from the hardness of the heartwood. The fruit is acid-sweet, but after eating it, acid and sour foods like limes will taste sweet, and the effect can last for two or three hours.

signatus, -a, -um [sig-NAY-tus]
Well-marked.

Silene [sy-LEE-ne]
Catchfly. Campion. The Greek name for another plant (*Viscaria*), now applied to these common herbs.

siliceus, -a, -um [sy-LISS-eus]
Growing in sand.

Silphium [SIL-fium]
Rosinweed. Perennial herbs with the Greek name for another plant also producing resin, perhaps *Ferula assafoetida*.

silvaticus, -a, -um [sil-VAT-ik-us]
   silvestris, -is, -e [sil-VEST-ris]
Growing in woods.

Silybum [SILL-i-bum]
Lady's thistle. Milk thistle. Blessed thistle. The Greek name

for some other thistlelike plant. The English names apply to
S. *marianum*, also called Our Lady's thistle from the white
spots on the leaves supposed to have been the result of milk
dropped on them by the Virgin.

similis, -is, -e   [SIM-ill-is]
Similar; like.

simplex   [SIM-plex]
Simple; unbranched. Also:

simplicicaulis   with simple stems
simplicifolius   with simple leaves

simulans   [sim-YEW-lans]
Resembling.

sinicus, -a, -um   [SIN-ik-us]
Chinese.

Sinningia   [sin-IN-jia]
Tropical herbs named for Wilhelm Sinning (1794-1874),
head gardener, University of Bonn. This is the gloxinia of
the florists (S. *speciosa*).

Sinomenium   [sy-no-MEE-nium]
Chinese moonseed. A shrubby vine. Gr. *sinai*, Chinese;
menas, the moon.

sinuatus, -a, -um   [sin-yew-AY-tus]
sinuosus, -a, -um   [sin-yew-o-sus]
With a wavy margin.

Sinowilsonia   [sy-no-will-so-nia]
A shrub or tree like *Hamamelis* named for Dr. E. H. Wilson
(1876-1930), of the Arnold Arboretum, Boston. Known as
Chinese Wilson (Gr. *sinai*, Chinese), he traveled widely
in China and introduced more than a thousand plants, including the regal-lily, to the gardens of England and America. English-born and Kew-trained, he brought unusual
imagination and perception to all he did, including a remarkable ability to get along with Chinese at all levels.
Among his books, *China, Mother of Gardens* is well worth
reading both for its botanical descriptions and as a story of
adventurous travel in the distant parts of a China now, alas,
no more.

sisalanus, -a, -um   [sy-sal-AY-nus]
Pertaining to sisal.

Sisyrinchium [sis-i-RINK-ium]
Blue-eyed grass. The ancient Greek name for another plant.

Sium [SY-um]
Ancient Greek name for S. *sisarum*, skirret, which is sometimes grown for its edible roots.

Skimmia [SKIM-ia]
From the Japanese name for these ornamental shrubs.

smaragdinus, -a, -um [sma-RAG-din-us]
Emerald-green.

Smilacina [smy-lass-SY-na]
False Solomon's seal. False spikenard. Diminutive of *Smilax*.

smilacinus, -a, -um [smy-lass-SY-nus]
Relating to *Smilax*.

Smilax [SMY-lax]
Greenbrier, the Greek name for these climbers although the smilax of florists is generally *Asparagus asparagoides*.

Sobralia [so-BRAY-lia]
Terrestrial orchids named for F. M. Sobral, Spanish botanist, c. 1790.

soboliferus, -a, -um [so-bo-LIFF-er-us]
Having creeping rooting stems.

socialis, -is, -e [so-si-AY-lis]
Forming colonies.

socotranus, -a, -um [so-ko-TRAY-nus]
Of the island of Socotra.

sodomeum [sod-om-EE-um]
Of the Dead Sea area.

Solandra [so-LAN-dra]
Showy-flowered vines named for Daniel Carl Solander (1736-1782), a pupil of Linnaeus, who sailed with Sir Joseph Banks as botanist on Captain Cooks' first voyage of exploration in the *Endeavour* in 1768.

Solanum [so-LAY-num]
Latin name for some plant assigned to this huge and varied genus which includes such plants as the potato, Jerusalem cherry, and woody nightshade.

solaris, -is, -e [so-LAY-ris]
Growing in sunny situations.

Soldanella [sol-dan-ELL-a]
L. *soldo*, a small coin; in allusion to the form of the leaf of this perennial herb.

Solidago [sol-i-DAY-go]
Goldenrod. L. *solido,* to make whole; in allusion to the reputed healing qualities of these perennial herbs.

solidus, -a, -um [SOL-id-us]
Solid; dense.

Sollya [SOLL-ya]
Evergreen climbers named for Richard Horsman Solly (1778-1858), English natural scientist.

somniferus, -a, -um [som-NIFF-er-us]
Sleep-producing.

Sonchus [SON-kus]
Sowthistle. The Greek name.

Sonerila [so-ner-RY-la]
From the native Malabar name for these herbs and small shrubs.

Sophora [SOFF-or-a]
From the Arabic name for these ornamental plants.

Sophronitis [so-fron-NY-tis]
Gr. *sophron,* modesty; in allusion to the small but pretty flowers of one species of these epiphytic orchids.

Sorbaria [sor-BAY-ria]
False spiraea. Deciduous shrubs. From the Latin, meaning resembling *Sorbus.*

sorbifolius [sor-bi-FO-lius]
With leaves like *Sorbus.*

Sorbus [SOR-bus]
Mountain ash. Rowan. L. *sorbum,* the fruit of the service tree (*Sorbus domestica*).

sordidus, -a, -um [SOR-did-us]
Dirty.

spadiceus, -a, -um [spad-ISS-eus]
With a spathe.

Sparaxis [spar-AX-is]
Wandflower. Gr. *sparasso,* to tear. The spathes of these bulbous plants appear torn.

Sparmannia [spar-MAN-ia]
Shrubs or trees named for Dr. Andreas Sparrman (1748-1820), Swedish botanist who sailed with Captain Cook in 1772 on his second voyage of exploration in the *Resolute.*

sparsus, -a, -um [SPAR-sus]
Few; far-between.

sparteus, -a, -um [SPAR-teus]
Pertaining to *Spartium.*

Spartium [SPAR-tium]
Weavers' broom. Gr. *spartium,* a kind of grass used for weaving and cordage, not this shrub.

Spathiphyllum [spath-i-FILL-um]
Gr. *spathe; phyllon,* a leaf; from the leaflike spathe of these low herbs.

Spathodea [spath-o-dea]
Greek word, meaning resembling a spathe; in allusion to the form of the calyx of these evergreen trees.

Spathoglottis [spath-o-GLOT-tis]
Gr. *spathe; glottis,* a tongue; in allusion to the form of the lip of these terrestrial orchids.

speciosus, -a, -um [spess-i-o-sus]
Showy.

spectabilis, -is, -e [spek-TAB-il-is]
Spectacular; showy.

spectandrus, -a, -um [spek-TAN-drus]
Showy.

spectrum [SPEK-trum]
An apparition.

Specularia [spek-yew-LAY-ria]
Venus' looking-glass. L. *speculum,* a mirror; from the old name for these annuals, *speculum veneris,* literally, the looking glass of Venus.

speculatus, -a, -um [spek-yew-LAY-tus]
Shining (as if with mirrors).

sphacelatus, -a, -um [sfass-ee-LAY-tus]
Dead; diseased.

Sphacele [SFASS-ee-lee]
Gr. *sphakos,* sage; which the foliage of these shrubs resembles.

Sphaeralcea [sfee-RAL-sea]
Globe-mallow. Gr. *sphaira,* a globe; *Alcea,* marsh-mallow. There are points of resemblance.

sphaericus, -a, -um [SFEE-rik-us]
Spherical. Also:

sphaerocarpus	with round fruits
sphaerocephalus	with a round head
sphaeroides	resembling a sphere

spiciformis, -is, -e [spy-si-FORM-is]
Spike-shaped. Also :

spicigerus   spike-bearing
spiculifolius   with leaves in the form of small spikes

Spigelia [spy-JEE-lia]
Indian pink. Pink-root. North American herbs named for Adrian van der Spiegel (1578-1625), Professor of Anatomy at Padua and a writer on botany.

Spinacia [spy-NAY-sia]
Spinach. L. *spina,* a spine; in allusion to the spiny husk of the fruit.

spinarum [spy-NAY-rum]
spinescens [spy-NESS-ens]
spiniferus, -a, -um [spy-NIFF-er-us]
spinifex [SPY-ni-fex]
spinosus, -a, -um [spy-NO-sus]
Spiny.

Spiraea [spy-REE-a]
Bridal wreath. Spirea. Deciduous flowering shrubs. Gr. *speiraira,* a plant used for garlands.

spiralis, -is, -e [spy-RAY-lis]
Spiral.

Spiranthes [spy-RANTH-ees]
Ladies' tresses. Gr. *speiros,* spiral; *anthos,* a flower; from the spiral inflorescence of these terrestrial orchids.

Spironema [spy-ro-NEE-ma]
Gr. *speiros,* spiral; *nema,* a thread, from the character of the stalks of the anthers of this Mexican herb.

splendens [SPLEN-dens]
splendidus, -a, -um [SPLEN-did-us]
Splendid.

Spondias [SPON-dias]
Greek for the plum. Assigned to this genus of tropical trees because of a similarity in the fruit. It includes the Jamaica plum, mombin, etc.

Sprekelia [sprek-EE-lia]
Bulbous plants named for J. H. von Sprekelsen (d. 1764), botanical author, of Hamburg.

spumarius, -a, -um [spew-MAY-rius]
Frothing.

spurius, -a, -um [SPEW-rius]
False.

Spyridium [spy-RID-ium]
Gr. *spyris,* a basket; *eidos,* like; from the form of the calyx of these Australian shrubs.

squalens, -a, -um [SQUAY-lens]
squalidus, -a, -um [SQUAL-id-us]
Dirty.

squamatus, -a, -um [squam-AY-tus]
Squamate; with small scalelike leaves or bracts.

squamosus, -a, -um [squam-O-sus]
Full of scales.

squarrosus, -a, -um [squay-RO-sus]
With parts spreading or recurved at the ends.

stachyoides [stak-i-OY-deez]
Resembling *Stachys.*

Stachys [STAK-iss]
Betony. Woundwort. Betonica. The Greek name for some other plant with spike flowers.

Stachytarpheta [stak-i-tar-FEE-ta]
Gr. *stachys,* a spike; *tarphys,* thick; from the thick flower spikes of these herbs and shrubs.

Stachyurus [stak-i-YEW-rus]
Gr. *stachys,* a spike; *oura,* a tail; from the form of the racemes of these shrubs.

stamineus, -a, -um [stam-IN-eus]
With prominent stamens.

Stanhopea [stan-HO-pea]
Epiphytic orchids named for the Earl of Stanhope (1781-1855), President of the Medico-Botanical Society of London.

stans [stans]
Erect; upright.

Stapelia [stap-EE-lia]
Carrion-flower. *Cactus*-like plants named by Linnaeus for Johannes Bodaeus van Stapel (d. 1631), of Amsterdam.

Staphylea [staf-ill-EE-a]
Bladdernut. Gr. *staphyle,* a cluster; from the arrangement of the flowers of these shrubs or small trees.

Statice [STAT-iss-ee]
Marsh rosemary. Sea-lavender. Sea pink. Thrift. Greek name for thrift or sea pink, now abandoned due to confusion and

ambiguity. Thrift or sea pink has been assigned to *Armeria* and sea-lavender or marsh rosemary to *Limonium*. Gardeners, however, will probably continue to call the latter *Statice*.

Stauntonia [stawn-TO-nia]
Evergreen climbing shrubs named for Sir George C. Staunton (1737-1801), Irish traveler in China.

stauracanthus, -a, -um [staw-ra-KAN-thus]
With spines crossing.

Steironema [sty-ro-NEE-ma]
Loosestrife. Gr. *steira*, sterile; *nema*, a thread; from a technical characteristic of the flowers of these glabrous herbs.

Stellaria [stel-AY-ria]
Chickweed. Stitchwort. Starwort. L. *stella*, a star; from the starry flowers of these herbs.

stellaris, -is, -e [stell-AY-ris]
stellatus, -a, -um [stell-AY-tus]
Starry.

Stenandrium [sten-AN-drium]
Gr. *stenos*, narrow; *aner*, man. The stamens are narrow on these herbs with ornamental foliage.

Stenanthium [sten-ANTH-ium]
Gr. *stenos*, narrow; *anthos*, a flower. Parts of the flower are narrow on these bulbous plants.

Stenocarpus [sten-o-KARP-us]
Gr. *stenos*, narrow; *karpos*, fruit; from the flat, narrow fruits of these trees.

steno-
In compound words signifies narrow. Thus:

stenocarpus	with narrow fruits
stenopetalus	with narrow petals
stenophyllus	narrow-leaved
stenopterus	narrow-winged
stenostachyus	narrow-spiked

Stenochlaenia [sten-o-KLEE-nia]
Gr. *stenos*, narrow; *chlaina*, a cloak. In these ferns there is no indusium—that part which normally covers the sori.

Stenoglottis [sten-o-GLOT-tis]
Gr. *stenos*, narrow; *glotta*, a tongue. The lip of these terrestrial orchids is narrow.

336

Stenolobium [sten-o-LO-bium]
Gr. *stenos,* narrow; *lobos,* a lobe; in allusion to the narrow fruits of these shrubs.

Stenospermation [sten-o-sperm-AY-tion]
Gr. *stenos,* narrow; *sperma,* a seed. These are South American climbers.

Stenotaphrum [sten-o-TAFF-rum]
Gr. *stenos,* narrow; *taphros,* a trench; from the cavities in which the flower spikelets of these grasses are seated.

Stephanandra [steff-an-AND-ra]
Gr. *stephanos,* a crown; *aner,* a man. The stamens of these ornamental shrubs persist in a rather obvious crown.

Stephanotis [steff-an-o-tis]
Wax-flower. Madagascar jasmine. Gr. *stephanos,* a crown; *otos,* an ear; in reference to the auricles in the staminal crown on these evergreen twining shrubs.

Sterculia [ster-KEW-lia]
Trees named for Sterculius, Roman god of the jakes (L. *stercus,* dung). Some species stink.

sterilis, -is, -e [STER-ill-is]
Infertile; sterile.

Sternbergia [stern-BER-jia]
Winter daffodil. Bulbous herbs named for Count Kaspar von Sternberg (1761-1838), Austrian botanist.

Stevensonia [stee-ven-so-nia]
A palm named for Sir William Stevenson, Governor of Mauritius, 1857-1863.

Stevia [STEE-via]
Herbs or sub-shrubs named for Pedro Jaime Esteve (d. 1566), Spanish botanist.

Stewartia (also, incorrectly, **Stuartia**) [stew-ART-ia]
Deciduous flowering shrubs and trees named for John Stuart, Earl of Bute (1713-1792), for whom *Butia* was also named.

Stigmaphyllon [stig-ma-FILL-on]
Gr. *stigma; phyllon,* a leaf. The stigma is rather like a leaf on these woody vines.

Stipa [STY-pa]
Feather-grass. Gr. *stuppeion,* tow or flax; from the feathery inflorescence on these perennial grasses.

stipulaceus, -a, -um [stip-yew-LAY-seus]
stipularis, -is, -e [stip-yew-LAY-ris]
stipulatus, -a, -um [stip-yew-LAY-tus]
Having stipules, the outgrowths found at the base of the leaf stalks of many flowering plants.

Stizolobium [sty-zo-LO-bium]
Velvet-bean. Gr. *stizo*, to prick; *lobos*, a lobe. The pods of some species of these ornamental vines have stinging hairs.

Stokesia [sto-KEE-sia]
Stokes' aster. A perennial herb named for Dr. Jonathon Stokes (1755-1831), botanical author.

stoloniferus, -a, -um [sto-lon-IFF-er-us]
Having stolons or rooting runners.

stramineus [stram-IN-eus]
Straw-colored.

strangulatus, -a, -um [strang-GEW-lay-tus]
Constricted.

Stranvaesia [stran-VEE-sia]
Handsome evergreen trees and shrubs named for William Fox-Strangways (1795-1865), Earl of Ilchester and a botanist.

Stratiotes [strat-i-o-teez]
Water soldier. Gr. *stratiotis*, a soldier; from the sword-shaped leaves of this aquatic herb.

Strelitzia [strel-ITS-ia]
Bird-of-paradise flower. Perennial herbs named for Charlotte of Mecklenberg-Strelitz (1744-1818), who became Queen to George III.

Streptocarpus [strep-to-KARP-us]
Cape primrose. Gr. *streptos*, twisted; *karpos*, fruit. The seed capsules of these herbs are twisted in a spiral.

strepto-
In compound words signifies twisted. Thus:

streptocarpus	with twisted fruits
streptopetalus	with twisted petals
streptophyllus	with twisted leaves
streptosepalus	with twisted sepals

Streptopus [STREP-top-us]
Twisted stalk. Gr. *streptos*, twisted; *pous*, a foot. The flower stalks are twisted on these perennials.

Streptosolen [strep-to-so-len]
Gr. *streptos*, twisted; *solen*, a tube. The tube of the corolla is twisted on this shrub.

striatus, -a, -um [stry-AY-tus]
Striped.

strictus, -a, -um [STRIK-tus]
Erect; upright.

strigosus, -a, -um [strig-O-sus]
With stiff bristles.

striolatus, -a, -um [stry-o-LAY-tus]
Faintly striped or with fine lines.

Strobilanthes [stro-bil-ANTH-eez]
Gr. *strobilos*, a cone; *anthos*, a flower; from the form of the bud and the emergent flower on these herbs or shrubs.

strobiliferus, -a, -um [stro-bil-IFF-er-us]
Cone-bearing.

Stromanthe [stro-MAN-the]
Gr. *stroma*, a bed; *anthos*, a flower; from the form of the inflorescence on these perennial herbs.

Strombocactus [strom-bo-KAK-tus]
Gr. *strombos*, a spinning-top; plus *Cactus*; from the shape of the plants.

strumarius, -a, -um [strew-MAY-rius]
strumatus, -a, -um [strew-MAY-tus]
strumosus, -a, -um [strew-MO-sus]
Having cushionlike swellings.

Strychnos [STRIK-nos]
Greek name for some other poisonous plant and applied here by Linnaeus because so many of these shrubs and trees are poisonous. The genus includes S. *nux-vomica* or strychnine. One or two of the species are the source of some of the most effectively fatal arrow poisons known.

Stylidium [sty-LID-ium]
Gr. *stylos*, a column. The styles are joined to the stamens on these chiefly Australian plants.

Stylophorum [sty-LOFF-or-um]
Celandine poppy. Gr. *stylos*, a column; *phoreo*, to bear. The styles are columnar on these perennial herbs.

stylosus, -a, -um [sty-LO-sus]
With prominent styles.

styracifluus, -a, -um [sty-rass-IFF-lew-us]
Flowing with gum.
Styrax [STY-rax]
Snowbell. Storax-tree. The classical Greek name for these ornamental woody plants.
suavis, -is, -e [SWAY-vis]
Sweet.
suaveolens [sue-a-VEE-o-lens]
Sweet-scented.
sub-
In compound words possibly the most used prefix, signifying somewhat; almost; rather; slightly; partially; under; etc.
subacaulis, -is, -e [sub-ak-KAW-lis]
Without much of a stem.
subalpinus, -a, -um [sub-al-PY-nus]
Growing in the lower mountain ranges.
subauriculatus, -a, -um [sub-aw-rik-ew-LAY-tus]
Somewhat eared.
subcanus, -a, -um [sub-KAY-nus]
Graying.
subcarnosus, -a, -um [sub-kar-NO-sus]
Rather fleshy.
subcoeruleus, -a, -um [sub-see-ROO-leus]
Slightly blue.
subcordatus, -a, -um [sub-kord-AY-tus]
Rather heart-shaped.
subdentatus, -a, -um [sub-den-TAY-tus]
Nearly toothless.
subdivaricatus, -a, -um [sub-dy-var-ik-KAY-tus]
Somewhat spreading.
suberculatus, -a, -um [sue-ber-kew-LAY-tus]
Pertaining to cork; corky.
suberectus, -a, -um [sub-er-REK-tus]
Almost upright.
suberosus, -a, -um [sue-ber-o-sus]
Cork-barked.
subfalcatus, -a, -um [sub-fal-KAY-tus]
Somewhat curved or hooked.
subglaucus, -a, -um [sub-GLAW-kus]
Somewhat glaucous; covered with the white or grayish

powder which, owing to the green of the leaves below, gives
a conspicuous blue-green or gray-green effect.

subhirtellus, -a, -um [sub-her-TELL-us]
Somewhat hairy.

sublunatus, -a, -um [sub-loo-NAY-tus]
Rather crescent-shaped.

submersus, -a, -um [sub-MER-sus]
Submerged.

subpetiolatus, -a, -um [sub-pet-i-o-LAY-tus]
Partially petaled.

subscandens [sub-SKAN-dens]
Tending to climb.

subterraneus, -a, -um [sub-ter-RAY-neus]
Underground.

subulatus, -a, -um [sub-yew-LAY-tus]
Awl-shaped.

subvillosus, -a, -um [sub-vill-o-sus]
With rather soft hairs.

succotrinus, -a, -um [suk-ko-TRY-nus]
From the island of Socotra.

succulentus, -a, -um [suk-yew-LEN-tus]
Fleshy; juicy.

suecicus, -a, -um [su-EE-sik-us]
suionum [su-i-o-num]
Swedish.

surculosus, -a, -um [ser-kew-LO-sus]
Producing suckers.

suffrutescens [suf-froo-TESS-ens]
suffruticosus, -a, -um [suf-froo-tik-o-sus]
Somewhat shrubby.

sulcatus, -a, -um [sull-KAY-tus]
Furrowed.

sulfurens [sull-FEW-rens]
sulphureus, -a, -um [sull-FEW-reus]
Sulphur-yellow.

sumatranus, -a, -um [sue-mar-TRAY-nus]
From Sumatra.

superbiens [sue-PER-bi-ens]
superbus, -a, -um [sue-PER-bus]
Superb.

superciliaris, -is, -e [sue-per-sill-i-AY-ris]
Eyebrowlike.

superfluus, -a, -um [sue-PER-flew-us]
Redundant.

supinus, -a, -um [sue-PY-nus]
Prostrate.

susianus, -a, -um [sue-si-AY-nus]
From southern Persia.

suspensus, -a, -um [sus-PEN-sus]
Hanging.

Sutherlandia [suth-er-LAND-ia]
Shrubs named for James Sutherland (d. 1719), Super-intendent, Botanic Gardens, Edinburgh.

Suttonia [sut-TO-nia]
Evergreen trees and shrubs, named for the Reverend Charles Sutton (1756-1846), English botanist.

Swainsonia [swain-so-nia]
Darling River pea. Herbs and sub-shrubs named for Isaac Swainson (1746-1812), London horticulturist.

Swietenia [swy-TEE-nia]
Mahogany tree. Named for Gerard van Swieten (1700-1772), Dutch botanist. This is the original mahogany of Central America and the West Indies. African and Philippine mahogany, commercially so called, are members of several other genera although the wood, in most cases, bears some resemblance to *Swietenia*.

sylvaticus, -a, -um [sil-VAT-ik-us]
sylvester [sil-VEST-er]
sylvestris, -is, -e [sil-VEST-ris]
Growing in woods; forest-loving.

Symphoricarpos [sim-for-ik-KAR-pos]
Snowberry. Gr. *symphoreo*, to bear together; *karpos*, fruit. The berries are borne in clusters on these shrubs.

Symphyandra [sim-fi-AND-ra]
Pendulous bellflower. Gr. *symphio*, to grow together; *aner*, anther. The anthers of these perennial herbs are conjoined.

Symphytum [SIM-fit-um]
Comfrey. The ancient Greek name of this herb, which was reputed to heal wounds.

Symplocarpus [sim-plo-KARP-us]
Skunk-cabbage. Gr. *symploke*, a connection; *karpos*, fruit.

The ovaries of this swamp-loving perennial herb grow together to make one fruit.

Symplocos [sɪm-plo-kos]
Gr. *symploke*, a connection. The stamens are united at the base on these ornamental woody plants.

Synadenium [sin-a-DEE-nium]
Gr. *syn*, with; *aden*, a gland; from a technical characteristic of the glands of these tropical shrubs.

Synechanthus [sy-nee-KAN-thus]
Gr. *syneches*, continuous; *anthos*, a flower; from the form of the flower heads on these palms.

Synthyris [sɪn-thi-ris]
Gr. *syn*, together; *thyris*, a small door; in allusion to a characteristic of the fruits of these perennial herbs.

sylvicolus, -a, -um [sil-vɪK-o-lus]
Growing in woods.

syriacus, -a, um [si-RY-ak-us]
Syrian.

Syringa [si-RING-ga]
Lilac. Originally also applied to *Philadelphus*. The name is still very commonly applied to mock-orange. The name derives from Gr. *syrinx*, a pipe, and refers to the hollow stems.

syringanthus, -a, -um [si-ring-GAN-thus]
Lilac-flowered.

syringifolius, -a, -um [si-ring-gi-FO-lius]
With leaves like lilac.

T

Tabebuia [tab-bee-BEW-ia]
From the native Brazilian name for these ornamental trees.

Tabernaemontana [tab-ber-nee-mon-TAY-na]
Evergreen flowering trees or shrubs named for Jakob Theodor von Bergzabern (d. 1590), Professor of Botany, Heidelberg, who Latinized his name as Tabernaemontanus and who is also commemorated with species named for him in *Amsonia* and *Scirpus*. He was the author of *Icones Stirpium* (The Images of Plants), published in Frankfort in 1590 and illustrated with original woodcuts. The latter were

used by Gerard in his *Herball,* published seven years later. The assumption is that Gerard had the woodcuts copied.

tabulaeformis, -is, -e [tab-bew-lee-FORM-is]
tabularis, -is, -e [tab-bew-LAY-ris]
tabuliformis, -is, -e [tab-bew-li-FORM-is]
Flat, like a table or board.

Tacca [TAK-ka]
From the Malayan name for these perennial herbs.

taedigerus, -a, -um [tee-DIJ-er-us]
Torch-bearing.

Tagetes [ta-JEE-tees]
Marigold, African and French. Named for an Etruscan deity said to have sprung from the earth as it was being plowed.

taiwanensis, -is, -e [ty-wan-EN-sis]
From Taiwan (Formosa).

Taiwania [ty-WAN-ia]
From Taiwan (Formosa) where the one species of this evergreen tree, *T. cryptomerioides,* was found.

Talinum [ta-LY-num]
Derivation of the name for these fleshy herbs is obscure.

Tamarindus [tam-ar-IND-us]
Tamarind. From the Arabic name. The acid pulp of this tree's seed-pods is used in medicine.

tamariscifolius, -a, -um [tam-ar-risk-i-FO-lius]
With leaves like tamarisk.

Tamarix [TAM-ar-ix]
Tamarisk. The Latin name for these showy deciduous shrubs and trees.

Tamus [TAY-mus]
Black bryony. From the Latin name for another climbing plant.

tanacetifolius, -a, -um [tan-ass-ee-ti-FO-lius]
Tansy-leaved.

Tanacetum [tan-ass-EE-tum]
Tansy. From the medieval Latin name Tanazeta, still used in some European places. Once regarded as a specific for intestinal worms, it was used in some rural areas of New England in funeral winding sheets, presumably as a discouragement to worms.

Taraxacum [ta-RAX-ak-um]
Dandelion. From a very ancient name traceable through Latin and Arabic to Persian.

taraxicifolius, -a, -um [ta-rax-iss-i-FO-lius]
With leaves like dandelion.
tardiflorus, -a, -um [tard-i-FLO-rus]
Late-flowering.
tardivus, -a, -um [tar-DY-vus]
tardus, -a, -um [TAR-dus]
Late.
tartareus, -a, -um [tar-TAY-reus]
With a rough surface.
tartaricus, -a, -um [tar-TAY-rik-us]
From Central Asia.
tauricus, -a, -um [TAW-rik-us]
From the Crimea.
taurinus, -a, -um [taw-RY-nus]
From the neighborhood of Turin.
taxifolius, -a, -um [tax-i-FO-lius]
With leaves like yew.
Taxodium [tax-o-dium]
Swamp cypress. *Taxus,* yew; Gr. *eidos,* resemblance; from a similarity in the leaf shape in these deciduous and semi-evergreen trees and shrubs.
Taxus [TAX-us]
Yew. Both the Greek and Latin name for these evergreen trees and shrubs.
tazetta [tax-ET-ta]
Specific name of *Narcissus,* meaning a small cup, from the form of the corona.
technicus, -a, -um [TEK-nik-us]
Special.
Tecoma [TEE-ko-ma]
From the Mexican name for these ornamental shrubs.
Tecomaria [tee-ko-MAY-ria]
Cape honeysuckle. From *Tecoma* which it closely resembles.
Tectona [tek-TO-na]
From the Tamil name for the teak tree (*T. grandis*). This magnificent forest tree, growing up to 150 feet, supplies the teak of commerce. The wood is extremely durable and proof against the ravages of white ants. It is not particularly hard but is not easy on tools because the silicate content of the grain quickly blunts the best edges. Before the war, teak was exported in very large quantity from Rangoon. Nowadays, the teak which has been popularized for fine

furniture by the Danes and others seems mostly to be of the Siamese variety, distinguished by the handsome dark striations in the grain. The almost black hardwood stools and other furniture made in China are certainly not teak wood.

tectorum [tek-TAW-rum]
Of the roofs of houses. Specific name of *Sempervivum* (house-leek) which grows freely on stone and slate roofs and which, in some places, is thought to avert lightning.

tectus [TEK-tus]
Concealed; covered.

telephium [tel-EE-fium]
Specific name of *Sedum,* of uncertain meaning.

Tellima [tel-LY-ma]
Anagram of *Mitella* to which these herbaceous perennials are closely related.

Telopea [tel-o-pea]
Gr. *telopos,* seen from afar. The crimson flowers of these tall shrubs are visible at a distance.

temulentus, -a, -um [tem-yew-LEN-tus]
temulus, -a, -um [TEM-yew-lus]
Drunken.

tenax [TEE-nax]
Strong; tough; matted.

tenebrosus, -a, -um [ten-eb-RO-sus]
Of shaded places.

tenellulus, -a, -um [ten-ELL-yew-lus]
tenellus, -a, -um [ten-ELL-us]
Tender; delicate.

tenens [TEE-nens]
Enduring.

tenuis, -is, -e [TEN-yew-is]
Slender; thin. Also:

tenuicaulis	slender-stemmed
tenuiflorus	with slender flowers
tenuifolius	slender-leaved
tenuipetalus	with slender petals

Tephrosia [teff-RO-sia]
Gr. *tephros,* ash-colored; from the appearance of the leaves of these perennial herbs.

terebinthaceus, -a, -um [ter-eb-inth-AY-seus]
terebinthinus, -a, -um [ter-eb-in-THY-nus]
Pertaining to turpentine.
teres [TEE-rees]
Cylindrical; circular in section.
Terminalia [ter-min-AY-lia]
Indian almond. L. *terminus*, end. The leaves of these tropical trees are borne at the ends of the shoots.
terminalis, -is, -e [ter-min-AY-lis]
terminans [TER-min-ans]
Ending.
ternatea [ter-nay-TEE-a]
From the island of Ternate in the Moluccas.
ternatus, -a, -um [tern-AY-tus]
In clusters of three.
Ternstroemia [tern-STREEM-ia]
Evergreen trees or shrubs named for Christopher Ternström (d. 1745), Swedish naturalist in China.
terrestris, -is, -e [ter-REST-tris]
Of the ground; growing in the ground as opposed to growing in trees or in water.
tessellatus, -a, -um [tess-el-LAY-tus]
Checkered in square spots.
testaceus, -a, -um [test-AY-seus]
Brick-colored.
testicularis, -is, -e [tes-tik-yew-LAY-ris]
testiculatus, -a, -um [tes-tik-yew-LAY-tus]
Like testicles.
testudinarius, -a, -um [tes-tew-din-AY-rius]
Like tortoise shell.
testudo [tes-TEW-do]
A tortoise.
tetra-
In compound words signifies four. Thus:

tetracanthus	four-spined
tetragonus	with four angles
tetrandrus	with four anthers
tetranthus	four-flowered
tetraphyllus	with four leaves
tetrapterus	four-winged

Tetracentron [tet-ra-SEN-tron]
Gr. *tetra*, four; *kentron*, a spur. The fruit of this deciduous ornamental tree is four-spurred.

Tetraclinis [tet-ra-KLY-nis]
Gr. *tetra*, four; *kline*, a bed. The leaves of this evergreen tree are grouped in fours making a kind of bed.

Tetragonia [tet-ra-GO-nia]
New Zealand spinach. Gr. *tetra*, four; *gonia*, an angle; from the form of the fruits of this succulent, edible annual.

Tetrapanax [tet-ra-PAY-nax]
Rice paper tree. Gr. *tetra*, four, plus *Panax*. The flowers are in fours and there is a resemblance to *Panax*.

Tetratheca [tet-ra-THEE-ka]
Gr. *tetra*, four; *theke*, a cell. The anthers of these heathlike shrubs are often four-celled.

teucrioides [tew-kri-OY-deez]
Resembling *Teucrium*.

Teucrium [TEW-krium]
Germander. The Greek name, probably named for Teucer, first king of Troy, who first used the plant in medicine.

texanus, -a, -um [tex-AY-nus]
Texan.

textilis, -is, -e [tex-TY-lis]
Used in weaving.

Thalia [THAY-lia]
Aquatic or marsh herbs named for Johann Thal (1542-1583), German botanist.

thalictroides [thal-ik-TROY-deez]
Like *Thalictrum*.

Thalictrum [thal-IK-trum]
Meadow rue. The Greek name for another plant than these showy perennial herbs.

Thea [tee-a]
Tea. From the Dutch rendering of the Chinese (Amoy) word for tea, T'E. *Thea sinensis* is now often classified under *Camellia*. Virtually a Chinese monoply, in the 1840's Robert Fortune exported both tea plants and skilled labor to India to establish the industry there. This, however, was not the first attempt to grow tea outside China. In the Western world, as early as 1772, tea-growing was tried in Georgia. For the next hundred years several attempts were made to

348

establish the industry in the mountains from North Carolina southward, some of them large scale and government sponsored. They seem to have failed, not because the plants could not be grown, but because the skills of manufacture were never mastered.

thebaicus, -a, -um [thee-BAY-ik-us]
Of Thebes.

theiferus, -a, -um [tee-IFF-er-us]
Tea-bearing.

Thelesperma [thel-es-PERM-a]
Gr. *thele,* a nipple; *sperma,* a seed; in allusion to the form of the seeds in some species of these glabrous herbs or subshrubs.

Thelocactus [thel-o-KAK-tus]
Gr. *thele,* a nipple, plus *Cactus.* The ribs have a nipplelike appearance.

Theobroma [thee-o-BRO-ma]
Cacao. A translation into Greek of the Aztec name; *theos,* a god; *broma,* food. The source of both cocoa and chocolate, and a highly profitable crop both on a large and on a small scale, cacao is grown throughout the tropics wherever the right climatic and other conditions prevail. The cacao tree requires protection of shade from other trees, hence a plantation may often take on a rather unkempt look. The fruit is borne on the bark of the larger branches. It is shaped like a football, with pointed ends, and may be as long as ten inches. The seeds are about the size of lima beans and are embedded in a whitish pulp which becomes ill-smelling as the beans are fermented.
The cocoa-butter of commerce is derived from coconut and has no connection with cacao.

thermalis, -is, -e [ther-MAY-lis]
Of warm springs.

Thermopsis [therm-OP-sis]
Gr. *Thermos,* lupin; *opsis,* like. There is a resemblance to lupin in the flower heads of these herbaceous perennials.

Thespesia [thes-PEE-sia]
Mahoe. Gr. *thespesios,* divine. These trees are often planted around Oriental temples.

Thevetia [thev-EE-shia]
Small trees and shrubs named for André Thevet (1502-1592), French monk, who traveled in Brazil and Guiana.

Thlaspi [THLAS-pi]
Penny-cress. The Greek name for a cress.
Thomasia [tom-ASS-ia]
Mostly Australian shrubs and small trees named for Peter and Abraham Thomas, collectors of Swiss plants, c. 1750.
Thrinax [THRY-nax]
Thatch palm. Fan palm. Gr. *thrynax*, a fan.
Thryallis [thry-AL-is]
Greek name for another plant.
Thuja (also **Thuya**) [THEW-ya]
Arbor-vitae, Northern white cedar. The Greek name for these resinferous, pyramidal, evergreen trees and shrubs.
Thujopsis [thew-YOP-sis]
Gr. *Thuja; opsis*, like. There is a similarity in these evergreen trees to *Thuja*.
Thunbergia [thun-BER-ja]
Flowering shrubs and climbers named for Dr. Carl Peter Thunberg (1743-1828), one of the young men Linnaeus sent out to various parts of the world botanizing. He traveled widely in Java and Japan and became Professor of Botany at Uppsala. Black-eyed Susan is a familiar name for *T. alata*.
thuriferus, -a, -um [thew-RIFF-er-us]
Incense-bearing.
thuyoides, thyoides [thew-OY-deez, thy-OY-deez]
Resembling *Thuja*.
thymifolius, -a, -um [ty-mi-FO-lius]
Thyme-leaved.
thymoides [ty-MOY-deez]
Like *Thyme*.
Thymus [TY-mus]
The ancient Greek name for these aromatic herbs and subshrubs.
Thysanotus [thy-san-o-tus]
Gr. *thysanotos*, fringed. The inner perianth of these perennials has three fringes.
Tiarella [ty-a-RELL-a]
False mitrewort. Foamflower. Gr. diminutive of *tiara*, a small crown in reference to the form of the pistil on these perennial herbs.
tibeticus, -a, -um [tib-ET-ik-us]
Of Tibet.

tibicinus, -a, -um [tib-is-SY-nus]
Of a flute-player.

Tibouchina [tib-book-KY-na]
Spider-flower. From the native name in Guiana for these tropical South American flowering shrubs and herbs.

Tigridia [ty-GRID-ia]
Tiger-flower. L. *tigris*, a tiger; because of the spots on the flowers (see *tigrinus*) on these Central American bulbous plants.

tigrinus, -a, -um [ty-GRY-nus]
Either striped like the Asiatic tiger or spotted like the animal known as a tiger in South America. Also, tiger-toothed.

Tilia [TIL-ia]
The Latin name for the linden or lime tree. Also bass wood.

tiliaceus, -a, -um [til-i-AY-seus]
Linden-like.

tiliaefolius, -a, -um [til-i-ee-FO-lius]
Linden-leaved.

Tillandsia [til-LAND-sia]
Spanish moss. American herbs, mostly epiphytic named for Elias Tillands, a Swedish botanist and Professor of Medicine at Abo, Finland, c. 1750.

Tinantia [ty-NAN-tia]
Erect herbs named for François A. Tinant (1803-1858), botanist of Luxemburg.

tinctorius, -a, -um [tink-TOR-ius]
Used in dyeing.

tinctus, -a, -um [TINK-tus]
tingens [TIN-jens]
Colored.

tingitanus, -a, -um [tin-jit-TAY-nus]
Of Tangiers.

Tinnea [TIN-nea]
A genus of herbs or sub-shrubs, hairy or woolly, whose name commemorates a scientific expedition up the Nile undertaken in 1863 by three Dutch ladies—Henriette Tinne, her sister, and her daughter.

Tipuana [tip-yew-AY-na]
From the South American name for these showy trees.

tipuliformis, -is, -e [tip-yew-li-FORM-is]
Shaped like a daddy-long-legs.

tirolensis, -is, -e [ty-ro-LEN-sis]
Of the Tyrol.

Titanopsis [ty-tan-OP-sis]
L. *Titan*, the sun god; Gr. *opsis*, like; from the resemblance of the flower to the sun in these stemless succulents.

titanus, -a, -um [ty-TAY-nus]
Very large.

Tithonia [ty-THO-nia]
Annual herbs named for Tithonus, a young man much loved by Aurora, the dawn-goddess.

Tococa [to-KO-ka]
From the native name for these shrubs in Guiana.

Tolmiea [toll-mi-EE-a]
A perennial herb named for Dr. William Fraser Tolmie (d. 1886), surgeon to the Hudson's Bay Company, Puget Sound.

Tolpis [TOL-pis]
Yellow hawkweed. Derivation of the name of these showy daisylike herbs is unknown.

tomentosus, -a, -um [to-men-TO-sus]
Densely woolly; with matted hairs.

tonsus, -a, -um [TON-sus]
Sheared; smooth-shaved.

Torenia [to-REN-ia]
Pretty annuals named for the Reverend Olaf Toren (1718-1753), chaplain to the Swedish East India Company at Surat, India, and in China.

torminalis, -is, -e [tor-min-AY-lis]
Relating to or effective against colic.

torosus, -a, -um [to-RO-sus]
Cylindrical, with contractions at intervals.

Torreya [to-REE-a]
Ornamental evergreens named for Dr. John Torrey (1796-1873), one of the giants of American botany and co-author with Asa Gray of *The Flora of North America*. He was regarded as an ultimate authority and in his lifetime described many thousands of plants brought back by such explorers as Fremont and Pickering.

torridus, -a, -um [TOR-rid-us]
Growing in hot, dry places.

tortilis, -is, -e [TORT-il-us]
  tortus [TORT-us]
  Twisted.

Townsendia [town-SEN-dia]
  Rocky Mountain herbs named for David Townsend of Pennsylvania in the first half of the 19th century.

toxicarius, -a, -um [tox-ik-KAY-rius]
  toxicus, -a, -um [TOX-ik-us]
  toxiferus, -a, -um [tox-IFF-er-us]
  Poisonous.

Trachelium [trak-EE-lium]
  Throatwort. Gr. *trachelos,* a neck. These perennial herbs were suppose to be good for afflictions of the throat (trachea).

Trachelospermum [trak-ee-lo-SPERM-um]
  Gr. *trachelos,* a neck; *sperma,* a seed, the seed of these shrubby climbers with fragrant flowers has a neck.

Trachycarpus [trak-i-KARP-us]
  Gr. *trachys,* rough; *karpos,* a fruit. The allusion is to the fruit of some species of these palms.

Trachymene [trak-KIM-ee-nee]
  Gr. *trachys,* rough; *hymen,* a membrane; in reference to the channels on the fruits of some species of these annual and perennial herbs.

Trachystemon [trak-iss-TEE-mon]
  Gr. *trachys,* rough; *stemon,* a stamen. The filaments are rough in one species of these hairy perennial herbs.

Tradescantia [trad-ess-KAN-tia]
  Widow's-tears. Wandering-Jew. Spiderwort. Perennial herbs named for John Tradescant (d. 1638), gardener to King Charles I.

translucens [trans-LOO-sens]
  Translucent.

transparens [trans-PAY-rens]
  Transparent.

transylvanicus, -a, -um [tran-sil-VAN-ik-us]
  From Rumania.

trapeziformis, -is, -e [trap-ee-zi-FORM-is]
  With four unequal sides.

Tragopogon [trag-o-PO-gon]
  Goat's-beard Salsify. Vegetable oyster. Gr. *tragos,* a goat;

pogon, a beard. The pappus of these biennial or perennial herbs is silky.

Trapa [TRAY-pa]
Water-chestnut. Aquatic floating herbs with edible fruit. A contraction of L. *calcitrapa,* called a caltrop or crow's foot—a weapon of defensive war consisting of four sharp, iron points which, thrown on the ground has one point always pointing upward particularly to pierce the hooves of cavalry horses. The reference here is to the similarly four-pointed seed. It might be added that French troops met with a similar device recently in Indo-China, the uppermost point generally having been well infected with some bacteria-laden substance, as from the dung-hill.

Trautvetteria [trout-vet-EE-ria]
Perennial herbs named for Ernst Rudolf von Trautvetter (1809-1889), Russian botanist.

tremuloides [trem-yew-LOY-deez]
Resembling the quivering poplar.

tremulus, -a, -um [trem-YEW-lus]
Quivering; trembling.

Trevesia [trev-EE-sia]
Showy tropical Asian shrubs and small trees named for the family of Treves de Bonfigli of Padua, 18th-century supporters of botanical research.

tri-
In compound words signifies three. Thus:

triancanthus	three-spined
triandrus	with three stamens
triangularis } triangulatus }	with three angles
tricaudatus	three-tailed
tricephalus	three-headed
trichotomus	three-branched
tricoccus	with three seeds
tricolor	three-colored
tricornis	with three horns
tricuspidatus	three-pointed
tridens } tridentatus }	three-toothed
trifidus	cut in three
trifloris	three-flowered

trifoliatus trifolius	}with three leaves
trifurcatus trifurcus	three-forked
trigonophyllus	with three-cornered leaves
trilobatus	three-lobed
trimestris	of three months
trinervis	three-nerved
trinotatus	three-spotted or -marked
tripetalus	three-petaled
triphyllus	three-leaved
tripterus	three-winged
trispermis	with three seeds
tristachyus	three-spiked
triternatus	thrice in threes

Trichilia [try-KILL-ia]
Gr. *tricha*, three parts. Ovary and capsule are usually three-celled on these tropical trees and shrubs.

tricho-
In compound words signifies hairy. Thus:

trichocalyx	with a hairy calyx
trichophyllus	with hairy leaves
trichosanthus	hairy-flowered
trichospermis	hairy-seeded

trichocereus [try-ko-SEE-reus]
Gr. *thrix*, a hair, plus *Cereus*. The flowering parts of these cacti are hairy.

Tricholaena [try-ko-LEE-na]
Gr. *thrix*, a hair; *chlaena*, a cloak. The spikelets of these ornamental grasses have a hairy coating.

Trichopilia [try-ko-PILL-ia]
Gr. *thrix*, a hair; *pilion*, a cap. The anthers of these epiphytic orchids are concealed under a cap.

Trichosanthes [try-ko-SAN-thees]
Snakegourd. Gr. *thrix*, hair; *anthos*, a flower. The corolla of these climbers is fringed.

Trichostema [try-ko-STEE-ma]
Bluecurls. Bastard pennyroyal. Gr. *thrix*, hair; *stemon*, a stamen. The filaments of these herbs are very slender.

Tricyrtis [try-SER-tis]
Japanese toad-lily. Gr. *treis,* three; *kyrtos,* a cavity; because
the three outer petals of these pretty perennials are baglike
at the base.

Tridax [TRY-dax]
Greek name for another plant used as a vegetable, not these
perennial herbs.

Trientalis [try-en-TAY-lis]
Star flower. Latin word meaning one-third of a foot in
height, approximately that of these small perennials.

Trifolium [try-FO-lium]
Clover. The Latin name, from *tres,* three; *folium,* a leaf;
because of the trifoliate leaves of these annual and perennial herbs.

Trigonella [try-go-NELL-a]
Fenugreek. Gr. *treis,* three; *gonu,* an angle. The flowers of
these herbs appear triangular.

Trilisa [TRIL-i-sa]
Carolina vanilla. Gr. *trilix,* triple; from the three divisions of
the pappus of these autumn-blooming plants related to
Liatris.

Trillium [TRILL-ium]
Wake-robin. Birthroot. Gr. *trilix,* triple. Leaves and other
parts of these rhizomalous perennial herbs are in threes.

Trimeza [try-MEE-za]
Gr. *treis,* three; *megas,* great. The three outer flower segments of these bulbous plants are bigger than the inner.

Triosteum [try-os-teum]
Horse-gentian. Gr. *treis,* three; *osteon,* a bone; from the three
bony seeds of these perennial herbs.

Triphasia [try-FAY-sia]
Limeberry. Gr. *triphasios,* triple. The parts of the flowers are
in threes on these small ornamental shrubs or trees.

Triplaris [TRIP-la-ris]
Gr. *triplex,* triple. The parts of the flowers of these trees are
in threes.

Tripterygium [trip-ter-RIJ-ium]
Gr. *treis,* three; *pteryx,* a wing. The fruits of these shrubs
are equipped with three membranous wings.

Tristania [tris-TAY-nia]
Evergreen flowering shrubs and trees named for Jules Tristan
(1776-1861), French botanist.

tristis, -is, -e [TRIS-tis]
Dull; sad.

Trithrinax [try-THRY-nax]
Gr. *treis*, three; *thrinax*, a fan; because of the form of the
leaves of these palms.

Triticum [TRIT-ik-um]
Wheat. The classical Latin name. Next to rice, wheat is the
most important cereal crop grown. It is so old that it is unknown as a wild plant and its geographic origins cannot be
traced.

Tritonia [try-TO-nia]
Blazing star. Gr. *triton*, a weather cock. The stamens vary
in direction in different species of these showy cormous
plants.

triumphans [try-UM-fans]
Splendid; triumphant.

trivialis, -is, -e [triv-i-AY-lis]
Common; ordinary.

Trochodendron [trok-o-DEN-dron]
Gr. *trochos*, a wheel, *dendron*, a tree; in allusion to the
spreading stamens on this aromatic evergreen tree.

trolliifolius [trol-li-i-FO-lius]
With leaves like *Trollius*.

Trollius [TROL-ius]
Globe flower. From the German name, *trollblume*, with the
same meaning. Sometimes called double buttercup.

Tropaeolum [tro-PEE-o-lum]
The nasturtium, of gardeners, though not that of botanists.
Named by Linnaeus, from Gr. *tropaion*, trophy. The plant
growing on a post reminded Linnaeus of a classical trophy—
round shields and golden helmets, arranged on a pillar.
The word *nasturtium* is Latin for water-cress.

tropicus, -a, -um [TROP-ik-us]
Of the tropics.

truncatus, -a, -um [trunk-KAY-tus]
Cut-off square.

Tsuga [TSOO-ga]
Hemlock. From the Japanese name for these coniferous evergreen trees.

tubaeformis, -is, -e [tew-bee-FORM-is]
tubatus, -a, -um [tew-BAY-tus]
Trumpet-shaped.

tuberculatus, -a, -um [tew-ber-kew-LAY-tus]
  tuberculosus, -a, -um [tew-ber-kew-LO-sus]
  Covered with wartlike excrescences; tubercled.
tuberosus, -a, -um [tew-ber-o-sus]
  Tuberous.
tubiferus, -a, -um [tew-BIFF-er-us]
  tubulosus, -a, -um [tew-bew-LO-sus]
  Tubular; pipelike.
tubiflorus, -a, -um [tew-bi-FLO-rus]
  Trumpet-flowered.
Tulbaghia [tul-BAG-ia]
  Perennial herbs in the lily family named for Ryk Tulbagh
  (d. 1771), Dutch Governor of the Cape of Good Hope.
Tulipa [TEW-lip-a]
  Tulip. The Latin version of the Arabic for a turban. With
  many species native to the Caucasus, Anatolia, and the
  Middle East generally, tulips have been grown in Turkish
  gardens for centuries. They seem to have been introduced
  to the West by Ogier Ghiselin de Busbecq, Ambassador of
  the Holy Roman Empire to Suleiman the Magnificent, who
  saw them growing on his way to Constantinople in 1554.
  Conrad von Gesner described tulips he saw growing in
  Augsburg in 1559. It is likely that Clusius sent tulips to
  England around 1578. He took bulbs to Holland in 1593
  when he became Professor of Botany at Leyden, where tulips
  must already have been known and appreciated, for he soon
  lost his bulbs by theft. A few years later there developed in
  Holland and, afterwards, in Turkey the extraordinary
  hysteria known as the "Tulipomania." It reached its most
  extravagant heights and sudden collapse in Holland in 1634-
  1637. Fabulous prices were asked and paid—up to 100,000
  florins for a single bulb. Regular markets were established,
  and the bulbs were sold by weight in "perits" of less than a
  gram. One bulb of "Admiral Liefken" of less than 440 perits
  fetched 4,400 florins; "Semper Augustus" at 200 perits
  fetched 5,500 florins. Normally shrewd merchants who were
  making fortunes in a boom period in the spice and East
  India trades plunged deeply until finally the government
  stepped in with restrictive legislation to bring these specula-
  tions to a sudden and, to many, a shattering halt.
tulipiferus, -a, -um [tew-lip-IFF-er-us]
  Tulip-bearing.

tumidus, -a, -um [TEW-mid-us]
Swollen.

Tunica [TEW-nik-a]
L. *tunica,* an undergarment; in reference to the bracts at
the base of the calyx of these annual and perennial herbs.

Tupidanthus [tew-pid-ANTH-us]
Gr. *tupis,* a mallet; *anthos,* a flower; from the shape of the
flower buds on this tall climber.

turbinatus, -a, -um [ter-bin-AY-tus]
Shaped like a spinning top.

turgidus, -a, -um [TER-jid-us]
Inflated; full.

Turraea [ter-REE-a]
Trees or shrubs named for Giorgia della Turre (1607-1688),
Professor of Botany at Padua.

Tussacia [tuss-AY-sia]
Tropical American shrubs named for Richard de Tussac
(1751-1837), French botanist and author of a book on the
Flora of the Antilles.

Tussilago [tuss-il-AY-go]
Coltsfoot. L. *tussis,* a cough. The leaves of this herb with
dandelion-like flowers were supposed to cure coughs.

Typha [TY-fa]
Cat-tail. Reed-mace. The Greek name. In England *Typha*
is commonly called bulrush, which is properly a *Scirpus.*
The biblical bulrushes were almost certainly *Cyperus papy-*
rus, the source of papyrus and the material used for making
small rafts. The infant Moses is reported to have been
found by Pharaoh's daughter in an ark of bulrushes laid
in the flags by the river's brink.

typhinus, -a, -um [ty-FY-nus]
Resembling *Typha.*

typicus, -a, -um [TIP-ik-us]
Typical; agreeing with the type of a group.

U

Ulex [YEW-lex]
Gorse. The ancient Latin name for these ornamental spiny
evergreen shrubs.

ulicinus, -a, -um [yew-LISS-in-us]
Resembling *Ulex.*

uliginosus, -a, -um [yew-lij-in-o-sus]
Of swamps and wet places.

Ullucus [ULL-yew-kus]
From the native Peruvian name for these fleshy herbs.

ulmifolius, -a, -um [ull-mi-FO-lius]
With leaves like elm.

ulmoides [ull-MOY-deez]
Resembling elm.

Ulmus [ULL-mus]
Elm. The Latin name for these deciduous trees. The Romans were accustomed to use pollarded elms in vineyards over which to grow their vines.

Umbellularia [um-bell-yew-LAY-ria]
California laurel. L. *umbella*, an umbel; from the shape of the inflorescence on this evergreen tree.

umbellatus, -a, -um [um-bell-AY-tus]
Furnished with umbels.

umbonatus, -a, -um [um-bo-NAY-tus]
Having a stout projection at the center.

umbraculiferus, -a, -um [um-brak-yew-LIFF-er-us]
Umbrella-bearing.

umbrosus, -a, -um [um-BRO-sus]
Shade-loving.

uncinatus, -a, -um [un-sin-NAY-tus]
Hooked at the end.

undatus, -a, -um [un-DAY-tus]
undulatus, -a, -um [un-dew-LAY-tus]
Waved, wavy, as in *undulifolius*, wavy-leaved.

Ungnadia [ung-NAY-dia]
Mexican buckeye. A small tree or shrub named for Baron David von Ungnad, Austrian Ambassador at Constantinople (1576-1582), who sent horse-chestnut and other seeds to Clusius.

unguicularis, -is, -e [ung-gwik-yew-LAY-ris]
unguiculatus, -a, -um [ung-gwik-yew-LAY-tus]
Furnished with claws.

unguipetalus, -a, -um [ung-gwi-pet-AL-us]
With claw-shaped petals.

unguispinus, -a, -um [ung-gwi-SPY-nus]
With hooked spines.

uni-

In compound words signifies one. Thus:

unicolor	of one color
unicornis	with one horn
unidentatus	with a single tooth
uniflorus	one-flowered
unifolius	with one leaf
unilateralis	one-sided
univittatus	with one stripe

Uniola [yew-ni-o-la]
Latin name for another, and unidentifiable, plant than these perennial grasses.

urbanus, -a, -um [er-BAY-nus]
urbicus, -a, -um [ER-bik-us]
Belonging to towns.

urceolatus, -a, -um [er-see-o-LAY-tus]
Urn-shaped.

urens [YEW-rens]
Stinging; burning.

Urera [YEW-ree-ra]
Cow-itch. L. *ura*, a burn or sting. This genus of trees and shrubs is also called chichaste and described as "one of the most dangerous plants of Central America. . . . When one is struck by the coarse hairs, the effect is almost like that of an electric shock and there often follows the most intense pain. . . . The plant is often used for hedges, which few larger animals care to penetrate." (Standley, *Flora of Costa Rica*)

Urginea [er-JIN-ea]
From an Arabic name. These bulbous herbs, closely related to *Scilla*, are the source of the commercial "squill."

urnigerus, -a, -um [er-NIJ-er-us]
Pitcher-bearing.

urophyllus, -a, -um [yew-ro-FILL-us]
With leaves like a tail.

Ursinia [er-SIN-ea]
Annuals, perennials, and sub-shrubs named for John Ursinus (1608-1666) of Regensberg, a botanical author.

ursinus, -a, -um [er-SY-nus]
Like a bear, in smell or other respects. Also, sometimes, Northern (from the Great Bear).

Urtica [er-TY-ka]
Stinging nettle. The Latin name. All species sting, but some are so virulent (e.g., *U. urentissima*) as sometimes to cause death. The power to sting lasts even in the dried plant. For instance, when the great Linnaean herbarium was being moved out of London to a place of safety prior to the outbreak of World War II, the specimen of *U. urens* (the common annual nettle of Great Britain) stung the individual handling it.

urticaefolius, -a, -um [er-tiss-ee-FO-lius]
Nettle-leaved.

urticoides [er-tik-OY-deez]
Resembling nettle.

usitatissimus, -a, -um [yew-sit-tay-TISS-im-us]
Most useful.

ustulatus, -a, -um [us-tew-LAY-tus]
Burned; sere.

utilis, -is, -e [YEW-till-is]
Useful.

Utricularia [yew-trik-yew-LAY-ria]
Bladderwort. L. *utriculus*, a small bottle; in allusion to insect-trapping bladders borne on the leaves and runners of these aquatic and terrestrial herbs.

utriculatus, -a, -um [yew-trik-yew-LAY-tus]
utriculosus, -a, -um [yew-trik-yew-LO-sus]
Bladderlike.

uva-ursi [yew-va-ER-see]
Bear's grape. Specific name of *Arctostaphylus*.

uviferus, -a, -um [yew-VIFF-er-us]
Bearing grapes.

Uvularia [yew-vew-LAY-ria]
Bellwort. L. diminutive of *uva*, a bunch of grapes, from the bunched fruits on these woodland perennial herbs.

V

vaccinifolius, -a, -um [vax-in-i-FO-lius]
With leaves like *Vaccinium*.

vaccinioides [vax-in-i-OY-deez]
Resembling *Vaccinium*.

Vaccinium [vax-IN-ium]
Blueberry. Bilberry. Cranberry. The Latin name for these deciduous and evergreen flowering and edible berry-bearing shrubs.

vacillans [vas-SIL-ans]
Variable.

vagans [VAY-gans]
Of wide distribution; wandering.

vaginalis, -is, -e [vaj-in-AY-lis]
vaginatus, -a, -um [vaj-in-AY-tus]
Sheathed; having a sheath.

valdivianus, -a, -um [val-div-i-AY-nus]
Of Valdivia, Chile.

valentinus, -a, -um [val-en-TY-nus]
From Valentia in Spain.

Valeriana [val-ee-ri-AY-na]
Valerian. The medieval Latin name for these perennial herbs, possibly derived from L. *valere*, to be healthy; in allusion to the plant's medicinal uses in nervousness and hysteria.

Valerianella [val-ee-ri-an-ELL-a]
Corn-salad. Lamb's lettuce. Diminutive of *Valeriana*, from the resemblance to *Valeriana* of these herbs.

validus, -a, -um [VAL-id-us]
Strong; well-developed.

Vallaris [val-LAY-ris]
L. *vallus*, a stake in a palisade. These twining shrubs are said to be used in Java for fences.

Vallisneria [val-liss-NEE-ria]
Eelgrass. Named for Antonio Vallisnera (1661-1730), Professor at Padua. These are fresh-water plants. Salt-water eelgrass so much appreciated by wild ducks is *Zostera marina*.

Vallota [val-LO-ta]
Scarborough-lily. Bulbous plants named for Pierre Vallot (1594-1671), French botanical author.

Vancouveria [van-koo-VEE-ria]
Perennial herbs named for Captain George Vancouver, Royal Navy (1757-1798), British explorer. He sailed twice with

Captain Cook in his early years. His outstanding feat was his seven-year voyage (1791-1798) during which he carried out the first detailed surveys of the Pacific coast of North America as far north as Cook Inlet. Vancouver Island is named for him.

Vanda [VAN-da]
From the East Indian name for these epiphytic orchids.

Vandopsis [van-DOP-sis]
From *Vanda*, plus Gr. *opsis*, similar to. (See *Vanda*.)

Vanilla [van-ILL-a]
Vanilla bean. Sp. *vainilla*, a small pod; with reference to the shape of the fruit. Vanilla is the only genus of orchid with an economic value, but even that is much reduced now by the introduction of synthetic vanillas, some of which can be produced very cheaply in very large quantities.

variabilis, -is, -e [vair-ri-AB-il-is]
  varians [VAY-ri-ans]
  variatus, -a, -um [vair-ri-AY-tus]
  Variable; varying.

variegatus, -a, -um [vair-ree-GAY-tus]
  Irregularly colored; variegated.

varius, -a, -um [VAIR-ri-us]
  Differing; diverse.

vegetatus, -a, -um [vej-et-TAY-tus]
  vegetus, -a, -um [VEJ-et-us]
  Vigorous.

Veitchia [VEECH-ia]
Palms named for James Veitch (1815-1869), and his son John Gould Veitch (1839-1870), of Exeter and Chelsea, England. The Veitchs were the leading nurserymen of their day and their family was in business continuously for 106 years when the Chelsea firm was finally liquidated in 1914. Meanwhile, many good plants were introduced by them, as shown by the number of times their name is commemorated in species names (*Veitchianus, Veitchii, Veitchiorum*). They sent their own collectors abroad and trained a legion of excellent gardeners. Dr. E. H. (Chinese) Wilson was among their alumni (see *Sinowilsonia*).

velaris, -is, -e [vel-AY-ris]
Pertaining to a veil.

velox [VEE-lox]
Quick-growing.

Veltheimia [vel-TY-mia]
Bulbous plants named for August Ferdinand von Veltheim (1741-1801), German patron of botany.

velutinus, -a, -um [vel-YEW-tin-us]
Velvety.

venanatus, -a, -um [vee-nan-AY-tus]
Poisonous. Also, *venenosus*, very poisonous.

Venidium [ven-ID-ium]
L. *vena*, a vein; because of the appearance of the ribbed fruits of these ornamental herbs.

venosus, -a, -um [vee-NO-sus]
Full of veins.

ventricosus, -a, -um [ven-trik-o-sus]
Having a swelling on one side.

venustus, -a, -um [vee-NUS-tus]
Handsome; charming.

Veratrum [vee-RAY-trum]
False hellebore. The Latin name from *vere*, truly; *ater*, black; from the color of the roots of these perennial herbs.

verbascifolius, -a, -um [ver-bask-i-FO-lius]
With leaves like mullein.

Verbascum [ver-BAS-kum]
Mullein. The ancient Latin name for these mainly biennial herbs.

Verbena [ver-BEE-na]
Vervain. The Latin name. These annual and perennial herbs or sub-shrubs once had a considerable reputation in medicine, the flowers being used to restore defective vision.

Verbesina [ver-bes-SY-na]
From the resemblance of these herbs to *Verbena*.

verecundus, -a, -um [ver-e-KUN-dus]
Modest.

veris [VEE-ris]
Of the spring; spring-flowering. Specific name of the cowslip (*Primula veris*).

vermicularis, -is, -e [ver-mik-yew-LAY-ris]
vermiculatus, -a, -um [ver-mik-yew-LAY-tus]
Wormlike.

365

vernalis, -is, -e [ver-NAY-lis]
Of spring; spring-flowering.
verniciferus, -a, -um [ver-ni-SIFF-er-us]
Producing varnish.
vernicosus, -a, -um [ver-ni-KO-sus]
Varnished.
vernix [VER-nix]
Varnish.
vernus, -a, -um [VER-nus]
Of the spring.
Vernonia [ver-NO-nia]
Ironweed. North American perennial herbs named for
William Vernon (d. 1711), botanist and traveler in North
America.
Veronica [ver-ON-ik-a]
Speedwell. Herbs, shrubs, and some trees, named for St.
Veronica. (See *Hebe*.)
Verschaffeltia [ver-shaff-ELT-ia]
A palm named for Ambrose Colletto Alexandre Verschaffelt
(1825-1886), Belgian author of a book on *Camellias*.
versicolor [ver-SIK-kol-or]
Variously colored.
verticillaris, -is, -e [ver-tiss-ill-AY-ris]
verticillatus, -a, -um [ver-tiss-ill-AY-tus]
Having whorls; forming a ring around an axis.
Verticordia [ver-ti-KORD-ia]
Juniper-myrtle. The name of these shrubs is a compliment
to Venus to whom myrtle was sacred (L. *verto*, I turn;
cor, the heart).
verus, -a, -um [VEE-rus]
True to type; standard.
vescus, -a, -um [VES-kus]
Thin; feeble.
vesicarius, -a, -um [ves-sik-KAY-rius]
vesiculosus, -a, -um [ves-sik-yew-LO-sus]
Bladderlike; furnished with small bladders.
Vesicaria [ves-sik-KAY-ria]
L. *vesica*, a bladder; from the inflated pods following the
flowers on these herbs.
vespertinus, -a, -um [ves-per-TY-nus]
Of the evening; evening-blooming.

366

vestitus, -a, -um [ves-TIT-tus]
Covered; clothed.

vexans [VEX-ans]
Annoying; wounding.

vexillaris, -is, -e [vex-ill-AY-ris]
Having a standard (flag). Also *vexillarius,* a standard-bearer.

vialis, -is, -e [vy-AY-lis]
viarum [vy-AY-rum]
Of the waysides.

viburnifolius, -a, -um [vy-ber-ni-FO-lius]
With leaves like *Viburnum.*

Viburnum [vy-BER-num]
Arrow-wood. Latin name of one species of this genus of
evergreen and deciduous flowering shrubs.

Vicia [VISS-ia]
Vetch. The Latin name for these herbs.

viciaefolius, -a, -um [viss-i-ee-FO-lius]
vicifolius, -a, -um [viss-i-FO-lius]
Vetch-leaved.

Victoria [vik-TO-ria]
Royal water-lily. Queen Victoria water-lily. Named for Queen
Victoria (1819-1901). The great water-lily *V. amazonica,*
(*V. regia*), was found in Guiana by Schomburgk and obtained from him by Paxton, head gardener to the Duke of
Devonshire at Chatsworth where a special house and pool
were constructed to Paxton's design to contain it. This was
one of Paxton's first glass-houses which were to reach their
climax in the Crystal Palace (see *paxtonii*). The feat of
bringing the plant into bloom caused a sensation and a
special telegram was dispatched to announce the fact to
Her Majesty. The leaves, which may be up to six feet across,
are reputed to be able to support the weight of a small
child—provided he does not fidget and his weight is dis-
tributed correctly.

victorialis, -is, -e [vik-to-ri-AY-lis]
Victorious. It is said that bulbs of *Allium victorialis* were
once worn by Bavarian miners as a protection against evil
spirits.

Vigna [VIG-na]
Twining and prostrate herbs named for Dominico Vigna
(d. 1647), Professor of Botany at Pisa.

Villaresia [vill-a-REE-sia]
Evergreen climbing shrubs or small trees named for Matthias
Villarez, Superintendent of the Gardens at Santa Espina,
Chile, c. 1790.

villosus, -a, -um [vill-O-sus]
Covered with soft hairs.

viminalis, -is, -e [vim-in-AY-lis]
vimineus, -a, -um [vim-IN-eus]
With long slender shoots—like osiers.

Vinca [VIN-ka]
Periwinkle. The Latin name for these evergreen and deciduous trailing sub-shrubs or herbs.

Vincetoxicum [vin-see-TOX-ik-um]
L. *vinco*, to conquer; *toxicum*, poison. This genus of herbs
and sub-shrubs was supposed to be an antidote to poisons.

viniferus, -a, -um [vy-NIFF-er-us]
Wine-bearing.

vinosus, -a, -um [vy-NO-sus]
Wine-red.

Viola [VY-o-la]
Pansy. Heart's-ease. Violet. The Latin name for these herbaceous annuals and perennials.

violaceus, -a, -um [vy-o-LAY-seus]
Violet-colored.

violescens [vy-o-LESS-ens]
Almost violet-colored.

virens [VY-rens]
Green. Also *virescens*, light green.

virgatus, -a, -um [ver-JAY-tus]
Twiggy.

Virgilia [ver-JILL-ia]
A tree named for the Latin poet Virgil (70-19 B.C.).

virginalis, -is, -e [ver-jin-AY-lis]
virgineus, -a, -um [ver-JIN-eus]
White; virginal.

virginianus, -a, -um [ver-jin-i-AY-nus]
virginicus, -a, -um [ver-JIN-ik-us]
virginiensis, -is, -e [ver-jin-i-EN-sis]
virginieus, -a, -um [ver-jin-i-EE-us]
Virginian.

viridis, -is, -e [VI-rid-is]
Green. Also in compound words *viri-*, thus:

viridescens	greenish
viridiflorus	with green flowers
viridifolius	green-leaved
viridifuscus	green-brown
viridissimus	very green
viridulus	somewhat green

viscidus, -a, -um [VISS-id-us]
viscosus, -a, -um [viss-KO-sus]
Sticky; clammy.
vitaceus, -a, -um [vy-TAY-seus]
Vinelike.
vitellinus, -a, -um [vy-tell-LY-nus]
Color of egg yolk.
Vitex [VY-tex]
Latin name for V. *agnus-castus* or chaste tree; one species of these aromatic deciduous flowering shrubs.
vitifolius, -a, -um [vy-ti-FO-lius]
With leaves like grape.
Vitis [VY-tis]
Grape. The Latin name.
V. *vinifera* is the European grape. It has been used by man since prehistoric times but no one knows when the secret of wine-making was discovered. Long ago, grapes were grown and wine made in the southern counties of England, as instanced by many place names. Today, grape-growing for wine is hardly practiced north of a line through Brittany, Liège in Belgium to Silesia. Whether this is due to climatic change or to more discriminating taste is not certain, perhaps some of both.
From their first arrival in the New World, the American settlers made determined efforts to grow acceptable wine from imported stocks. As early as 1639, the Virginia Assembly made it mandatory for all growers of corn and tobacco to grow a certain number of vines. That measure being unsuccessful, a heavy premium of 10,000 pounds of tobacco was offered for each two tuns of wine from grapes grown in the Colony. In spite of these inducements, the industry never succeeded.

It took Americans nearly three hundred years to discover that imported stocks could not be made to produce. It was only when John Adlum in about 1820 introduced the Catawba grape that a truly satisfactory wine grape became available to American wine growers. Catawba is still the outstanding American wine grape.

It remained for Georg Engelmann (see *engelmannii*), the German-born St. Louis physician, to discover that American grape stocks were virtually proof against the minute plant louse, the phylloxera. It had already devastated the vineyards of Madeira and was beginning serious attacks on the famous vineyards of Europe. Presumably they would have been lost had not Engelmann stepped in with his timely discovery.

Vittadinia [vit-a-DIN-ia]
Thick-stemmed herbs and sub-shrubs named for Dr. C. Vittadini (1800-1865), Italian botanical author.

vittatus, -a, -um [vit-TAY-tus]
Striped lengthwise.

vittigerus, -a, -um [vit-IJ-er-us]
Marked with stripes.

volgaricum [vol-GAR-ik-um]
Of the Volga River.

volubilis, -is, -e [vol-YEW-bil-is]
Twining.

volutus, -a, -um [vo-LEW-tus]
With rolled leaves.

vomitorius, -a, -um [vom-it-OR-ius]
Emetic.

Vriesia [VREE-sia]
Tropical American plants with stiff leaves, named for W. H. deVriese (1806-1862), Dutch botanist.

vulcanicus, -a, -um [vul-KAN-ik-us]
Growing on a volcano.

vulgaris, -is, -e [vul-GAY-ris]
vulgatus, -a, -um [vul-GAY-tus]
Common.

vulpinus, -a, -um [vul-PY-nus]
Relating to foxes; used for species with an inferior sort of fruit.

W

Wahlenbergia [wah-len-BER-jia]
Bellflower. Annual and perennial herbs named for Georg Wahlenberg (1780-1851), Swedish botanist.

Waldsteinia [wald-STY-nia]
Creeping herbs like strawberries named for Count Franz Adam Waldstein-Wartenberg (1759-1823), Austrian botanist.

Wallichia [woll-ISH-ia]
Palms named for Nathaniel Wallich (1786-1854), Danish botanist.

Warscewiczella [var-shev-ich-ELL-a]
Epiphytic orchids named for Joseph Warszewicz (1812-1866), who escaped from Poland after taking an active part in the 1830 rebellion. He traveled widely in South America collecting orchids for Messrs. van Houtte, Dutch nurserymen. Eventually he was able to return home to become Inspector of the Botanic Gardens in Krakow.

Warzewiczia [var-shev-IK-sia]
See *Warscewiczella.*

Washingtonia [wash-ing-TO-nia]
Named for George Washington (1732-1799), first President of the United States. They are tall, not very handsome, fan-palms native in California and southern United States.

Watsonia [wat-SO-nia]
Bugle lily. Bulbous herbs named for Sir William Watson (1715-1787), scientist and physician.

Wedelia [wed-EE-lia]
Herbs and sub-shrubs named for Georg Wolfgang Wedel (1645-1721), Professor of Botany at Jena.

Weigela [wy-GEE-la]
Deciduous flowering shrubs named for Christian Ehrenfried von Weigel (1748-1831), German botanist.

Weinmannia [wyn-MAN-nia]
Evergreen shrubs or trees with fernlike foliage named for Johann Wilhelm Weinmann (1737-1745), apothecary of Ratisbon.

Westringia [west-RINJ-ia]
Australian rosemary. Shrubs named for Johann Peter Westring (1753-1833), physician to the King of Sweden.

Wigandia [wy-GAN-dia]
Foliage plants named for Johannes Wigand (1523-1587), Bishop of Pomerania, who wrote on plants.

Wilcoxia [wil-KOX-ia]
Cacti named for General Timothy E. Wilcox, U. S. Army, a keen student of plants, c. 1900.

Wisteria (sometimes, incorrectly, **Wistaria**) [wis-TEE-ria]
Deciduous climbing flowering shrubs named for Caspar Wistar (1761-1818), Professor of Anatomy at the University of Pennsylvania and one of the early owners of what is now Vernon Park, Philadelphia. Despite the apparent anomaly Wisteria *remains* the preferred spelling.

wolgaricus, -a, -um [vol-GAY-rik-us]
Of the Volga River region.

Woodsia [WOOD-sia]
Ferns named for Joseph Woods (1776-1864), English botanical author.

Woodwardia [wood-WAR-dia]
Chain-fern. Named for Thomas Jenkinson Woodward (1745-1820), English botanist.

Wulfenia [Wulf-EE-nia]
Herbaceous perennials named for Franz Xavier, Freiherr von Wulfen (1728-1805), Austrian botanical author.

Wyethia [wy-ETH-ia]
Mule-ears. Named for Nathaniel B. Wyeth, mid-19th-century American botanist who discovered the plants.

X

xanthinus, -a, -um [zan-THY-nus]
Yellow. In compound words *xanth-*, thus:

xanthacanthus	yellow-spined
xanthocarpus	yellow-fruited
xantholeucus	yellowish white
xanthonervis	yellow-nerved
xanthophyllus	with yellow leaves
xanthorrhizus	yellow-rooted
xanthoxylon	with yellow heartwood

Xanthisma [zan-THIS-ma]
Gr. *xanthos*, yellow; alluding to the color of the flowers of this daisylike annual.

Xanthoceras [zan-THOS-ee-ras]
Gr. *xanthos,* yellow; *keras,* a horn; from the yellow hornlike growths between the petals of this deciduous flowering tree.

Xanthorrhoea [zan-tho-REE-a]
Gr. *xanthos,* yellow; *rheo,* to flow. A yellow resinous gum is extracted from these perennials which are known as Botany Bay gum or blackboy.

Xanthosoma [zan-tho-so-ma]
Gr. *xanthos,* yellow; *soma,* a body; with reference to the yellow inner tissues of some species of these milky herbs.

Xeranthemum [zee-RAN-them-um]
Immortelle. Gr. *xeros,* dry; *anthos,* a flower. The flower heads are dry and retain their form and color for years.

Xerophyllum [zee-ro-FILL-um]
Turkey's beard. Gr. *xeros,* dry; *phyllon,* a leaf. The leaves of this perennial sub-aquatic herb are dry and grasslike.

xylobium [zy-LO-bium]
Gr. *xylon,* wood; *bios,* life. The plants grow on trees.

xylocanthus, -a, -um [zy-lo-KAN-thus]
With woody spines.

Y

Yucca [YUK-ka]
From the Carib name for manihot or cassava, erroneously used here for these evergreen shrubs or small trees with rosettes of sword-shaped leaves. Adam's needle and Spanish bayonet are familiar names of some species.

Z

Zaluzianskya [za-loo-zi-an-SKY-a]
Annual or perennial herbs named for Adam Zaluziansky von Zalusian (1558-1613), botanist of Prague.

Zamia [ZAY-mia]
Evergreen palmlike plants. L. *zamia,* damage or loss. Named by Linnaeus because of the barren appearance of the male cones. The roots of the coontie (*Z. floridana*) were used by the Indians to make soap. Also, when the poisonous principle has been removed the roots can be ground to make a palatable arrowroot.

Zantedeschia [zan-tee-DESH-ia]
Calla-lily (U. S.); arum-lily (U. K.). Perennial herbs named for Francesco Zantedeschi (b. 1797), Italian botanist.

Zanthoxylum [zan-THOX-ill-um]
Prickly ash. Hercules' club. Tooth-ache tree. Gr. *xanthos,* yellow; *xylon,* wood; from the color of the heartwood of some species of these ornamental shrubs.

Zea [ZEE-a]
Corn (U. S.); maize, Indian corn (U. K.). From the Greek name for another food grass. The plant is widely cultivated in the tropical and temperate zones from sea level to about 12,000 feet. It is the staple grain in Mexico, Central America, and southern Africa. In the United States, about 90 per cent of the crop is fed to animals and goes to market as meat, milk, and eggs. The leaves provide the wrappers of the "whacking white cheroot" of Burma.

Zebrina [zee-BRY-na]
L. *zebra;* in allusion to the stripings on the leaves of one species of these herbaceous trailing perennials.

zebrinus, -a, -um [zee-BRY-nus]
Zebra-striped.

Zelkova [zel-KO-va]
From the Caucasian name for these deciduous trees.

Zenobia [zee-NO-bia]
An ornamental shrub named for Zenobia, Queen of Palmyra c. A.D. 266.

Zephyranthes [zef-fy-RANTH-eez]
Zephyr-lily. Gr. *zephyros,* the west wind; *anthos,* a flower. These bulbous herbs are natives of the Western hemisphere.

zeylanicus, -a, -um [zee-LAN-ik-us]
Of Ceylon.

zibethinus, -a, -um [zib-eth-THY-nus]
Ill-smelling like a civet cat. Specific of the durian (*Durio*) whose fruit contains a pith which can smell horribly. In it are embedded the fruit segments which have a delightful flavor.

Zingiber [ZIN-jib-er]
Ginger. From the Greek name which, in turn, is said to derive from the Malayan. The root of Z. *officinale* is the source of commercial ginger.

374

Zinnia [ZIN-nia]
Showy annuals named for Johann Gottfried Zinn (1727-1759), Professor of Botany, Göttingen.

Zizania [zy-ZAY-nia]
Wild rice. Canadian wild rice. Greek name for another wild grain, not this. Z. *aquatica* is eagerly eaten by wild ducks and gives their flesh an especially fine flavor. Similarly, it is especially good when eaten with wild duck.

zizanioides [zy-zay-ni-OY-deez]
Resembling *Zizania*.

Zizyphus [ZY-ziff-us]
Jujube. From the Arabic name for this small tree.

zonalis, -is, -e [zo-NAY-lis]
zonatus, -a, -um [zo-NAY-tus]
Banded or with a girdle usually of a distinct color.

Zoysia [ZOY-sia]
Named for Karl von Zoys (1756-1800), Austrian botanist. There is a new vogue for this turf grass for sandy lawns in warmish climates.

Zygadenus (also, incorrectly, **Zigadenus**) [zy-GAD-ee-nus]
Gr. *zygos*, a yoke; *aden*, a gland. The glands of these herbs are in pairs at the base of the perianth.

Zygocactus [zy-go-KAK-tus]
Christmas cactus. Gr. *zygos*, a yoke, plus *Cactus*; from the way in which the stems are jointed.

Zygopetalum [zy-go-PET-al-um]
Gr. *zygos*, a yoke; *petalon*, a petal; from the form of the flowers of these epiphytic orchids.

Index of Common Names

3

A

acacia	Acacia
acacia, false	Robinia
aconite	Aconitum
aconite, winter	Eranthis
Adam and Eve	Aplectrum
Adam's needle	Yucca
adder's mouth	Pogonia
adder's tongue	Erythronium
adder's tongue fern	Ophioglossum
African corn-lily	Ixia
African lily	Agapanthus
African marigold	Tagetes
African ragwort	Othonna
African valerian	Fedia
African violet	Saintpaulia
agrimony	Agrimonia
ague-weed	Eupatorium
akee tree	Blighia
alder	Alnus
Alexandrian laurel	Danaë
alfalfa	Medicago
alkanet	Anchusa
Allegheny vine	Adlumia
alligator pear	Persea
allspice	{ Calycanthus / Pimenta }
allspice tree	Pimenta
alum-root	Heuchera
alyssum, sweet	Lobularia
amaranth, globe	Gomphrena
amaryllis	{ Amaryllis / Hippeastrum }
Amazon lily	Eucharis
American cowslip	Dodecatheon

379

American cranberry	**Oxycoccus**; now, Vaccinium
American cress	Barbarea
American feverfew	Chrysanthemum parthenium
American pennyroyal	Hedeoma
American wayfaring-tree	Viburnum
Andromeda	Pieris
angel's trumpet	Datura
anise	Pimpinella
aniseed tree	Illicium
Antarctic forget-me-not	Myosotidium
apple	Malus
apple berry	Billardiera
apple-of-Peru	Nicandra
aralia, false	Dizygotheca
arbor-vitae	Thuja
arbutus, trailing	Epigaea
arrow-arum	Peltandra
arrowhead	Sagittaria
arrowroot	Maranta
arrow-wood	Viburnum
artichoke	Cynara
arum-lily	Zantedeschia
ash	Fraxinus
aspen	Populus tremula
aster, annual ⎱ aster, China ⎰	Callistephus
aster, Stokes'	Stokesia
aster, tree	Olearia
astilbe	Astilbe
Australian Desert kumquat	Eremocitrus
Australian honeysuckle	Banksia
Australian laurel	Pittosporum
Australian rosemary	Westringia
Australian sarsaparilla	Hardenbergia
Australian sword lily	Anigozanthus
Autumn crocus	Colchicum
avens	Geum
avens, mountain	Dryas
avocado	Persea
azalea	Rhododendron

B

baby's breath	Gypsophila
baby's tears	Helxine
bachelor's button	Centaurea
bael fruit	Aegle
baldmoney	Meum
balloon flower	Platycodon
balm	Melissa
balm, bastard	Melittis
balm-of-Gilead	Cedronella
balsam	Impatiens
bamboo	Bambusa
banana	Musa
baneberry	Actaea
baobab tree	Adansonia
Barbados-cherry	Malpighia
barberry	Berberis
barley	Hordeum
barren strawberry	Waldsteinia
barren-wort	Epimedium
basil	Ocimum
bass-wood	Tilia
bastard balm	Melittis
bastard jasmine	Cestrum
bastard pennyroyal	Trichostema
bay	Laurus
bayberry	{ Myrica Pimenta
bay, sweet	Magnolia
bay-tree	{ Laurelia Laurus
beach grass	Ammophila
beach heather	Hudsonia
beach pea	Lathyrus
beach plum	Prunus maritima
bead-tree	Melia
bean	{ Faba Glycine Phaseolus Vicia
bearberry	Arctostaphylos

bear-grass	{ Camassia { Nolina
bear-tongue	Clintonia
beard grass	Andropogon
beard-tongue	Penstemon
bear's breech	Acanthus
beauty bush	Kolkwitzia
bedstraw	Galium
bee-balm	Monarda
beech	Fagus
beech, southern	Nothofagus
beefsteak plant	Perilla
beet	Beta
beggar's ticks	Bidens
belladonna	Atropa
bellflower	{ Campanula { Wahlenbergia
bellflower, Chilean	Nolana
bellflower, Chinese	Platycodon
bellflower, giant	Ostrowskia
bellflower, gland	Adenophora
bellflower, pendulous	Symphyandra
bellwort	Uvularia
Belvedere	Kochia
Benjamin bush	Lindera benzoin
bent grass	Agrostis
benzoin	Lindera benzoin
bergamot	Monarda
Bermuda grass	Cynodon
Bethlehem sage	Pulmonaria
betelnut	Areca
betonica betony	Stachys
betony, wood	Pedicularis
big tree	Sequoiadendron
bilberry	Vaccinium
bindweed	Convolvulus
birch	Betula
bird-of-paradise flower	Strelitzia
birthroot	Trillium
birthwort	Aristolochia

bishop'scap	Mitella
bishopsweed	Aegopodium
bittersweet	Celastrus
bitterwort	Lewisia
blackberry	Rubus
blackberry lily	Belamcanda
blackboy	Xanthorrhoea
black bryony	Tamus
black cohosh	Cimicifuga
black-eyed Susan	{ Rudbeckia Thunbergia
bladder campion	Silene
bladder fern	Cystopteris
bladdernut	Staphylea
bladder senna	Colutea
bladderwort	Utricularia
blanket-flower	Gaillardia
blazing star	{ Chamaelirium Liatris Mentzelia Tritonia
bleeding-heart	Dicentra
blessed thistle	{ Cnicus Silybum
blistercress	Erysimum
blood-lily	Haemanthus
bloodroot	Sanguinaria
bloodwood tree	Haematoxylum
bluebell	{ Campanula (Scotland) Mertensia (Virginia) Scilla or Endymion (England)
bluebell, California	Phacelia
blueberry	Vaccinium
bluebonnet, Texas	Lupinus
blue cohosh	Caulophyllum
bluecurls	Trichostema
blue daisy	Felicia
blue-eyed grass	Sisyrinchium
blue-eyed Mary	Collinsia
blue gum	Eucalyptus
blue lace-flower	Trachymene

blue oxalis	Parochetus
blue palmetto	Rhapidophyllum
blue poppy	Meconopsis
blue spiraea	Caryopteris
bluet	Houstonia
bogbean	Menyanthes
bog myrtle	Myrica
bog-orchid	{ Arethusa / Calypso
bog rosemary	Andromeda
boneset	Eupatorium
borage	Borago
Boston ivy	Parthenocissus
Botany Bay gum	Xanthorrhoea
bottlebrush tree	{ Callistemen / Melaleuca
bottle-gourd	Lagenaria
bottle tree	Brachychiton
bouncing Bet	Saponaria
bowstring hemp	Sansevieria
box	Buxus
box, sweet	Sarcococca
box-thorn	Lycium
bracken / brake	{ Pteridium / Pteris
bramble	Rubus
Brazil-nut	Bertholletia
breadfruit	Artocarpus
bridal wreath	Spiraea
broad bean	Vicia
brome grass	Bromus
brookweed	Samolus
broom	{ Cytisus / Genista / Spartium
broom, butcher's	Ruscus
bryony	Bryonia
bryony, black	Tamus
buckbean	Menyanthes
bucket orchid	Coryanthes
buckeye	Aesculus

384

buckthorn	Rhamnus
buckthorn, sea	Hippophae
buckwheat	Fagopyrum
bugbane	Cimicifuga
bugle	Ajuga
bugle lily	Watsonia
bugleweed	Ajuga
bugloss	Anchusa
bugloss, viper's	Echium
bulbous chervil	Chaerophyllum
bulrush	Scirpus
bunchberry	Cornus
bunchflower	Melanthium
bur, New Zealand	Acaena
bur-cucumber	Sicyos
bur-marigold	Bidens
burnet	{ Poterium Sanguisorba
burning bush	Dictamnus
burstwort	Herniaria
bush clover	Lespedeza
bush honeysuckle	Diervilla
butcher's broom	Ruscus
butter-and-eggs	Linaria
butter-bur	Petasites
buttercup	Ranunculus
buttercup, double	Trollius
butterfly bush	Buddleia
butterfly flower	Schizanthus
butterfly iris	Moraea
butterfly pea	Clitoria
butterfly-weed	Asclepias
butterwort	Pinguicula
button bush	Cephalanthus
buttonwood	Platanus

C

cabbage	Brassica
cabbage tree	Andira
calaba tree	Calophyllum

calabash tree	Crescentia
calamint	Calamintha
calico-bush	Kalmia
California golden bells	Emmenanthe
California laurel	Umbellularia
California-bluebell	Phacelia
California poppy	Eschscholtzia
calla-lily	Zantedeschia
calvary-clover	Medicago
camas	Camassia
camomile (see chamomile)	
campeachy-wood	Haematoxylum
campion	Silene
campion, evening	Lychnis
Canadian wild rice	Zizania
canary-grass	Phalaris
candle-tree	Parmentiera
candlewood	Fouquiera
candy carrot	Athamanta
candytuft	Iberis
cane palm	Calamus
Canterbury-bell	Campanula
Cape chestnut	Calodendrum
Cape cowslip	Lachenalia
Cape gooseberry	Physalis
Cape honeysuckle	Tecomaria
Cape jasmine	Gardenia
Cape marigold	Dimorphotheca
Cape pondweed	Aponogeton
Cape primrose	Streptocarpus
Cape stock	Heliophila
caper	Capparis
caraway	Carum
cardamon	Elettaria
cardinal-flower	Lobelia
cardoon	Cynara
carline thistle	Carlina
carnanba palm	Copernica
carnation	Dianthus
carob	Ceratonia
Carolina allspice	Calycanthus

carrion-flower	{ Smilax { Stapelia
carrot	Daucus
cashew nut	Anacardium
cassava	Manihot
castor bean } castor-oil plant }	Ricinus
catbrier	Smilax
catchfly	{ Lychnis { Silene
catmint } catnip }	Nepeta
cat-tail	{ Scirpus { Typha
cat's claw	Doxantha
cat's ear	Hypochoeris
cauliflower	Brassica
cedar	Cedrus
cedar, incense	Libocedrus
cedar, Japanese	Cryptomeria
cedar, of Lebanon	Cedrus libani
cedar, northern white	Thuja
cedar, red	Juniperus
celandine	Chelidonium
celandine poppy	Stylophorum
celery	Apium
centaury	Centaurium
centaury, American	Sabbatia
century plant	Agave
cereus, night-blooming	Selenicereus
chain-fern	Woodwardia
chamomile	Anthemis
chamomile, false	Boltonia
chamomile, wild	Matricaria
chard, Swiss	Beta
chaste tree	Vitex
checker-berry	Gaultheria
cherry	Prunus
cherry, ground	Physalis
cherry, Jerusalem	Solanum
cherry-laurel	Laurocerasus

COMMON NAMES

cherry-pie	Heliotropium
chervil, bulbous	Chaerophyllum
chervil, salad	Anthriscus
chestnut	Castanea
chestnut, horse	Aesculus
chestnut-oak	Lithocarpus
chick pea	Cicer
chickweed	Stellaria
chickweed, mouse-ear	Cerastium
chicory	Cichorium
Chilean bellflower	Nolana
Chilean boldo tree	Peumus
China aster	Callistephus
chinaberry	Melia
China-grass	Boehmeria
Chinese moonseed	Sinomenium
chive	Allium
chokeberry	Aronia
Christmas-berry	Heteromeles
Christmas-rose	Helleborus
Christmas fern	Polystichum
cinnamon fern	Osmunda
cinnamon vine	Apios
cinquefoil	Potentilla
citronella	Collinsonia
clary	Salvia
cleavers	Galium
cliff-brake fern	Pellaea
climbing cactus	Acanthocereus
climbing-fern	Lygodium
clove tree	Eugenia
clover, bush	Lespedeza
clover, hop	Trifolium
clover, sweet	Melilotus
club of Hercules	Zanthoxylum
club-moss	{Lycopodium
	{Selaginella
cob-nut	Corylus
cock's comb	Celosia
cock's foot grass	Dactylis
cockspur thorn	Crataegus

coco-de-mer	Lodoicea
cocoa	Cacao
coconut	Cocos
coconut, double	Lodoicea
coffee	Coffea
coffee, wild	Psychotria
cohosh	Actaea
cohosh, black	Cimicifuga
cohosh, blue	Caulophyllum
coltsfoot	Tussilago
columbine	Aquilegia
comb fern	Schizaea
comfrey	Symphytum
cone-flower	{ Echinacea, Lepachys, Rudbeckia
cone-plant	Conophytum
copper leaf	Acalypha
coral tree	Erythrina
coral vine	Antigonum
coriander	Coriandrum
cork-tree	Phellodendron
corn	Zea
corncockle	Lychnis
cornel, cornel, dwarf, cornelian cherry	Cornus
cornflower	{ Centaurea, Echinacea
corn-salad	Valerianella
costmary	Chrysanthemum
cottage pink	Dianthus
cotton	Gossypium
cotton, lavender	Santolina
cottongrass	Eriophorum
cotton tree	Bombax
cotton-weed	Diotis
cottonwood	Populus
cowbane	Cicuta
cow-itch	Urera
cow-parsnip	Heracleum

cowslip	{Caltha Mertensia (Virginia) Primula
cowslip, American	Dodecatheon
cranberry	Vaccinium
cranberry bush	Viburnum
cranesbill	Geranium
creeping-Charlie	Lysimachia
creosote bush	Larrea
cress, American	Barbarea
cress, bitter	Cardamine
cress, garden	Lepidium
cress, rock	Arabis
cress, spring	Cardamine
cress, stone	Aethionema
cress, upland	Barbarea
cress, water	Nasturtium
cress, winter	Barbarea
crested poppy	Argemone
crocus	Crocus
crocus, Autumn	Colchicum
cross vine	Bignonia
crosswort	Crucianella
croton	Codiaeum
crowberry	Empetrum
crowfoot	Ranunculus
crown-imperial lily	Fritillaria
crown vetch	Coronilla
cuckoo-flower	Cardamine
cuckoo-pint	Arum
cucumber	Cucumis
cucumber, prickly	Echynocystus
cudweed	Gnaphalium
cup-flower	Nierembergia
cupid's dart	Catananche
currant	Ribes
curry-leaf	Murraya
custard-apple	Annona
cypress	Cupressus
cypress, false	Chamaecyparis

cypress, summer	Kochia
cypress, swamp	Taxodium
cypress pine	Callistris

D

daffodil	Narcissus
dahlia	Dahlia
dahlia, climbing	Hidalgoa
daisy	Bellis
daisy, blue	Felicia
daisy bush	Olearia
daisy, Michaelmas	Aster
daisy, New Zealand	Celmisia
daisy, ox-eyed	Chrysanthemum
daisy, Swan River	Brachycome
daisy, Transvaal	Gerbera
daisy, white	Chrysanthemum
dame's violet	Hesperis
dammar pine	Agathis
dandelion	Taraxacum
dandelion, dwarf	Krigia
Darling River pea	Swainsonia
date palm	Phoenix
date plum	Diospyros
date-yucca	Samuela
day-flower	Commelina
day-lily	Hemerocallis
dead-nettle	Lamium
deadly nightshade	Atropa
deer-foot	Achlys
deer-grass	Rhexia
desert-candle	Eremurus
devil's bit	Chamaelirium
devil's paintbrush	Hieracium
dewberry	Rubus
diamond-flower	Ionopsidium
dill	Anethum
dish-cloth gourd	Luffa
distaff thistle	Carthamus
ditchmoss	Elodea

COMMON NAMES

dittany	{ Cunila { Dictamnus
dock	Rumex
dockmackie	Viburnum
dodder	Cuscuta
dogbane	Apocynum
dog's-tooth violet	Erythronium
dogwood	Cornus
Douglas fir	Pseudotsuga
dove orchid	Peristeria
dragon arum	{ Arisaema { Dracunculus
dragonhead	Dracocephalum
dragonhead, false	Physostegia
dragon's mouth	Helicodiceros
dragon-root	Arisaema
duckweed	Lemna
dusty miller	Centaurea
Dutchman's breeches	Dicentra
Dutchman's pipe	Aristolochia
dwale	Atropa
dwarf alder	Fothergilla
dwarf dandelion	Krigia
dyer's greenweed	Genista

E

ebony	Diospyros
edelweiss	Leontopodium
eelgrass	Vallisneria
eggplant	Solanum
elder	Sambucus
elecampane	Inula
elephant-ear fern	Elaphoglossum
elephant's ear	Colocasia
elm	Ulmus
endive	Cichorlum
eryngo	Eryngium
evening primrose	Oenothera
evening-star	Cooperia

everlasting	{ Antennaria Helichrysum Helipterum
everlasting, Australian	Helipterum
everlasting, pearly	Anaphalis
everlasting, winged	Ammobium
everlasting, pea	Lathyrus

F

fairybells	Disporum
false acacia	Robinia
false aralia	Dizygotheca
false chamomile	Boltonia
false cypress	Chamaecyparis
false dragon-head	Physostegia
false gromwell	Onosmodium
false heath	Fabiana
false hellebore	Veratrum
false indigo	Amorpha
false mallow	{ Malvastrum Sidalcea
false mitrewort	Tiarella
false plantain	Heliconia
false saffron	Carthamus
false Solomon's seal false spikenard	Smilacina
false spirea	Sorgaria
false tamarisk	Myricaria
fanwort	Cabomba
feather-grass	Stipa
fennel	Foeniculum
fennel-flower	Nigella
fenugreek	Trigonella
fern, adder's tongue	Ophioglossum
fern, bladder	Cystopleris
fern, bracken or brake	{ Pteridium Pteris
fern, chain	Woodwardia
fern, Christmas	Polystichum
fern, cinnamon	Osmunda
fern, cliffbrake	Pellaea

fern, climbing	Lygodium
fern, comb	Schizaea
fern, elephant-ear	Elaphoglossum
fern, gold	Pityrogramma
fern, grape	Botrychium
fern, hare's foot	Davallia
fern, hart's tongue	Phyllitis
fern, hayscented	Dennstaedtia
fern, holly	Polystichum
fern, interrupted	Osmunda
fern, Japanese	Cyclophorus
fern, lady	Athyrium
fern, lip	Cheilanthes
fern, maidenhair	Adiantum
fern, moonwort	Botrychium
fern, ostrich	{ Onoclea Pteretis
fern, polypody	Polypodium
fern, rattlesnake	Botrychium
fern, rock brake	Cryptogramma
fern, royal	Osmunda
fern, rush	Schizaea
fern, sensitive	Onoclea
fern, shield	Pityrogramma
fern, silver	Dryopteris
fern, spleenwort	Asplenium
fern, staghorn	Platycerium
fern, swamp spleenwort	Athyrium
fern, sword	Nephrolepis
fern, sweet	Comptonia
fern, tree	Cyathea
fern, wall	Polypodium
fern, wood	Dryopteris
fescue	Festuca
feverbush	Lindera
feverfew	{ Chrysanthemum Matricaria Pyrethrum
feverfew, American	Chrysanthemum parthenium
fiddle-wood	Citharexylum

fig	Ficus
fig-marigold	Mesembryanthemum
fig-wort	Scrophularia
filbert	Corylus
finger-grass	Chloris
finger lime	Microcitrus
fir	Abies
fire-thorn	Pyracantha
fireweed	Epilobium
fish grass	Cabomba
flag	Iris
flag, sweet	Acorus
flamboyant tree	Poinciana
flame-lily	Pyrolirion
flamingo flower	Anthurium
flannel-bush	Fremontia
flax	Linum
flax, New Zealand	Phormium
flax lily	Dianella
fleabane	Erigeron
fleur-de-lis	Iris
floral firecracker	Brevoortia
floss silk tree	Chorisia
flowering moss	Pyxidanthera
flowering rush	Butomus
flywort	Myanthus
foamflower	Tiarella
forget-me-not	Myosotis
forget-me-not, Antarctic	Myosotidium
four-o'clock	Mirabilis
foxglove	Digitalis
foxglove, false	Gerardia
foxtail lily	Eremurus
frangipani	Plumeria
fraxinella	Dictamnus
French marigold	Tagetes
fringe flower	Schizanthus
fringe-tree	Chionanthus
fringed orchis	Habenaria
fritillary	Fritillaria
frost flower	Aster

fruiting myrtle	Eugenia
fumitory	{ Corydalis Fumaria
fumitory, climbing	Adlumia
fuchsia	Fuchsia
fuchsia, Australian	Correa
furze	Ulex

G

gale	Myrica
gall-of-the-earth	Prenanthes
garbanzo	Cicer
garden cress	Lepidium
garden heliotrope	Valeriana
gardenia	Gardenia
garget	Phytolacca
garlic	Allium
gas plant	Dictamnus
gay-wings	Polygala
gentian	Gentiana
geranium	Pelargonium
germander	Teucrium
ghostflower	Monotropa
giant bamboo	Dendrocalamus
giant bellflower	Ostrowskia
giant fennel	Ferula
giant scabious	Cephalaria
giant summer hyacinth	Galtonia
gill-over-the-ground	Nepeta
ginger	Zingiber
ginger, wild	Asarum
ginger-lily	Hedychium
ginseng	Panax
glasswort	Salicornia
globe daisy	Globularia
globe flower	Trollius
globe-mallow	Sphaeralcea
globe thistle	Echinops
glory-bush	Tibouchina
glory flower	Eccremocarpus

glory-lily	Gloriosa
glory-of-the-snows	Chionodoxa
glory-pea	Clianthus
goat's-beard	{ Aruncus Spiraea Tragopogon
goatsrue	Galega
gold fern	Pityrogramma
gold thread	Coptis
golden aster	Chrysopsis
golden-bell	Forsythia
golden club	Orontium
golden drop	Onosma
golden larch	Pseudolarix
goldenrod	Solidago
goldenrod, plumed	Bigelovia
golden seal	Hydrastis
golden spider-lily	Lycoris
golden star	Chrysogonum
good-King-Henry	Chenopodium
gooseberry	Ribes
goosefoot	Chenopodium
gorse	Ulex
goutweed	Aegopodium
grape	Vitis
grape, Oregon	Mahonia
grape, seaside	Coccoloba
grape fern	Botrychium
grape-hyacinth	Muscari
grass, brome	Bromus
grass, canary	Phalaris
grass, Pampas	Cortaderia
grass, pink	Calopogon
grass, quaking	Briza
grass-of-Parnassus	Parnassia
great burnet	Poterium
Greek valerian	Polemonium
greenbrier	Smilax
gromwell	Lithospermum
ground-cherry	Physalis
ground-ivy	Nepeta

397

ground-laurel	Epigaea
groundnut	{ Apios / Arachis / Aralia
ground-oak	Chamaedrys
ground pine	Lycopodium
ground rattan	Rhapis
groundsel	Senecio
groundsel-tree	Baccharis
guava	Psidium
guelder-rose	Viburnum
gum myrtle	Angophora
gumplant	Grindelia
gum tree	Eucalyptus

H

hackberry	Celtis
hair grass	Aira
harbinger-of-spring	Erigenia
hardhack	Spiraea
harebell	Campanula
hare's ear	Bupleurum
hare's-foot fern	Davallia
hare's-tail grass	Lagurus
hart's-tongue fern	Phyllitis
hatchet vetch	Securigera
hawk's-beard	Crepis
hawkweed	Hieracium
hawkweed, yellow	Tolpis
hawthorn	Crataegus
hazel	Corylus
heal-all	Prunella
heart's-ease	Viola
heath	Erica
heath, fake	Fabiana
heath, Irish	Daboëcia
heath, spike	Bruckenthalia
heather	Calluna
heather, beach	Hudsonia
hedge-bindweed	Convolvulus

hedge-hyssop	Gratiola
hedge-mustard	Erysimum
hedge-nettle	Stachys
heliotrope	Heliotropium
heliotrope, garden	Valeriana
hellebore	Helleborus
hellebore, false	Veratrum
helmet flower	Coryanthes
hemlock	Tsuga
hemlock, poison	Conium
hemlock, water	Cicuta
hemp	Cannabis
hempweed, climbing	Mikania
hen-and-chickens	Sempervivum
henbane	Hyoscyamus
henna	Lawsonia
herb-bennet	Geum
herb-grace	Ruta
herb-Mercury	Mercurialis
herb-Paris	Paris
herb-Robert	Geranium
herb-of-St. Barbara	Barbarea
Hercules' club	Zanthoxylum
heron's bill	Erodium
herniary	Herniaria
hickory	Carya
Himalayan poppy	Meconopsis
hoarhound	Marrubium
hoarhound, water	Lycopus
hobblebush	Viburnum
holly	Ilex
holly, American mountain	Nemopanthus
hollyhock	Althaea
holy grass	Hierochloë
honesty	Lunaria
honey-bell	Mahernia
honey berry	Meliococca
honey bush	Melianthus
honey locust	Gleditsia
honeysuckle	Lonicera
honeysuckle, bush	Diervilla

399

honeywort	Cerinthe
hop	Humulus
hop-hornbeam	Ostrya
horehound	Marrubium
horehound, water	Lycopus
hornbeam	Carpinus
horned poppy	Glaucium
horn-of-plenty	Fedia
horse balm	Collinsonia
horse bean	Vicia
horse-chestnut	Aesculus
horse-gentian	Triosteum
horse-mint	Monarda
horse-radish	Armoracia
horseshoe vetch	Hippocrepis
horsetail	Equisetum
horse weed	Collinsonia
hound's tongue	Cynoglossum
house-leek	Sempervivum
huckleberry	Gaylussacia
hyssop	Hyssopus

I

iceplant	Mesembryanthemum
immortelle	⎧Helichrysum ⎨Helipterum ⎩Xeranthemum
incense cedar	Libocedrus
India hawthorn	Raphiolepis
India lotus	Nymphaea
India-rubber plant	Ficus
Indian almond	Terminalia
Indian cress	Tropaeolum
Indian crocus	Pleione
Indian cucumber root	Medeola
Indian fig	Opuntia
Indian grass	Arundo
Indian hemp	Apocynum
Indian mulberry	Morinda
Indian paint brush	Castilleja
Indian physic	Magnolia

Indian pink	Spigelia
Indian pipe	Monotropa
Indian poppy	Meconopsis
Indian shot	Canna
Indian strawberry	Duchesnea
Indian tobacco	Lobelia
Indian turnip	Arisaema
indigo	Indigofera
indigo, wild	Baptisia
inkberry	Phytolacca
innocence	Collinsia
interrupted fern	Osmunda
Irish heath	Daboëcia
iron tree	Metrosideros
ironweed	Vernonia
ironwood	Ostrya
ironwort	Sideritis
ivory-nut palm	Phytelephas
ivy	Hedera
ivy, Boston	Parthenocissus
ivy arum	Scindapsus
ivy, ground	Nepeta
ivy, poison	Rhus

J

Jack-in-the-pulpit	Arisaema
Jacobea	Senecio
Jacob's ladder	Polemonium
Jacob's rod	Asphodeline
Jamaica pepper	Pimenta
Jamestown weed	Datura
Japanese bellflower	Platycodon
Japanese bitter orange	Poncirus
Japanese cedar	Cryptomeria
Japanese quince	Chaenomeles
Japanese raisin tree	Hovenia
Japanese toad-lily	Tricyrtis
Japanese yew	Cephalotaxus
Japonica	{ Chaenomeles { Camellia
jasmine	Jasminum

jasmine, bastard	Cestrum
Jerusalem artichoke	Helianthus
Jerusalem cherry	Solanum
Jerusalem oak	Chenopodium
Jerusalem sage	Phlomis
Jerusalem thorn	Parkinsonia
jewel-weed	Impatiens
Job's tears	Coix
Joe-Pye-weed	Eupatorium
jonquil	Narcissus
joy-weed	Alternanthera
Judas tree	Cercis
June berry	Amelanchier
juniper	Juniperus
juniper-myrtle	Verticordia
Jupiter's beard	{ Anthyllis { Centranthus
jute	Corchorus

K

Kaffir lily	{ Clivia { Schizostylis
Kamila tree	Mallotus
kangaroo's paw	Anigozanthus
Kansas gay-feather	Liatris
Kauri pine	Agathis
kidney bean	Phaseolus
kidney vetch	Anthyllis
king-cup	Caltha
knapweed	Centaurea
knotweed	Polygonum
kudzu-vine	Pueraria
kumquat	Fortunella

L

Labrador tea	Ledum
laburnum	Laburnum
ladies' fingers	Anthyllis
ladies' tresses	Spiranthes
lady fern	Athyrium

lady's mantle	Alchemilla
lady's slipper	Cypripedium
lady's smock	Cardamine
lady's thistle	Silybum
lady's thumb	Polygonum
lamb-kill	Kalmia
lamb's-quarters	Chenopodium
lamb's lettuce	Valerienella
lamb's tail grass	Alopecurus
lantana, wild	Abronia
larch	Larix
larch, golden	Pseudolarix
larkspur	Delphinium
laurel	Laurus
laurel, Alexandrian	Danaë
laurel, cherry	Laurocerasus
laurel, mountain	
laurel, sheep	Kalmia
laurel, swamp	
laurestinus	Viburnum
lavender	Lavandula
lavender, sea	Limonium / Statice
lavender cotton	Santolina
leadwort	Plumbago
leatherwood	Dirca
lemon	Citrus
lemon verbena	Lippia
lentil	Lens
leopard flower	Belamcanda
leopard lily	Sansevieria
leopard's bane	Doronicum
lettuce	Lactuca
licorice	Glycyrrhiza
licorice, wild	Abrus
lilac	Syringa
lily	Lilium
lily, African	Agapanthus
lily, blackberry	Belamcanda
lily, day	Hemerocallis
lily, golden spider	Lycoris

lily, Kaffir	Clivia
lily, leopard	Sansevieria
lily, Mariposa	Calochortus
lily, Mediterranean	Pancratium
lily, Peruvian	Alstroemeria
lily, spider	Hymenocallis
lily-of-the-Nile	Agapanthus
lily-of-the-valley	Convallaria
lily-of-the-valley, wild	Maianthemum
lily thorn	Catesbaea
lime	Citrus
lime, finger	Microcitrus
limeberry	Triphasia
linden, or lime	Tilia
ling, ling-heather	Calluna
lion's foot	Leontopodium
lion's-tail	Leonurus
lip fern	Cheilanthes
liverleaf, liverwort	Hepatica
lizard's-tail	Saururus
locust	Robinia
locust, honey	Gleditsia
locust, yellow	Robinia
logwood	Haematoxylum
London pride	Saxifraga
loosestrife	Steironema
loosestrife, purple	Lythrum
loosestrife, swamp	Decodon
loosestrife, yellow	Lysimachia
lords-and-ladies	Arum
lotus	Nelumbium
louse-wort	Pedicularis
lovage	{ Levisticum Ligusticum
love-apple	Lycopersicon
love-grass	Eragrostis
love-in-a-mist	Nigella
love-lies-bleeding	Amaranthus
lucerne	Medicago
lungwort	{ Pulmonaria Mertensia
lupin, lupine	Lupinus

M

madder	Rubia
Madiera vine	Boussingaultia
madwort	Alyssum
mahoe	Thespesia
mahogany tree	Swietenia
maidenhair fern	Adiantum
maidenhair tree	Gingko
maize	Zea
male-fern	{ Aspidium { Dryopteris
mallow	Malva
mallow, false	Malvastrum
mallow, globe	Sphaeralcea
mallow, marsh	Althaea
mallow, musk	Malva
mallow, rose	Hibiscus
mallow, tree	Lavatera
Maltese cross	Lychnis
mammee-apple	Mammea
mandrake	{ Mandragora { Podophyllum
mango	Mangifera
mangosteen	Garcinia
manna grass	Glyceria
maple	Acer
maple, flowering	Abutilon
maplewort	Aceranthus
mare's tail	Ephedra
marlberry	Ardisia
marigold	Calendula
marigold, African	Tagetes
marigold, fig	Mesembryanthemurm
marigold, French	Tagetes
marigold, marsh	Caltha
marigold, pot	Calendula
Mariposa lily	Calochortus
marjoram	Origanum
marjoram, sweet	Majorana
marram grass	Ammophila
marsh-marigold	Caltha

marsh rosemary	{ Limonium Statice
marsh samphire	Salicornia
marvel-of-Peru	Mirabilis
mask-flower	Alonsoa
masterwort	Astrantia
martrimony vine	Lycium
May-apple	Podophyllum
Mayflower	Epigaea
mayweed	{ Anthemis Matricaria
meadow-beauty	Rhexia
meadow foam	Limnanthes
meadow foxtail	Alopecurus
meadow rue	Thalictrum
meadow saffron	Colchicum
meadow-sweet	{ Filipendula Spiraea
medick	Medicago
Mediterranean lily	Pancratium
medlar	Mespilus
melic grass	Melica
melilot	Melilotus
melon	Cucumis
melon, water	Citrullus
mercury	Chenopodium
mesquite	Prosopis
Mexican buckeye	Ungnadia
Mexican lily	Hippeastrum
Mexican orange	Choisya
Mexican poppy	Argemone
Michaelmas daisy	Aster
migonette	Reseda
mint-bush	Prostanthera
milfoil	Achillea
milk thistle	Silybum
milk vetch	Astragalus
milkweed	{ Asclepias Gomphocarpus
milkwort	Polygala
millet	{ Panicum Paspalum

mint	Mentha
mint-bush	Prostanthera
mistletoe	Viscum
mitrewort	Mitella
mitrewort, false	Tiarella
mock-orange	Philadelphus
mock strawberry	Duchesnia
monarch-of-the-East	Sauromatum
moneywort	Lysimachia
monkey-bread tree	Adansonia
monkey-dinnerbell	Hura
monkey-flower	Mimulus
monkeynut	Arachis
monkey-pod tree	Samanea
monkey-puzzle tree	Araucaria
monkshood	Aconitum
moonflower	Calonyction
moonseed	{ Cocculus / Menispermum }
moonwort	{ Botrychium / Soldanella }
moonwort, blue	Soldanella
moosewood	Dirca
morning-glory	Ipomaea
moth orchid	Phalaenopsis
motherwort	Leonurus
mountain ash	Sorbus
mountain avens	Dryas
mountain-fringe	Adlumia
mountain holly	Nemopanthus
mountain-laurel	Kalmia
mountain mint	Pycnanthemum
mountain spurge	Pachysandra
mountain-tea	Gaultheria
mourning bride	Scabiosa
mouse-ear chickweed	Cerastium
mulberry	Morus
mulberry, Indian	Morinda
mule-ears	Wyethia
mullein	Verbascum
mullein pink	Lychnis
mushroom, field	Agaricus

COMMON NAMES

muskmallow	Malva
muskmelon	Cucumis
mustard, black	Brassica
myrtle	{Myrtus Vinca

N

nailwort	{Draba Paronychia
nasturtium	Tropaeolum
navelwort	{Cotyledon Omphalodes
nectarine	Prunus
nemu tree	Albizzia
nettle	Urtica
New Jersey tea	Ceanothus
New Zealand bur	Acaena
New Zealand daisy	Celmisia
New Zealand flax	Phormium
New Zealand spinach	Tetragonia
New Zealand wineberry	Apristotelia
night-blooming cereus	Selenicereus
nightshade	Solanum
nightshade, deadly	Atropa
nightshade, Malabar	Basella
nightshade, woody	Solanum
nine bark	{Neillia Physocarpus
northern white cedar	Thuja

O

oak	Quercus
oak, poison	Rhus
oak-of-Jerusalem	Chenopodium
oats	Avena
obedient-plant	Dracocephalum
old-man cactus	Cephalocereus
oleander	Nerium

olive	Olea
olive, Russian	Eleagnus
olive, sweet	Osmanthus
onion	Allium
orach	Atriplex
orange	Citrus
orange jessamine	Murraya
orange root	Hydrastis
orchid	Orchis
Oregon grape	Mahonia
osage orange	Maclura
osoberry	Osmaronia
ostrich fern	{ Onoclea / Pteretis
Oswego-tea	Monarda
ox-eyed daisy	Chrysanthemum
oyster-plant	Tragopogon

P

paeony	Paeonia
painted-cup	Castilleja
palmetto	Sabal
pampas grass	Cortadeidria
Panama candle-tree	Parmentiera
pansy	Viola
parchment bark	Pittosporum
parsley	Petroselinum
parsnip	Pastinaca
parsnip, cow	Heracleum
partridgeberry	Mitchella
partridge-pea	Cassia
pasque-flower	Pulsatilla
passion-flower	Passiflora
patience	Rumex
paw-paw	Asimina
pea	Pisum
pea, Darling River	Swainsona
pea, everlasting	Lathyrus
pea, shamrock	Parochetus
pea, sweet	Lathyrus

COMMON NAMES

peach	Prunus
peanut	Arachis
pear	Pyrus
pearl-bush	Exochorda
pearlwort	Sagina
pearly everlasting	Anaphalis
pebble plants	Lithops
pellitory	Parietaria
penny-cress	Thlaspi
pennyroyal	Mentha
pennyroyal, American	Hedeoma
pennyroyal, bastard	Trichostema
pennywort	Cotyledon
peony	Paeonia
pepper	Piper
pepper-and-salt	Erigenia
pepperbush, sweet	Clethra
pepper-grass	Lepidium
peppermint	Mentha
pepper-root	Dentaria
pepper-tree	Schinus
pepper vine	Ampelopsis
pepperwort	Lepidium
periwinkle	Vinca
persicaria	Polygonum
persimmon	Diosypyros
Peruvian lily	Alstroemeria
pheasant's-eye	Adonis
pickerel-weed	Pontedaria
picotee	Dianthus
pigeonberry	Phytolacca
pignut	Carya
pignut palm	Hyophorbe
pimpernel, water	Samolus
pincushion flower	Scabiosa
pindo palm	Buteia
pine	Pinus
pineapple	Ananas
pink ⎫	Dianthus
pink, cottage ⎭	
pink, ground	Phlox

pink, Indian	Spigelia
pink, moss	Phlox
pink, mullein	Lychnis
pink, rose	Sabbatia
pink, sea	Armeria
pink, swamp	Calopogon, Helonias
pink-root	Spigelia
pink siris	Albizzia
pinxterflower	Rhododendron
pipsissewa	Chimaphila
pistachio	Pistacia
pitcherplant	{ Nepenthes, Sarracenia }
plane tree	Platanus
plantain	Plantago
plantain, false	Heliconia
plantain, rattlesnake	Goodyera
plantain, poor Robin's	Hieracium
plantain, water	Alisma
plantain lily	{ Funkia, Hosta }
pleurisy root	Asclepias
plum	Prunus
plum yew	Cephalotaxus
plumbago	Plumbago
plume-grass	Erianthus
plume poppy	{ Bocconia, Macleaya }
poison hemlock	Conium
poison-ivy, -oak, -sumach	Rhus
pokeberry / pokeweed	Phytolacca
polyanthus	Primula
polypody	Polypodium
pomegranate	Punica
pompion	Curcurbita
pond-lily, yellow	Nuphar
poor man's weatherglass	Anagallis
poor Robin's plantain	Hieracium

poplar popple	Populus
poppy	Papaver
poppy, blue	Meconopsis
poppy, California	Eschscholzia
poppy, crested	Argemone
poppy, Himalayan	Meconopsis
poppy, horned	Glaucium
poppy, Indian	Meconopsis
poppy, plume	Bocconia Macleaya
poppy, prickly	Argemone
poppy, sea	Glaucium
poppy, snow	Eomecon
poppy, water	Hydrocleys
poppy-mallow	Callirhoë
potato	Solanum
potato-bean	Apios
prairie-button	Liatris
prairie-clover	Petalostemum
prairie gentian	Eustoma
prairie-lily	Cooperia Mentzelia
prickly ash	Zanthoxylum
prickly cucumber	Echynocystis
prickly date-palm	Acanthophoenix
prickly pear	Opuntia
prickly-poppy	Argemone
prickly thrift	Acantholimon
primrose	Primula
primrose, evening	Oenothera
primrose willow	Jussiaea
Prince Albert's yew	Saxegothea
prince's feather	Amaranthus
prince's pine	Chimaphila
privet	Ligustrum
prophet-flower	Arnebia
pulse	Lathyrus
purple loosestrife	Lythrum
purple-sage	Salvia
purslane	Portulaca

pussy's toes	Antennaria
puttyroot	Aplectrum
pyrola, one-flowered	Moneses
pyxie	Pyxidanthera

Q

Quaker ladies	Houstonia
quaking grass	Briza
Queen Anne's lace	Daucus
queen palm	Arecastrum
Queen Victoria waterlily	Victoria
quince	Cydonia

R

radish	Raphanus
ragged Robin	Lychnis
raffia	Raphia
ragweed	Ambrosia
ragwort	Senecio
ragwort, African	Othonna
rain-tree	Samanea
ramie	Boehmeria
rampion	Phyteuma
raspberry	Rubus
rat-tail cactus	Aporocactus
rattan	Calamus
rattle-box	Crotolaria
rattlesnake fern	Botrychium
rattlesnake orchid	Pholidota
rattlesnake-master	Eryngium
rattlesnake plantain	Goodyera
rattlesnake root	Prenanthes
rattlesnake-weed	Hieracium
redbud	Cercis
red Cape tulip	Haemanthus
red cedar	Juniperus
red-hot poker	Kniphofia
redroot	Ceanothus

COMMON NAMES

red valerian	Centranthus
redwood	Sequoia
reed-mace	Typha
rein orchis	Habernaria
rest-harrow	Ononis
rheumatism root	Jeffersonia
rhododendron ⎫ rhodora ⎭	Rhododendron
rhubarb	Rheum
ribbon-grass	Phalaris
ribbon wood	Plagianthus
rice	Oryza
rice, Canadian wild	Zizania
rice-flower	Pimelea
rice paper tree	Tetrapanax
rock-cress	Arabis
rock-cress, purple	Aubrietia
rocket, sweet	Hesperis
rocket, yellow	Barbarea
rockfoil	Saxifraga
rock jasmine	Androsace
rock-rose	Cistus
rogation flower	Polygala
rose	Rosa
rose bay	⎰Nerium ⎱Rhododendron
rose-campion	Lychnis
rose-mallow	Hibiscus
rosemary	Rosmarinus
rosemary, marsh	Statice
rosemary, wild	Ledum
rose-of-Sharon	⎰Hibiscus ⎱Hypericum
rose pink	Sabbatia
rosinweed	Silphium
rouge plant	Rivina
rowan	Sorbus
royal fern	Osmunda
royal poinciana	Delonix
royal waterlily	Victoria

rubber tree	Hevea
rubber vine	Cryptostegia
rue	Ruta
rue-anemone	Anemonella
rupturewort	Herniaria
rush	Juncus
rush fern	Schizaea
Russian olive	Eleagnus
Russian sage	Perovskia
Russian thistle	Salsola
rye, wild	Elymus
rye-grass	{ Lolium Secale

S

safflower	Carthamus
saffron	Crocus
saffron, false	Carthamus
saffron, meadow	Colchicum
sage	Salvia
sage, Bethlehem	Pulmonaria
sage, Jerusalem	Phlomis
Sago palm	Cycas
sainfoin, saintfoin	Onobrychis
Saint Agnes' flower	Leucojum
Saint Andrew's cross	Ascyrum
Saint Barbara's herb	Barbarea
Saint Barnaby's thistle	Centaurea
Saint Bernard's lily	Anthericum
Saint Bruno's lily	Paradisea
Saint Dabeoc's heath	Daboëcia
Saint George's herb	Valeriana
Saint John's bread	Ceratonia
Saint John's wort	{ Hypericum Symphoricarpos
Saint Martin's flower	Alstroemeria
Saint Mary's wood	Calophyllum
Saint Patrick's cabbage	Saxifraga

Saint Peter's wort	⎧ Ascyrum ⎨ Hypericum ⎪ Primula ⎩ Symphoricarpos
salad chervil	Anthriscus
salsify	Tragopogon
salsify, black	Scorzonera
salt-bush	Rhagodia
salt tree	Halimodendron
saltwort	Salsola
samphire	Crithmum
samphire, marsh	Salicornia
sandalwood	Santalum
sandalwood, red	Adenanthera
sand-box tree	Hura
sand lily	Leucocrinum
sand-myrtle	Leiophyllum
sand verbena	Abronia
sandwort	Arenaria
sanicle, bear's-ear	Cortusa
sapodilla	Sapota
sarsaparilla	Aralia
sarsaparilla plant	Smilax
sassafras	Sassafras
satin-flower	Lunaria
satinwood tree	Murraya
sausage-tree	Kigelia
savin	Juniperus
savory	Satureja
savoy	Brassica
saw cabbage palm	Acoelorraphe
saxifrage	Saxifragra
scabious	Scabiosa
scallion	Allium
scammony	Convolvulus
Scarborough-lily	Vallota
scarlet runner	Phaseolus
sclarea	Salvia
Scotch thistle	Onopordum
screw-pine	Pandanus
scurfy pea	Psoralea

scurvy grass	Cochlearia
scythian lamb	Cibotium
sea-buckthorn	Hippophaë
sea daffodil	Pancratium
sea-heath	Frankenia
sea-holly	Eryngium
seakale	Crambe
sea-lavender	{ Limonium / Statice
sea-pink	{ Armeria, also see / Limonium / Statice
sea poppy	Glaucium
sea-purslane	Atriplex
sea-ragwort	Cineraria
seaside grape	Coccoloba
sea-urchin cactus	Echinopsis
sedge	Carex
self-heal	Prunella
senna, wild	Cassia
sensitive fern	Onoclea
sensitive-plant	Mimosa
service-berry	Amelanchier
service tree	Sorbus domestica
setwall	Valeriana
shadblow / shadbush	Amelanchier
shaddock	Citrus
shallot	Allium
sheep-laurel	Kalmia
sheep's-bit scabious	Jasione
shepherd's beard	Andropogon
shepherd's club	Verbascum
shield fern	Dryopteris
shield-wort	Peltaria
shingle-plant	Monstera
shinleaf	Pyrola
shooting star	Dodecatheon
side-saddle flower	Sarracenia
silk-cotton tree	Bombax

417

silk-tassel bush	Garrya
silk-tree	Albizzia
silk vine	Periploca
silver bell tree	Halesia
silver fern	Pityrogramma
silver morning-glory	Argyreia
silver-rod	{ Solidago Asphodeline
silver tree	Leucadendron
silverweed	Argyreia
simpler's joy	Verbena
sisal	Agave
skirret, skirwort	Sium
skullcap	Scutellaria
skunk-cabbage	Symplocarpus
slipper-flower	Pedilanthus
slipper-wort	Calceolaria
sloe-tree	Prunus
smartweed	Polygonum
smoke-tree	Cotinus
snail-seed	Cocculus
snakegourd	Trichosanthes
snake plant	Sansevieria
snakeroot	{ Aristolochia Cimicifuga Eupatorium Liatris
snake's-mouth orchid	Pogonia
snake's-tongue	Ophioglossum
snapdragon	Antirrhinum
snapweed	Impatiens
sneezeweed	Helenium
sneezewort	Achillea
snowball tree	Viburnum
snowbell	Styrax
snowberry	{ Chiococca Symphoricarpos
snowberry, creeping	Chiogenes
snowdrop	Galanthus
snowdrop-tree	Halesia
snowflake	Leucojum

snow-glory	Chionodoxa
snow-in-summer	Cerastium
snow-on-the-mountain	Euphorbia
snow poppy	Eomecon
snow wreath	Neviusia
snowy mespilus	Amelanchier
soap-bark tree	Quillaja
soap-berry	Sapindus
soap-bush	Noltea
soapwort	Saponaria
Solomon's seal	Polygonatum
Solomon's seal, false	Smilacina
sorghum	Holcus
sorrel, garden	Rumex
sorrel, wood	Oxalis
sorrel-tree	Oxydendrum
sour gum	Nyssa
soursop	Annona
sour-wood	Oxydendrum
southern beech	Nothofagus
southernwood	Artemisia
sowbread	Cyclamen
sowthistle	Sonchus
soybean	Glycine
Spanish bayonet	Yucca
Spanish bluebell	Scilla
Spanish broom	Spartium
Spanish moss	Tillandsia
Spanish oyster-plant	Scolymus
spatter-dock	Nuphar
spearflower	Ardisia
spear-grass	Stipa
spear lily	Doryanthes
spearmint	Mentha
spearwort	Ranunculus
speedwell	Veronica
spice-bush	{ Lindera / Benzoin }
spider-flower	Cleome
spider-flower, Brazilian	Tibouchina
spider lily	Hymenocallis

spider lily, golden	Lycoris
spiderwort	Tradescantia
spike heath	Bruckenthalia
spikenard, American	Aralia
spikenard, false	Smilacina
spinach	Spinacia
spinach, New Zealand	Tetragonia
spindle-tree	Euonymous
spine-areca	Acanthophoenix
spiral-flag	Costus
spire lily	Galtonia
spirea	Spiraea
spirea, blue	Caryopteris
spirea, false	Sorbaria
spleenwort	Asplenium
spleenwort, swamp	Athyrium
spoonwood	Kalmia
spring-beauty	Claytonia
spruce	Picea
spurge	Euphorbia
spurge-laurel	Daphne
spurge olive	Cneorum
squaw-weed	Senecio
squill	Scilla
squill, striped	Pushkinia
squirrel-corn	Dicentra
squirrel-tail grass	Hordeum
squirting cucumber	Ecballium
stagger-bush	Lyonia
staghorn sumach	Rhus
staghorn fern	Platycerium
star flower	Trientalis
star grass	{ Aletris Hypoxis
star-of-Bethlehem	Ornithogalum
starwort	{ Aster Stellaria
statice	Limonium
steeple-bush	Spiraea
stick-tight	Bidens
stinging nettle	Urtica

stitchwort	Stellaria
stock	Matthiola
stock, Virginia	Malcomia
Stokes' aster	Stokesia
stone cress	Aethionema
stonecrop	Sedum
stone-root	Collinsonia
storax-tree	Styrax
stork's-bill	Pelargonium
straw flower	Helichrysum
strawberry	Fragaria
strawberry, barren	Waldsteinia
strawberry, Indian or mock	Duchesnea
strawberry tree	Arbutus
striped squill	Puschkinia
stud flower	Helonias
succory	Cichorium
sugarcane	Saccharum
sumach sumach, poison sumach, staghorn	Rhus
sundew	Drosera
sundrops	Oenothera
sunflower	Helianthus
sunrose	Helianthemum
swamp cypress	Taxodium
swamp loosestrife	Decodon
swamp pink	Calopogon Helonias
Swan River daisy	Brachycome
sweet alyssum	Lobularia
sweet basil	Ocimum
sweet bay	Laurus Magnolia
sweet brier	Rosa eglanteria
sweet cicely	Myrrhis
sweet clover	Melilotus
sweet fern	Comptonia
sweet flag	Acorus
sweet gale	Myrica

sweet gum	Liquidambar
sweet marjoram	Majorana
sweet olive	Osmanthus
sweet pea	Lathyrus
sweet pepper bush	Clethra
sweet potato	Ipomoea
sweet rocket	Hesperis
sweet sultan	Centaurea
sweet vernal grass	Anthoxanthum
sweet William	Dianthus
sword fern	Nephrolepis
sword-lily	Gladiolus
sycamore	{ Acer Platanus
sycamore-maple	Acer

T

tamarind	Tamarindus
tamarisk	Tamarix
tamarisk, false	Myricaria
tanbank	Lithocarpus
tansy	Tanacetum
tapioca	Manihot
taro-root	Colocasia
tarragon	Artemisia
tarweed	Madia
tassel flower	Emilea
tea	{ Camellia Thea
tea-berry	Gaultheria
teak tree	Tectona
tear-thumb	Polygonum
teasel	Dipsacus
thatch palm	Thrinax
thimbleweed	Anemone
thistle	{ Carduus Cnicus
thistle, blessed	{ Cnicus Silybum
thistle, cotton	Onopordum

thistle, distaff	Carthamus
thistle, globe	Echinops
thistle, golden	Scolymus
thistle, hedgehog	Echinocactus
thistle, plumed	Cirsium
thistle, plumeless	Carduus
thistle, Russian	Salsola
thistle, saffron	Carthamus
thistle, Scotch	Onopordum
thistle, sow	Sonchus
thorn, Jerusalem	Parkinsonia
thorn-apple	Datura
thoroughwort	Eupatorium
thunder-plant	Sempervivum
thrift	Armeria
throatwort	Trachelium
thyme	Thymus
tickseed	{ Bidens Coreopsis
tick-trefoil	Desmodium
tidy-tips	Layia
tiger-flower	Tigridia
tiger's chaps	Faucaria
timothy	Phleum
toadflax	Linaria
toadflax, ivy-leaved	Cymbalaria
tobacco	Nicotiana
tomato	Lycopersicon
tooth-ache tree	Zanthoxylum
toothwort	Dentaria
torch-lily	Kniphofia
touch-me-not	Impatiens
toyon	Heteromeles
trailing arbutus	Epigaea
trailing cactus	Acanthocereus
Transvaal daisy	Gerbera
traveler's joy	Clematis
traveler's tree	Ravenala
tree aster	Olearia
tree fern	Cyathea
tree-mallow	Lavatera

423

tree-of-heaven	Ailanthus
tree-poppy	Dendromecon
trefoil	Trifolium
trout-lily	Erythronium
true-love	Paris
trumpet creeper	{ Bignonia Campsis
trumpet flower	{ Clytostoma Datura
tuberose	Polianthes
tulip	Tulipa
tulip tree	Liriodendron
tupelo	Nyssa
turmeric	Curcuma
turnip	Brassica rapa
turnip, Indian	Arisaema
turkey's beard	Xerophyllum
turtlehead	Chelone
twayblade	{ Liparis Listera
twinflower	Linnaea
twin leaf	Jeffersonia
twist-arum	Helicodiceros
twisted stalk	Streptopus

U

umbrella palm	Hedyscepe
umbrella pine	Sciadopitys
umbrella plant	Peltiphyllum
umbrella tree	{ Magnolia Melia Thespesia
upas tree	Antiaris

V

vanilla	Vanilla
vanilla, Carolina	Trilisa
vanilla leaf	Achlys

valerian	Valeriana
valerian, African	Fedia
valerian, red	Centranthus
vegetable-oyster	Tragopogon
vegetable-sponge	Luffa
velvet-bean	Stizolobium
Venus flytrap	Dionaea
Venus' hair	Adiantum
Venus' looking-glass	Specularia
Venus' navelwort	Omphalodes
verbena, lemon	Lippia
verbena, sand	Abronia
vervain	Verbena
vetch	Vicia
vetch, crown	Coronilla
vetch, milk	Astragalus
vine	Vitis
violet	Viola
violet, African	Saintpaulia
violet cress	Ionopsidium
viper's bugloss	Echium
Virginia cowslip	Mertensia
Virginia creeper	{ Ampelopsis / Parthenocissus
Virginia-stock	Malcomia
Virginian poke	Phytolacca
virgin's bower	Clematis
viscaria	Lychnis

W

wake-robin	Trillium
wallcress	Arabis
wall fern	Polypodium
wallflower	Cheiranthus
wall-pennywort	Cotyledon
wall-pepper	Sedum acre
wall-rue	Asplenium
walnut	Juglans
wandering-Jew	Tradescantia

wandflower	{ Dierama / Sparaxis
wand plant	Galax
water-arum	Calla
water-chestnut	Trapa
water-cress	{ Nasturtium / Rorippa
water-elm	Planera
water-flag	Iris
water hemlock	Cicuta
water hoarhound, horehound	Lycopus
water-hyacinth	Eichhornia
water-leaf	Hydrophyllum
water-lettuce	Pistia
water-lily	{ Nelumbium / Nymphaea
water-lily, yellow	Nuphar
watermelon	Citrullus
water milfoil	Myriophyllum
water-pennywort	Hydrocotyle
water-pimpernel	Samolus
water plantain	Alisma
water poppy	Hydrocleys
water-shield	Brasenia
water soldier	Stratiotes
waterweed	Elodea
wattle	Acacia
wax-flower	{ Hoya / Stephanotis
wax myrtle	Myrica
wax palm	Ceroxylon
waxweed	Cuphea
waxwork	Celastrus
wayfaring tree	Viburnum
weavers' broom	Spartium
West Indian kale	Colocasia
wheat	Triticum
whin	{ Genista / Ulex
white cedar, northern	Thuja
whitlow-grass	Draba

whitlow-wort	Paronychia
whorl-flower	Morina
widow's-tears	Tradescantia
wild rice	Zizania
willow	Salix
willow-herb	Epilobium
wind-flower	Anemone
wing-nut	Pterocarya
winged everlasting	Ammobium
winter aconite	Eranthis
winterberry	Ilex
winter daffodil	Sternbergia
wintergreen	Gaultheria
witch-grass	Panicum
witch-hazel	Hamamelis
withe-rod	Viburnum
woad, dyer's	Isatis
woad, waxen	Genista
woad, wild	Reseda
wolfberry	Symphoricarpos
wolfchop	Mesembryanthemum
wolf's-bane	Aconitum
wolf's-milk	Euphorbia
wood-apple	Feronia
wood-betony	Pedicularis
woodbine	{ Lonicera Ampelopsis Parthenocissus
wood fern	Dryopteris
woodruff	Asperula
wood-sorrel	Oxalis
woody nightshade	Solanum
woman's-tongue-tree	Albizia
wormwood	Artemisia
woundwort	{ Anthyllis Stachys

Y

| yam | Dioscopea |

yarrow	Achillea
yellow locust	Robinia
yellow-wood, Kentucky	Cladastris
yerba buena	Micromeria
yew	Taxus
yew, plum	Cephalotaxus

Z

zephyr-lily	Zephyranthes

Marco Bruno

El entrenador de fútbol

De la formación del futbolista a la
táctica y los modelos de juego

Traducido por: **Mariano Bas**
Editor: **Tektime**

La sensación de placer al ponerse las botas, el olor de la hierba recién cortada al principio de la temporada; las bolsitas de plástico en los pies para que no entre el agua durante los entrenamientos bajo la lluvia que cae. Los amigos que lo son por una sola temporada, pero siguen siéndolo siempre. Crecer con un sueño y no alcanzarlo del todo y luego darse cuenta de que el motivo era porque mi vocación era la de entrenador. De pequeños y grandes. Con una naturalidad inesperada. Probablemente el talento que me faltaba como jugador lo tengo como entrenador. O tal vez tampoco: quién puede decirlo... El camino para llegar a obtener lo que deseaba es a veces increíblemente tortuosa y también te puedes perder. Con las botas o con un silbato, la pasión es la misma. Y cuando te acompaña la pasión, no puedes perder nunca.

Índice general

QUÉ ES EL FÚTBOL

El fútbol es un juego sencillo y fácilmente comprensible en sus reglas y su desarrollo. Puede ser practicado por cualquiera, porque no exige una estructura física particular ni determinadas dotes atléticas; permite al deportista una amplia libertad de movimientos y por tanto la posibilidad de dar lo mejor de uno mismo,

Por esto, el fútbol se define como una actividad libre, que, partiendo de una técnica común de base, permite a todos expresar su propia personalidad y su propio estilo y sin embargo es una actividad incierta, ligada a las normas del azar, por lo que es imposible prever su desarrollo.

Filosóficamente, **el fútbol es una aventura siempre nueva** y llena de interés, que puede convertirse en espectacular: es una actividad del presente, porque el jugador construye durante cada partido su devenir, el pasado no cuenta.

El fútbol gusta

Porque es un juego sencillo.

Puede ser practicado por todos.

Es una actividad libre.

Es una actividad incierta.

Es una aventura.

Es una actividad del presente.

Existen factores que se consideran fundamentales sobre los que trabajar para poder formar a un futbolista en todas sus características: técnicas, tácticas, físicas, psicológicas y sociales. Evidentemente hace falta aclarar de inmediato que entrenar a un futbolista joven es completamente diferente a entrenar a un futbolista adulto. Por este motivo es preferible hablar primero de la formación del futbolista joven y luego del entrenamiento del futbolista adulto.

En estos años el error que he visto cometer más frecuentemente por entrenadores de jóvenes ha sido (y continúa siendo) entrenar a jóvenes y niños como si se estuviera entrenando a adultos.

LOS PRINCIPIOS DEL ENTRENAMIENTO

Todo entrenador, cuando se dispone a asumir la responsabilidad de dirigir un equipo debe tener muy claro el significado de la palabra "entrenamiento". De un modo muy general, el entrenamiento es un proceso que produce un cambio físico, motor, cognitivo y afectivo.

El entrenamiento deportivo del atleta incluye:

- Preparación física,
- Preparación técnico-táctica,
- Preparación intelectual, psicológica y moral.

Todo esto se lleva a cabo mediante diversos ejercicios físicos. Podríamos por tanto definir al entrenamiento como *«La unión de todas las acciones dirigidas a la mejora de los factores modificables que influyen en las prestaciones para obtener el mejor rendimiento»*.

Los factores sobre los cuales es posible intervenir son múltiples. Podemos hablar de:

- Entrenamiento de las capacidades físicas.

- Entrenamiento de las capacidades técnicas.

- Entrenamiento de las capacidades tácticas.;

- Entrenamiento de las capacidades psicológicas.

No es posible intervenir sobre una sola de ellas sin influir positiva o negativamente en las otras.

Si los estímulos de los entrenamientos son diversos y se dirigen a todas las capacidades, el organismo se confunde y no sabe qué respuesta dar a esos esfuerzos. En el entrenamiento, la combinación de más capacidades no provoca una suma de adaptaciones, sino, por el contrario, una resta de adaptaciones. Por tanto, el entrenador no debe entrenar siempre todo, porque de lo contrario entrenará mal, poco o nada. A los preparadores físicos siempre les interesan las adaptaciones de nuestro organismo a la exposición crónica al ejercicio físico (entrenamiento) y en particular:

Al principio de la subjetividad, según el cual el programa de entrenamiento se establece teniendo en cuenta las posibles variaciones de persona a persona. Personas diversas responden de distinta manera a un mismo programa de entrenamiento.

Al principio de la especificidad, según el cual el entrenamiento debe reflejar perfectamente el tipo de actividad motora desarrollada, a fin de optimizar los beneficios. Un levantador de pesas no puede entrenarse con carrera continua.

6

Al principio de la reversibilidad, según el cual los beneficios del entrenamiento se pierden cuando el entrenamiento se interrumpe o disminuye. Para interrupciones largas, conviene sugerir siempre actividades de mantenimiento.

Al principio de la sobrecarga progresiva, según el cual hay que estimular el organismo (músculos, sistema cardiovascular) con cargas progresivamente crecientes a las que el organismo se adapta paulatinamente.

Al principio del «difícil/fácil», según el cual a los periodos de entrenamiento intenso «difícil» (carga en aumento) deben seguir periodos de entrenamiento «fácil» (de descarga o asimilación) para permitir que el organismo se recupere y se adapte antes de afrontar el próximo incremento.

Al principio de la periodificación, entendido como programación de megaciclos, macrociclos, mesociclos o microciclos, en el ámbito de los cuales veremos variar la intensidad y el volumen de carga y los tipos de entrenamiento para la búsqueda continua de mejores condiciones de forma.

Muchos atletas acaban sobreentrenados y cuando sus prestaciones empeoran a causa del *overtraining*, entrenan más, porque creen que más entrenamiento supone más mejora. *(J.H Wilmore–D. L. Costill, 2005)*.

Por el contrario, el entrenamiento será tanto más eficaz y preciso cuanto más completas y destinadas

a un fin sean las intervenciones sobre las partes que lo compongan. Por desgracia, en el fútbol se dan ahora casos en los que el entrenamiento se limita a «dar unas vueltas al campo, partidillos y tiros a puerta». No hay nada que pueda sustituir a la práctica, todas las teorías resultan abstractas si no consiguen ilustrar los conceptos formados sobre la experiencia práctica. La complejidad del juego del fútbol requiere intervenciones precisas, cualificadas y estudiadas,

El problema más difícil de afrontar es el de establecer la tipología, la calidad y la intensidad del trabajo a proponer a los jugadores y verificar el grado de adaptación a las cargas del entrenamiento (ENTRENABILIDAD).

La entrenabilidad es un parámetro dinámico que depende de factores personales internos y externos y puede manifestarse de diversas maneras en los diversos sistemas funcionales y orgánicos del mismo sujeto. En la edad infantil y en la adolescencia, desempeñan un papel esencial las llamadas «fases sensibles» (Martin, 1982), que se refieren a aquellos periodos de crecimiento que son particularmente favorables al desarrollo y la formación de habilidades y capacidades decisivas para las prestación motora-deportiva. Aplicando todos los principios del entrenamiento, es preciso disponer previamente de un programa de trabajo que se adapte a los jugadores que lo deben seguir y al tipo de juego que pretende imponer el entrenador. El

entrenador debe tener siempre presente la pregunta «qué debo hacer en cada momento».

Buscamos por tanto aclarar cuáles son;

- Los principios del aprendizaje (cómo aprende el futbolista).

- Los principios de la enseñanza (cómo debe enseñar el entrenador).

La finalidad principal debe ser la de inducir cambios positivos en el comportamiento y los hábitos de vida. El comportamiento humano distingue:

Acciones innatas, que no tenemos que aprender y que no requieren ninguna experiencia previa.

Acciones descubiertas, que descubrimos solos mediante un proceso personal de prueba-error-reintento.

Acciones asimiladas, que adquirimos de otras personas con un proceso inconsciente de emulación.

Acciones aprendidas, que deber ser enseñadas y requieren un esfuerzo voluntario, basado en una observación analítica precisa.

Los principios del aprendizaje

La afirmación de que «si un futbolista se entrena, mejora y perfecciona sus capacidades» no es realmente verdad, porque el entrenamiento determina comportamientos y adaptaciones que pueden llevarse a cabo de forma adecuada o inadecuada. No todas las adaptaciones ni los comportamientos son útiles para la realización de las diversas actividades deportivas.

Un entrenamiento eficaz y su consiguiente aprendizaje en el juego del fútbol están muy ligados a la formación de actitudes, hábitos y movimientos correctos.

Lo primero en orden de importancia es la actitud hacia el aprendizaje, tanto por parte del entrenador como del jugador. Esta actitud debería estará caracterizada por dos cualidades:

- Mentalidad abierta.

- Mentalidad ávida de saber.

Las actitudes mentales son esenciales para recibir y valorar nuevas ideas y aplicarlas, para ponerlas continuamente en cuestión y para sencillamente estar al día de forma continua.

No todas las ideas son buenas, por lo que es un error aceptar de inmediato una idea nueva basándose solo

en el criterio de la novedad, igual que es un error no darle crédito sin valorarla.

Algunos deportes requieren de manera predominante la atención a los aspectos técnicos, otros a los atléticos: el fútbol es un deporte donde es más importante la capacidad de juicio.

Se llega a esta conclusión con un análisis sencillo:

- Un partido de fútbol dura 90 minutos.

- El balón está en juego unos 60 minutos.

- En los 60 minutos se supone que algún equipo tendrá la posesión del balón al menos 30 minutos.

- Durante estos 30 minutos el balón está a menudo en vuelo y fuera del control de los jugadores.

- Cada jugador de media no puede tener la posesión del balón durante más de 2 o 3 minutos.

Después de este análisis, se produce inmediatamente una pregunta:

¿Qué hace el jugador en los otros 57-58 minutos en los que el balón está en juego?

La respuesta es:

Aplica su propia capacidad de juicio, toma decisiones y escoge.

Observamos además que el fútbol es uno de los deportes con aspectos más cambiantes, tanto porque los jugadores y el balón pueden moverse por todo el campo, como porque las reglas a seguir son pocas, por lo que entendemos que las situaciones cambian rápidamente y requieren por parte de los jugadores rapidez de ejecución y concentración. Todo lo cual nos lleva al *problema fundamental que no es cómo se entrena, sino cómo aprende un futbolista*.

Para estimular a los futbolistas con éxito, el entrenador debe tener en consideración los siguientes factores:

1) El interés: El jugador poco interesado y motivado dedica poco esfuerzo a las actividades propuestas.

2) El entusiasmo: El jugador al que le falta entusiasmo no es útil ni a sí mismo ni al grupo.

3) La colaboración: Trabajar junto al grupo para alcanzar un fin común.

4) El ejemplo: Ver jugar a las estrellas o mejor ver acciones correctas de juego mediante el uso de grabaciones puede aportar mejoras en el

aprendizaje, tanto sobre la actitud como sobre los hábitos.

5) La frecuencia de los entrenamientos: La calidad del entrenamiento es más importante que la frecuencia. Si hay calidad, cuanto más tiempo se dedique al entrenamiento, mayores serán las mejoras.

6) La consciencia de las mejoras: Quien obtiene buenas mejoras entrena con más entusiasmo. En un entrenamiento bien realizado, los futbolistas se dan cuenta de los progresos obtenidos.

7) El sufrimiento: Para desarrollar las habilidades propias es necesaria una búsqueda continua de la superación de las capacidades propias y los límites propios. Los futbolistas mejorarán si cumplen siempre con sus tareas, a condición de que no sean excesivamente exigentes.

8) La confianza: Los entrenadores deberían enseñar a los futbolistas a tener confianza, pero sobre todo animarlos y darles esperanzas y ambiciones alcanzables.

Después de haber establecido cómo aprende el futbolista, hay que establecer qué tiene que aprender en el entrenamiento futbolístico.

Hay cuatro áreas en el entrenamiento futbolístico:

- La técnica y la táctica (*capacidad coordinativa*).

- La condición física (*capacidad condicional*).

- La comprensión (*qué hacer y qué no hacer*);

- La condición psico-social (*comportamientos*).

1) **La técnica y la táctica**: Son los instrumentos del oficio, cuanto mejores sean, más eficaces, útiles y sorprendentes serán los resultados alcanzados.

2) **La condición física**: Las habilidades no se pueden ejercer si no vienen acompañadas por una buena condición física. Este será el argumento predominante de nuestras lecciones.

3) **La comprensión**: Consiste en entender qué se puede hacer y qué es necesario hacer y distingue al buen futbolista de los demás en igualdad de condiciones físicas y técnico-tácticas. Probar algo que se sabe que no se podrá hacer es tan grave como hacer bien cualquier cosa en el momento equivocado.

La comprensión requiere:

- Conocimiento de los principios y las reglas del juego.

- Intuición de lo que va a ocurrir.

- Decisiones sobre qué es mejor hacer.

- Percepción del espacio y el tiempo.

- Acción, ejecución rápida e inmediata de lo que se ha decidido.

4) **La condición psico-social**: Saber estar dentro de un grupo (equipo), aceptando la diversidad (habilidades, comportamientos, capacidades físicas, experiencia...) colaborando a alcanzar el objetivo común es una condición indispensable para completar las demás.

Antes de iniciar el tratamiento de los elementos fundamentales para alcanzar una buena condición física es necesario indicar brevemente cómo debe enseñar el entrenador y los principios sobre los que se basa una acción entrenadora eficaz.

Los principios de la enseñanza

Los principios o reglas de la enseñanza deportiva sirven para optimizar la capacidad metódica de acción de entrenadores y deportistas. Esos principios se refieren a todos los aspectos y tareas de la enseñanza, de la cual determinan contenidos, métodos y organizaciones.

1) **Conocer la materia**: Hay que conocer el fútbol desde el punto de vista técnico y táctico, los principios de la preparación física, no dejarse influir

por factores externos y ambientales de tipo emotivo e impedir que los futbolistas se vean afectados por ellos.

2) **Conocer cómo se aprende**: No es posible realizar un entrenamiento rentable sin conocer los principios del aprendizaje que hayamos elegido antes.

3) **Conocer los factores clave de la enseñanza**: Los factores clave de la enseñanza son:

a) *El objetivo general*: Buscar objetivos que habitualmente sean a medio y largo plazo, por ejemplo, la mejora del juego de ataque del equipo o la mejora de la fuerza. Del objetivo general derivan los objetivos a corto plazo.

b) *Los objetivos*: Se refieren:

- Al juego con pelota (pases, controles, triangulaciones, etc.).

- Al juego sin balón (movimiento combinado, acciones de apoyo, cruces, etc.).

No se puede enseñar todo de una vez, sino determinar un orden de prioridad y una secuencia lógica de entrenamiento.

c) *El orden de prioridades y la secuencia lógica*. No se pueden enseñar eficazmente diversos aspectos del juego de una sola vez.

Entre dos factores, siempre habrá una precedencia lógica sobre otra. Si no se respeta una secuencia lógica se hace mucho más difícil. Lo mismo pasa si se insiste en enseñar cosas apropiadas, pero en un momento inapropiado. Debe prestarse mucha atención a la proyección y la organización.

d) *La proyección y la organización*:

La proyección conlleva el mejor uso del equipo y debe llevarse a cabo al principio para dar lugar a la mejor organización posible.

La organización de una sesión eficaz de entrenamiento prevé:

- La elección de la zona del campo a utilizar en el entrenamiento.
- El número exacto de jugadores que participarán.
- Un entrenamiento realista (los jugadores deben estar colocados en sus posiciones reales y en los ejercicios deben jugar de modo realista; las porterías deben ser siempre de tamaño normal, porque los dos aspectos esenciales del fútbol son los tiros a puerta y la indicación de las porterías).

- Un inicio adecuado del ejercicio y calidad en los pases (muchos entrenamientos se realizan de forma cansina porque se presta poca atención al modo de iniciar el ejercicio y los pases son poco apropiados).
- Sencillez y claridad (todos los jugadores deben entender bien qué se quiere hacer con cada tipo de entrenamiento).

e) *La capacidad de observación*: La observación de una sesión de entrenamiento debe llevar al técnico a saber si:

- Los entrenamientos se desarrollan de acuerdo con la organización.

- La actitud de los jugadores se ve estimulada e interesada.

- Las acciones del juego colectivo cumplen los objetivos generales.

- La acción concreta de cada uno es beneficiosa para el trabajo del grupo.

Si no se cumple todo esto, hay que preguntarse:

- ¿Está el jugador físicamente en situación de realizar esa tarea?

Si la respuesta es «no», no hay razón para continuar el ejercicio.

- ¿El ejercicio asusta al jugador?

Si la respuesta es «sí» conviene empezar con ejercicios más sencillos y animar más al jugador.

- ¿Es un problema técnico?

- ¿De qué técnica se trata?

Asegurarse de que el jugador entienda dónde se equivoca y explicarle cómo hacerlo de modo correcto y ejercitarlo en ese sentido.

- ¿Es un problema táctico?

1. Falta de comprensión (aislar y explicar las distintas partes).
2. Falta de intuición (el jugador no entiende la acción que se desarrolla por tres motivos):

- **Acción demasiado complicada.**

- **Acción demasiado veloz,**

- **Juega con desgana.**

3. Falta de empeño (el jugador comprende lo que se quiere de él, pero se equivoca en la ejecución porque trata de hacer cosas demasiado difíciles).

f) *La comunicación,* Todo lo que se ha dicho hasta ahora importa poco si el entrenador no es capaz de comunicar. Un entrenador puede comunicar de dos maneras;

1. Mediante demostración, mostrando las siguientes cualidades:

- Acciones correctas de juego.

- Acciones desarrolladas de modo sencillo.

- Demostración clara, mostrando el factor principal.

- Establecer un objetivo mínimo,

2. A través de la palabra: La comunicación mediante palabras es muy importante, pero depende de la convicción con la que habla el entrenador. El entrenador, antes de hablar, debe pensar por un momento a quién debe hablar para estar seguro del significado de las palabras, debe evitar palabras o discursos complicados y mirar a los oyentes mientras habla. Finalmente debe hablar siempre en clave positiva porque es más eficaz decir «haz esto» en lugar de decir «te has equivocado al hacer esto».

La comunicación en cifras

El 70% de nuestra vida lo pasamos comunicando verbalmente. Este tiempo se reparte así:

A escuchar   45%

A hablar   30%

A leer   15%

A escribir   10%

De todo esto recordamos:

De lo que leemos	el 10%
De lo que escuchamos	el 20%
De lo que observamos	el 30%
De lo que escuchamos y observamos	el 50%
De lo que decimos	el 80%
De lo que explicamos	el 90%

En una conversación, recordamos:

Oímos el 50% de lo que se dice.

Escuchamos el 50% de lo que se oye (solo el 25%).

Comprendemos el 50% de lo que escuchamos (solo el 12,5%).

Creemos el 50% de lo que comprendemos (solo el 6,25%).

Recordamos el 50% de lo que creemos (solo el 3,125%).

¿Cuántas veces hemos hablado un rato largo con nuestros jugadores?

¿Qué ha quedado de nuestras palabras?

¡¡¡¡¡¡¡¡¡ El 3,125% !!!!!!!!!!

El resto se olvida.

Entrenar significa comunicar. Hay quien habla, pero comunica poco y le cuesta relacionarse, Otros por el contrario hablan mucho y dedican poco tiempo a escuchar.

Todo enseñante debe tener siempre presente la importancia de la secuencia:

ESCUCHO = OLVIDO

VEO = RECUERDO

EJECUTO = APRENDO

La enseñanza durante el juego

El entrenador debe estar capacitado y atento en los partidos de entrenamiento. El partido de entrenamiento representa la culminación de la sesión, el desarrollo final de una buena actividad de juego de equipo. Las técnicas y los ejercicios en grupos pequeños son como piezas de un mosaico y enseñar a ponerlos en práctica durante el partido es como tratar de completar el mosaico. Esperar que esas piezas se pongan por sí solas en su lugar es un

optimismo excesivo. Para obtener resultados satisfactorios conviene establecer:

- Qué enseñar.

- Dónde enseñar.

- Cómo enseñar.

1) Qué enseñar:

Hay que dedicarse principalmente a objetivos dirigidos a la mejora del juego en equipo.

Defensa: reducir tiempo y espacio; acosar y cubrir; defensa en bloque.

Ataque: creación y aprovechamiento de espacios; pases y movimientos, ataque en bloque.

Esto independientemente de una estrategia de juego. Cada jugador debe aprender a comportarse eficazmente en toda situación.

Habituar a los jugadores a realizar los cálculos apropiados:

- Entre seguridad y riesgo.

- De las posibilidades: saber elegir y hacer aquello que resulta ser lo mejor en una situación concreta **(elegir lo mejor)**.

2) Dónde enseñar:

Los jugadores deben ejercitarse en la realización de acciones de juego en todas las partes del campo. La mejora del juego en equipo en ataque debería conseguirse a partir de los tres cuartos defensivos del campo, del mismo modo que la mejora del sistema defensivo debería conseguirse partiendo de los tres cuartos de ataque. Considero oportuno efectuar ejercicios situacionales en las diversas zonas del campo, es decir, en las zonas donde queramos que estos comportamientos se desarrollen realmente en el partido.

3) Cómo enseñar: Los métodos que están en la base de la enseñanza son:

- *Control del juego* (por ejemplo, si un equipo debe entrenarse en crear espacios en la zona central del campo, el entrenamiento debe limitarse a esa zona).

- *Condiciones de juego* (por ejemplo, si hay que concentrarse en los pases rápidos hay que imponer el juego al primer toque, cuando sea posible, y por tanto un movimiento continuo sin balón previendo las decisiones del compañero para poder dar solución al pase antes de que reciba el balón. Si se requiere desbordar en el apoyo hay que imponer que el jugador deba superar en carrera al compañero al que han pasado el balón).

- *Parar el juego.* Es un método para mostrar a los jugadores las ventajas y desventajas de sus posiciones.

Para este propósito, es necesario que:

a) Se establezca una señal conocida por todos para parar el juego (por ejemplo, dos silbidos, aunque en este sentido estoy convencido de que la señal debe ser necesariamente visual, ya que en el partido el entrenador no puede usar el silbato y por tanto los jugadores deben reconocer visualmente una situación común para todos, de modo que, al reconocerla, todos se comporten como se estableció en el entrenamiento.

b) Los jugadores se detengan sin alterar la situación de juego que se quiere corregir (conviene parar el juego para poner el acento en el tema tratado, no para tratar varios temas).

- *Corregir y repetir*: Después de haber parado el juego es importante hacer repetir en el modo correcto lo que se ha hecho de modo equivocado.

- *Pensar en voz alta*: Se trata de un método por el cual el entrenador piensa en voz alta en el lugar del jugador, anticipando sus acciones. Este método se usa a menudo para hacer más eficaz la repetición correctiva.

ENTRENAMIENTO Y CRECIMIENTO

Mediante el entrenamiento se busca la mejora de las capacidades motoras. Algunas capacidades pueden entrenarse y mejorarse, otras pueden educarse y transformarse. Ya hemos dicho que no es posible intervenir en una de ellas sin influir positiva o negativamente en las otras, En los juegos deportivos son importantes las influencias de las diversas capacidades sobre la eficacia del gesto deportivo y este hecho ha producido la noción de «régimen de manifestación». El régimen de manifestación representa el modo de manifestarse de una capacidad motora (por ejemplo, la resistencia en el régimen de velocidad; la velocidad en el régimen de fuerza) y representa también el modo de manifestarse en la mezcla de los factores del entrenamiento (por ejemplo, la preparación física en el régimen técnico, la preparación técnica en el régimen táctico).

1

Los componentes de la preparación físico-motora son:

- La preparación física general y multilateral, que realizada de modo particular y global se dedica

especialmente a las grandes funciones del organismo y es muy apropiada para los jóvenes.

- La preparación física específica, que se dirige a las funciones y la motricidad propia de cada deporte, correspondiente a los requerimientos de las prestaciones de la competición a conseguir después de ciclo preparatorio juvenil.

La figura muestra que las prestaciones del futbolista, o más bien su eficiencia en una competición, dependen de múltiples habilidades, capacidades y cualidades, que se influyen entre sí.

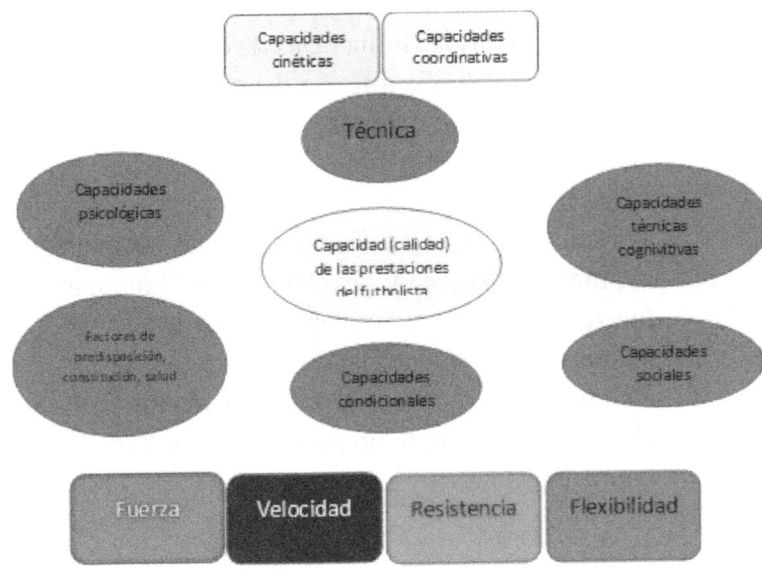

Componentes de las capacidades del futbolista
(Weineck-Erlangen, 1994)

La figura muestra que las prestaciones del futbolista, o más bien su eficiencia en una competición, dependen de múltiples habilidades, capacidades y cualidades que se influyen entre sí.

En la estructura del rendimiento representada en la figura anterior, las capacidades condicionales son fundamentales, porque constituyen la base para una prestación técnica, táctica y psicológica estable durante la competición *(Stiehler-Kinzag-Döbler, 1988)*.

Para enfrentarse seriamente a los problemas del entrenamiento, hay que llevar a cabo tres operaciones: La primera consiste en definir las cualidades físicas dominantes en el juego del fútbol:

- *La resistencia en régimen de fuerza.*

- *La velocidad (aceleración).*

- *La destreza (capacidad de realizar velozmente movimientos complejos).*

La segunda es definir las características del esfuerzo específico que requiere el fútbol. El esfuerzo físico se caracteriza en general por los siguientes parámetros:

- Intensidad.
- Duración.
- Complejidad.

- Procesos metabólicos para la producción de energía.

Desde el punto de vista de la intensidad, el esfuerzo puede ser:

Intensidad	Frec.cardiaca-Puls/m.	Frec. respiratoria-Insp/m.
Máxima	Superior a 210	Superior a 40 – 50
Límite	Entre 200 – 210	Entre 35 – 40
Sublímite	Entre 180 - 200	Entre 30 – 40
Grande	Entre 120 - 180	Entre 25 – 35
Moderada	Inferior a 120	Inferior a 25

La intensidad del ejercicio debe relacionarse con la edad del sujeto. Para sujetos adultos, una indicación a seguir es la de considerar la frecuencia cardiaca máxima a alcanzar, respetando:

Las fórmulas de *Cooper:*

FC max = 220 - edad   para las mujeres

FC max = 205 - (edad/2)   para los hombres

O bien la fórmula de *Karvonen:*   FC max = 220 – frecuencia en reposo

O mejor todavía la fórmula de *Tanaka*:   FC max = 208 - (0,7 x edad)

Hay que recordar que:

- Entre el 50-60% de la FC max, se realiza un trabajo moderado.

- Entre el 60-70% de la FC max, se realiza un trabajo grande, también llamado «cardiotraining».

- Entre el 70-80% de la FC max, se realiza un trabajo sublímite aeróbico cercano al umbral.

- Entre el 80-90% de la FC max, se realiza un trabajo límite anaeróbico.

- Más allá del 90% se realiza un trabajo máximo (poco aconsejado).

Desde el punto de vista de la duración, el esfuerzo puede ser:

- Corto o largo.
- Continuo o variable.
- Con o sin interrupciones.

Desde el punto de vista de la complejidad, el esfuerzo puede ser:

- Simple (por ejemplo, la maratón).
- Complejo (por ejemplo, el fútbol).

Desde el punto de vista de los procesos metabólicos de producción de energía, el esfuerzo puede ser:

- Aeróbico.
- Anaeróbico.
- Mixto.

Para el fútbol, el esfuerzo específico se considera:

Por intensidad:

-Sublímite (frec. card. 180/200 – frec. resp. 30/40)

Por duración:

-Variable con numerosas interrupciones.

Por complejidad:

-Complejo, porque recurre a cualidades físicas diversas (velocidad, fuerza, etc.) para acciones técnicas y tácticas con situaciones de contacto físico.

Por procesos metabólicos:

-Mixto, con notable esfuerzo anaeróbico aláctico.

La tercera componente es la de establecer el aumento y la disminución de los esfuerzos durante el entrenamiento.

En la práctica, establecer el plan de entrenamiento y el programa de preparación física.

El objetivo principal de todo entrenamiento futbolístico debe ser la mejora de la capacidad de actuar del futbolista *(Bisanz-Gerisch, 1990)*. Esta afirmación sirve para revisar la importancia de los factores de las condiciones para evitar su excesiva sobrevaloración o infravaloración en el entrenamiento. En un entrenamiento futbolístico dirigido se tratará de favorecer ejercicios de velocidad de acción que se dirijan a la práctica del juego, teniendo en cuenta todos los factores de prestaciones a nivel psicofísico, técnico-táctico y social. Las siguientes citas demuestran que una teoría específica del entrenamiento futbolístico se debe basar en las exigencias de la competición y que el entrenamiento de las condiciones debe semejarse a la práctica del juego o, si es posible, integrarse en esta.

«El mejor maestro para el entrenamiento es la competición» *(Cramer, 1987)*.

«De la competición aprendemos qué debemos entrenar» *(Krauspe-Rauhut-Teschner, 1990)*.

«Si la competición es el mejor entrenamiento entonces es verdad que un buen entrenamiento debe por fuerza tener las características de una competición» *(Northpoth, 1988)*.

«El secreto del fútbol está siempre en el entrenamiento de la competición» *(Beenhakker, 1990)*.

«El objetivo central de todo entrenamiento futbolístico debe ser la mejora de la capacidad de acción del jugador» *Bisanz-Gerisch, 1990)*.

De estas citas se deduce que **el entrenamiento futbolístico debe asemejarse a la práctica del juego** o, si es posible, integrarse en esta. El entrenamiento no es por tanto un fin en sí mismo, sino que persigue el objetivo de «mejorar la capacidad de jugar y optimizar la capacidad de actuar».

Si por una parte se quiere revisar la importancia de los factores de la condición física, por otra será oportuno favorecer en el entrenamiento futbolístico un ejercicio de la velocidad de acción que se oriente a la práctica de juego, teniendo siempre presente todos los factores de prestaciones a nivel técnico-táctico y psicosocial. Esto significa que es necesario atribuir más importancia a un entrenamiento similar a la práctica del juego con métodos y medios cada vez más especializados *(Lottermann, 1990)*.

EL ENTRENADOR DEBE

1) Conocer bien a los deportistas y trabajar para mejorar constantemente su aprendizaje y su formación.

2) Analizar con los deportistas y los dirigentes las razones del éxito o las causas de los malos resultados.

3) Contribuir a la formación del grupo y a su sentido de la responsabilidad y el respeto.

4) Inducir a los deportistas a seguir un entrenamiento regular.

5) Preocuparse por el estado de salud de los deportistas.

6) Inculcar en los deportistas el sentimiento de los colores del club y el respeto por la propiedad social.

7) Animar a los deportistas a participar de forma activa en cada entrenamiento.

8) Estar profesionalmente al día.

9) Documentar diariamente los entrenamientos.

10) Preparar el entrenamiento de modo que suscite el interés de los futbolistas por los ejercicios físicos, técnicos y tácticos.

EL ENTRENAMIENTO DE LOS FUTBOLISTAS JÓVENES

Es oportuno detenerse en primer lugar a analizar los graves errores que se cometen con respecto a los objetivos del entrenamiento juvenil.

El primer error está en considerar a los jóvenes una imagen reducida de los adultos, sin considerar que tienen una personalidad todavía en formación, un modo de pensar todavía en evolución y sobre todo un físico y capacidades completamente diferentes. No es posible trasladar a la esfera juvenil el entrenamiento de los adultos, limitándonos a prestar atención solo a reducir la cantidad y la intensidad.

El aumento de las capacidades físicas no puede proponerse de la misma manera a los jóvenes que a los adultos, más bien debe haber una diferenciación ulterior en el mismo ámbito juvenil, de acuerdo con las franjas de edad.

Por ejemplo, dirigir un ciclo de entrenamiento para niños de 12-13 años (muy jóvenes) teniendo como objetivo el máximo rendimiento para alcanzar un éxito inmediato significa alterar el espíritu del propio entrenamiento, Por el contrario, se debe

llevar al joven gradualmente y a pequeños pasos y a lo largo de los años hacia el rendimiento deseado.

Una preparación demasiado veloz y precoz, que en general siempre está ligada al cumplimiento de objetivos ambiciosos entre los adultos, producirá resultados notables a corto plazo, pero seguramente producirá daños, que casi siempre son irreversibles.

Cuando los jóvenes y los adolescentes en particular son sometidos a una carga física y psicológica excesiva disminuye su motivación por lo que están haciendo, disminuye su deseo hasta llegar a un verdadero rechazo ante los primeros fracasos. Así se puede entender cómo muchas veces los jóvenes futbolistas después del entrenamiento con su equipo se reúnen (en un gimnasio, en un patio o en un espacio abierto) para jugar por fin al fútbol.

Un entrenamiento gradual y cuidadoso conduce a un grado más alto de preparación física y atlética en edad adulta y la mantiene estable durante más tiempo.

Al acabar el ciclo juvenil, el jugador deberá:

- Haber alcanzado la maduración física apropiada.
- Haber adquirido un bagaje técnico completo.
- Haber adquirido un sentido táctico correcto.
- Haber desarrollado la llamada «cualidad de la voluntad» indispensable para obtener resultados duraderos, es decir:
  - Disposición al trabajo en grupo.

- Espíritu de colaboración.
- Disposición a aprender y trabajar.
- Conciencia de la mejora mediante el empeño.
- Deseo de progresar.

Estas cualidades actúan positivamente no solo en el ámbito deportivo, sino que son de gran ayuda para afrontar la vida y las dificultades cotidianas.

Junto a estos objetivos primarios, debemos considerar otros aspectos que revisten gran importancia para la formación de los jóvenes:
- El mantenimiento y el cuidado de la salud y de la higiene personal.
- La organización y la ocupación del tiempo libre.
- El fútbol y su entrenamiento correspondiente deben permanecer en segundo plano con respecto a la escuela o el trabajo.
- El entrenamiento no debe comportar riesgos para la salud y el futuro crecimiento del joven.
- La alegría y la serenidad deben estar siempre en primer plano: hay que evitar por tanto entrenamientos fatigosos, monótonos o repetitivos (esto no significa que no se puedan repetir ejercicios ya efectuados).
- Los jóvenes deben poder siempre obtener del entrenamiento experiencias constructivas y socializadoras.
- Además del fútbol, los jóvenes deben poder cultivar otros intereses, sobre todo a nivel cultural.

El entrenador de juveniles debe saber reconocer un potencial futbolista valorando sus capacidades y competencias en relación con:

TÉCNICA:
- Actitud global ante el movimiento.
- Sensibilidad al contacto con el balón y habilidad en su control.
- Buena actitud al defender el balón en situaciones concretas de juego.

TÁCTICA:
- Sentido de la orientación.
- Rapidez en la capacidad de juicio para prever por anticipado situaciones de juego en ataque y en defensa.

CUALIDADES DEL CARÁCTER:
- Capacidad de autoafirmación.
- Resolución en los propósitos.
- Voluntad constante.
- Buen comportamiento social.
- Modestia para saber ponerse también al servicio de los demás.

CARACTERÍSTICAS FÍSICAS:
- Constitución física que deja entrever un desarrollo adecuado y regular.
- Dotes atléticas potenciales.

Entrenar a los jóvenes significa sobre todo poner en práctica correctamente todas las fases de la estrategia general de la educación.

- Conocimiento del alumno en relación con su desarrollo motor.
- Conocimiento de los problemas educativos en las diversas franjas de edad.
- Valoración continua de las variaciones inducidas en la personalidad y la maduración del joven, de la influencia ambiental y de la acción educativa físico-motora.

El entrenador debe ajustarse, sobre todo para los jóvenes hasta los 14/15 años, en la medida de lo posible, el principio de la polivalencia.

La polivalencia constituye la vía principal para hacer que los alumnos se inicien de una manera seria, correcta y válida la práctica deportiva.

Requiere:
- *Intervenciones de tipo analítico* (desarrollo de las percepciones auditiva, visual, coordinación sensomotora, movimientos concretos).
- *Intervenciones de tipo global* (secuencias múltiples, recorridos mixtos, juegos polivalentes, juegos en equipo).
- *Intervenciones apropiadas* (lo justo en el momento justo).

Efectos de algunas disciplinas deportivas sobre los jóvenes

DEPORTE	EFECTO
Natación	Aumento de la laxitud
Carrera	Limitación de la movilidad en algunas articulaciones
Tenis- Esgrima	Entrenamiento asimétrico
Fútbol	Desequilibrio de las extremidades inferiores

(G. Frohner, 2002)

Esto podría llevar a pensar que realizar todas estas actividades podría garantizar un desarrollo completo del individuo.

Eso no es verdad si no se organizan las actividades de tal modo que se integren entre sí sin que una predomine sobre la otra. Motivo por el cual se aconseja siempre, con respecto a la formación del futbolista, que se realicen actividades polivalentes, sobre todo en edad preadolescente y adolescente, independientemente de la actividad que esté practicando la persona. Por tanto, resulta importante que las propuestas de entrenamiento comprendan todos los factores (sin olvidarse de cuál es la actividad principal).

LA RESPONSABILIDAD DEL ENTRENADOR

Muchos entrenadores, como ofrecen gratuitamente su tiempo, piensan que no tienen responsabilidad en el progreso y la salud de los chicos a los que entrenan, sino solo en el resultado deportivo de sus acciones. Al entrenador de juveniles sin embargo se le considera responsable del daño psicológico que pueda producir al joven y sobre todo de los daños físicos causados por negligencia o inconsciencia: los dirigentes (corresponsables) deberían acordarse de informar siempre al entrenador acerca de sus responsabilidades antes de que empiece su trabajo.

Sería importante saber por lo menos que existen unas fases de progreso en las que se desarrollan diferentes características y capacidades coordinativas, llamadas FASES SENSIBLES.

Las fases sensibles
Fases de mayor sensibilidad de las diversas capacidades motoras y cualidades psicofísicas en las edades de seis a quince años.

▶ **Entre los 5 y los 9/10 años** se consiguen los patrones motores de base y aumenta la precisión en los movimientos.

▶ **Entre los 6 y los 8 años** mejora rápidamente el equilibrio.

▶ **Entre los 7 y los 10 años** mejora la rapidez de movimientos.

▶ **Entre los 8 y los 10 años** madura la aptitud para prever la velocidad y la dirección de objetos en movimiento.

▶ **Entre los 9 y los 10 años** se alcanza la máxima frecuencia de paso.

▶ **Entre los 9 y los 11 años** se consiguen progresos en la coordinación senso-motora (ojo-mano, ojo-pie y dinámica general).

▶ **Entre los 11 y los 12 años** se completa el desarrollo de la lateralización.

▶ **Entre los 12 y los 18 años** se redobla la fuerza muscular. Para las chicas, a partir de los 13 no aumenta sustancialmente.

▶ **Hasta los 14 años** hay que evitar ejercicios pasivos de movilidad, en la práctica, de aquellos que se realizan con la ayuda de los otros.

▶ **A partir de los 10 años** hay que iniciar la educación en el estiramiento muscular y la movilidad.

Fases de la preparación deportiva

Antes de enumerar las diversas fases de la preparación deportiva es necesario recordar que las edades cronológicas indicadas son puramente indicativas, en la preparación de los jóvenes es mucho más serio y correcto considerar la edad biológica de los distintos sujetos.

Etapas o niveles	Todas las actividades deportivas	El fútbol en particular
6-10 años	Preparación general preliminar.	Yo y el balón.
10-13 años	Iniciación al deporte.	Yo, el balón y el compañero.
13-15 años	Entrenamiento especializado en un deporte.	Yo, el balón, los compañeros y los adversarios.
15-18 años	Perfeccionamiento deportivo: 1. Zona de los primeros grandes éxitos. 2. Zona de las posibilidades óptimas. 3. Zona de la estabilización y de las máximas prestaciones.	El equipo.

Estas indicaciones son importantes para poder establecer cuáles serán las propuestas de entrenamiento y para poder programar la actividad.

Principio del ejercicio con un fin

Fases del entrenamiento	Entrenamiento motor general	Entrenamiento específico o condicional	Entrenamiento especial	Competición
Entrenamiento de base 8-10 años	30%	20%	40%	10%
Entrenamiento de construcción 10-13 años	10%	25%	45%	20%
Entrenamiento de alto nivel 13-15 años	10%	20%	35%	35%
Entrenamiento de muy alto nivel 15-18 años	0%	25%	35%	40%

(Schonborn, 1984)

El camino a recorrer en el entrenamiento juvenil es el del incremento gradual del ejercicio. Los

estímulos deben aplicarse progresivamente de modo adecuado al desarrollo.

La sucesión metodológica aconsejable es la de aumentar:
- Primero la frecuencia del entrenamiento (número de sesiones).
- Luego el volumen (cantidad de trabajo).
- Finalmente la intensidad (velocidad de ejecución y carga).

(Helens, Grosser, Zimmermann, 1983)

EXPLORACIÓN *Experimentación*	FIJACIÓN *Asimilación*	ESTABILIZACIÓN *Automatización*
8-12 años	**13-15 años**	**16-20 años**
Sentido táctico y capacidad técnica.	Comportamiento táctico y técnico.	Táctica (sentido de la posición) y técnica.

Según Martin (1982) las **fases sensibles** encuentran sus momentos de mayor mejora en las edades indicadas en los gráficos siguientes.

EDAD

Capacidades		6	7	8	9	10	11	12	13	14	15	16
Capacidades coordinativas	Capacidad aprendizaje motor			■	■	■					■	■
	Capacidad de diferenciar			■	■	■	■	■			■	
	Capacidad de reaccionar ante estímulos ópticos y acústicos				■	■						
	Capacidad de orientación en el espacio		■	■	■				■	■		
	Capacidad de ritmo		■	■								
	Capacidad de equilibrio					■	■	■				
Capa. físicas	Resistencia		■	■	■	■	■	■	■	■	■	■
	Fuerza			■	■					■	■	■
	Rapidez		■	■								
C. afectivo-cognitiva	Calidad afectivo-cognitiva			■	■	■	■			■	■	■
	Voluntad de aprender		■									

No es posible un entrenamiento de las capacidades coordinativas y condicionales que tenga la misma eficacia para todas las edades. Por tanto, ninguna

capacidad puede entrenarse en la misma medida a cualquier edad *(Israel 1976)*.

Con la llegada de la adolescencia se registran disminuciones en las prestaciones o estancamientos en el campo coordinativo *(Sharma, 1993)*.

En los chicos de desarrollo retardado, se descubren prestaciones coordinativas mejores con respecto a las de aquellos con un desarrollo anticipado o normal.

Los periodos del desarrollo en los cuales la entrenabilidad es más favorable para una determinada capacidad motora o clase de tareas deportivas (por ejemplo, desarrollo de la movilidad articular, perfeccionamiento de la técnica deportiva) han de considerarse fases sensibles para esa clase de tareas. Hay que prestar mucha atención al hecho de que existe la misma sensibilidad entre los métodos de entrenamiento adecuados e inadecuados. Si no se usan los años de la infancia más favorables para la formación de la coordinación y la técnica deportivas o se permite que en ellos se formen comportamientos deportivos equivocados, las consecuencias negativas serán seguramente más visibles y por tanto más duraderas que en otros periodos.

Pasamos a analizar cuáles son las capacidades a desarrollar en el deportista joven.

Capacidades neutras
Resistencia aeróbica
Es posible desarrollarla ya en edad preescolar, para continuar con ella en las posteriores etapas

evolutivas, hasta llegar al periodo de «impulso» adolescente, que, de acuerdo con los conocimientos actuales, parece ser el más favorable.

Capacidades precoces
- **Coordinativa.**
- **Rapidez de reacción y frecuencia motora.**
- **Movilidad articular.**
- **Aprendizaje motor** (con tareas de aprendizaje que no requieran supuestos altos de fuerza máxima o de fuerza relativa).

Capacidades intermedias
Hacia el final del periodo escolar elemental y durante toda la primera fase adolescente, se consideran, con atención creciente:
- **Movilidad articular.**
- **Fuerza rápida.**
- **Resistencia a la fuerza** (con carga natural).
- **Rapidez de movimiento, de locomoción y aceleración.**

Capacidades tardías
- **Fuerza máxima.**
- **Resistencia anaeróbica.**
- **Fuerza rápida contra oposición.**
- **Resistencia a la fuerza contra oposición.**

Crecimiento, desarrollo y maduración son palabras que sirven para describir las modificaciones que se producen en el organismo hasta alcanzar la edad adulta:

✓ **El crecimiento**

Se refiere a un aumento en las dimensiones totales del organismo o de cualquier parte del cuerpo.

✓ **El desarrollo**

Se refiere a la diferenciación de las células siguiendo líneas de especialización funcional y a las competencias conseguidas para enfrentarse a las situaciones (habilidad, capacidad, personalidad).

✓ **La maduración**

Se refiere al proceso de alcanzar la condición biológica de la edad adulta y la funcionalidad completa. Se produce en mucho tiempo. Se refiere:
- A la edad cronológica
- A la edad física.
- Al estado de maduración sexual. La madurez fisiológica en las chicas se produce 2-3 años antes que en los chicos.

En resumen, los indicadores útiles para determinar la evolución del joven son:

El crecimiento   Dimensiones corporales.
El desarrollo   Competencias adquiridas.
La maduración   Condiciones biológicas.

Los especialistas del sector del crecimiento y del desarrollo han dedicado mucho tiempo al estudio de las modificaciones de la estatura y del peso que acompañan al crecimiento. El crecimiento en altura es muy rápido en los dos primeros años de vida.

La tasa máxima de crecimiento se verifica:
- Cerca de los 11,4 años para las niñas.
- Cerca de los 13,4 años para los niños.

La altura definitiva se alcanza:
- Cerca de los 16-17 años para las niñas.
- Cerca de los 18-20 años para los niños.

El aumento máximo del peso corporal se produce:
- Cerca de los 12,5 años para las niñas.
- Cerca de los 14,5 años para los niños.

Huesos, articulaciones, cartílagos y ligamentos forman el soporte de la estructura del cuerpo: los huesos proporcionan puntos de inserción de los músculos, protegen los tejidos delicados y representan depósitos de calcio y fósforo. Entre los 14 y los 22 años, las membranas y los cartílagos se transforman en hueso. Durante un tiempo igualmente largo, entre los 13 y los 20 años, se produce la osificación completa de los diversos huesos. La edad preadolescente es la más indicada para reforzar los huesos en respuesta al estímulo de la actividad física.

La masa muscular aumenta regularmente desde el nacimiento hasta el fin de la adolescencia con arreglo al aumento del peso. Las chicas alcanzan el máximo desarrollo muscular entre los 16 y los 20 años, los chicos entre los 18 y los 25.

Pero de esto hablaremos de modo más específico cuando tratemos las diversas capacidades motoras.

Incluyo a título informativo dos gráficos sobre la frecuencia de lesiones en espalda y rodillas en edad juvenil causadas por entrenamientos inadecuados. Edades comprendidas entre los 10 y los 18 años.

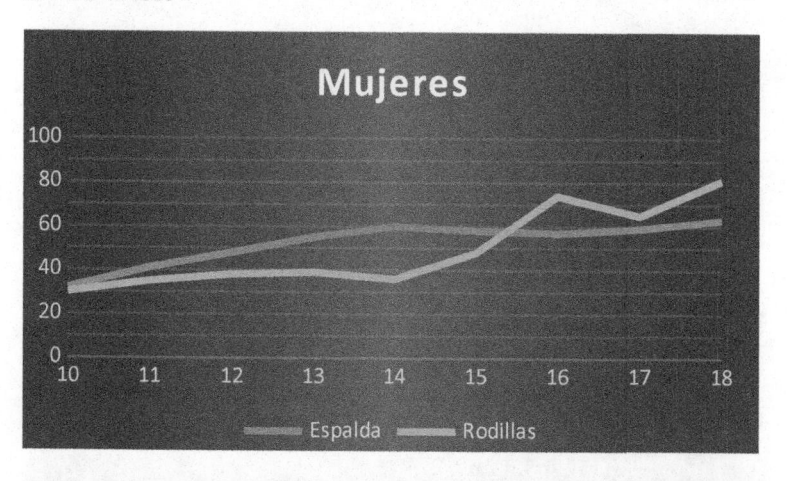

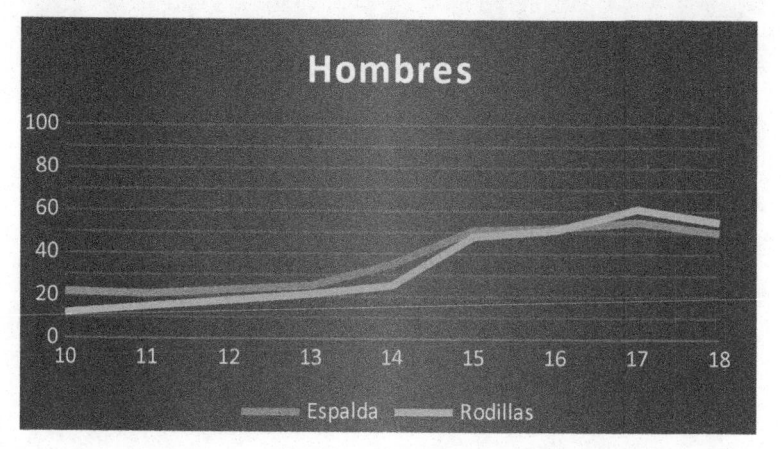

EFECTOS FISIOLÓGICOS DEL ENTRENAMIENTO

La condición física

El organismo humano puede aumentar sus capacidades funcionales de manera notable mediante el proceso fisiológico del entrenamiento. Cuando nuestro cuerpo se somete a un ejercicio físico de cierta intensidad, se verifican inmediatamente estas reacciones:
- Aumento de los latidos del corazón.
- Aumento del ritmo respiratorio.
- Aumento de la profundidad de las acciones respiratorias.
- Aumento de la secreción de sudor.

Estas reacciones se manifiestan independientemente de la condición física del sujeto, aunque esta última puede determinar el comportamiento y la entidad. Se trata de cambios temporales, porque en cuanto cesa el ejercicio físico también desaparecen estos cambios y en poco tiempo el organismo vuelve a su estado normal. El intervalo de tiempo para la vuelta a la normalidad es normalmente más breve cuanto mejor es la condición del individuo.

La expresión «**condición física**» indica ese estado concreto por el que el deportista se encuentra en la mejor disposición, desde el punto de vista físico, para ofrecer una determinada prestación.

Una de las manifestaciones típicas de la condición física es el alejamiento del «**umbral de la fatiga**».

¿Qué es la fatiga? ¿Qué es el umbral de la fatiga?

Por **fatiga** entendemos la disminución del poder funcional de un órgano o de todo el organismo, debida a un exceso de trabajo.

El **umbral de la fatiga** representa el límite de demarcación entre la completa eficiencia y el inicio del descenso del poder funcional.

El entrenamiento mediante múltiples actividades se propone obtener una mejora de las prestaciones y **retrasar el momento del surgimiento de la fatiga**.

En la práctica, el entrenamiento se manifiesta como una **repetición sistemática y racional de determinados movimientos y comportamientos** con el objetivo de obtener una mejora de prestaciones.

Los cambios estructurales y funcionales que se verifican en nuestro cuerpo a causa del entrenamiento tienen una relación estrecha con el tipo de prestación motora que los ha provocado: a

cada forma de movimiento le corresponde un tipo de adaptación.

En la práctica ocurre que, en las fases inmediatamente posteriores al esfuerzo físico, las estructuras orgánicas y musculares requeridas para producirlo y soportarlo no se limitan a superar la situación de fatiga con una vuelta a las condiciones de normalidad, sino que tienen una reacción reconstructiva que los lleva a superar la situación precedente al estímulo.

Estos momentos de **sobrecompensación** tienen una duración limitada y se vuelve progresivamente a la situación de normalidad.

Se hace necesario provocar otras situaciones de sobrecompensación antes de que se agoten las precedentes, es decir, provocar una «suma total de las acciones de entrenamiento» *(Matwejew, 1972)*.

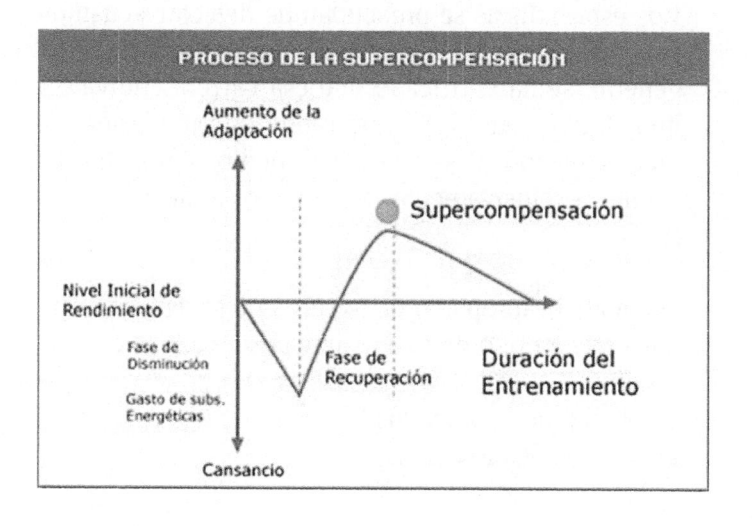

Repetir estas situaciones de estrés provocará la adecuación gradual de las capacidades atléticas, poniendo al organismo en situación de superar cargas de trabajo con menos acumulaciones de fatiga o de mostrar prestaciones siempre más elevadas. La sobrecompensación no debe entenderse desde un punto de vista fisiológico, sino solamente como una mejora de la acumulación de glucógeno.

Cuanto más grandes sean los depósitos de glucosa (reservas de glucógeno) en el músculo del futbolista, más tarde acusará el cansancio y más tiempo mantendrá la capacidad de cumplir con su tarea con una muy alta intensidad *(Cogan Coyle, 1989)*.

El elemento básico de la prestación futbolística en lo que se refiere al empleo y el consumo de energía es la actividad de carrera.

Los especialistas se preocupan de detectar «cuánto» corre el futbolista aficionado durante un partido: en general, se ha verificado que esa carrera equivale a unos 8.000 metros. Eso no representaría ni siquiera una prestación atlética de nivel medio, si tenemos en cuenta exclusivamente el tiempo total de juego (90').

Un análisis apropiado de la carga de trabajo muestra que en el ámbito de esta distancia se realizan:
- Saltos.
- Detenciones y frenados.
- Cambios de dirección.

- Controles del balón.
- Enfrentamientos con adversarios.

En otras palabras, el partido de fútbol es una sucesión de prestaciones diversas por tipo de intensidad de acuerdo con el desarrollo del juego y se producen en un periodo determinado de tiempo. Toda comparación de la prestación futbolística con otras disciplinas (por ejemplo, el atletismo) es en realidad arbitraria y errónea. El jugador de futbol, desde el punto de vista atlético, ha de ser considerado solo un futbolista y nada más. Los 8.000 metros de carrera del futbolista se reparten así:

- Caminar 20%   (~1.600 metros).
- Carrera lenta 35%   (~2.800 metros).
- Carrera 25%   (~2.000 metros).
- Sprint 15%   (~1.200 metros).
- Carrera hacia atrás 5% (~ 400 metros).

Los centrocampistas habitualmente recorren distancias superiores con respecto a defensas y delanteros. La cantidad de carrera y el tipo de marcha varía mucho de posición a posición y en el mismo puesto en relación con las características físico-atléticas y sobre todo de carácter del futbolista.

Las distancias recorridas a la máxima velocidad varían desde los 3/4 metros a los 25/30 metros, siendo las más frecuentes de 10/15 metros y se repiten unas 50/60 veces.

Creo interesante indicar también los resultados de un estudio sobre las frecuencias cardiacas manifestadas por los futbolistas durante una competición. Los valores registrados demuestran que el futbolista no está sometido a tensiones muy elevadas.

A lo largo de un partido, se han manifestado las siguientes pulsaciones:

Pulsaciones por minuto	Delanteros	Centrocampistas y laterales	Centrales
126/131	11'45''	2'45''	29'00''
132/155	9'45''	5'15''	29'00''
156/173	12'00''	27'30''	16'00''
174/185	9'00''	8'45''	0'00''
186/204	2'30''	0'45''	0'00''

Esas cifras generan algunas consideraciones de carácter general:
1. Existen diferencias importantes entre las prestaciones medias de los distintos jugadores.
2. Con la excepción de los centrales, todos los demás jugadores están sometidos a una amplia gama de estímulos.
3. Entre los defensas y centrocampistas prevalece el periodo de intensidad media, mientras que para los delanteros tenemos el periodo más largo de intensidad mínima,

pero también el más largo de intensidad máxima.

Tratemos ahora de analizar cómo el movimiento y el entrenamiento pueden producir cambios en nuestro cuerpo. Para facilitar las cosas, describiré por separado los efectos del movimiento producidos sobre los músculos, sobre las articulaciones, sobre los huesos, sobre los órganos internos, sobre la mente y también sobre las relaciones con otros, pero hay que tener presente que a menudo esos efectos se manifiestan al mismo tiempo.

EFECTOS SOBRE LOS MÚSCULOS

Los músculos son los órganos activos del movimiento, están de hecho constituidos por fibras que se contraen ante la presencia de impulsos (órdenes nerviosas). El movimiento produce sobre el músculo las siguientes transformaciones:

1. Aumento del volumen: El músculo, si se le hace trabajar para elevar pesos o vencer una resistencia, se hace más grueso y al mismo tiempo aumenta su fuerza.

2. Aumento de la longitud: El músculo mantiene o aumenta su longitud por medio del trabajo continuo al que es sometido, el estiramiento muscular permite aprovechar plenamente la amplitud articular.

3. Aumento de los capilares: El músculo, dedicado a un trabajo de baja intensidad, pero de larga duración, aumenta su capilarización, es decir, el número de vasos que hacen llegar el oxígeno (transportado por la sangre) a las fibras musculares. Se

consigue una mejor capacidad de abastecer de oxígeno al músculo, condición que permite al músculo resistir más tiempo la fatiga.

4. Aumento de las sustancias energéticas: El movimiento permite el aumento de las sustancias energéticas (glucógeno) necesarias para la contracción muscular.

5. Mejora de la transmisión de los estímulos nerviosos: El entrenamiento hace más veloz y precisa la transmisión de los estímulos nerviosos del cerebro a los músculos, mejorando así la velocidad y la coordinación de movimientos.

EFECTOS SOBRE LAS ARTICULACIONES

Las articulaciones constituyen el sistema de «cruce» de nuestro cuerpo. Permiten el movimiento de las diversas secciones corpóreas. La articulación está constituida por la unión de dos huesos, cuyos extremos se llaman cabezas articulares. El movimiento produce sobre las articulaciones las siguientes transformaciones:

1. Mantenimiento de la movilidad fisiológica: La articulación, para mantener su movilidad normal, debe utilizarse al máximo de sus posibilidades de movimiento.

2. Aumento o recuperación de la movilidad: Para que sea posible recuperar la movilidad perdida y aumentar la que se posee es necesario utilizar formas especiales de entrenamiento y movimiento.

3. Robustecimiento de las cápsulas articulares: La cápsula articular, formada por ligamentos y músculos, tiene la misión de mantener firmemente ligadas las cabezas articulares e impedir que las articulaciones se salgan de su lugar y se produzcan torceduras y luxaciones.

EFECTOS SOBRE LOS HUESOS

Los huesos constituyen la armazón de nuestro cuerpo, desempeñan la función de protección (el cráneo protege el cerebro, la columna vertebral protege la médula) y contribuyen, como órganos pasivos, al movimiento y al desplazamiento del cuerpo y de sus extremidades. El movimiento produce sobre los huesos las siguientes transformaciones:

1. Una mejor nutrición: El aumento de circulación sanguínea provocado por el ejercicio físico nutre mejor el tejido óseo reforzándolo con calcio.

2. Desarrollo de longitud: El movimiento favorece la producción de nuevas células óseas, lo que determina el crecimiento en longitud del propio hueso.

3. Desarrollo en anchura y grosor: Las flexiones de los huesos, ejercitadas por los músculos durante el movimiento, favorecen el desarrollo de estos en grosor y anchura. Se consigue un aumento de la resistencia.

EFECTOS SOBRE LA RESPIRACIÓN

La tarea del aparato respiratorio es el suministro de oxígeno al organismo y la eliminación de anhídrido carbónico. El movimiento produce sobre la respiración los siguientes beneficios:

1. Reducción del tiempo de recuperación: El que entrena emplea menos tiempo en volver a la respiración normal después del esfuerzo.
2. Menor aumento de la frecuencia respiratoria: El que entrena, a igualdad de trabajo, tiene una frecuencia respiratoria básica más baja con respecto al sedentario (12-16 veces por minuto).
3. Aumento de la capacidad vital: La capacidad vital es la cantidad de aire, medida en litros con el espirómetro, que se consigue emitir con una expiración forzada después de haber realizado una inspiración máxima.
4. Aumento del tiempo de apnea: La apnea, o suspensión voluntaria de la respiración, aumenta su duración en quien entrena.
5. Potenciación de la mecánica respiratoria: Con el ejercicio, los músculos respiratorios, especialmente el diafragma, aumentan su potencia y la eficacia de sus contracciones.

EFECTOS SOBRE EL CORAZÓN Y LA CIRCULACIÓN

El aparato circulatorio está constituido por el corazón (bomba), la circulación sistémica (arterias y venas que llevan la sangre a los diversos tejidos y órganos del cuerpo y la devuelven al corazón) y la circulación pulmonar (que lleva la sangre a los

pulmones para oxigenarlos y la devuelve al corazón). La actividad física produce efectos evidentes sobre el sistema cardiocirculatorio y entre los más importantes están:

1. Cambia la forma del corazón: El corazón de un deportista se convierte en casi esférico.
2. El corazón se hace más grueso: Aumentan de volumen las cavidades internas (aurículas y ventrículos) y las paredes musculares aumentan de grosor.
3. Aumenta el gasto sistólico: La cantidad de sangre impulsada por cada contracción (sístole) del corazón es mayor, porque han aumentado los volúmenes internos y la fuerza muscular.
4. Aumenta la aportación cardiaca: La cantidad de sangre que circula por minuto.
5. Aumenta la frecuencia cardiaca: Durante el trabajo aumenta el número de pulsaciones por minuto. Recordemos que en igualdad de trabajo el que entrene tendrá un número menor de pulsaciones gracias a la capacidad de su corazón de bombear una mayor cantidad de sangre,
6. Reducción de las pulsaciones en reposo: Este es uno de los efectos más fácilmente controlables, pero solo se consigue gracias a un entrenamiento constante y prolongado.
7. Reducción del tiempo de recuperación después del esfuerzo: El que entrena vuelve más rápidamente al ritmo cardiaco de reposo con respecto al sedentario.

8. Aumento de la capilaridad del corazón: El corazón está mejor irrigado y nutrido.

9. Aumento de la capilaridad en los músculos: La apertura de nuevos capilares sanguíneos es importante para mejorar la nutrición de los músculos y eliminar más velozmente los residuos producto de las contracciones musculares.

10. Desvío de la sangre: Cuando se lleva a cabo un trabajo físico intenso la sangre se canaliza hacia los músculos utilizados y se resta de otras partes. Son principalmente el intestino, el estómago, el hígado y el bazo los que ceden sangre para el trabajo muscular. Por esto quien entrena poco sufre dolores en ambos costados.

11. Facilitación de la vuelta de la sangre al corazón: Durante el movimiento, los músculos, con sus contracciones, «masajean» y «exprimen» las venas, que, gracias a las válvulas semilunares, dirigen la sangre hacia el corazón.

EFECTOS SOBRE LA FUNCIÓN DIGESTIVA

El ejercicio físico acelera todas las actividades de la digestión, tanto las mecánicas como las químicas y secretoras. El ejercicio refuerza y hace más veloces los movimientos del estómago y el intestino.

EFECTOS SOBRE EL SISTEMA NERVIOSO

El Sistema Nervioso Central (S.N.C.) está constituido por:
- Cerebro.
- Cerebelo (equilibrio).
- Bulbo raquídeo.
- Médula espinal.

El Sistema Nervioso Periférico (S.N.P.) está constituido por:
- 12 pares de nervios craneales.
- 31 pares de nervios espinales.
- El sistema simpático (regula los latidos cardiacos, las acciones respiratorias, la presión sanguínea).
- El sistema parasimpático (regula el aparato digestivo y equilibra las reacciones provocadas por el sistema simpático).

El movimiento es la acción más visible producto del sistema nervioso: es la respuesta motora a una excitación nerviosa.

Para que se realice el movimiento, hacen falta tres fases:
1) Información.
2) Elaboración.
3) Conciencia.

Recibida la información (dar una patada al balón) se pone en marcha un dispositivo ideomotor que utiliza la memoria de movimientos similares ya realizados previamente. Una vez preparado el dispositivo, el cerebro produce los estímulos nerviosos adecuados

para contraer los músculos apropiados con la fuerza apropiada y en la sucesión apropiada. En el movimiento voluntario, sobre todo si no se ha realizado antes, los tiempos relativos a las tres fases serán largos. Cuando el movimiento ya se ha repetido muchas veces se convierte en automático, porque el dispositivo motor ya lo conoce y está preparado. La ejecución del gesto se hace más veloz y precisa: el control del movimiento se ha automatizado. Por tanto, el ejercicio motor entrena y educa a los órganos sensoriales, mejora y hace más aguda la sensibilidad visual, auditiva, táctil, propioceptiva (capacidad de analizar la posición de nuestro cuerpo con los ojos cerrados) y de equilibrio.

EFECTOS PSICOLÓGICOS Y SOCIALES

La actividad motora desarrolla:
a) La capacidad cognoscitiva.
b) La capacidad imaginativa.
c) La capacidad práctica.

La actividad motora mejora:
a) La atención.
b) La memoria.

Cuando alguien se apresta a realizar un ejercicio deportivo, se comporta como cuando se apresta a entender un concepto, a captar una verdad, a resolver un problema matemático. Primero se enfoca en los datos, es decir, valora aquello de lo que dispone y los objetivos a alcanzar; luego analiza

las dificultades a superar; después reflexiona y pasa a la acción; finalmente controla los resultados y verifica la exactitud. Resulta fácil entender también cómo los deportes colectivos reclaman nuestro estado emotivo y nuestra pasión (alegría, entusiasmo, orgullo, etc.). La actividad deportiva ayuda a quien tiene problemas de timidez y de inseguridad porque habitúa al valor y a la confianza en uno mismo.

LAS FUENTES DE PRODUCCIÓN DE ENERGÍA

Las fibras musculares

Es sabido que la calidad de la contracción de un músculo depende esencialmente del porcentaje de tipos de fibras que lo componen. La dotación y la distribución de las diversas fibras musculares están determinadas genéticamente *(Weineck 2001)*.

Se distinguen dos tipos de fibras musculares:

Las fibras rojas de tipo I, finas y lentas, denominadas ST (slow twitch = fibras de contracción lenta). Esas fibras intervienen en el trabajo muscular de baja intensidad (alta capacidad oxidativa, baja capacidad glucolítica). Su capilaridad es de 4,8 capilares de media por fibra.

Las fibras blancas de tipo II, claras, espesas y rápidas, denominadas FT (fast twitch = fibras de contracción rápida). Esas fibras entran en acción en los requerimientos musculares intensos y de fuerza rápida. Su capilaridad es de 2,9 capilares de media por fibra.

Hay tres subcategorías de fibras FT, en concreto:

1. Las fibras de tipo IIa (Capacidad oxidativa-glucolítica).
2. Las fibras de tipo IIb (Elevada capacidad glucolítica).
3. Las fibras de tipo IIc (Alta capacidad oxidativa y buena capacidad glucolítica, llamadas también fibras intermedias).

Según algunas investigaciones, los deportistas campeones disfrutan de privilegios genéticos. La investigación ha descubierto un gen del ADN llamado «alfa-actinina-3», que dirige en el músculo la producción de la actinina, un constitutivo clave de las fibras de contracción veloz. El gen alfa-actinina-3 existe de dos maneras alternativas principales, llamadas «alelos», obtenidas de cada uno de los padres, que pueden ser iguales o diferentes. Se pueden presentar con los siguientes pares:

♣ Alelos RR, que determinan la presencia en el músculo de la proteína del sprint.

♣ Alelos XX, no ordenan, por el contrario, la producción de actinina.

♣ Alelos RX, con producción parcial de actinina, la mayoría de la población.

Por investigaciones se ha verificado que los deportistas de élite en los deportes de velocidad están dotados de una cuota muy alta de la variante de RR, los atletas de élite en las especialidades de resistencia están dotados con respecto a los velocistas y la población normal de una cuota muy alta de la variante XX. Según investigadores

australianos, sería en realidad la mayor o menor presencia de los alelos RR lo que haría rápida o resistente nuestra musculatura. Todo gesto realizado en la actividad humana, caminar, correr, saltar, chutar, etc., se produce debido a contracciones musculares. Los músculos pueden considerarse como verdaderos motores, es decir, máquinas capaces de transformar en energía mecánica otras formas de energía. Los motores de cualquier género necesitan carburante para poder funcionar. También los músculos utilizan un carburante: **EL ÁCIDO ADENOSÍN TRIFOSFATO**, al que se alude más normalmente con las siglas **ATP**. Sin el ATP, los músculos no están en disposición de contraerse ni por tanto de crear movimiento.

El ATP es una molécula grande que contiene tres grupos fosfato, dos de los cuales están unidos por enlaces altamente energéticos cuya ruptura libera una cantidad notable de energía.

La reacción química de escisión del ATP en ADP + P (ácido adenosín difosfato + grupo fosfato) produce la energía para la contracción muscular, reacción que puede esquematizarse como sigue:

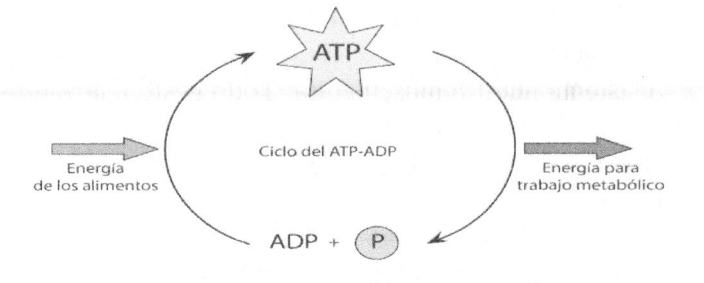

La cantidad de ATP depositada en el músculo y disponible para ser empleada de inmediato está bastante limitada: es necesario por tanto que el ATP se reconstituya constantemente.

El ATP presente en los músculos consiente a duras penas la sucesión de algunas contracciones con una duración de 2 o 3 segundos, por lo que se utiliza para «empezar» cualquier tipo de trabajo de máxima intensidad. Para poder continuar trabajando, el músculo necesita más ATP que debe producirse o reproducirse entretanto.

Esa producción se realiza por medio de tres sistemas (fuentes o mecanismos) distintos:

ANAERÓBICO ALÁCTICO	De la fosfocreatina PC.
ANAERÓBICO LÁCTICO	Glucólisis – transformación de los azúcares.
AERÓBICO	Oxidación de los azúcares y las grasas.

Analizamos los tres sistemas de producción de energía.

1) Sistema ATP-CP (anaeróbico aláctico)
En el músculo están presentes y almacenadas moléculas de «fosfocreatina (PC)». La fosfocreatina se divide en creatina (C) y fósforo (P). Este último va a reconstruir el ATP junto al ADP.

Este proceso de reconstrucción de ATP es muy rápido, casi simultáneo, pero la cantidad de PC presente en el músculo es relativamente baja y se agota en un plazo muy breve (8-10 segundos). Este sistema permite al músculo realizar contracciones muy rápidas, incluso de intensidad límite, pero por periodos de tiempo bastante limitados. Se utiliza en el ámbito deportivo en las carreras de velocidad sobre distancias cortas (aproximadamente hasta los 100 metros) y en pruebas como saltos, lanzamientos, etc., que requieren el uso de energía límite. La utilización de este sistema puede funcionar bien más allá de los 8-10 segundos siempre que el esfuerzo muscular sea tal que no requiera la máxima potencia del proceso, sino un porcentaje por encima de la base. El mecanismo ANAERÓBICO ALÁCTICO desempeña un papel muy importante tanto en los esfuerzos breves de máxima velocidad, como en aquellos más largos (duración máxima 40-45 segundos) de intensidad menor a la máxima.

2) Sistema del ácido láctico (anaeróbico láctico)

Cuando el deportista ha agotado toda la reserva de PC presente en el músculo y por tanto no puede reconstruir el ATP con las reservas químicas propias, su actividad no cesa, sino que logra continuarla porque entra en su lugar el sistema de ácido láctico o glucólisis.

El glucógeno muscular (azúcares que hayamos acumulado con la alimentación) se transforma y produce directamente ATP y ácido láctico. Este último ha de eliminarse porque limita el trabajo del músculo. Si el requerimiento de ATP es muy elevado y prolongado en el tiempo, el ácido láctico no puede eliminarse del todo y se acumula y cuando alcanza cierta concentración causa la fatiga muscular y en breve tiempo lleva al deportista al agotamiento. La capacidad de trabajo del individuo decrece gradualmente en relación con el aumento de la concentración del ácido láctico en la sangre. El proceso anaeróbico láctico es de importancia fundamental para cumplir con las prestaciones físicas en las siguientes especialidades deportivas:

- *Individuales continuas* sublímite de duración comprendida entre los 40-45 segundos y cerca de los 4 minutos.

- *De equipo* en relación con deportistas con un trabajo intenso y continuo (esto raramente ocurre en el fútbol).

En el uso corriente se vienen utilizando erróneamente los términos **ácido láctico y lactato** como sinónimos: el ácido láctico y el lactato son compuestos químicos distintos.

• El ácido láctico es un ácido con la fórmula química $C_3H_6O_3$.

• El lactato es cualquier sal del ácido láctico. Cuando el ácido láctico libera un H+ (ion positivo de hidrógeno), el compuesto resultante se une a Na+ o K+ (iones positivos de sodio y potasio) para formar una sal. La glucólisis anaeróbica produce ácido láctico, que sin embargo se disocia rápidamente formando una sal,

El lactato.

3) Sistema del oxígeno (aeróbico)

Si la cantidad de ATP requerida por el músculo para desempeñar su actividad no es muy elevada, el oxígeno (O_2) que entra en nuestro organismo por medio de la respiración tiene la posibilidad de oxidar (combinar) las sustancias presentes (azúcares, proteínas y grasas) y reconstruir ATP produciendo anhídrido carbónico (CO_2) y agua (H_2O), que se expulsan mediante la respiración y el sudor.

En esas situaciones, el trabajo muscular puede prolongarse más tiempo, teóricamente sin límite. Utilizando este sistema, la cantidad de oxígeno transportada a los músculos no es nunca inferior a la necesaria para reconstruir el ATP y por tanto el organismo puede trabajar en «steady-state», es decir, en estado de equilibrio.

Incluyo a continuación una tabla indicativa de cómo transformar la velocidad en energía:

Relación entre velocidad y transformación de energía				
Combustible	**Proceso**	**Duración potencia**	**Duración capacidad**	**Rapidez**
ATP preexistente		Hasta 3''	Hasta 3''	Máxima
PC	Anaeróbico aláctico	De 0'' a 7''	De 7'' a 15''	Máxima
Glucólisis	Anaeróbico láctico	De 15'' a 45''	De 45'' a 2'	Elevada
Oxidación de los azúcares	Aeróbico	De 2' a 10'	De 10' a 30'	Moderada
Oxidación de las grasas	Aeróbico	Desde cerca de 20' a horas		Baja

Reconstrucción de las fuentes de producción de energía

Después de haber examinado por qué vías nuestro organismo procede a la producción del ATP necesario para la contracción muscular, es oportuno entender cuáles son las maneras y tiempos que permiten que se reconstruyan estas fuentes energéticas después de agotarse o sencillamente usarse. La reposición de las reservas energéticas consumidas durante la actividad muscular se realiza completamente en el proceso respiratorio.

Al término de una actividad física, durante el reposo o fase de recuperación, la necesidad de ATP baja notablemente, pero por el contrario no cesa la necesidad de oxígeno que se mantiene elevada por un periodo más o menos largo, de acuerdo con la intensidad y duración del trabajo precedente.

La cantidad de oxígeno necesaria para restablecer el equilibrio de nuestro organismo recibe el nombre de **«deuda de oxígeno»**.

El pago completo de la deuda de oxígeno no significa que el organismo se encuentre de nuevo en estado de total eficiencia: el tiempo necesario para la completa recuperación energética puede variar desde algunos minutos (saltos y lanzamientos) a algunas horas (carreras de velocidad prolongada) hasta uno o más días (partidos de fútbol, rugby, baloncesto, etc.).

Para algunos deportes especialmente duros (como el boxeo) hacen falta algunas semanas.

En lo que se refiere a los partidos de fútbol, la experiencia actual aconseja dejar pasar al menos **48 horas** entre ellos, recordando sin embargo que, en general durante las 24-36 horas ya se han completado los procesos de recuperación.

Esquema resumen:

FINALIDAD DE LA TAREA	DURACIÓN EJERCICIO	INTENSIDAD EJERCICIO	TIEMPO DE RECUPERACIÓN	NÚMERO REPETICIONES
FUERZA RÁPIDA Anaeróbico	Hasta 6''	Límite	2'' tras las pruebas 5'' tras las series	7 pruebas 6 series
RESIETENCIA A LA VELOCIDAD Anaeróbico láctico	Entre 20'' y 45',' una sola prueba	Sublímite	---	---
	Entre 20'' y 45',' más pruebas	Sublímite	2'' tras las pruebas 5'' tras las series	3 pruebas 4 series
TODAS LAS CAPACIDADES CONDICIONALES Anaeróbico aeróbico	12''	Grande	30'' tras las pruebas 3' tras las series	4 pruebas 6 series
	30''/90''	Grande	30'' tras las pruebas 90'' tras las series	10 pruebas 6 series
	3'/10'	Grande	Hasta la recuperación completa	De 2 a 6
	30''	Media-grande	---	---
RESISTENCIA GENERAL aeróbico	De 1' a 3'	Media	90''	Desde 10
	De 3' a 10'	Media	Sin límite, según el estado de forma	De 6 a 8
	30'	De baja a grande	---	---

La tabla anterior es indicativa. Los tiempos se establecerán normalmente después de las pruebas físicas, que indicarán el estado de forma de los deportistas.

Conviene recordar que la recuperación se completa en el sistema:

- **ANAERÓBICO ALÁCTICO** en aproximadamente 3'-5', Con la siguiente progresión (1/2 en los primeros 30", 1/4 en los segundos 30", 1/8 en los terceros 30" y así sucesivamente).

- **ANAERÓBICO LÁCTICO** Si la prestación es intensa en unos 45'. Con la siguiente progresión (1/2 en los primeros 15', 1/4 en los segundos 15', 1/8 en los terceros 15' y así sucesivamente).

El lactato producido se elimina en ¾ partes por el O_2 formado por el trabajo de las fibras lentas, el resto por el O_2 respiratorio y también por ¾ partes de los músculos no dedicados al trabajo y ¼ por el hígado. Solo una cantidad mínima se elimina por la orina y el sudor.

- **RECUPERACIONES COMPLETAS**

RESISTENCIA	48/72 HORAS
FUERZA	24 HORAS
VELOCIDAD	12 HORAS

- **DESPUÉS DE UN PARTIDO**, para recuperar los depósitos de glucógeno hacen falta 72 horas.

- **LOS DEPORTISTAS CON FUERTE CAPACIDAD AERÓBICA** pueden desarrollar una gran cantidad de trabajo, pero mantienen una capacidad de recuperación aláctica de la misma duración que los deportistas poco entrenados.

Utilización de energía por parte de nuestro organismo

– Nuestro cuerpo llega a utilizar el 35% de nuestra energía disponible.

- Un 10% adicional de esta energía está disponible, pero no se utiliza casi nunca, sobre todo con el paso de los años.

- El 55% restante es el que nuestro organismo emplea solo en caso de peligro extremo de vida, en otro caso no llega a utilizarla.

LAS CAPACIDADES MOTORAS

Las capacidades motoras son aquellos factores que influyen sobre la prestación y pueden mejorarse, educarse, transformarse y mantenerse mediante las distintas formas de movimientos. Esas capacidades son múltiples y es oportuno recordar que no intervienen separadas unas de otras, sino que forman parte de un proceso unitario que presenta relaciones importantes. Estas relaciones deben considerarse atentamente y valorarse en la programación y la determinación de la carga de trabajo.

CAPACIDADES MOTORAS	
CAPACIDADES COORDINATIVAS	**De base**: Aprendizaje, organización y control motor. **Especiales**: Propias de cada disciplina.
CAPACIDADES CONDICIONALES	**Fuerza**. **Resistencia**. **Velocidad**. **Flexibilidad** (movilidad articular y estiramiento muscular).

LAS CAPACIDADES COORDINATIVAS

La coordinación es una manifestación externa de funciones del sistema nervioso central y viene influida:

- Genéticamente.
- Por las modificaciones ambientales.
- Y llega a su máximo desarrollo entre los 7 y los 13 años. Las capacidades coordinativas son las mismas que las capacidades utilizadas para aprender, controlar y organizar (adaptar y transformar) un movimiento. Constituyen la base para el aprendizaje y la mejora de las capacidades técnicas y están en estrecha relación con las capacidades condicionales.

El desarrollo de las capacidades coordinativas depende estrechamente del sistema nervioso, en particular:

- Del aparato perceptivo (vista, oído, tacto).
- Del aparato sensomotor (equilibrio, percepción del espacio y del tiempo).
- De la capacidad expresiva (lenguaje del cuerpo).

Un proceso correcto de aprendizaje de las capacidades coordinativas permitirá la ejecución de gestos motores funcionales, rápidos, precisos, coordinados, válidos y expresivos. Para poder perfeccionar las capacidades coordinativas hay que conocer las fases cronológicas y biológicas del crecimiento humano.

En general, el desarrollo de las capacidades coordinativas se realiza entre los 7-13 años.

Por esa razón, la mejor edad para el aprendizaje de los gestos motores deportivos es:
- Para los chicos, entre los 8 y los 13 años.
- Para las chicas, entre los 7 y los 12 años.

Volviendo al esquema inicial de las capacidades motoras, podríamos decir que las coordinativas de base (o generales) se reflejan con contundencia en las coordinativas especiales. En los niños y jóvenes, son dotes que pueden ser educadas y contribuyen a la solución rápida y adecuada de las tareas de movimiento en todos los aspectos de la vida. Las capacidades coordinativas generales, que constituyen la destreza deportiva, poseen un grado elevado de universalidad y se pueden referir a todo el sector de la motricidad deportiva.

Pueden por tanto clasificarse en:

Aprendizaje motor

Capacidad de aprender, asimilar y adquirir movimientos, desde los más sencillos a los más complejos. Permite modificar el comportamiento motor propio a través del aprendizaje de nuevos gestos con el uso de medios de trabajo (ejercicios, juegos, situaciones). Para poder automatizar los gestos, el sujeto deberá corregir y adaptar su proyecto para hacerlo estable en el tiempo sobre la base de informaciones provenientes de estímulos propioceptivos y exteroceptivos, de la memoria y de la propia experiencia motora personal.

Control motor
Capacidad de controlar los movimientos para lograr exactamente el propósito previsto por el gesto a realizar. La capacidad de control motor permite al niño controlar el movimiento a fin de llevar a cabo su proyecto motor previamente establecido.

Adaptación y transformación
Capacidad de cambiar, transformar y adaptar los movimientos aprendidos ante cambios improvisados de las condiciones externas, para permitir alcanzar siempre y de todas formas el resultado motor previsto. Esta capacidad permite al niño adaptar, transformar y corregir su proyecto motor en situaciones que pueden cambiar durante el desarrollo de la acción motora para sustituirlo por uno más eficaz. En el fútbol la variedad de las situaciones hace que esta capacidad coordinativa esté presente casi continuamente durante las fases del juego. Ese mecanismo requiere por otro lado una

buena capacidad de anticipación motora, que se estructura en sinergias con esta capacidad coordinativa general. Las tres capacidades coordinativas estás ligadas estrechamente entre sí mediante un circuito circular.

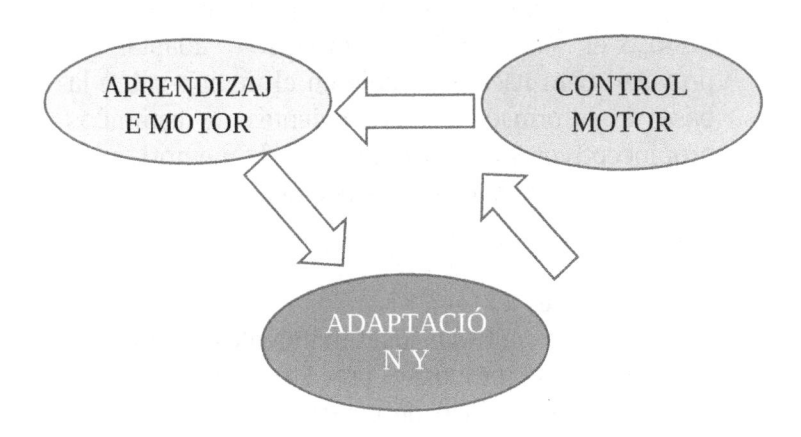

Capacidades coordinativas especiales que prevalecen en el fútbol

- Habilidad en detalles.
- Capacidad de equilibrio.
- Elasticidad de movimientos.
- Capacidad de combinación motora.
- Imaginación motora.
- Orientación espacio-temporal.
- Diferenciación dinámica.
- Anticipación motora.
- Reacción motora.
- Memorización motora.
- Ritmo.

Principios metodológicos para el entrenamiento de las capacidades coordinativas

1. Las capacidades coordinativas, a diferencia de las demás formas principales de requisitos motores, no pueden mejorarse y entrenarse de un modo unilateral, sino que van mejorando de una manera compleja.

2. Solo mediante el principio de la variación y la combinación continua de los métodos y los contenidos del entrenamiento se puede lograr un desarrollo elevado de la destreza.

3. Gracias a la adquisición y uso de las habilidades motoras se perfeccionan en paralelo las funciones psicofísicas (analizativas) y coordinativas necesarias para el aprendizaje de nuevas habilidades motoras.

4. Las capacidades coordinativas se adiestran desde pequeños, dado que los procesos de recepción y elaboración de la información empeoran con la edad y disminuyen la eficacia del entrenamiento.

5. El entrenamiento de la destreza no se realiza en condiciones de fatiga, porque en tales condiciones los procesos de control no pueden entrenarse de manera óptima.

Métodos para la variación y combinación de ejercicios para el aumento de la coordinación

1. Variaciones de la posición de partida (partida boca arriba, mirando al suelo, etc.).
2. Variaciones de la ejecución del movimiento (ejecución al contrario de un movimiento).
3. Variaciones de la dinámica del movimiento (ejecución más lenta o más rápida).
4. Variaciones de la estructura espacial del movimiento (reducir el campo de juego).
5. Variaciones de las condiciones externas (partidos sobre terrenos no habituales).
6. Variaciones de la recepción de la información (un jugador recibe el balón dando la espalda al compañero y solo se gira después de una señal acústica).
7. Combinación de habilidades motoras, cada habilidad motora debe ser controlada hasta su forma exacta para combinarlas.
8. Ejercicios bajo presión temporal (recibir y pasar el balón con oposición del adversario).

NIVELES DE COORDINACIÓN EN EL DEPORTE		
NIVELES	**TIPO DE COORDINACIÓN**	**DEPORTE**
Todas las capacidades coordinativas	Precisión de los movimientos	Kárate, patinaje, tiro con arco
Movimientos precisos y veloces	Precisión y velocidad de movimiento	Patinaje artístico, gimnasia deportiva, saltos, ciclismo en pista, levantamiento de peso
Movimientos, precisos, veloces y variables	Precisión y velocidad de movimientos en condiciones cambiantes	Hockey, balonmano, baloncesto, **FÚTBOL**, voleibol, judo y lucha libre, combate de kárate, esgrima, tenis, piragüismo, esquí alpino, ciclismo, salto de esquí

LAS CAPACIDADES CONDICIONALES

Las capacidades condicionales son
* La resistencia.
* La fuerza.
* La velocidad.
* La flexibilidad.

Que tienen su fundamento en la condición orgánica y neuromuscular del jugador.

Esas capacidades tienen como factor limitador la cantidad de energía que el sujeto tiene a su disposición. Con el progreso del entrenamiento, el organismo mejora tanto las reservas energéticas como la capacidad de producirlas y usarlas, hasta el punto de que las capacidades condicionales puedan activarse más tiempo y con una mayor intensidad.

Para las capacidades condicionales, conviene recordar que:

- En relación con la **FUERZA** podemos distinguir:
1. FUERZA RÁPIDA.
2. FUERZA MÁXIMA.
3. FUERZA RESISTENTE.

- En relación con la **VELOCIDAD** podemos distinguir:

1. FUERZA RÁPIDA.
2. RAPIDEZ MÁXIMA.
3. RESISTENCIA A LA VELOCIDAD.

- En relación con la **RESISTENCIA** podemos distinguir:
1. RESISTENCIA DE PERIODO BREVE (45" – 2').
2. RESISTENCIA DE PERIODO MEDIO (2' – 8').
3. RESISTENCIA DE PERIODO LARGO (> 8').
4. RESISTENCIA A LA FUERZA.
5. RESISTENCIA A LA VELOCIDAD (< 45").

Las capacidades que pueden entrenarse en los jóvenes (6-14 años) son:

- **VELOCIDAD.**
- **FUERZA RÁPIDA.**
- **RESISTENCIA DE PERIODO LARGO.**

Dos consideraciones importantes constituyen el concepto general de una programación seria y competente del entrenamiento:

1) El desarrollo de las capacidades motoras del futbolista está ligado estrechamente al factor técnico-táctico. **Es completamente inútil aumentar, por ejemplo, la velocidad de base si el sujeto no tiene también la misma medida de habilidad técnica para transformarla en velocidad en el juego.**

2) El tiempo requerido por la preparación física es bastante elevado. Si nos limitáramos a este tipo de trabajo quitaríamos demasiado tiempo a la preparación técnica y táctica del equipo. **Resulta de importancia fundamental, especialmente para los equipos que dedican poco tiempo al entrenamiento, aunar ambas preparaciones, al menos todas las veces que sea posible**.

LA RESISTENCIA

La resistencia es la capacidad de mantener inalterado en el tiempo el nivel de una prestación duradera.

Una clasificación muy importante para la organización de los programas de entrenamiento distingue la resistencia en:

Resistencia general u orgánica, capacidad que pone en marcha sobre todo los grandes sistemas del organismo (cardiocirculatorio y respiratorio), de intensidad no elevada y prolongada por un tiempo medio o largo.

Resistencia específica o local, capacidad de mantener las cargas de trabajo propias de un deporte en particular, con intensidad que puede ser incluso elevada. La duración del esfuerzo puede ser reducida, pero puede requerir un número notable de repeticiones.

La resistencia futbolística

Considerando la duración del esfuerzo competitivo (90'), es indudable que se requiere un proceso aeróbico. Si pensamos además en las acciones normales de juego, observamos que se requieren siempre movimientos breves, paradas improvisadas, cambios repentinos de dirección, desmarques, toques de balón, en la práctica esfuerzos muy elevados de duración breve. Todas estas acciones están sin duda a cargo de los procesos anaeróbicos alácticos. La intervención del proceso anaeróbico

láctico se requiere más en el juego moderno, en algunas fases del partido. Los porcentajes de intervención de los procesos energéticos que se requieren en la prestación de futbolista están ligados a muchos factores, siendo la más importante la elección del entrenador en relación con el juego a adoptar.

Otros factores pueden variar de partido a partido:
- Capacidad de los adversarios.
- Evolución de la competición.
- Condiciones psicológicas de los jugadores.
- Condiciones ambientales.

Por esto es muy difícil establecer de modo exacto los porcentajes de intervención de los diversos procesos energéticos. El objetivo que debe proponerse el entrenador es el de hacer a todos los futbolistas capaces de soportar provechosamente durante 90' el esfuerzo requerido por el juego del equipo. Todo buen entrenamiento de resistencia debe prolongarse en el tiempo y superar un umbral mínimo, llevando al organismo al umbral de la fatiga. **El trabajo debe ser lo más individualizado posible**, pero en el entrenamiento futbolístico no es fácilmente realizable: El modo más práctico de afrontar este problema es el de subdividir a los jugadores en algunos grupos (3 o 4) en relación con su capacidad. En los ejercicios colectivos, el ritmo del grupo será aquel que pueda seguirse con buen trabajo de los jugadores menos dotados de resistencia.

La intensidad del trabajo de resistencia debe ser valorada atentamente por el entrenador y este ha de tener en cuenta las siguientes variables:
- Velocidad de ejecución.
- Duración del ejercicio.
- Número de ejecuciones.
- Duración del periodo de recuperación.
- Tipo de actividad desarrollada en la recuperación.

ES FÁCIL ENTENDER LO IMPORTANTE QUE ES PODER PROGRAMAR LAS SESIONES DE ENTRENAMIENTO EN FUNCIÓN DEL NÚMERO DE JUGADORES A DISPOSICIÓN.

EJERCICIOS DE RESISTENCIA		
TRABAJO CONTINUO (Resistencia general y orgánica)	**A RITMO UNIFORME**	Sin formación de ácido láctico.
		Con acumulación progresiva de ácido láctico.
	CON VARIACIONES DE RITMO	Variaciones libres (fartlek).
		Variaciones obligadas a ritmo variado o creciente.
TRABAJO INTERRUMPIDO CON PAUSAS (Resistencia específica)	**CON RECUPERACIÓN COMPLETA**	Pruebas repetidas.
	CON RECUPERACIÓN	Pruebas escalonadas a ritmo lento.
		Pruebas escalonadas a

		ritmo medio.
	PARCIAL	Pruebas escalonadas a ritmo elevado.
TRABAJO BASADO EN EL JUEGO	**CIRCUITO**	
	RECORRIDO	
	COMBINACIÓN DE JUEGOS	

El parámetro más común para medir la resistencia sigue siendo el control de pulsaciones. Como indicación, podemos definir que el trabajo será de:

Capacidad aeróbica
- Para pulsaciones entre 120/140.
- Con formaciones de lactato inferiores a 2 mmol/L.

Potencia aeróbica
- Para pulsaciones entre 150/170.
- Con formaciones de lactato entre 2-4 mmol/L.

Resistencia anaeróbica
- Para pulsaciones superiores a 180.
- Con formaciones de lactato superiores a 4 mmol/L.

Capacidad
Se entiende como tal la cantidad global de energía que puede liberarse, independientemente del tiempo.

Potencia
Indica la cantidad global de energía liberada por unidad de tiempo o la velocidad con la que las fuentes de energía pueden convertirse en trabajo.

Capacidad aeróbica

Expresa el concepto de un trabajo largo de intensidad baja o media-baja.

Potencia aeróbica

Se refiere a una actividad de intensidad media o alta, en la escala de los valores del trabajo aeróbico.

Resistencia aeróbica

Típica de los deportes largos, donde la resíntesis del ATP se produce gracias a la energía liberada por la combustión de azúcares y grasas.

Resistencia anaeróbica

Específica de las competiciones de velocidad prolongada y medio fondo, donde la energía deriva en buena parte de escisión anaeróbica de los azúcares.

Al empezar a correr o en cualquier actividad deportiva de movimiento podéis apreciar después de pocos minutos una sensación desagradable de falta de aire, casi de ahogo. Esa sensación se debe al hecho de que aumenta la necesidad de carburante (ATP) por parte de todos los músculos, pidiendo un mayor aporte de oxígeno. La solicitud de oxígeno es inmediata, pero el aumento del ritmo respiratorio no se realiza en sincronía, sino un poco más lentamente. Por ese motivo sois presas de la sensación de que «os falta el aliento», problema que desaparece en cuanto el mecanismo aeróbico suministra la cantidad de oxígeno necesaria, con lo que habremos «recuperado el aliento», como se

suele decir. Al desarrollar el entrenamiento este estado se hará cada vez menos evidente, hasta desaparecer completamente.

Trabajo continuo (resistencia general)

Este tipo de trabajo se dirige principalmente a la mejora de la resistencia general, busca aumentar en el organismo la capacidad de trabajar de forma continua y crea una base más amplia para la inserción del trabajo específico. Mejora la capacidad de recuperación y busca un aumento del volumen cardiaco.

1) Trabajo continuo, a ritmo uniforme, sin formación de ácido láctico.
Es necesario que el trabajo se lleva a cabo a ritmo suave que permita mantenerse en el ámbito del «steady-state», por debajo del «umbral aeróbico». El umbral aeróbico varía para cada persona, por lo que el trabajo deberá mantenerse en unas pulsaciones de 120-140 por minuto para personas no entrenadas y aumentar hasta los 150-160 para personas bien entrenadas.

2) Trabajo continuo, a ritmo uniforme, con acumulación progresiva del ácido láctico.
Si el trabajo descrito antes se lleva a cabo a ritmos superiores, por encima del llamado «steady-state», se genera una producción de ácido láctico que se acumula progresivamente. La duración de este trabajo será mucho más limitada. El objetivo es conseguir un rendimiento elevado en presencia de una cierta cantidad de ácido láctico. Esta situación se produce a lo largo de un partido, pero raramente.

3) Trabajo continuo, con variaciones libres de ritmo

Esta forma de trabajo se llama «fartlek sueco»: prevé una actividad de carrera libre, sin interrupciones, en la que el futbolista inserta variaciones voluntarias del ritmo. Representa un magnífico estímulo para entrenar, dirigido a la mejora de la resistencia general, pero prevé estímulos para entrenar la resistencia específica. Es preferible al trabajo de carrera continua a ritmo uniforme.

4) Trabajo continuo, con variaciones de ritmo variado o creciente y obligatorias

Este trabajo es una variación del fartlek en el que las variaciones de ritmo están predispuestas por el entrenador. Puede desarrollarse también en el campo, utilizando también el balón y otros accesorios. Existe la posibilidad de hacer muy específico el trabajo: las variaciones de ritmo pueden ser muy breves (30-40 metros), veloces y numerosas o pueden ser más largas (80-120 metros), a buen paso y de número reducido.

Trabajo interrumpido con pausas (Resistencia específica)

Este tipo de trabajo prevé el logro del efecto del entrenamiento solo con una buena cantidad de repeticiones. La atención debe dirigirse sobre todo al ritmo de ejecución. Si este es muy elevado, será necesaria una recuperación completa; si el ritmo es inferior, podrían reducirse las pausas. La

concentración máxima de lactato en los músculos se alcanza con trabajos de duración cercana a los 30".

De acuerdo con los grupos musculares que participan en el trabajo, podemos distinguir la resistencia en:

Resistencia local: Cuando participa en el trabajo menos de un tercio de la musculatura.
Resistencia sectorial: Cuando participan en el trabajo entre un tercio y dos tercios de la musculatura.
Resistencia global: Cuando participan en el trabajo más dos tercios de la musculatura.

1) Trabajo interrumpido por pausas, con recuperación completa
La duración e intensidad varían según los objetivos a alcanzar, basando el número en la duración y la intensidad. La pausa debe permitir una recuperación completa: El jugador debe volver a un ritmo cardiaco bajo y advertir la sensación personal de haber recuperado la frescura. Este tipo de trabajo está indicado para el final de pruebas repetidas.
La acción puede realizarse de diversas formas:
- Esfuerzos breves con ejecuciones límite (30-40-50 metros) dirigidos a mejorar la capacidad del sistema nervioso (que analizaremos más en detalle cuando hablemos de la velocidad).
- Esfuerzos de duración media con intensidad elevada, permaneciendo por debajo de los 15-16 segundos (80-120 metros) cuando se quiere

intervenir con un trabajo predominantemente aláctico.

- Esfuerzos prolongados, por tiempos de 40"/90" (200-500 metros) con intensidad elevada proporcional a la distancia: se activa también el mecanismo láctico.

La primera forma de trabajo se produce con muy elevada frecuencia en el curso del partido.

La segunda forma de trabajo resulta menos frecuente.

La tercera forma de trabajo es ajena a la especificidad del juego del fútbol y entendemos que puede eliminarse de los entrenamientos.

2) Trabajo interrumpido con pausas, con recuperación parcial

Es una forma de entrenamiento en la que la reanudación del ejercicio debe realizarse cuando el organismo no ha completado aún la fase de recuperación. Este título agrupa las diversas formas de «interval-training». En la aplicación práctica del interval-training están previstas diversas clasificaciones en relación con la intensidad de los tramos de trabajo o el ritmo de ejecución o la duración de la pausa de recuperación. Se entiende que la reanudación del trabajo después de un esfuerzo puede producirse cuando la frecuencia cardiaca ha descendido a cerca de 120-130 pulsaciones por minuto. Durante el esfuerzo la frecuencia aumenta generalmente a 180 pulsaciones o más. Busca un robustecimiento de las paredes cardiacas.

Veamos por tanto cuáles son las formas más difundidas de entrenamiento con interval-training para comprobar la adaptabilidad a las exigencias del futbolista.

INTERVAL-TRAINING A RITMOS DE MEDIOS A ELEVADOS

Cuando la intensidad en los ejercicios sea elevada será necesaria una pausa de cierta duración entre una prueba y otra.
En este tipo de trabajo, se usan ejercicios de duración de 1' a 3': si la intensidad es elevada hará falta una pausa de recuperación de 5' a 10'.
El número de repeticiones será muy reducido.
Este tipo de interval-training se aleja mucho del trabajo realizado en un partido, no creo que deba usarse para entrenamiento de futbolistas.

INTERVAL-TRAINING A RITMOS SUAVES

Cuando la ejecución del ejercicio se realiza con una intensidad no elevada tras las repeticiones bastará con una pequeña pausa.
El tiempo de trabajo para cada repetición tiende a ser más largo (de 2' a 6') y el de recuperación de 3'-6'.
El número de repeticiones podrá ser mayor.
También este tipo de interval-training se aleja mucho del trabajo del futbolista y su utilización es muy limitada.

INTERVAL-TRAINING FRIBURGUÉS

Se conoce con este término por el nombre de la ciudad de Friburgo, sede de una escuela de fútbol

que estudió por primera vez el uso de un entrenamiento similar. Prevé ejercicios de trabajo de duración de 15' a 30', repetidos un número elevado de veces, a una velocidad que permite, en un tiempo de 90", una recuperación de la frecuencia cardiaca a 120/130 pulsaciones por minuto.

Resulta ser lo contrario de los métodos anteriores: Mientras que antes la velocidad de ejecución determinaba la duración de la recuperación, en este caso es la capacidad de recuperación en el tiempo indicado la que determina la intensidad de la ejecución. Este tipo de trabajo se adapta a las exigencias del futbolista al aproximarse bastante a la práctica del juego.

Trabajo basado en el juego

Quien juega al fútbol necesita una resistencia específica basada en la aplicación de situaciones de juego. **El análisis de jugadores de diverso nivel ha constatado que la capacidad lactácida de jugadores que no practicaban ningún tipo de entrenamiento de resistencia no era muy distinta de la de los demás. De esto se deduce que los estímulos del entrenamiento que se ejercitan sobre el propio juego y el entrenamiento bajo forma de juego son suficientemente determinantes.**

UN EJERCICIO BASADO EN EL JUEGO PUEDE EJERCITAR DE MODO COMPLETO LA RESISTENCIA ESPECÍFICA NECESARIA PARA

LA PRESTACIÓN DEPORTIVA DEL FUTBOLISTA.

Con la ayuda de este método se entrenan de modo completo las capacidades específicas de resistencia que requiere el juego del fútbol. El valor concreto de un entrenamiento de la resistencia basado en el juego está sobre todo en el enfrentamiento continuo con el adversario, que provoca una mejora singular de las funciones de todos los sistemas afectados, que no se obtendría nunca con el entrenamiento normal. El método de entrenamiento basado en el juego, es decir, el entrenamiento de la resistencia integrado en el juego representa el método de entrenamiento más completo, porque ejercita al mismo tiempo todas las capacidades que requiere el fútbol. En el ámbito aficionado bastan con los estímulos que se ejercitan en el juego para impulsar la resistencia.

Un trabajo que se base exclusivamente en la carrera se puede llevar a cabo solamente en un entrenamiento realizado por cuenta propia.

Observaciones sobre el trabajo de resistencia
En el trabajo de resistencia, la realización de carreras prolongadas en el ámbito del umbral anaeróbico (distancias superiores a los 300 m.) son raramente apropiadas porque: comportan un agotamiento veloz de los depósitos de glucógeno; son muy comprometidas a nivel psicológico; se acaba «quemando» a los futbolistas, porque los tiempos de recuperación raramente son suficientes para reconstruir los depósitos de glucógeno. Un

entrenamiento planteado en demasía sobre el aumento de la resistencia general llevaría a una adaptación demasiado marcada de los músculos a este tipo de esfuerzo, lo que perjudicaría el desarrollo de las capacidades de velocidad y fuerza instantánea. Haciendo eso, el futbolista adquiriría todos los requisitos para participar en las carreras de resistencia del atletismo, pero no los que harían de él un jugador excelente. La resistencia del futbolista no está determinada por el aumento de la VO2 max. (trabajo aeróbico), sino por la capacidad láctica (resistencia específica), trabajo con intervalos de velocidad del 110-130% de la velocidad del umbral aeróbico.

Los jóvenes y la resistencia
Para los jóvenes por debajo de los 15/16 años está especialmente aconsejado el trabajo para la resistencia general, aunque con alguna inserción de trabajos de resistencia específica (después de los 11 años).

La resistencia general (aeróbica) en los jóvenes:
- Influye positivamente en el bienestar físico y la salud.
- Previene las enfermedades cardiovasculares.
- Mejora la economía del trabajo cardiaco.
- Coincide con la edad de oro para el desarrollo del VO2 max.
- Ayuda a regular y controlar la emotividad.
- Influye positivamente en la eficacia de los actos respiratorios.

- Es un buen sistema para hacer disminuir la masa grasa.

Resistencia y juegos

Una buena resistencia general permite:
- Jugar más tiempo.
- Recuperarse mejor y antes.
- Estar menos cansado en los momentos decisivos.

Dificultades que se encuentran en el ejercicio de la resistencia de los jóvenes
- Incapacidad de encontrar el ritmo oportuno.
- Escaso control de la intensidad del esfuerzo.
- Mala distribución de las energías.
- Motivación débil en el trabajo.

Cómo proceder en el trabajo
- El mayor error: Utilización de la carrera como castigo.
- Evitar ejercicios demasiado largos, demasiado difíciles, demasiado fatigosos o aburridos.
- Informar siempre acerca del objetivo de la propuesta de trabajo.
- Intervenir activamente para animar, variar o mantener.

Metodología a usar
- No agobiar ni renunciar al trabajo.
- Programar solo algunos periodos de trabajo limitados en el tiempo (septiembre/noviembre y marzo/mayo) o en

todo caso anteriores a la actividad competitiva profesional.

- Proporcionar siempre un objetivo final (carrera escolar por el campo, competiciones atléticas, torneos deportivos).
- Ir paso a paso.
- Aspirar a la implicación de todo el grupo o clase en la clasificación de los equipos.

El entrenamiento intenso prolongado provoca una remodelación del músculo cardiaco. Se tiene una condición patológica de cardiomiopatía hipertrófica o dilatada cuando el espesor cardiaco supera los 13 mm. y la cavidad ventricular supera el diámetro de 66 mm. En deportes de resistencia, como por ejemplo el ciclismo de carretera, el esquí de fondo, el piragüismo y el remo, se ha hallado en los deportistas: aumento de la cavidad del ventrículo izquierdo < 55 mm.; aumento del espesor de las paredes cardiacas < 13 mm.

El mecanismo que provoca la remodelación del ventrículo izquierdo está representado principalmente por el aumento del caudal cardiaco (en reposo, 5 litros/minuto; durante el esfuerzo, 30 litros/minuto e incluso más) y de la presión arterial (que supera durante el esfuerzo los 200 mm. de mercurio).

En deportes de potencia, como la halterofilia y los lanzamientos, se ha descubierto en los atletas un

aumento en el espesor de las paredes ventriculares derecha e izquierda, no se modifica notablemente la cavidad ventricular izquierda y aumenta la presión durante el esfuerzo (la presión sistólica supera los 200 mm. y a veces incluso los 300 mm.).

En deportes de equipo como el **fútbol** o el baloncesto, se han descubierto modificaciones cardiacas modestas en los deportistas.

Recordemos que después de alcanzar la edad adulta en el organismo humano aparecen algunas modificaciones importantes:

- ✓ La fortaleza cardiaca se reduce con la edad hasta un 50% en la ancianidad.
- ✓ La capacidad aeróbica disminuye al menos un 30% entre los 25 y los 60 años a causa de la disminución de la fortaleza cardiaca y la capacidad periférica de uso del oxígeno.
- ✓ Las fibras de tipo 2 o FT de contracción rápida que contienen las enzimas para la glucólisis anaeróbica disminuyen en número hasta el 50%.
- ✓ Las fibras de tipo 1 o ST de contracción lenta que contienen las enzimas oxidativas o aeróbicas disminuyen de una manera menor, hasta el 30%.
- ✓ El volumen sistólico no sufre modificaciones después de la edad adulta.

CONSEJOS E INDICACIONES SOBRE EL TRABAJO DE RESISTENCIA EN EL FÚTBOL

	QUÉ HACER
Hasta 10/11 años	La resistencia, como las demás capacidades condicionales, se ejercita mediante el juego.
Hasta 15/16 años	Se inicia el trabajo sobre la resistencia general, empezando con el trabajo a ritmo uniforme para pasar gradualmente a las variaciones de ritmo. – Se puede realizar alguna sesión de resistencia específica. – Se continúa con el trabajo de resistencia basado en el juego.
Desde 16 años	En el caso de equipos que tengan menos de 3 entrenamientos semanales, no realizar más trabajo de resistencia general, sino solo trabajo de pruebas escalonadas sobre distancias cortas (80-120 m.) y resistencia basada en el juego. En el caso de equipos que tengan más de 3 entrenamientos semanales, se puede programar un momento de resistencia general, pero solo en la primera sesión semanal de trabajo. – Trabajo de pruebas escalonadas sobre distancias cortas (80-120 m.) y resistencia basada en el juego.

	CUÁNDO HACERLO
Hasta 10/11 años	Durante los juegos y ejercicios en todos los periodos del año.
Hasta 15/16 años	Distribuir el trabajo de resistencia general en dos bloques de tiempo, el primero en los tres primeros meses, el segundo después de unos cuatro meses y en los tres meses siguientes. Al término de cada sesión. - La resistencia específica basada en el juego se realiza en cada sesión de principio de semana, intercalando alguna vuelta al trabajo en pruebas escalonadas.
	En el caso de equipos que tienen menos de 3 entrenamientos semanales, preparar un solo bloque de trabajo de resistencia general en la primera fase de la pretemporada (y la pausa invernal) 2-3 semanas y al final de la sesión de entrenamiento.

	- La resistencia específica en pruebas escalonadas junto a aquella basada en el juego se realizan en cada sesión de inicio de semana.
Desde 16 años	En casos de equipos con más de 3 entrenamientos semanales, prever: □ En la 1ª y2ª fase de pretemporada, un bloque de trabajo de resistencia sobre la capacidad aeróbica. □ En la 3ª fase de pretemporada, un bloque de trabajo basado en la potencia aeróbica, igual que en la pausa invernal. - Durante el periodo de competición, prever un momento de resistencia general (potencia aeróbica) pero solo en la primera sesión semanal y al final de la sesión. - La resistencia específica a pruebas escalonadas junto a la basada en el juego se realizan en cada sesión de principio de semana.

CUÁNTO HACER	
Hasta 10/11 años	En proporción a la duración del entrenamiento, normalmente sin superar los 15'/20'.
Hasta 15/16 años	Para la resistencia general, pasar de 15' a 25'/30' con aumentos de 3'/5' por sesión adaptando a la edad la intensidad y las variaciones de ritmo. – Para la resistencia específica, con el aumento de la edad, efectuar cargas de trabajo cada vez más ajustadas con respecto al número e intensidad de las pruebas. – Para la resistencia basada en el juego (realizar siempre) con cantidades que completen la específica para no exagerar con las cargas.
Desde 16 años	En el caso de equipos que tengan menos de 3 entrenamiento semanales. – Para la resistencia general en la primera fase de la pretemporada (y la pausa invernal), pasar de 15' a 25'/30' de trabajo sobre la capacidad aeróbica con una cadencia de 2 sesiones sí, una sesión no. – Para la resistencia específica a pruebas escalonadas, un número adecuado de repeticiones con intensidad personal. – Para la resistencia basada en el juego (realizar siempre) con cantidades que complementen la específica para no exagerar con las cargas.
	En el caso de equipos que tengan más de 3 entrenamientos

semanales, preparar. – Para la resistencia general, prever: ▫ En la 1ª y 2ª fase de pretemporada de 15' a 25'/30' de trabajo sobre la capacidad aeróbica con una cadencia de 2 sesiones sí, una sesión no. ▫ En la 3ª fase de pretemporada, mantenerse sobre los 15'/20' de trabajo basado en la potencia aeróbica, igual que en la pausa invernal. ▫ En las fases de competición, programar volúmenes de trabajo de 15'. - Para la resistencia específica a pruebas escalonadas, un número adecuado de repeticiones a intensidad personal. – Para la resistencia basada en el juego (realizar siempre) con cantidades que completen la específica para no exagerar con las cargas.

LA FUERZA

La fuerza es la capacidad que posee el músculo humano de desarrollar tensiones útiles para superar u oponerse a resistencias externas.

La fuerza muscular, capacidad motora importante para toda actividad deportiva, está condicionada:

- Por la maduración del sistema nervioso.
- Por el tipo de fibras musculares (presencia de unidades motoras de contracción rápida con respecto a las de contracción lenta).
- Por la sección transversal del músculo.
- Por la inclinación muscular (orientación de las fibras en relación con el movimiento).
- Por la frecuencia de los impulsos nerviosos transmitidos.
- Por el nivel de activación en la misma unidad de tiempo (sincronización) de más unidades motoras que constituyen las unidades funcionales de relación entre el

sistema nervioso y las estructuras musculares.

- Por la técnica correcta de ejecución.

Entre las capacidades motoras que caracterizan la prestación de un futbolista, la fuerza representa un caso especial. Se trata de una fuerza muy concreta que encuentra su expresión más evidente al saltar, chutar, acelerar, defender, lanzar. No se utiliza en cantidad muy elevada, debiendo el jugador, como máximo, vencer el peso de su propio cuerpo, dándose el caso de que se requiera una actuación de grado límite, como la velocidad, e instantáneo, como aplicación en el tiempo. Hay que recordar además que la fuerza mejora en el futbolista relativamente poco durante la realización de ejercicios técnicos (como la repetición de remates de cabeza) y que para obtener mejoras importantes hay que recurrir a ejercicios específicos. <u>La fuerza es la capacidad de oponerse a una resistencia externa por medio de contracciones musculares.</u>

Podemos distinguir dos tipos de fuerza:

1. **Fuerza general**: Se refiere a la fuerza de todos los grupos musculares, independientemente del deporte practicado.
2. **Fuerza específica** o especial: Se refiera a la forma de manifestación de la fuerza típica de cada deporte.

En las diversas disciplinas deportiva, la fuerza se presenta siempre de una forma mixta y en combinación con las demás capacidades condicionales. La fuerza general es la base sobre la

que se debe construir la específica y su entrenamiento prevalece en la primera parte del trabajo.

LAS TENSIONES MUSCULARES

Para realizar el trabajo de fuerza, se distinguen las siguientes formas de tensiones musculares:

Isométricas
Cuando los elementos contráctiles del músculo se contraen mientras se alargan los elementos elásticos y externamente no se produce un acortamiento visible del músculo.

Isotónicas (concéntricas)
Cuando los elementos contráctiles del músculo se contraen mientras no se alargan los elásticos y no se produce un acortamiento muscular.

Isotónicas (excéntricas)
Cuando los elementos contráctiles del músculo se contraen mientras no se alargan los elásticos y se produce un estiramiento muscular.

Auxotónicas
Representan una combinación entre las dos tensiones isométricas e isotónicas, en la que el sistema neuromuscular se adecúa mediante una continua inserción y desinserción de las unidades neuromusculares, con el cambio de los momentos de fuerza del peso y las variaciones de velocidad.

En relación con las tensiones que acabamos de describir, el trabajo muscular distingue entre:

Trabajo muscular superador (concéntrico)
Las inserciones extremas de los tendones del músculo se asemejan y la carga se desplaza o levanta. Es el tipo de trabajo que prevalece en la mayor parte de los deportes.

Trabajo muscular cedente (excéntrico).
Es lo contrario del anterior, las inserciones extremas de los tendones del músculo se alejan durante la contracción, el músculo trata de oponerse a la carga y cede lentamente. Sirve para la amortiguación de los saltos y de los movimientos de carga.

Trabajo muscular estático (isométrico)
Aunque se ejerce tensión muscular, la distancia entre las cabezas de los tendones extremos no cambia, por lo que la carga no es vencida ni se cede ante ella. Sirve para fijar determinadas posturas del cuerpo y las extremidades.

Los músculos que
trabajan en tensión se alargan,
si trabajan en flexión se espesan
- los flexores son músculos gruesos;
- los extensores son músculos largos.

La carrera hacia atrás es útil para el desarrollo de los flexores de la pierna y para estabilizar las rodillas.

La fuerza límite

La fuerza límite representa la máxima fuerza posible que llega a alcanzar el sistema neuromuscular en una contracción máxima voluntaria.

Todavía más elevada que la fuerza límite es la fuerza extrema, que representa la suma de la fuerza límite y las reservas de fuerza que pueden movilizarse solo en condiciones particulares (peligro de vida, hipnosis, etc.). La diferencia entre la fuerza extrema y la fuerza límite se define como «déficit de fuerza», que según el estado de entrenamiento puede ir del 30% (personas no entrenadas) al 10% (personas entrenadas). En la fuerza límite, con referencia a las diversas tensiones musculares podemos distinguir:

Fuerza límite estática, en la práctica, la que consigue alcanzar el sistema neuromuscular en una contracción voluntaria, contra una oposición insuperable.

Fuerza límite dinámica, es decir, la que el sistema neuromuscular consigue alcanzar durante el proceso de movimiento y se puede manifestar de forma:

✓ Positiva o concéntrica, superante.
✓ Negativa o excéntrica, cedente, frenante.

La fuerza límite estática es siempre mayor que la dinámica, porque puede producirse solo cuando la

carga a superar y la fuerza contráctil del músculo mantengan el equilibrio.

La fuerza límite depende de tres componentes:

1. La sección transversal fisiológica del músculo.
2. La coordinación intermuscular, es decir, la sinergia entre los músculos en el mismo movimiento.
3. La coordinación intramuscular, es decir, la interna del mismo músculo.

El entrenamiento de la fuerza máxima empeora la fuerza elástica porque elude la reutilización elástica del músculo.

La fuerza rápida

La fuerza rápida (veloz) es la capacidad del sistema neuromuscular de mover el cuerpo, parte de él u objetos externos a la máxima velocidad posible. En la misma persona se pueden expresar distintos niveles de fuerza rápida: un atleta puede tener articulaciones superiores veloces, pero movimientos lentos de las inferiores. Los movimientos de fuerza rápida están dirigidos por un programa motor archivado en el sistema nervioso central. Para estos movimientos, los deportistas con talento disponen del llamado «programa motor de tiempo corto», mientras que los menos dotados disponen de un «programa motor de tiempo largo». Esos programas pueden verse influidos solo hasta cierto punto (*Bauersfeld, Voß, 1992*).

Los programas cortos se caracterizan por el hecho de que en ellos se encuentran impulsos rápidos dirigidos a los músculos principales.

El **patrón** de activación nerviosa se caracteriza por:
- Fases pronunciadas de preactivación (mejora la capacidad de reacción de los husos musculares).
- Entrada rápida en la actividad principal (base para una contracción rápida y potente).
- Concentración de la actividad en la primera mitad de la fase de trabajo.
- Buena actividad coordinativa de los músculos principales.

Desde el punto de vista de la metodología del entrenamiento de la fuerza rápida, se puede distinguir entre:

Fuerza inicial, capacidad de llegar a realizar la máxima subida posible en la curva fuerza-tiempo al inicio de la tensión muscular, hecho muy importante en todos los movimientos que requieren una velocidad inicial elevada. Resulta relevante la capacidad de recurrir al mayor número de unidades motoras al inicio de la contracción.

Fuerza explosiva, capacidad de llegar a realizar una subida lo más rápida posible en la curva fuerza-tiempo. Resulta relevante la capacidad y velocidad de contracción del número de unidades motoras que se contraen a la vez y de la fuerza contráctil de las fibras requeridas.

La fuerza resistente

La resistencia a la fuerza es «**la capacidad del organismo de oponerse a la fatiga en prestaciones de fuerza de larga duración**». La capacidad de resistencia a la fuerza es un factor que determina la prestación en todas las disciplinas de resistencia. Una forma especial de resistencia a la fuerza es la resistencia a la fuerza rápida, que depende, de manera determinante, de la capacidad de recuperación rápida de la musculatura afectada, de la capacidad de resistencia general y local aeróbica y anaeróbica bien desarrolladas. Generalmente se hace una diferencia entre resistencia a la fuerza general y local, igual que entre resistencia dinámica y estática a la fuerza.

Por resistencia general a la fuerza se entiende la capacidad de la periferia del cuerpo de resistir la fatiga. Los criterios para un entrenamiento eficaz de la fuerza resistente son:

- Resistencia a movimientos mayores que en la competición.
- Repetir más veces los estímulos de entrenamiento.
- Hacer coincidir o acercar lo más posible las formas de entrenamiento a las curvas fuerza-tiempo del movimiento de competición,
- Dirigir los medios de entrenamiento hacia los principales grupos musculares (agonistas y antagonistas): El número de las posibles repeticiones disminuye cuando aumenta el peso que debe soportarse.

Formas especiales de fuerza

Junto a los tipos de fuerza que hemos examinado, algunos autores proponen otras formas especiales:

- **La fuerza extrema**: Representa la fuerza límite voluntaria más las reservas de prestaciones que pueden movilizarse mediante productos farmacéuticos y componentes psicológicos (hipnosis).
- **La fuerza absoluta**: Representa la fuerza que puede desarrollarse independientemente del peso corporal.
- **La fuerza relativa**: Representa la fuerza que puede desarrollarse en relación con el peso corporal.

La no entrenabilidad de la fuerza

En edad infantil, las diferencias de entrenabilidad entre niños y niñas son muy escasas. Pero la entrenabilidad en los adolescentes y los adultos masculinos crece rápidamente, alcanzando su máximo entre los 20 y 30 años, para luego disminuir. En las mujeres los cambios de entrenabilidad de la fuerza durante la vida son relativamente escasos y se puede asegurar que su subida más rápida se produce en la primera pubertad, en la adolescencia.

Según algunas investigaciones estadounidenses, debe prestarse atención especial al periodo que va de los 12 a los 14 años, ya que en este periodo el porcentaje de las fibras intermedias asciende al 14%

entre los niños y al 10% entre las niñas. Mediante un entrenamiento adecuado esas fibras pueden transformarse en fibras ST o fibras FT, después no resulta ya posible la transformación en fibras FT. Resulta por tanto indispensable a esa edad hacer hincapié en el entrenamiento de la fuerza rápida, ya que en esta fase del crecimiento la rapidez (cíclica y acíclica) es particularmente bien entrenable. En la infancia, hasta los 11 años aproximadamente, en la práctica, niños y niñas tienen la misma fuerza. Sin embargo, con la edad, la fuerza de los varones aumenta rápidamente. La causa de la diferencia de fuerza entre hombres y mujeres está en la mayor producción de las hormonas sexuales masculinas (testosterona) en el hombre, que tiene un efecto anabolizante: De ahí el hecho de que las secciones transversales de la musculatura femenina sean aproximadamente el 75% de las masculinas. Además, a igualdad de secciones musculares, la fuerza de las mujeres es menor, al haber diversos porcentajes de tejidos: La mujer posee un porcentaje de tejido adiposo que es cerca del doble del del hombre. La fuerza de una mujer adulta, en lo que se refiere a la musculatura de las extremidades (brazos y piernas) llega a ser dos tercios de la del hombre.

Clasificación de la fuerza en relación con el gesto a realizar

RESISTENCIA A LA FUERZA	Fuerza de sprint resistente. Fuerza de salto. Fuerza de tracción. Fuerza de tiro.	
FUERZA VELOZ	Fuerza de sprint. Fuerza de salto (elevación). Fuerza de lanzamiento.	
FUERZA LÍMITE	Estática	Fuerza de parada. Fuerza de tracción. Fuerza de empuje.
	Dinámica	Fuerza de parada. Fuerza de tracción. Fuerza de empuje.

(Letzelter, 1987)

Métodos para el entrenamiento de la fuerza

El entrenamiento dinámico o isotónico de la fuerza se subdivide en:

1. **Entrenamiento dinámico positivo**, también llamado superante, concéntrico, con acortamiento o acelerador.
2. **Entrenamiento dinámico negativo**, también llamado cedente, excéntrico, con estiramiento o ralentizador.

El <u>entrenamiento dinámico positivo</u> es la forma más frecuente en el deporte y se obtiene un desarrollo de la fuerza según la fórmula

Trabajo = Fuerza x Desplazamiento

que viene acompañado por un acortamiento del músculo.

El <u>entrenamiento dinámico negativo</u> es el movimiento de amortización del propio cuerpo o de reducción de sobrecargas límites.

La recepción del peso corpóreo propio mediante saltos hacia abajo desde alturas adaptadas a los niveles correspondientes de prestación sirve para mejorar la coordinación intramuscular y entrenar la «componente elástica» del músculo. Con el método de cesión a cargas muy elevadas se produce sobre todo un estímulo hipertrofiante.

Permite obtener picos de tensión notablemente superiores a los valores límites de fuerza dinámica positiva y estática (30/40% superior al máximo estático y 10/15% del máximo dinámico positivo).

El entrenamiento de la fuerza

Para poder comprender en qué dirección es más oportuno actuar para conseguir un efecto eficaz de entrenamiento de la fuerza del futbolista, aclaramos cuáles son los factores que influyen en general en la fuerza.

FUNDAME NTOS DE LA FUERZA	FACTORES CONSTITUT IVOS	Conformación física. Composición del músculo. Velocidad de conducción del estímulo nervioso.
	FACTORES MEJORABL ES	Capacidad de activación de un número elevado de fibras musculares. Capacidad de activación de los procesos voluntarios. Capacidad de activación de los procesos bioquímicos específicos. Capacidad técnica.

Los factores constitutivos condicionan notablemente el entrenamiento de la fuerza. Un jugador con una masa muscular reducida llega a la máxima capacidad personal de fuerza en poco tiempo, un jugador cuya musculatura representa un porcentaje bajo de fibras blancas (veloces) tiene una capacidad baja de mejora en su fuerza explosiva.

Los factores mejorables representan aspectos fundamentales e importantes en el entrenamiento de la capacidad de fuerza.

Determinación de la fuerza límite

Cada vez que decimos que la carga de un ejercicio es del 60% o el 90% nos referimos al porcentaje con respecto a la carga máxima sostenible en ese ejercicio concreto. Se trata por tanto de buscar la

fuerza máxima que cada futbolista puede ejercer en un ejercicio concreto.

Con personas ya preparadas, se puede adoptar el siguiente método: Después de valorar de forma aproximada la carga máxima que puede superar un futbolista en un ejercicio concreto, se calcula el porcentaje un poco por debajo del máximo y se hacen repeticiones del ejercicio hasta el agotamiento. Sabiendo entonces que con el 95% del máximo son posibles 3 repeticiones, con el 90% cerca de 5/6 repeticiones, resulta fácil calcular la máxima capacidad de fuerza.

Para los principiantes se debe actuar con la máxima cautela y mantener amplios márgenes de seguridad en los porcentajes. Si el programa de entrenamiento puede realizarse de la mejor manera, la mejora de la fuerza se manifiesta de forma visible después de 4/6 semanas. De esto se deduce que después de ese periodo, o mejor después de 6/8 semanas, hacen falta adaptaciones de los porcentajes de carga del trabajo.

Formas de trabajo para la mejora de la fuerza

	Contracciones isotónicas	CARGA NATURAL
ENTRENA MIENTO DE LA FUERZA	TRABAJO DINÁMICO concéntrico y excéntrico	CON SOBRECARGA
	Contracciones isométricas TRABAJO ESTÁTICO	
	TRABAJO MIXTO	
	ELECTROESTIMULACIONES	

ENTRENAMIENTO CON TRABAJO DINÁMICO

- Con carga natural, la mejora de la fuerza se obtiene mediante ejercicios que no utilizan resistencias externas. Ejercicios concretos: Carrera hacia arriba, saltos y ejercicios pliométricos sencillos (hablaremos en particular de estos).
- Con sobrecarga se usan elementos externos (pesas, máquinas, elásticos, etc.) o interviene un compañero.

En este tipo de trabajo se consideran los siguientes valores:
- Ejercicios con cargas límite (por encima del 90%).
- Ejercicios con cargas elevadas (entre el 80 y el 90%).
- Ejercicios con cargas medias (entre el 55 y el 75%).

- Ejercicios con cargas ligeras (hasta el 50%).

ENTRENAMIENTO CON TRABAJO ESTÁTICO

Se lleva a cabo con ejercicios en los que está previsto un aumento de tensión del músculo sin variar la longitud y el mantenimiento de esa tensión durante cierto tiempo: Se trata de ejercicios isométricos.

ENTRENAMIENTO CON TRABAJO MIXTO

Se habla de trabajo mixto cuando está prevista una combinación apropiada de esfuerzos dinámicos y estáticos. En la práctica, no es muy habitual.

ENTRENAMIENTO CON ELECTROESTIMULACIÓN

La contracción no viene provocada por un impulso voluntario, controlado por el sistema nervioso central, sino mediante un estímulo eléctrico externo. Gracias a la activación límite del aparato contráctil, se obtiene una tensión muscular elevada y por tanto una hipertrofia muscular marcada. Se evita la fatiga del SNC y por tanto es posible un volumen elevado de carga. Se pueden entrenar aisladamente grupos musculares y es excelente para objetivos rehabilitativos. Un entrenamiento de 30 minutos permite lograr los mismos resultados que un entrenamiento normal de cerca de dos horas. Este método de potenciación presenta una serie de efectos negativos.

♣ Pasa completamente a un segundo plano el funcionamiento de los circuitos coordinadores.

♣ Se activan primero las unidades motoras grandes y rápidas y luego las pequeñas y lentas.

♣ La electroestimulación anula la eficacia de las funciones de control y protección de los propioceptores.

♣ Se activan las fibras musculares que se encuentran en el exterior y no se les unen las fibras más internas.

♣ Los mecanismos fisiológicos y psicológicos de protección del cansancio desaparecen debido una señal de estimulación proveniente del exterior, con posibilidad de daños musculares.

CONCEPTOS A TNEER EN CUENTA EN EL ENTRENAMIENTO DE LA FUERZA

1) Dirigir al trabajo hacia el aumento del tipo de fuerza indispensable para el jugador de fútbol.
2) Aprender bien los ejercicios antes de usar cargas elevadas.
3) El aumento de la masa muscular en el futbolista no debe ser excesivo, para evitar incidencias negativas sobre las capacidades técnicas.
4) Variar periódicamente el trabajo para evitar condicionamientos que disminuyan la eficacia del trabajo.
5) La mejora de la fuerza debe encontrar de inmediato respuesta en la técnica.

6) El entrenamiento de la fuerza solo es eficaz si es continuo.

7) El trabajo de potenciación específica debe venir precedido por un trabajo de potenciación general.

8) En el ámbito de los ejercicios de fuerza se puede actuar sobre las siguientes variables:
✓ Cantidad de carga.
✓ Número de repeticiones.
✓ Número de series.
✓ Velocidad de ejecución.
✓ Tiempo de pausa.

9) La pausa entre una serie de ejercicios y otra debe ser tal que permita cumplir beneficiosamente la nueva repetición (no inferior a los 2' ni superior a los 5'). La pausa debe ser activa.

10) A todo trabajo de fuerza deben seguir ejercicios de impulso muscular rápido.

11) El trabajo debe programarse de modo que afecte tanto a los músculos principales como a sus antagonistas.

12) La carga de trabajo debe aumentar progresivamente.

13) Hay que personalizar la carga de trabajo.

14) El volumen de carga debe determinarse por el tipo de ejercicio que se debe realizar.

Entrenamiento con sobrecargas

<u>Método del contraste o método «búlgaro»</u>
Se propone proveer al sistema muscular estímulos nuevos de entrenamiento, no habituales, pero extremadamente eficaces, mediante tareas de fuerza completamente opuestas.

Método clásico del contraste	El cambio o contraste viene determinado por el uso alternado de pesas ligeras y pesadas con una ejecución explosiva del movimiento.
Variante del método clásico	El contraste se puede lograr, no solo con la alternancia «pesado-ligero», sino también combinando la repetición de tareas de fuerza límite, tareas de fuerza resistente y tareas explosivas de fuerza rápida.

Métodos clásicos «americanos»

Super serie	- Para músculos antagonistas: Primero se entrena el agonista e inmediatamente después el antagonista. - Para los músculos agonistas: Se trabaja el mismo grupo muscular mediante 2 series consecutivas de ejercicios diversos.
Series ardientes	Realizar un máximo de 10 repeticiones para 10 series, seguido por 5-6 repeticiones de movimientos parciales del mismo ejercicio.

Series forzadas	Después de una serie de 10 repeticiones, le siguen 3-4 repeticiones del mismo ejercicio, recurriendo a la ayuda de un compañero que mantiene el movimiento mientras resulta posible continuar y repetir.
Serie de super bombeo	Utilizado sobre todo por los culturistas, consiste en realizar 15-18 series del mismo ejercicio.
Serie con truco	El inicio del movimiento viene facilitado por movimientos suplementarios. De esta manera el atleta desplaza cargas que no podría desplazar de otra manera.
Método Bulk	Se realizan series con un máximo de 5 a 6 repeticiones.

El trabajo con sobrecargas puede organizarse con:
- Carga constante.
- Variaciones de carga.

La carga constante supone un trabajo por series. Establecida la entidad de la carga (en torno al 70%) se realiza un número de repeticiones que al inicio es de 4/6 y va aumentando hasta 8/10, lo que constituye una serie. Antes de repetir la serie, debe estar prevista una pausa de 5' a 2' con disminución progresiva.

El trabajo con variaciones de carga se organiza según el sistema llamado de pirámide, por ejemplo:
- 5 repeticiones con el 75% de la carga.
- 4 repeticiones con el 80% de la carga.
- 3 repeticiones con el 85% de la carga.
- 2 repeticiones con el 90% de la carga.
- 1 repetición con el 95% de la carga.
La velocidad debe ser bastante elevada; la pausa, como la precedente,

Para el jugador de fútbol es más útil una metodología que une las dos formas de trabajo usando una sucesión de trabajo del siguiente tipo, llamado pirámide larga:
- 8 repeticiones con el 60% de la carga.
- 7 repeticiones con el 65% de la carga.
- 6 repeticiones con el 70% de la carga.
- 5 repeticiones con el 75% de la carga.
- 4 repeticiones con el 80% de la carga.
La ejecución debe hacerse a velocidad media-alta.

Otro método, llamado de la carga decreciente, ofrece la ventaja de que las cargas máximas se realizan en condiciones de «reposo», mientras que las sublímite se desarrollan en condiciones de prefatiga hasta el agotamiento completo de la musculatura.

Los objetivos que se logran son solo la coordinación intramuscular y la construcción muscular:
- Carga decreciente con variación del número de repeticiones:
- 1 repetición con el 95% de la carga.

- 3 repeticiones con el 85% de la carga.
- 5 repeticiones con el 80% de la carga.
- 7 repeticiones con el 75% de la carga.
- 8 repeticiones con el 70% de la carga.

- Carga decreciente con número constante de repeticiones:
  - 1 repetición con el 95% de la carga.
  - 1 repetición con el 85% de la carga.
  - 1 repetición con el 80% de la carga.
  - 1 repetición con el 75% de la carga.
  - 1 repetición con el 70% de la carga.

Circuit-training
Prevé series de ejercicios que requieren sucesivamente diversos grupos musculares, de modo que a la fase de trabajo le siga una forma de reposo localizado mientras se trabaja otro grupo muscular.

Se puede preparar la siguiente sucesión:
- Extremidades superiores.
- Dorsales.
- Abdominales.
- Extremidades inferiores.

El trabajo previsto por serie es de 6/8 repeticiones con cargas del 70% y ejecución bastante veloz. Normalmente se prevén 2 o 3 ejercicios por cada grupo muscular para un total de 8/12 etapas.

MEJORA DE LA FUERZA GENERAL Y DE LA FUERZA RESISTENTE

Escogiendo determinados ejercicios, es posible realizar intervenciones específicas. Pueden convertirse en tipo orgánico si se disminuyen mucho las cargas y los ritmos de ejecución.

Body building system
Utiliza el trabajo en circuito para realizar series de ejercicios con cargas y velocidad que permitan 8/10 repeticiones. Este sistema busca un desarrollo armónico general y puede utilizarse en el primer periodo de entrenamiento como trabajo de preparación para el subsiguiente trabajo de fuerza. El intervalo de recuperación de 4/5 minutos desciende gradualmente hasta los 2/3 minutos. Para cada sesión se eligen 10/12 ejercicios.

Power training
Es una metodología particular dirigida esencialmente a la mejora de la fuerza veloz explosiva. Utiliza tres formas distintas de trabajo, siempre en forma de circuito.
- Se preparan ejercicios con cargas pesadas.
- Se preparan ejercicios con cargas medias-ligeras.
- Se preparan ejercicios con carga natural.
La ejecución se caracteriza por la máxima velocidad posible (6/8 repeticiones), con pausa proporcional a la carga: los ejercicios serán 8/10. El circuito ha de repetirse de una a 2/3 veces. A emplear con jugadores ya expertos y como trabajo de mantenimiento y recuperación de fuerza.
Ejercicios pliométricos sencillos

En el ámbito de los ejercicios de carga natural, la mejora de las extremidades inferiores se realiza principalmente con el método «pliométrico» o «reactivo». Son todos aquellos métodos que prevén una fase de amortización (en la que se alargan los músculos) durante la cual se frena el cuerpo al caer de lo alto, seguida por una fase reactiva (contracción muscular) en la que el futbolista supera la resistencia constituida por el peso del cuerpo con una acción de salto.

Se utiliza principalmente fuerza elástica y se realizan únicamente cargas en las extremidades inferiores y son muy apropiados para el fútbol. Mejora la fuerza explosiva-reactiva-balística (elástica). Es oportuno usar una altura de caída entre 30/40 cm. y una ejecución de 10 repeticiones y 6/8 series. Después de cada serie es oportuno realizar ejercicios de descompresión para la espalda (posición de huevo). Entran en el ámbito pliométrico sencillo todas las formas de salto, tanto sencillo como con superación de obstáculos. Un número de saltos entre 60 y 100 puede considerarse un entrenamiento favorable.

Prestar mucha atención al ángulo (entre 125° e 160°) de flexión de las rodillas en la fase de apoyo en el terreno, de modo que el tiempo de contacto sea muy corto, lo que permite utilizar la **fuerza instantánea** (o inicial), un 30% de la fuerza máxima. Con este tipo de ejercicio se obtienen mejoras inmediatas. Al día siguiente al entrenamiento se obtienen efectos positivos sobre la

prestación, pero si no se mantiene el trabajo esas mejoras se pierden rápidamente,

En la ejecución del trabajo pliométrico conviene prestar mucha atención a posibles señales provenientes de los deportistas: si sufren dolores en las rodillas o la columna que permanecen a pesar de los ejercicios de descompresión y estiramiento, suspender para ellos el trabajo pliométrico y sustituirlo por trabajos de fuerza veloz y aceleración.

Recordar que al contacto con el terreno después de cada salto descargamos sobre la zona lumbar de la columna vertebral:
- Cerca de 340 kg. para caídas de 30 cm.
- Cerca de 440 kg. para caídas de 40 cm.

Para apreciar los peligros a los que está sometida nuestra columna, propongo un ejemplo sencillo. Consideremos un joven de 1,60 m. y un peso de 45 kg. Su peso se repartiría así:
- La cabeza pesa unos 3 kg.
- Los brazos pesan unos 10 kg.
- El tronco pesa unos 19 kg.
- Total, excluidas las piernas: 32 kg.
En posición erecta, flexionando y extendiendo las piernas, la columna vertebral y sus músculos espinales soportan un peso corporal de 32 kg.; si flexiona el pecho hacia delante y prosigue el mismo movimiento de flexión y extensión de las piernas o incluso en posición estática el peso soportado por la

columna y los músculos espinales aumenta de 6 a 7 veces hasta los 200-250 kg. La situación que se crea es de gran peligro.

La importancia del entrenamiento de la fuerza en los jóvenes

Un entrenamiento de la fuerza en edad juvenil desarrolla un papel importante en la formación física general y multilateral. Hay que considerar como pertenecientes a la categoría «jóvenes» todas aquellas personas comprendidas entre la infancia (6-10 años), la preadolescencia (11-13 años) y el inicio de la adolescencia (14-15 años). El aumento de la fuerza sigue el siguiente desarrollo:

♣ Hasta los 11 años, es insignificante.

♣ De los 12 a los 15 años está en aumento notable.

♣ De los 15 a los 18 años el desarrollo es más intenso.

Según algunas estadísticas, en los primeros dos años de escuela hay un aumento del 70% de los defectos de la postura. En el mismo periodo, el porcentaje de niños con sobrepeso aumenta del 3 al 20%, mientras que con el aumento del porcentaje de gordura disminuye la capacidad de las prestaciones en aquellos movimientos que requieren sobre todo fuerza muscular, rapidez y resistencia general. El entrenamiento de la fuerza apropiado para la edad se convierte en absolutamente necesario como medida preventiva y medio para aumentar la capacidad de prestación motora.

Es importante señalar que las condiciones de los jóvenes débiles y desentrenados mejoran con un entrenamiento dosificado de la fuerza, Con un entrenamiento de ocho semanas (20 minutos tres veces por semana) se obtiene una disminución del déficit de fuerza del 15 al 74% *(Breuning, 1985 - da Weineck 2001)*.

En el periodo del estirón infantil, el aparato locomotor responde a los estímulos del entrenamiento de fuerza rápida. Con un entrenamiento regular de la fuerza rápida a medida del niño aumentan sus capacidades generales de prestación. Por el contrario, un entrenamiento extremadamente específico que prevea solo formas de carga específicas de un deporte produce desequilibrios musculares que posteriormente impiden un desarrollo de las prestaciones y abren la puerta a problemas musculares *(Weineck, 2001)*.

Se puede afirmar que en la edad juvenil (infancia y adolescencia) un entrenamiento de la fuerza sirve tanto para mejorar la prestación como como prevención de las posturas y prevención de problemas.

Riesgos en el entrenamiento de la fuerza en los jóvenes

En el desarrollo de la fuerza hay que prestar atención a la particularidad del organismo en vías de crecimiento: La estructura ósea de los jóvenes, debido a la escasez de calcio, es más elástica, pero menos resistente a la presión y la flexión. La osificación del sistema esquelético termina

generalmente entre los 17 y los 20 años y en consecuencia la capacidad de carga en los jóvenes es reducida con respecto a la de los adultos.

Mediante requerimientos de presión y tracción de los huesos, producto de la actividad muscular, se pueden aplicar estímulos «formativos» y provocar fenómenos de adaptación sobre la estructura del hueso y la resistencia a la tracción del tejido conjuntivo. En el entrenamiento de la fuerza de los jóvenes hay que atenerse a algunas indicaciones.

♣ Hay que tener siempre en cuenta las capacidades de carga de los huesos y el tejido cartilaginoso al elegir y dosificar la carga de trabajo.

♣ Evitar forzar incorrectamente el aparato locomotor, especialmente la columna vertebral, durante la ejecución de ejercicios concretos.

♣ Todo ejercicio, incluso el más sencillo, si no se realiza bien, tiene siempre peligros para el deportista joven.

♣ No conviene, por razones de prudencia, usar ejercicios por parejas, es decir, que utilizan el peso del cuerpo de un compañero.

♣ Si se puede aumentar la carga, se hará con el número de repeticiones.

♣ La masa muscular, y por tanto la fuerza, aumentan con la edad.

♣ Los periodos de mayor riesgo para los huesos son los comprendidos entre los 11 y 14 años, pero sobre todo 6 meses antes del inicio de la pubertad, cuando se registra el pico máximo de crecimiento estructural, mientras que al llegar la pubertad aumenta el peso (el desarrollo muscular se retrasa unos dos años con respecto al estiramiento óseo). La

figura muestra que en la infancia (hasta los 11-12 años) en la práctica hombres y mujeres tiene la misma fuerza. Con el paso del tiempo, la fuerza de los hombres aumenta rápidamente.

Contenidos del entrenamiento de la fuerza en edad juvenil

La infancia o primera edad escolar (de 6 a 10 años)
En esta edad del crecimiento, es primordial el robustecimiento del aparato locomotor y de sostenimiento, realizado de forma lúdica y armónica. La tendencia natural al movimiento del niño debe dirigirse a un entrenamiento de la fuerza adecuado para su edad, utilizando solo entrenamiento dinámico y ejercitando la fuerza rápida (fuerza de salto, fuerza de lanzamiento, fuerza de tiro y fuerza de patada). Dado que los niños generalmente solo se pueden concentrar en una tarea y por un periodo limitado de tiempo, es especialmente apropiado el entrenamiento en circuito porque satisface la necesidad de prestaciones singulares y de breve duración y garantiza una buena formación general del aparato muscular.

Para robustecer todo el cuerpo se pueden usar juegos de empuje y tracción, así como juegos de lucha que empleen una gran cantidad de grupos musculares.

La preadolescencia o segunda edad escolar (de 11 a 13 años)

En la segunda edad escolar, que termina con el inicio de la pubertad, en las mujeres hacia los 11-12 años, en los hombres hacia los 12-13 años, los ritmos de desarrollo están en una fase especial: En las chicas estamos en el periodo cerca de su madurez sexual y aparece una aceleración de las funciones motoras; los chicos están en plena fase transitoria, en la que se registra una ralentización del desarrollo de las capacidades motoras. El desarrollo de la fuerza en esta fase asume un papel esencial y lo tendrá hasta los 14-15 años, donde podrán iniciar un trabajo sistemático de aumento de la fuerza máxima.

El reforzamiento general y multilateral de los principales grupos musculares se aumenta posteriormente mediante ejercicios de carga natural o con sobrecargas ligeras, Conviene usar ejercicios dirigidos al refuerzo de la musculatura dorsal y abdominal y de los músculos extensores de las extremidades superiores.
Para la mejora de la fuerza de salto, gracias a la gran agilidad y los óptimos presupuestos coordinativos, se pueden utilizar ejercicios de salto más exigentes.
Los ejercicios deben mantener la característica lúdica, pero pueden insertarse en los juegos ejercicios con objetivos precisos.

La adolescencia (14-15 años)
El inicio de la pubertad significa el fin de la edad infantil y la entrada en la adolescencia, En las chicas la edad puberal empieza cerca de un año antes que

en los chicos. En la primera parte de la fase puberal se produce un aumento acentuado del peso que provoca una desarmonía temporal de las proporciones del cuerpo. Existen relaciones desfavorables de levantamiento con respecto al rendimiento potencial de la musculatura. Los cartílagos de crecimiento sufren una serie de modificaciones morfológicas funcionales que disminuyen la capacidad mecánica de carga. Este periodo es particularmente sensible a cargas «equivocadas» y a cargas prolongadas, sobre todo en la región de la columna vertebral. Sin embargo, gracias al repentino aumento de las hormonas sexuales anabolizantes (testosterona), la entrenabilidad de la fuerza aumenta de forma notable, aunque ese aumento se acompaña de una disminución de la capacidad de carga mecánica. Aparte del adiestramiento de la fuerza general, para el joven de esta edad son apropiados diversos ejercicios de salto, lanzamiento y fútbol, junto a juegos de lucha en los que se tira y empuja y ejercicios gimnásticos con aparatos pequeños. En la segunda fase puberal asistimos a un crecimiento en la anchura, mientras que las proporciones del cuerpo vuelven a ser armónicas. Se registra un aumento ulterior de las hormonas sexuales.

Variaciones de la tasa de testosterona (mg./100 ml.)		
Edad	Mujeres	Hombres
8-9	20	21-34
10-11	10-65	41-60
12-13	30-80	131-349
14-15	30-85	328-643

Es el periodo de la máxima entrenabilidad de la fuerza y de su máxima tasa de incremento *(Komadel 1975; Zurbrügg 1982; da Weineck 1981).* Gracias a la creciente estabilización del sistema óseo se pueden utilizar cada vez más las cargas y los métodos de entrenamiento de los adultos.

Incremento de las expresiones de fuerza en las diversas edades			
Edad	**FUERZA VELOZ**	**FUERZA RESISTENTE**	**FUERZA MÁXIMA**
6-10 años	Mínima	Mínima	Nula
11-13 años	Baja	Discreta	Nula
14-15 años	Baja	Buena	Baja
16-17 años	Elevada	Elevada	Discreta
18 años	Óptima	Óptima	Buena-óptima
Otros	Mantenimiento de los valores alcanzados, con tendencia a disminuir	Mantenimiento de los valores alcanzados, con tendencia a disminuir	Mantenimiento de los valores alcanzados, con tendencia a disminuir
QUÉ HACER			
Hasta los 10/11 años	La fuerza hasta esta edad se ejercita mediante el juego o ejercicios lúdicos. El método sigue exclusivamente el método dinámico de carga natural. Se ejercita principalmente la fuerza instantánea de salto, de patada, de lanzamiento, etc. Deben utilizarse todos los grupos musculares. También se pueden utilizar ejercicios con circuitos simples de trabajo y de contraposición, tirar, empujar, desplazar, resistir, superar, etc.		

Hasta los 15/16 años	Es una fase muy particular y difícil del crecimiento. Recordar valorar siempre, más que la edad anagráfica la edad biológica del chico y la chica. - El entrenamiento de la fuerza se dirige ahora hacia el trabajo dinámico con carga natural (fuerza instantánea, fuerza de aceleración y frenado), ejercicios de gimnasia específica con y sin aparatos pequeños. - Se empiezan a introducir ejercicios de fuerza especifica que se hacen cada vez más duros al final del ciclo. - Es un periodo de la adolescencia, edad de la máxima disponibilidad y de las máximas tasas de incremento. - Se utilizarán también ejercicios para la fuerza resistente en circuito o con otras metodologías de trabajo.
Desde los 16 años	En el caso de equipos que realizan menos de 3 entrenamientos semanales, el trabajo de fuerza continuará realizándose como en el periodo precedente, con utilización también de pequeñas sobrecargas. – Se inicia la introducción de modo sistemático de ejercicios de pliometría sencilla. En el caso de equipos que realizan más de 3 entrenamientos semanales, continuará realizándose el trabajo de fuerza como en el periodo precedente, con utilización también de pequeñas sobrecargas. – Se empezarán a introducir de modo sistemático ejercicios de pliometría sencilla. – Si las condiciones lo permiten, con disponibilidad de gimnasio con máquinas y de personal especializado, se podrán iniciar trabajos específicos de potenciamiento con sobrecargas.

	CUÁNDO HACERLO
Hasta los 10/11 años	Durante los juegos y los ejercicios en cualquier periodo del año.
Hasta los 15/16 años	En el periodo preparatorio se puede iniciar el trabajo tanto de la fuerza general como de la específica, con cantidad en progresión y en sesiones alternas. – Al acercarse el inicio del campeonato (dos semanas antes) se debe dedicar esencialmente a la fuerza específica, sin aumentar la carga (a veces reduciéndola), pero aumentando la velocidad de ejecución. – La frecuencia desciende a una vez por semana, en la sesión de inicio de semana, para mantener el

148

	grado de fuerza alcanzado. – Con ocasión de partidos poco exigentes o de una semana de reposo, se puede programar un aumento del trabajo de fuerza. En el caso de equipos que realizan menos de 3 entrenamientos semanales, la distribución temporal del trabajo es similar a la descrita en el periodo precedente. – Deben desarrollarse eventuales trabajos de pliometría en el último entrenamiento de la semana, después de los ejercicios de velocidad específica.
Desde los 16 años	En el caso de equipos que realizan más de 3 entrenamientos semanales, la programación es siempre la precedente. – Si se programa un trabajo con sobrecargas, hay que recordar que en fase preparatoria la frecuencia de trabajo debe ser bisemanal o trisemanal; durante la fase de competición una vez por semana en las sesiones de inicio de semana. La sesión con las cargas debe realizarse en grupos pequeños y si es posible fuera de los entrenamientos normales.

	CUÁNTO HACER
Hasta los 10/11 años	En proporción a la duración del entrenamiento, en todo caso sin superar los 10'/15'.
Hasta los 15/16 años	Cerca de 15', también mediante ejercicios contrapuestos y de juego.
Desde los 16 años	En el caso de equipos que realizan menos de 3 entrenamientos semanales. - En la fase preparatoria, hasta un máximo de 20'. - En la fase de competición, no superar los 15'. - Para el trabajo de pliometría sencilla, mantener la prudencia en relación con las dificultades mostradas por los diversos futbolistas. En el caso de equipos que realizan más de 3 entrenamientos semanales, prever. - Para la fuerza con carga natural y la pliometría sencilla, utilizar las mismas cantidades anteriores. - Para un eventual trabajo con sobrecargas, acordar tiempos y cargas con el experto, basándonos en las necesidades y posibilidades individuales del futbolista.

LA VELOCIDAD

Por velocidad se entiende la capacidad de realizar el mayor número de acciones motoras por unidad de tiempo.

Si nos referimos a la física, podemos definirla como la capacidad de desplazamiento en el espacio con respecto al tiempo. La velocidad depende del sistema nervioso y de la composición muscular y es poco mejorable, porque está ligada estrechamente a la velocidad de conducción del estímulo nervioso y el número de fibras blancas (veloces) presentes en el músculo. Esas fibras no son mejorables ni pueden aumentar en número, porque es patrimonio genético personal.

La velocidad es el efecto de la aplicación de una fuerza y es el resultado de una serie de cualidades que influyen en la longitud y frecuencia de los pasos:

1) Fuerza.
2) Ritmo.
3) Técnica.

Podemos distinguir dos tipos de velocidad:

- **Velocidad general** o de base, entendida como capacidad de realizar con velocidad elevada movimientos fundamentales (correr, saltar, lanzar, etc.).
- **Velocidad específica**, entendida como capacidad de realizar en el tiempo más corto posible las acciones técnicas de un deporte determinado.

La velocidad se puede expresar con:

- **Movimientos cíclicos,** es decir, movimientos biomecáni-camente similares, por ejemplo, la carrera.
- **Movimientos acíclicos,** es decir, movimientos biomecánica-mente únicos o diversos, por ejemplo, deportes de situación.

La velocidad está condicionada por las capacidades técnicas adquiridas por la persona y se realiza en cinco fases:

1. Reacción motora.
2. Aceleración.
3. Frecuencia de movimiento o de acción.
4. Velocidad punta.
5. Resistencia a la velocidad.

La reacción motora

Entendida como la capacidad de percepción de una señal y su correspondiente elaboración de respuesta, está en buena medida relacionada con las dotes naturales y por tanto poco entrenables. Sin embargo, conviene ejercitarla siempre, estimulándola con señales lo más variadas posibles de percibir con diversos canales sensitivos (oído, vista, tacto). La reacción motora incluye un factor importante denominado «**anticipación**», que en los deportes de equipo se llama «**instinto**».

El tiempo que transcurre entre la percepción de la señal o estímulo y la actuación de la respuesta motora se llama «tiempo de latencia». En relación

con la tipología de la señal, puede manifestarse de modo:
Simple, si la reacción motora y la señal se advierten precedentemente (por ejemplo, en la salida de una carrera).
Complejo, si la reacción motora se refiere a un objeto en movimiento o a la elección entre dos o más soluciones a una situación que ejerce como señal (por ejemplo, el movimiento condicionado por la dirección de un balón o de los desplazamientos imprevistos de un adversario en los deportes de equipo).

La aceleración

Entendida como la capacidad de expresar y producir una fuerza de elevada a máxima en el tiempo más breve posible manteniendo una amplitud adecuada en los movimientos.
Reclama por tanto fuerza veloz, capacidad entrenable y mejorable (ver capítulo «Fuerza»).

La frecuencia de movimiento o de acción

Capacidad de contracción o descontracción muscular rápida para realizar movimientos frecuentes, amplios y veloces en todo el cuerpo o sus extremidades,
Se puede considerar la parte coordinativa de la velocidad, porque está ligada estrechamente al sistema nervioso.

Velocidad punta

Máxima velocidad instantánea personal que se alcanza en un solo momento y luego se tiende a desacelerar.

Resistencia a la velocidad

Capacidad de oponerse lo más posible a la desaceleración. Depende de la capacidad de resistencia anaeróbica, que está escasamente desarrollada en los jóvenes y por tanto poco adaptada a ellos. Su entrenabilidad aumenta gradualmente después de la adolescencia, pero solo después de los 18 años se aprecian mejoras eficaces.

LOS COMPONENTES DE LA VELOCIDAD			
RAPIDEZ DE REACCIÓN MOTORA	ACELERACIÓN	VELOCIDAD DE MOVIMIENTO	MANTENIMIENTO DE LA VELOCIDAD
Percepción de la señal	Fuerza veloz	Rapidez de ejecución	Velocidad lanzada – Pico máximo de velocidad
Elaboración de la respuesta		Frecuencia de los movimientos	Velocidad prolongada en el tiempo
Respuesta motora		Amplitud de movimientos	

LOS FUNDAMENTOS DE LA VELOCIDAD	
FACTORES CONSTITUCIONALES	**FACTORES MEJORABLES**
Velocidad de conducción del estímulo nervioso	Capacidad neuromuscular de contracción rápida
	Capacidades técnicas específicas
	Capacidad de expresión de fuerza veloz
Composición del músculo: Número de fibras blancas	Capacidad de recurrir a los procesos voluntarios
Conformación física	Capacidad de recurrir a las fibras musculares
	Capacidad de activación de los procesos bioquímicos

Son importantes las correlaciones entre la velocidad y las demás capacidades motoras:

Entre la velocidad y la fuerza veloz (entendida en sus distintas expresiones: rápida, instantánea y explosiva).

Entre velocidad y destreza (capacidad de realizar un gesto con la máxima eficacia, en el menor tiempo posible y con el menor gasto energético).

Entre velocidad y flexibilidad (entendida como capacidad de realizar movimientos disfrutando de la máxima amplitud articular y elasticidad muscular).

Entre velocidad y resistencia específica (entendida como la capacidad de prolongar en el tiempo prestaciones rápidas y resistir a su ralentización por la aparición de la fatiga).

No existe correlación entre velocidad y resistencia general porque:

- La primera usa las fibras blancas (veloces) y el mecanismo anaeróbico aláctico.
- La segunda usa las fibras rojas (lentas) y el mecanismo aeróbico.

La velocidad en el fútbol

La velocidad constituye una de las dotes esenciales del futbolista y está siempre condicionada por las situaciones del juego y la capacidad técnica. Es una capacidad muy compleja, pero los márgenes de mejora son grandes. Es un tipo de velocidad que debe permitir al futbolista realizar correctamente los gestos técnicos, mantenerse en equilibrio con facilidad y cambiar rápidamente de dirección y velocidad.

En relación con la prestación futbolística, hablaremos de **velocidad controlada** (velocidad de anticipación y de decisión), que incluye los siguientes aspectos mejorables:

1. Capacidad de actuar y reaccionar rápidamente a las señales.
2. Capacidad de salida y parada.
3. Capacidad de mantener la velocidad máxima.

4. Prontitud en encarar el balón.
5. Capacidad de leer el partido.
6. Capacidad de percepción.
7. Capacidad de tomar las decisiones apropiadas,

Para un análisis más profundo y oportuno, distinguimos la velocidad del futbolista en dos grupos:
- Velocidad con balón.
- Velocidad sin balón.

En el primer caso, la velocidad con balón, esta será más elevada cuanto más desarrollada esté la capacidad técnica del futbolista. Cuando se abre un espacio amplio delante del jugador que posee el balón, la acción será bastante fluida y será seguramente muy cercana al máximo. Sin embargo, si el jugador está siendo perseguido o defendido por el adversario, el balón no solo será un obstáculo para la carrera, sino que también la presencia del adversario ocasionará una dificultad en la propia carrera, por lo que habrá que recurrir a gestos técnicos como fintas, cambios de ritmo, de dirección o paradas repentinas.

En el segundo caso, velocidad sin balón, se pueden alcanzar puntas de velocidad mayores, pero siempre condicionadas por las diversas situaciones de juego. Hay que tener en cuenta también el momento en el que el futbolista ha perdido la posesión del balón y debe perseguir al adversario. Este tipo de carrera «defensiva» puede ser a plena velocidad en casos

extremos o de velocidad diversa si se puede disponer de cobertura por parte de los compañeros. El compañero en situación más ventajosa debe detener al poseedor del balón para permitir a su compañero recuperar la posición más eficaz. *Sobre la base de estas observaciones, resulta que los componentes técnico-tácticos reducen la posibilidad obtener la máxima velocidad y por tanto al jugador no se le requiere un trabajo veloz absoluto, sino una capacidad mixta a la que podemos llamar* **«habilidad veloz»**.

Cómo ejercitar la velocidad

La velocidad, entre las capacidades condicionales, es la menos mejorable porque está estrechamente ligada a factores de tipo nervioso y coordinativo. Una capacidad elevada de conducción nerviosa no se debe a la práctica deportiva, sino que está ligada a una «grandeza funcional de origen constitutivo». Por tanto, «un asno puede entrenarse todo lo que quiera, pero no será nunca un caballo, lo más que puede ser es un asno veloz».

Los esquemas que hemos presentado y las observaciones que hemos hecho nos ayudan a comprender mejor cuáles son los principios del entrenamiento de la velocidad. Las modalidades con las que la velocidad se puede emplear durante el juego pueden esquematizarse así:

VELOCI DAD ESPECÍ FICA	CON BALÓN	Con espacios amplios	
		Con adversario al lado	
		Con más adversarios	
	SIN BALÓN	Para llegar antes al balón	
		Para alcanzar a un adversario	
		Para cambiar de posición	*Para desmarcarse*
			Para crear espacio
			Para entrar al hueco

Mediante una observación atenta del partido, se ve que los rasgos de la carrera en velocidad muy raramente superan los 30 metros, más frecuentemente se limitan a 15/20 metros. De esto se deduce la importancia de la **capacidad de aceleración** (partiendo de parada o cambio de velocidad), que en la jerga se suele llamar «sprint».

Durante el partido se presenta la necesidad de realizar carreras de 40-60 metros, que, si deben repetirse frecuentemente, llevan a introducir el concepto de resistencia a la velocidad. Por eso debemos referirnos a todo lo que hemos dicho cuando hemos hablado de resistencia específica.

El entrenamiento de la velocidad

Los esquemas presentados y las observaciones realizadas nos ayudan de comprender cuáles son los principios que hay que seguir para entrenar la velocidad en el fútbol.

Un entrenamiento de la velocidad que se base solo en la carrera no basta para obtener la máxima aceleración o para saltar lo más alto posible para cabecear. En paralelo al entrenamiento de la velocidad, el futbolista debe mejorar también su calidad de fuerza instantánea, sobre todo en lo que se refiere a las extremidades inferiores, aplicando un entrenamiento de potenciación de la musculatura de las piernas.

FUERZA VELOZ	Saltos. Subidas. Descensos. Carreras con sobrecargas.
TÉCNICA DE LA CARRERA VELOZ	Andar al paso. Control del avance. Coordinación en velocidad.
CARRERA VELOZ	Carrera a la máxima velocidad de 30 a 100 m. como máximo.
ACELERACIÓN	Carreras con máxima aceleración

	de 5 m. a 30/40 m. como máximo.
CARRERA EN EL FÚTBOL	Aceleraciones con cambio de dirección, Aceleraciones con cambio de sentido. Aceleraciones con frenadas improvisadas. Aceleraciones combinadas con cambios de dirección, de sentido y frenadas.

Entrenamiento de la velocidad general

Será necesario programar ejercicios que busquen:
- **a)** Mejorar la velocidad.
- **b)** Mejorar la fuerza veloz.
- **c)** Mejorar la resistencia a la velocidad.

Ejercicios para la velocidad
- Deben desarrollar la velocidad límite, serán por tanto sin balón.
- Deben permitir concentrar la atención y la voluntad en la velocidad de ejecución. El jugador debe saber bien qué debe hacer.
- Deben ser ejercicios de duración limitada para poder mantener siempre alta la velocidad de ejecución.
- Deben realizarse cuando el jugador esté en condiciones de frescura.
- Las distancias de carrera podrán ser por tanto de 20-30-40 metros.
- La forma de trabajo que permite obtener los mejores efectos es la de las pruebas repetidas.

- La duración de las pausas no debe ser superior a 3-4' ni inferior a los 2', siempre en relación con la duración de la longitud de la carrera y el grado de entrenamiento.
- Carrera en descenso (máx. 10-12%) de unos 10-20 m. En la parte de descenso se realizará una aceleración fuerte (con control del paso). En la parte llana hay que buscar el aumento de la longitud del paso.

EJEMPLO DE PROGRESIÓN DE DIFICULTAD EN EL ENTRENAMIENTO DE CARRERA EN 20 M. EN EL FÚTBOL	
1	Carrera rectilínea con aceleración máxima.
2	Carrera con aceleración máxima con cambio de dirección a 90°.
3	Carrera con aceleración máxima con cambio de dirección de más de 90°.
4	Carrera con aceleración máxima con cambio de sentido.
5	Carrera rectilínea con aceleración máxima con parada y reanudación en la misma dirección.

Ejercicios para la fuerza veloz

Refiriéndonos a lo dicho acerca de la fuerza, recordemos que los ejercicios para la fuerza veloz más importantes para la velocidad son los que

permiten ejecuciones a una velocidad máxima o al menos muy elevada. Los ejercicios serán con carga natural o sobrecargas muy ligeras, sobre distancias de 25-30 metros. Los ejercicios dedicados a la mejora de esta capacidad específica pueden ser:
- Aceleración máxima con partidas diversas.
- Multisaltos y brincos variados.
- Carreras con rodillas en alto (skip bajo, skip medio y skip alto).
- Ejercicios pliométricos simples.
- Carreras en subida (máx. 10/12%, se deben admitir pendientes máximas 2"/3", debido a las distancias indicadas de 25-30 m.).
- Ejercicios de remolque. Evitar carreras con cinturones con lastre.

Ejercicios para la resistencia a la velocidad

En este caso, los ejercicios se refieren a lo ya dicho para la resistencia específica. Aquí nos debe preocupar mejorar la capacidad de repetir muchas veces tramos breves de velocidad, buscando aplazar el umbral de la fatiga. En entrenamiento se realiza usando una serie de carreras breves de 30-40-50-60 metros a velocidad casi máxima, repetidos con frecuencia elevada, es decir, con reducción del tiempo de las pausas tras las pruebas, más largo tras las series. El entrenamiento prevé 9/16 repeticiones subdivididas en 3/4 series.

Entrenamiento para la velocidad específica

Se debe recurrir a la carrera con y sin balón y a situaciones de juego. En la base de la posibilidad de mejorar la velocidad específica está una capacidad elevada de velocidad general. En este caso, resulta fundamental la importancia de la destreza como «dominio del balón» y de la «capacidad de juicio». Las indicaciones para el entrenamiento específico son exactamente las mismas que hemos examinado para el entrenamiento de la velocidad general con el añadido de la ejecución de un gesto técnico específico a realizar en velocidad (conducción, pase, cambio de dirección, etc.) con o sin balón. Solamente varían las modalidades para llegar a una ejecución veloz. Con respecto a la velocidad óptima hay que actuar gradualmente para poder aprender el gesto y las acciones.

Indicaciones metódicas para el entrenamiento de la velocidad

El entrenamiento de la velocidad debe estar siempre precedido por una puesta en acción apropiada, **evitando en todo caso ejercicios de estiramiento persistente** para evitar la inhibición del «circuito gamma» (motoneuronas γ, circuito neuromuscular que protege automáticamente la musculatura frente a estiramientos peligrosos).

Para conseguir la máxima eficacia del entrenamiento de la velocidad, hay que seguir las siguientes indicaciones metódicas:

1. El entrenamiento para la velocidad debe iniciarse pronto, ya en los primeros años de escuela elemental, porque en esta edad el sistema nervioso central y la estructura fibrosa de los músculos se modifican y mejoran con mucha facilidad.

2. Los estímulos para la velocidad y la fuerza instantánea deben estar presentes en cada sesión de entrenamiento.

3. El entrenamiento de la velocidad se realiza al inicio de la unidad de trabajo y en estado de reposo.

4. El entrenamiento de la velocidad solo tiene efectos si se realiza con intensidad límite.

5. Debe suspenderse el entrenamiento de la velocidad tras los primeros síntomas de fatiga.

6. Los tiempos y pausas de recuperación son muy importantes para que se restablezcan los depósitos de CP (fosfocreatina).

7. En los casos de dos entrenamientos diarios, el entrenamiento de velocidad se realiza solo en la primera unidad.

8. El entrenamiento de velocidad no se realiza solamente en el día posterior a una competición.

9. Para hacer más «brillantes o ágiles» a los deportistas es posible realizar el día anterior al partido una unidad limitada de saltos y aceleraciones breves.

10. Para evitar un «estereotipo» en los estímulos, es necesario que el entrenamiento

de la velocidad prevea una variación continua de las propuestas de entrenamiento (distancias y tipos de ejercicio).

11. Prestar atención a que los estímulos sean adecuados para las prestaciones necesarias del fútbol.

12. Tener siempre presente que todos los factores que determinan la velocidad, fuerza, coordinación, resistencia y flexibilidad deben entrenarse en paralelo.

13. El entrenamiento de la velocidad debe dirigirse siempre a las capacidades técnica con y sin balón:
    a) Situaciones de juego.
    b) Juegos de contraposición 1 contra 1, 2 contra 2, etc.
    c) Juegos con superioridad de los adversarios.
    d) Juegos en campos con dimensiones reducidas.

14. A menudo se debe buscar superar los valores de aceleración y velocidad límite adquiridos, con ejercicios especiales, los supermétodos:
    a) Carreras en ligero descenso (permiten sobrepasar los límites personales de concepción de velocidad).
    b) Pliometría simple (produce una potencia que no se consigue lograr en condiciones normales).

15. En la elección de los ejercicios, actuar de modo que el grado de dificultad de estos

aumente progresivamente para hacer que la aplicación de la velocidad sea siempre la máxima.

16. La potencia en la carrera veloz depende de la calidad de las fibras, de la longitud del brazo de palanca y de la longitud de las inclinaciones de las fibras.

La velocidad en los jóvenes

Para los chicos es una capacidad muy importante y entre los 9 y los 15 años se producen sus mayores incrementos. En este tramo de edad (infantil → juvenil), la elevada plasticidad de la corteza cerebral y la inestabilidad del sistema nervioso permiten una óptima formación básica de las capacidades veloces.

EDAD	CARACTERÍSTICA	HOMBRES	MUJERES
9-11 años	Máxima frecuencia de paso: número de pasos por unidad de tiempo	Más de 4 pasos por segundo	Hasta 4 pasos por segundo
11-15 años	Se registra un desarrollo intenso de la fuerza rápida	Mejora mucho la longitud del paso, del lanzamiento de objetos y la altura del salto	
De 10-11 a 13-14 años	Mejora la velocidad de desplazamiento en metros por segundo	De 5,5 a 6,5-7 m./s.	
15-16 años	La frecuencia máxima tiende a disminuir y estabilizarse	Cerca de 4 pasos por segundo	Cerca de 3,5 pasos por segundo

Primera edad escolar

Entre los 5 y los 7 años se produce un enorme perfeccionamiento del movimiento de carrera, con efectos positivos también sobre la velocidad de carrera. Se aconseja en este periodo un aumento de los ejercicios de velocidad.

Entre los 7 y los 11 años, la frecuencia y la velocidad motora sufren el mayor desarrollo absoluto. También es muy importante la notable mejora de la *reactividad* y con ella la mejora del tiempo de reacción o de latencia.

La disposición física es tal que permite entrenar la fuerza de salto.

Segunda edad escolar

Entre los 10 y los 13 años mejora posteriormente el tiempo de reacción y de latencia hasta prácticamente valores adultos. Los chicos que se entrenan al menos dos veces por semana consiguen un importante aumento de las cualidades de velocidad que son además superiores a los de la edad posterior. Se aconseja suministrar estímulos múltiples de velocidad y reacción motora con ejercicios de reactividad combinados con aceleraciones límite.

Pubertad

Entre los 12 y los 14/15 años se registran los grandes cambios hormonales (aumento de la

testosterona en los chicos) y mejora además la capacidad anaeróbica (resistencia a la velocidad). En ese periodo se logran importantes mejoras de la velocidad y la fuerza instantánea.

Adolescencia

En el tramo de edad entre los 14 y los 16 años se hace posible el ejercicio ilimitado de todos los aspectos atléticos y coordinativos de la velocidad. Los métodos y los contenidos del entrenamiento se corresponden más o menos con los de los jugadores adultos. Las carreras y los saltos muy explosivos y a velocidad límite, sobre todo a los 16 años, y se cuidan de modo especial.

	QUÉ HACER
Hasta 10/11 años	La fuerza veloz hasta esta edad se ejercita mediante el juego y ejercicios relacionados con este. - Diversas formas de relevos y juegos de velocidad, aceleraciones y paradas breves tipo «roba la bandera». - Siempre debe haber espacio en la sesión para el partidillo, porque si en ella escasean los estímulos veloces, este genera dichos estímulos en condiciones más reales.
Hasta 15/16 años	Ejercitar la velocidad general y específica siguiendo las indicaciones de las páginas anteriores. - Siempre debe haber espacio en la sesión para el partidillo, porque si en ella escasean los estímulos veloces, este genera dichos estímulos en condiciones más reales.
Desde los 16 años	Ejercitar la velocidad general y específica siguiendo las indicaciones de las páginas anteriores. - Siempre debe haber espacio en la sesión para el partidillo, porque si en ella escasean los estímulos veloces, este genera dichos estímulos en condiciones más reales.

	CUÁNDO HACERLO
Hasta 10/11 años	Ejercitar la velocidad (rapidez) en todas las sesiones de entrenamiento y siempre en forma de juego.
Hasta 15/16 años	En el periodo preparatorio, iniciar de inmediato con el trabajo de velocidad general y, después de algunas sesiones, con la específica en cada sesión de entrenamiento. - Al acercarse el inicio del campeonato y durante la competición, dedicarse sobre todo a la velocidad específica y en las sesiones inmediatamente vecinas a los partidos. En las demás sesiones, programar siempre un trabajo de velocidad general o de reclamación de velocidad (marcha y ejercicios de impulso). - El trabajo de velocidad debe desarrollarse siempre con la musculatura fresca, por tanto, en la primera parte del entrenamiento.
Desde los 16 años	En el periodo preparatorio, iniciar de inmediato con el trabajo de velocidad general y después de algunas sesiones con la específica, con volúmenes en progresión y en cada sesión de entrenamiento. - Al acercarse el inicio del campeonato y durante la competición, dedicarse sobre todo a la velocidad específica y en las sesiones inmediatamente vecinas a los partidos. En las demás sesiones, programar siempre un trabajo de velocidad general o de reclamación de velocidad (marcha y ejercicios de impulso). - El trabajo de velocidad debe desarrollarse siempre con la musculatura fresca, por tanto, en la primera parte del entrenamiento.

CUÁNTO HACER	
Hasta 10/11 años	Prestar mucha atención a los tiempos de trabajo individual, que deben ser inferiores a los 8" y a las señales de disminución de prestaciones.
Hasta 15/16 años	Para la cantidad de trabajo de velocidad, seguir las indicaciones de las páginas anteriores y respetar las necesidades individuales de cada futbolista sin generalizar nunca el volumen de carga.
Desde los 16 años	Para la cantidad de trabajo de velocidad, seguir las indicaciones de las páginas anteriores y respetar las necesidades individuales de cada futbolista sin generalizar nunca el volumen de carga.

N.B.: Los únicos periodos en los que la velocidad no puede entrenarse son los posteriores a las lesiones. El jugador debe volver a la ejecución veloz con cautela y gradualmente.

LA FLEXIBILIDAD

La flexibilidad es la capacidad de realizar movimientos muy amplios, en los límites permitidos por las articulaciones y la elasticidad muscular.

La flexibilidad se realiza mediante:

- **La movilidad articular**

Es decir, la capacidad de poder utilizar al máximo el recorrido de nuestras articulaciones. Influye de modo eficaz la amplitud de los movimientos y está condicionada por el estiramiento muscular. Para mejorar o mantener la movilidad a buen nivel, se deben realizar ejercicios de impulso, flexión, oscilación y rotación.

- **El estiramiento muscular**

Es decir, la capacidad de los músculos estriados de cambiar de forma y volver a su estado original.

Los músculos poseen tres propiedades fundamentales:

1. **Elasticidad**, es decir, la capacidad de las fibras musculares de aumentar su longitud.
2. **Contractibilidad**, es decir, la capacidad de las fibras musculares de reducir su longitud.
3. **Excitabilidad**, es decir, la capacidad de las fibras musculares de reaccionar a los estímulos nerviosos.

Para mejorar la elasticidad muscular se deben realizar ejercicios de estiramiento (stretching) mantenido y nunca amortiguado.

Realizando los ejercicios de estiramiento con regularidad se logra:
- Reducir las tensiones musculares.
- Mejorar la movilidad articular.

Son movilizantes todos los ejercicios y movimientos que llevan gradualmente a las articulaciones a su máximo recorrido. Los niños tienen en general una movilidad elevada, por lo que no necesitan ejercitar la flexibilidad de manera específica. Entre los 12 y los 15 años, a causa del aumento de la estatura y la tonicidad muscular, es posible que encuentren disminuciones rápidas de la flexibilidad y por tanto es útil iniciar una formación adecuada para mantener elevada esta capacidad. Evitar, sin embargo, el uso de ejercicios de movilidad pasiva, en la práctica, los realizados con la ayuda de un compañero o de sobrecargas.

La capacidad de relajar y descontraer los músculos antagonistas es el punto de partida para aumentar la flexibilidad.

La flexibilidad está condicionada por diversos factores:
- *Factores externos*

Hora del día.
Temperatura ambiente.
Fuerzas externas (gravedad, inercia, sobrecarga).
- *Factores internos cualitativos*

Edad y sexo.
Eficiencia en el movimiento.
Masas musculares.

Estructura articular.

- *Factores internos cuantitativos*

Capacidad de relajamiento de la musculatura antagonista. Elasticidad de las formaciones articulares. Capacidad de activación de los procesos neurofisiológicos.

Origen del stretching

Stretching es un término inglés (que significa alargamiento, estiramiento) usado en la práctica deportiva para indicar un conjunto de ejercicios dirigidos a la mejora muscular. Los ejercicios de stretching afectan a músculos, tendones, huesos y articulaciones y en gran parte consisten en movimiento de estiramiento muscular. Todos nosotros, al levantarnos por la mañana, sentimos la necesidad de estirarnos y alargarnos. Lo mismo hacen numerosos animales. Se trata, por tanto, al menos en alguna de sus formas, de un acto instintivo y natural. Esto ha llevado a un desarrollo de los estudios y las aplicaciones del stretching, además de a su difusión en el campo de la educación física, tanto como complemento de otros deportes como como actividad física autónoma.

Fisiología del stretching

Como ya hemos explicado antes, los músculos realizan su actividad alargándose y acortándose. Casi todos los músculos tienen una contraparte

complementaria: flexores y extensores, aductores y abductores, intrarrotadores y extrarrotadores. Cuando el flexor (por ejemplo, el bíceps del brazo) se contrae, el extensor correspondiente (el tríceps) se relaja, y viceversa.

El principal efecto de los ejercicios de estiramiento es el de llevar a los músculos a su máximo alargamiento. Cuando un músculo alcanza su alargamiento máximo, responde con un reflejo miotático para proteger el tejido muscular y conjuntivo frente a posibles daños. Consiste en una contracción muscular automática que acorta el músculo, inducida por unos órganos llamados husos neuromusculares.

Diversas tipologías de stretching

De acuerdo con la dinámica utilizada, se pueden definir diversas tipologías de stretching.

Stretching balístico
Es una técnica obsoleta de estiramiento muscular, muy utilizada en los años '70 y '80 (y todavía hoy enseñada en muchos gimnasios), que consiste en hacer oscilar repetidamente y de manera descontrolada las articulaciones o el torso tratando de forzar el alargamiento muscular más allá de su rango normal de movimientos. Este movimiento oscilatorio es contraproducente, porque activa de forma muy fuerte el reflejo miotático.

Stretching dinámico

Esta técnica difiere de la precedente en la modalidad de ejecución de los ejercicios.

El concepto es siempre el de hacer oscilar las articulaciones o el torso, pero de manera controlada y lenta, sin recurrir a arrebatos ni oscilaciones. El movimiento consiste en hacer rotar en una dirección determinada las articulaciones de forma controlada, evitando el efecto rebote y el amortiguamiento que causan las activaciones del reflejo miotático, llevando al músculo a reaccionar contrayéndose en lugar de relajándose.

Stretching estático pasivo

Consiste en asumir una postura concreta y mantenerla relajando el músculo afectado durante cierto tiempo, en general de 20 a 40 segundos, mediante el apoyo de una pareja, por tanto, sin la contracción de los músculos agonistas.

Stretching estático activo

Consiste en asumir una postura concreta y mantenerla relajando el músculo afectado durante cierto tiempo, 20-40 segundos, sin ayuda de una pareja. Están previstas dos fases: fase de preestiramiento, en la que se asume la postura lentamente, inspirando antes del movimiento y respirando durante el movimiento para asumir la postura pretendida. Alcanzada la postura, se mantiene durante un máximo de 10 segundos, sin llegar al estiramiento máximo del músculo afectado, sin sobrepasar el umbral del dolor, inspirando antes del movimiento y espirando durante el movimiento

y, una vez asumida la postura de máximo estiramiento, mantenerla por un máximo de 20 segundos.

Stretching isométrico

Es un tipo de estiramiento muy usado en la danza, las artes marciales y la gimnasia artística para conseguir la máxima agilidad muscular. Este método fue desarrollado en principio por el neurofisiólogo estadounidense Herman Kabat a finales de los '40 como reeducación neuromuscular y luego fue adoptado y adaptado como técnica de entrenamiento.

Existen varios métodos de stretching isométrico:

El PNF (Proprioceptive Neuromuscolar Facilitation, o "facilitación neuromuscular propioceptiva").

El CRAC (Contract Relax Antagonist Contract, es decir, "contracción, relajación y contracción de los músculos antagonistas").

El CRS (Contract Relax Stretch, es decir, "contracción, relajación y stretching").

PNF

Este sistema está compuesto por cuatro fases:
1. Estiramiento máximo gradual y lento del músculo.
2. Contracción isométrica durante unos 15-20 segundos (en posición de estiramiento).
3. Relajación de unos 5 segundos.
4. Posterior estiramiento del músculo contraído anteriormente durante al menos 30 segundos.

176

CRAC

Se diferencia del PNF en la fase final del estiramiento. Prevé la contracción de los músculos antagonistas a aquellos que se están estirando. En este método se disfruta del fenómeno de la inhibición recíproca, que facilita la relajación del músculo agonista.

CRS

Este sistema se basa en una contracción isométrica del músculo 10-15 segundos, seguida de una relajación de 5 segundos y un posterior estiramiento.

El método de Anderson (1984)

<u>Cómo estirar</u>

Aprender la técnica apropiada permite poder realizar los ejercicios de estiramiento independientemente de la forma física. El ejercicio correcto y regular permitirá realizar cada movimiento con mayor facilidad, aunque hará falta tiempo para poder eliminar la rigidez muscular.

El ejercicio del estiramiento no debe ser una actividad estresante, violenta o competitiva, sino serena, relajante y placentera. La ejecución del estiramiento debe adaptarse a cada uno de nosotros y debe estar en sintonía con nuestros músculos mediante la toma de conciencia de las diversas tensiones musculares.

Cada uno de nosotros es un ser física y mentalmente único, con sus propios ritmos, fuerza, resistencia, velocidad, flexibilidad y carácter, pero todos pueden

apreciar los beneficios producidos por un estiramiento muscular regular y correcto. La técnica equivocada y muy practicada del estiramiento muscular es la de realizar movimientos reboteadores y llevar el estiramiento hasta el umbral del dolor. Ese modo de actuar causa daños, efectos a veces traumáticos que no animan a realizar regularmente y con satisfacción el ejercicio de estiramiento muscular.

Veamos cómo es posible realizar un estiramiento muscular correcto, examinando las diversas fases de tensiones que pueden alcanzar y experimentar nuestros músculos.

Tensión fácil
Cuando se inicia el estiramiento es necesario quedarse 10"-30" en esta tensión fácil sin amortiguar, pasar luego a una *tensión media*, relajarse y buscar sentir un aligeramiento de dicha tensión. Estas fases reducen la oposición muscular al estiramiento y preparan a los tejidos para la tensión de desarrollo.

Tensión de desarrollo
Tras la fase anterior, se debe llegar lentamente a la fase de tensión de desarrollo sin amortiguar, hay que moverse lentamente hasta sentir una tensión discreta y mantener la posición por 10-30", repetir el ejercicio al menos tres veces. Esta fase aumenta el estiramiento muscular. No entrar nunca en tensión drástica, en la práctica, la que causa dolor. La respiración durante el ejercicio debe ser lenta,

rítmica y bajo control, no contener nunca la respiración durante el estiramiento. Si la postura alcanzada impide la acción respiratoria natural, no se está suficientemente relajado y es por tanto necesario disminuir la tensión del estiramiento hasta poder recobrar la respiración natural.

Efectos del stretching

En general, el stretching (excluyendo el tipo balístico) reduce la tensión muscular, mejora la coordinación y la propiocepción (es decir, la toma de conciencia del cuerpo propio), previene lesiones musculares y de tendones y mejora la rotación articular. Sin embargo, el entrenamiento para mantener el estiramiento por periodos largos genera una habituación del huso del músculo, reduciendo la señal que genera el reflejo del estiramiento.

Al reducir el umbral del reflejo miotático, existe la posibilidad potencial de favorecer ciertos tipos de lesiones, especialmente si se realiza el stretching antes de un partido.

Por tanto, es razonable sugerir una moderación en la actividad de estiramiento y un control del programa de entrenamiento por parte de personal cualificado.

Stretching y tendones
Los ejercicios de stretching afectan a las fibras musculares y poco a los tendones, porque su tejido

presenta características que no permiten el estiramiento:
- Tejido fibroso.
- Poco irrigado a nivel sanguíneo.
- Tiene poca capacidad de adaptación al entrenamiento.
- Tiene poca capacidad de reparación en caso de lesión.
- Pierde fácilmente la capacidad de desplazamiento con tejidos vecinos.

Stretching y edad

A pesar de la elevada eficacia del entrenamiento de stretching para la mejora de la flexibilidad, no está indicado para el entrenamiento infantil y juvenil y solo es idóneo a partir de una cierta edad. Como en entrenamiento-aprendizaje de los niños debe desarrollarse solamente de forma lúdica, el carácter realista y poco divertido del stretching está poco de acuerdo con su mentalidad. **En los niños el riesgo de lesiones provocadas por estiramientos musculares activos es tan insignificante que los ejercicios en ese sentido son inútiles y a veces contraproducentes.** La flexibilidad es la única capacidad condicional que alcanza el punto más alto de su desarrollo en edad infantil, después de la cual está destinada a empeorar si no se somete a ejercicios regulares. Por este motivo se aconseja iniciar un trabajo metódico de stretching a partir de los 14-15 años, pero **efectuarlo siempre lejos del entrenamiento**. El entrenamiento de la flexibilidad se debe organizar en ciclos anuales, pero conviene aplicarlo cotidianamente y durante todo el año, convenciendo

180

a los futbolistas desde el inicio a practicarlo regularmente de modo individual y personal. Cuanto más continuo sea, mayor será su efecto.

Stretching y calentamiento
Utilizado durante la fase de calentamiento, el stretching debería tener la función de aumentar la temperatura del cuerpo.
El aumento de la temperatura interna del músculo depende de su grado de vascularización.
El ejercicio muscular, mediante una alternancia de contracciones y descontracciones, permite al músculo desarrollar una acción de bombeo que tiene como consecuencia la mejora de la circulación sanguínea.
Una alternancia de contracciones concéntricas frente a una resistencia media constituye el método más apropiado para aumentar la temperatura del músculo.
Veamos ahora qué pasa durante el estiramiento muscular.
Alter (1996), autor de «Science of flexibility», ha demostrado que los estiramientos provocan en el músculo tensiones elevadas que comportan una interrupción de la irrigación sanguínea: <u>En la práctica se produce lo contrario del efecto «vascularizante» que se busca</u>.
Cuando se alternan acciones de estiramiento y contracciones, el paso de la sangre se produce durante las fases de relajamiento y por tanto la tensión en el estiramiento no parece el mejor medio para estimular el efecto «vascularizante».

Wiemann y Klee (2000) han ratificado la escasa eficacia del stretching para aumentar la temperatura muscular. Los estiramientos musculares clásicos no parecen por tanto los medios más apropiados para realizar un calentamiento muscular.

<u>Stretching y prestaciones</u>
Algunos investigadores han verificado el empeoramiento de las prestaciones y de los valores de los test en atletas sometidos previamente a ejercicios de stretching.
He aquí algunos datos de los análisis:
Wiemeyer (2003) ha confirmado una disminución en un test de salto del 3 al 5,3%.
Henning y Podzielny (1994) advirtieron un empeoramiento en saltos de altura.
Begert y Hillebrecth (2003) verificaron la reducción de la fuerza reactiva del 8 al 10%% en saltos hacia abajo.
El saltador Schmidtbleicher (1997), aumentó el tiempo de contacto con la tierra de 8 ms. (8%) y empeoró la altura de salto en 2,6 cm. (-7%).
Wiemann y Klee, registraron un empeoramiento de 0,14 seg. en carreras de 35 m.
Rosembaum y Henning (1997) explicaron que los efectos mecánicos del stretching limitan la capacidad de reproducir la fuerza.
Un estudio de Fowles y colaboradores (2000) ha demostrado que el estiramiento prolongado de un grupo muscular cusa la disminución de su activación de la fuerza relativa de contracción. La pérdida de fuerza está también presente una hora después del estiramiento. La disminución de la

activación muscular se recupera pronto (15 minutos), pero la fuerza contráctil, incluso después de 60 minutos, permanece inferior al 9%.

Esta hipótesis es apoyada por otras investigaciones, según las cuales después del stretching se presenta una disminución del stiffness (esfuerzo que realiza un músculo para acortarse después de ser estirado) de la unidad músculo-articular *(Enoka 1994; Rosenbaum y Henning 1995; Magnusson 1996; Klinge 1997; Hutton 1999; Wiemann y Klee 2000).*

Stretching como prevención
Muchos consideran que el uso de ejercicios de stretching es fundamental para prevenir lesiones musculares. Las conclusiones de numerosas investigaciones contradicen esta afirmación. Shrier (1999), en una investigación muy documentada (más de 12 artículos), ha constatado que el stretching antes del ejercicio no reduce realmente el riesgo de lesiones musculares.

Pope y colaboradores (1998, 2000) no encuentran ninguna diferencia significativa entre grupos de «stretch» y «no stretch» que sufrieron 214 lesiones de naturaleza muscular-tendinosa.

Van Mechelen y colaboradores (1993) estudiaron durante 16 semanas en una población de 320 marchadores los efectos del calentamiento con ejercicios de estiramiento y con trabajo de enfriamiento.

El grupo que no había realizado ni el calentamiento ni los estiramientos ni tampoco el enfriamiento sufrió menos lesiones musculares (4,9 incidentes por cada 1.000 horas de entrenamiento con respecto

al grupo que había sido sometido a calentamiento, estiramiento y enfriamiento (5,5 incidentes por cada 1.000 horas de entrenamiento).

Lally (1994) ha demostrado, sobre 600 maratonistas, que el número de lesiones musculares registradas resultaba superior (un 35% más) en el grupo de los atletas que habían utilizado ejercicios de stretching.

Albrecht y colaboradores (1999), afirman que, hasta ahora, en la literatura, no se ha logrado probar que gracias al estiramiento se impidan o reduzcan las lesiones, ni que influyan en la aparición o no de dolores musculares. Los resultados de estas investigaciones demuestran cómo la ciencia contradice clamorosamente tanto el comportamiento como las convicciones de entrenadores, preparadores e incluso deportistas.

	QUÉ HACER
Hasta los 10/11 años	La flexibilidad es en modo particular su componente de movilidad articular, hasta esta edad se ejercita a través del juego o los ejercicios lúdicos, por lo que se trata de un entrenamiento genérico.
Hasta los 15/16 años	Es una fase particular de desarrollo y crecimiento, el trabajo de la flexibilidad debe ser adecuado para la edad y las características individuales, usando ejercicios activos. Evitar por tanto ejercicios pasivos o excesivamente forzados.
Desde los 16 años	Empiezan a cerrarse las láminas cartilaginosas (en las jóvenes un poco antes), es la indicación de la adquisición de una mayor resistencia física. Desde este momento, el entrenamiento de la flexibilidad puede ser completado también con el uso de ejercicios pasivos con cargas externas.

	CUÁNDO HACERLO
Hasta los 10/11 años	Los ejercicios de estiramiento son potencialmente completamente superfluos. Los niños que hayan perdido repentinamente la flexibilidad deben realizar ejercicios domésticos cotidianos y constantes, pero fuera del entrenamiento.
Hasta los 15/16 años	Se inicia el crecimiento de la primera fase de la pubertad y se hace necesario un entrenamiento genérico de la flexibilidad. La ejercitación de la flexibilidad debe ser personal regular y diaria, pero hay que realizarla fuerza de las sesiones de entrenamiento.
Desde los 16 años	A partir de esta edad, los ejercicios de flexibilidad se orientarán hacia el stretching. El trabajo debe ser siempre personal, regular, diario y fuera de las sesiones de entrenamiento. Corresponde al entrenador explicar la importancia, las bases y la problemática.

185

CUÁNTO HACER	
Hasta los 10/11 años	No se puede indicar cantidad. En caso de necesidad, pocas repeticiones, con frecuencia diaria.
Hasta los 15/16 años	En relación con la condición de desarrollo muscular personal. Con cantidades adecuadas al objetivo a alcanzar.
Desde los 16 años	En relación con la tipología del entrenamiento que se realiza. Recordar que a cada entrenamiento de potenciación con sobrecargas deben corresponder al menos cinco sesiones de flexibilidad.

Organizar la prevención de lesiones evitando ejercicios equivocados

La mayor parte de las lesiones en las actividades motoras no deriva de acontecimientos traumáticos, sino de la ejecución de ejercicios en condiciones de fatiga excesiva.

O lo que es peor, de la ejecución de ejercicios no realizada correctamente o de que estos no son apropiados para la edad o a la capacidad de los alumnos.

En la elección de los ejercicios y en la carga de trabajo es importante respetar el principio de la gradualidad y la progresividad.

Los factores principales que pueden crear las condiciones para lesiones son:

- Una condición física insuficiente.
- Una ejecución técnica incorrecta.
- La utilización de equipo inadecuado.
- Ropa inapropiada.

- Asistencia superficial.
- Condiciones ambientales particulares (terreno de juego, clima, instalaciones).
- Alimentación incorrecta.
- Falta de respeto por las reglas.

Todas estas situaciones pueden evitarse con una atención adecuada por parte de todos y del formador, instructor o entrenador en especial. Sin embargo, es más importante la atención que se debe prestar a la actividad desarrollada y a la prudencia a la hora de evitar ejercicios potencialmente peligrosos, a veces propuestos por personas poco informadas sobre los daños que pueden provocar.

Evitar todos los ejercicios que conllevan una extensión forzada del tronco. Cuando la columna se dobla (hiperestesia) más allá de los límites fisiológicos, se provocan estados de peligro para los discos vertebrales a nivel lumbar, que pueden causar lesiones muy graves.

Evitar tiempos largos al mantener la máxima flexión, porque se requieren peligrosamente todos los ligamentos y tendones de las articulaciones de las rodillas y se impide la circulación sanguínea de las piernas y los pies.

Evitar ejercicios para los músculos abdominales con partida de posición supina y con piernas tensas, ya que al hacerlo se realizan tracciones peligrosas a nivel lumbar causadas por la acción del músculo ilipsoas. Tratar de recordar siempre que el ángulo de

las piernas con respecto al terreno debe ser superior a los 45 grados. Ese ángulo permite aislar la acción del músculo ilipsoas y favorece el trabajo correcto de los abdominales.

Recordamos algunas normas fundamentales

En la potenciación de la musculatura abdominal, se utilizan a veces ejercicios que en lugar de ejercitar esos grupos musculares requieren predominantemente otros grupos musculares del tronco (ilipsoas, glúteos, etc.). Por tanto, es necesario tomar algunas medidas para hacer eficaz su entrenamiento. Hay que recordar que los músculos abdominales están compuestos principalmente por fibras lentas.

Evitar en los jóvenes caminar con apoyo de manos, ya que se podría incurrir en lesiones graves debido al peso excesivo y las necesidades de torsión y tracción que recaen sobre brazos, manos y muñecas.

Evitar en los jóvenes ejercicios con sobrecargas y pesos, no apropiados para su estructura física (huesos, músculos y articulaciones) que está en fase evolutiva de crecimiento y por tanto podrían generar daños notables por ejercicios sobrecargados. En los jóvenes se pueden obtener mejoras notables en la fuerza muscular con la ejecución de toda la gama de ejercicios con carga natural. ¡No usarlos con los jóvenes!

Evitar en los jóvenes ejercicios de resistencia de periodo breve y medio, la que produce dosis

notables de ácido láctico. Es un tipo de trabajo no apropiado para su organismo, que no está listo para soportar situaciones de excesiva fatiga láctica.

Evitar, finalmente, comportamientos y actitudes vitales cotidianas que nos lleven a usar nuestra columna vertebral de forma dañina e incorrecta.

LA PUESTA EN ACCIÓN

Permite al futbolista adaptarse al esfuerzo tanto física como mentalmente.

La parte de actividad que lleva al verdadero y propio trabajo físico, ya sea en el partido o en la sesión de entrenamiento, se llama puesta en acción. Hay pareceres muy diversos sobre su cantidad y duración. Los pareceres son muy discordantes sobre todo sobre la utilidad y necesidad como medio para la protección de la salud y la prevención de las lesiones. Con la colaboración de los propios futbolistas, se deberán buscar las actividades más adaptadas a las exigencias de cada uno.

El objetivo de la puesta en acción

La puesta en acción se propone preparar al deportista para mantener la prestación deportiva de modo que el paso de la condición de reposo al estado de activación sea el más apropiado para el cambio de actividad que se realiza en un tiempo breve. En particular, antes del partido se trata de poner al futbolista en condiciones de ofrecer la prestación más elevada con respecto al grado de preparación, lo que equivale a mostrar al máximo y de inmediato la mejor calidad de rendimiento en la prestación.

<u>**La puesta en acción es inútil hasta la edad prepuberal (11-12 años)**</u>.

CONSIDERACIONES SOBRE EL «CALENTAMIENTO»

Pensemos en un grupo de chicos que se reúne para jugar a cualquier juego o deporte en un polideportivo o un patio.
Pensemos en dos tenistas que bajan al campo para un partido de un campeonato y una actividad amateur.
Pensemos en dos equipos de baloncesto que bajan al campo para un partido o un entrenamiento.
Pensemos en un grupo de amigos que se reúnen para jugar a fútbol o a fútbol sala.
Pensemos en un hombre que persigue un autobús, un tranvía u otra cosa.
Pensemos en vuestra actividad de futbolista o entrenador, en cuántas veces durante un partido nos sucede ver entrar en juego deportistas que hasta ese momento estaban sentados en el banquillo.
¿Les habéis visto realizar acciones preventivas de calentamiento o de stretching?
¿Les habéis visto alguna vez sufrir lesiones o problemas musculares?
Probablemente algunos de ellos habrán dedicado algunos minutos a repetir los gestos fundamentales de su actividad y nada más.
La pregunta que aparece espontáneamente es: ¿por qué lo hacen todos?
Hay que reflexionar ahora sobre la importancia y la utilidad de esas acciones y considerar de modo serio y responsable la elección de las actividades que hay que utiliza para introducir a los deportistas en las

variaciones de esfuerzo y tipología de trabajo (entrenamiento o partido).

Calentamiento y stretching

En el calentamiento, los ejercicios de stretching estimulan la circulación sanguínea, sobre todo a nivel capilar, activando un «efecto de bombeo», un reclamo sanguíneo notable para el músculo tras el aplastamiento vascular provocado por el estiramiento de las fibras musculares. Los ejercicios de stretching insistido inducen la inhibición del «circuito gamma» (motoneuronas γ, circuito neuromuscular que protege automáticamente la musculatura frente a estiramientos peligrosos). Ese efecto anestésico tiene una duración de unos 15' y deja al músculo sin protección.

Se aconseja, por tanto, para proteger la salud de los deportistas, al menos no realizar nunca stretching:

- Después de ejercicios lactácidos o de fuerza máxima.
- Antes de ejercicios de elasticidad, fuerza explosiva y velocidad máxima.

LA PROGRAMACIÓN DEL ENTRENAMIENTO

La preparación completa del futbolista se realiza superponiendo su organismo, su personalidad y su potencialidad motora a una gran cantidad de estímulos que tienen el objetivo de obtener:
1) Un reforzamiento general.
2) Un desarrollo de las capacidades motoras.
3) Un desarrollo de las habilidades motoras.
4) Un cuidado de la salud.

En cada periodo del año deportivo, pausa estival, precampeonato, fase de competición, pausa invernal, todos los ejercicios deben distribuirse basándose en el principio de la progresividad de la carga de trabajo y en relación con las capacidades a potenciar.

Para establecer la carga de cada sesión individual de entrenamiento debemos dosificar:
- El volumen o cantidad de trabajo.
- La intensidad o calidad de trabajo.

Todos coinciden en que existe una diversidad más o menos grande entre los diversos deportes, por lo que no es posible proponer las mismas cargas de trabajo ni tipologías de ejercicios a un maratonista, un saltador de altura, un futbolista, un jugador de

voleibol, un baloncestista, un jugador de tenis de mesa o cualquier otro. Solo individualizando las necesidades del atleta en condiciones de competición se logrará seleccionar el modo más útil y productivo para alcanzar la mejora de las condiciones del individuo y el grupo.

Hay que tener muy presente que **la combinación de más capacidades no provoca siempre una suma de adaptaciones, sino que por el contrario a veces provoca una resta de adaptaciones**. Si los estímulos del entrenamiento son varios y se dirigen a todas las capacidades, el organismo se confunde y no sabe qué respuesta dar a esos estímulos.

Por tanto, el entrenador no debe entrenar siempre todo, porque de esa manera entrenaría mal, poco o nada.

La organización de una programación racional del entrenamiento pasa por la **PERIODIFICACIÓN** o distribución de los objetivos a alcanzar en los diversos periodos.

Podemos distinguir:
- Programación a largo plazo si se trata de preparar el contenido del entrenamiento de dos o tres temporadas deportivas, **MEGACICLO**.
- Programación a medio plazo si se trata de preparar el contenido del entrenamiento de una temporada deportiva, **MACROCICLO**.
- Programación a corto plazo si se trata de preparar el contenido del entrenamiento de periodos

breves, **MESOCICLO** (trabajo de dos a tres o seis semanas).

- Programación a muy corto plazo o **MICROCICLO** si se trata de preparar el trabajo semanal (se deben tocar todos los elementos del entrenamiento futbolístico, incluido el partido).

En esos periodos, el entrenador compara el nivel deseado de rendimiento con el rendimiento efectivo alcanzado: Así se fijan a corto plazo nuevos objetivos «intermedios» a fin de alcanzar el valor previsto.

MEGACICLO	2 o 3 temporadas deportivas
MACROCICLO	1 temporada deportiva
MESOCICLO	De 2 a 6 semanas
MICROCICLO	Una semana completa (de partido a partido)

Muchos entrenadores no lograr no hacerse influir y creen poder tener éxito repitiendo programas de entrenamiento que han permitido triunfar a otros o programas de equipos de categoría superior.

COPIAR O REPETIR UN PROGRAMO SOLO PORQUE LO HA USADO UN ENTRENADOR DE ÉXITO O UN EQUIPO QUE HA GANADO UN CAMPEONATO ES LA PEOR DE TODAS LAS DECISIONES QUE SE PUEDEN TOMAR.

En este sentido, llamamos la atención sobre dos ideas equivocadas, pero bastante comunes entre los entrenadores:

1. «Lo que dice o hace el entrenador vencedor es verdad».
2. «Solo es bueno el entrenamiento de los equipos que han vencido».

PERIODIFICACIÓN DEL ENTRENAMIENTO

La forma deportiva máxima, predisposición óptima del deportista para lograr el máximo resultado deportivo, es un fenómeno de duración limitada.

Sin embargo, el estado de forma es recuperable y su pérdida es un momento determinante para llegar a un nivel más elevado en el ciclo siguiente. Para conseguirlo, es necesario que los mesociclos y los microciclos que componen el ciclo anual (macrociclo) estén modulados y preparados de manera oportuna.

El microciclo (duración: una semana):
Se diversifica en relación con su contenido y su posición en el curso del entrenamiento.

Por esto, podemos tener:
  a) Basándonos en el contenido:
    - Microciclos generalizados (típicos del inicio de la fase preparatoria).
    - Microciclos específicos (típicos de las fases anteriores a los partidos principales).
  b) Basándonos en el nivel de exigencia:

- Microciclos ordinarios (caracterizados por el crecimiento gradual de las cargas de entrenamiento: destacar volumen).
- Microciclos intensivos (caracterizados por la concentración de cargas de trabajo: destacar intensidad).
- Microciclos de recuperación o asimilación o descarga (disminución drástica del volumen de trabajo).

Se caracterizan por un bajo nivel de exigencia, numerosas fases de recuperación y cambio radical en los ejercicios. Sin embargo, la intensidad de los ejercicios permanece alta.

El mesociclo (duración: 2-6 microciclos):
Es el elemento fundamental del entrenamiento.

La elección de los microciclos y su combinación se determinan por la lógica general del proceso de entrenamiento y las exigencias particulares del momento.

Los mesociclos del periodo de competición con más breves (3 o 4 microciclos) que los del periodo preparatorio (5 o 6 microciclos).

En general, se pueden prever esquemas de este tipo:
- (3:1) Tres semanas de aumento del trabajo y una semana de recuperación (o descarga).

- (4:1 o 5:1) Si hay problemas de resistencia.
- (2:1 y también 1:1) Si hay problemas de velocidad o si es necesario ponerse en forma en poco tiempo.

Recordemos que:

- En la planificación de un microciclo el elemento más importante está representado por la alternancia justa de los esfuerzos y las pausas.
- En la planificación de un mesociclo, el rendimiento máximo (forma máxima relativa) se alcanza cuando se empieza a aumentar la intensidad de la carga de trabajo tras haber desarrollado un microciclo de asimilación o descarga.
- Cerca de partidos particularmente importantes es necesario reforzar la «curva de rendimiento» en busca de un buen momento de forma.
- La pausa de recuperación es importante para cada prueba, para la sesión completa o ciclo de sesiones Cada 3 sesiones de trabajo una costumbre aconsejable y correcta es introducir una sesión de reposo.
- El entrenamiento no es una cuestión de cantidad, sino de calidad.
- El objetivo principal es obtener un rendimiento elevado lo más rápidamente posible.
- La musculación en gimnasio se adapta mal a las necesidades del fútbol.

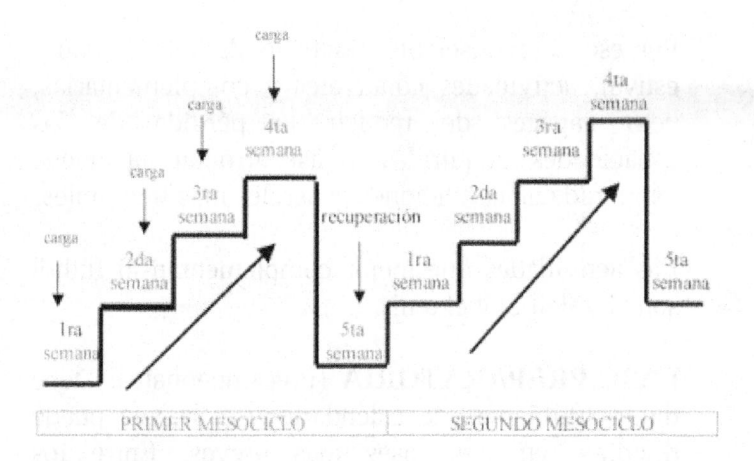

carga

carga

carga

carga

carga

4ta
semana

3ra
semana

2da
semana

1ra
semana

4ta
semana

3ra
semana

recuperación

2da
semana

1ra
semana

5ta
semana

5ta
semana

| PRIMER MESOCICLO | SEGUNDO MESOCICLO |

Para leer e interpretar correctamente el contenido de las próximas páginas, es útil fijarse en las siguientes notas:
- Por «Jornada de entrenamiento» se entiende el día de la semana en el que se suministra la carga de trabajo.
- Por «Sesión de entrenamiento» se entiende el entrenamiento que se realiza durante una reunión en el campo. Por tanto, en una jornada puede haber dos sesiones.

PERIODO DE LA PAUSA ESTIVAL: Conviene dedicar ahora algunas palabras a este periodo que resulta sí «posterior» a una temporada deportiva, pero es más importante examinarlo como «anterior» al periodo previo al campeonato.

Un largo periodo de reposo total es inoportuno, tanto para los jóvenes deportistas como para los más expertos. Las cualidades fisiológicas fatigosamente creadas se reducen muy rápido con la inactividad.

199

Por eso es aconsejable practicar, durante la pausa estival, actividades colaterales y complementarias, pero capaces de reducir la pérdida de las capacidades adquiridas y así afrontar la nueva temporada en condiciones generales más favorables.

Las actividades que mejor complementan al fútbol son el voleibol y el tenis.

FASE PREPARATORIA (Precampeonato): Debe durar 40-45 días de calendario y a su vez puede dividirse en tres fases más breves. Entre los aficionados es muy probable que el inicio del campeonato se fije antes del fin de la fase preparatoria. No es posible comprimir ni reducir esa fase en un periodo de tiempo inferior al indicado, por lo que el campeonato empezará, pero la fase preparatoria tendrá que completarse y solo después se iniciará la preparación del periodo competitivo.

PRIMERA FASE (duración: unos 13-15 días): Realizar 4-5 entrenamientos semanales incluidos posible amistosos (teniendo cuidado de incluir una jornada de reposo cada 3 días, en caso de dos sesiones diarias, una sesión de reposo cada 3 sesiones).

La actividad se basa en la polivalencia, utilizando inmediatamente los ejercicios con balón.

La velocidad en sus diversas formas debe atenderse desde los primeros días, igual que la potenciación con carga natural.

Solo para los juveniles y hasta los 15/16 años conviene dedicar atención también al trabajo aeróbico.
También deben usarse juegos de equipo con número reducido a 4 o 5 en la organización del trabajo sobre las capacidades condicionales.

En total:
- 8-10 jornadas de entrenamiento.
- 2 jornadas para los partidos.
- 3 jornadas de reposo.

SEGUNDA FASE (duración: unos 13-15 días): Se inicia programando ejercicios de intensidad más elevada. Sesión a sesión, los diversos ejercicios deben realizarse a velocidad siempre creciente hasta llegar al esfuerzo buscado. Para los jóvenes, disminuir el trabajo aeróbico a ritmo uniforme a favor de los trabajos con variaciones de ritmo. También aumentarán los ejercicios de potenciación.
Aumentan los partidos amistosos.
Se dedica más atención al trabajo técnico y táctico.
En total:
- 8-9 jornadas de entrenamiento.
- 3 jornadas para los partidos.
- 3 jornadas de reposo.

TERCERA FASE (duración: unos 13-15 días): La preparación física cada vez se realiza más con ejercicios de perfeccionamiento técnico y de aplicación al juego de equipo.
La carga de las sesiones es ahora de intensidad elevada y tenderá por tanto a disminuir su volumen.

El trabajo aeróbico para los juveniles se estabiliza en volúmenes medios.

En total:

- 8-9 jornadas de entrenamiento.
- 3 jornadas para los partidos.
- 3 jornadas de reposo.

PERIODO COMPETITIVO: Comprende todo el periodo del campeonato y posibles torneos, con posibilidad de una parada más o menos larga debido a la pausa invernal. Cada jornada de entrenamiento debe desarrollarse en dos fases:

- La primera dedicada al ejercicio de la técnica, la táctica y la velocidad (incluido partido).
- La segunda dedicada a los demás ejercicios físicos (si es posible, siempre con el balón y en situaciones de combinación de juego).

En los jóvenes, hacia la mitad de noviembre debe concluir el primer bloque de trabajo aeróbico. Ese trabajo deberá reanudarse en un segundo bloque en los meses de marzo, abril y mayo.

POSIBLE PERIODO DE PAUSA INVERNAL: Durante el periodo de suspensión del campeonato, será oportuno repetir los contenidos de los ejercicios programados en la tercera fase del periodo precampeonato, manteniendo sin embargo el esfuerzo y la intensidad del trabajo muy elevados, dado que ha crecido el nivel de capacidad.

Si el periodo de pausa es más largo, repetir antes los contenidos de la segunda fase del precampeonato

(en todo o en parte, en relación con la duración del periodo de pausa) y luego los de la tercera.

Recordemos que:

- En la planificación de un microciclo, el elemento más importante es la alternancia justa de esfuerzos y pausas.
- En la planificación de un mesociclo, el rendimiento máximo (forma máxima relativa) se alcanza cuando se empieza a aumentar la intensidad de la carga de trabajo después de haber desarrollado un microciclo de asimilación o descarga.
- La pausa de recuperación es importante para cada prueba, para la sesión y/o la jornada de entrenamiento. Como ya se ha indicado antes, cada tres jornadas de trabajo es aconsejable incluir una jornada de reposo. En el caso de dos sesiones por jornada, conviene incluir una sesión de reposo cada tres sesiones de trabajo.
- El entrenamiento no es una cuestión de cantidad, sino de calidad.
- El objetivo principal es obtener un rendimiento elevado lo antes posible. En el caso de un equipo que realiza pocos entrenamientos semanales, la musculación en el gimnasio es poco apropiada para las necesidades del futbolista.
- Hasta una edad de unos 15/16 años, en el entrenamiento debe haber lugar para todos los ejercicios técnicos, tácticos y físicos.
- Después de los 16/17 años, el deportista que se dedica al fútbol debe entrenar como un especialista, tanto en la última como en la

primera categoría. El especialista debe ejercitarse de modo apropiado a las necesidades y las características del trabajo competitivo y no en todas las capacidades condicionales y mecanismos energéticos. Si los estímulos del entrenamiento son varios y se dirigen a todas las capacidades, el organismo se confunde y no sabe qué respuesta dar a esos requerimientos.

- El entrenador no debe entrenar siempre todo, porque en ese caso entrenaría mal, poco o nada.

EL ENTRENADOR

La eficacia y la capacidad de un entrenador, además de en el campo de entrenamiento y en la gestión de las relaciones individuales y de grupo, se manifiesta sobre todo al preparar y dirigir el partido. Su comportamiento antes, durante y después del partido constituye un elemento esencial de su trabajo educativo y formativo.

Prescindiendo de la tensión por el resultado, el partido representa siempre una experiencia que se vive intensamente y que deja una fuerte impronta en el ánimo de los participantes.

Los hechos del partido se recuerdan detalladamente y por mucho tiempo y tienen una influencia determinante sobre el comportamiento futuro de cada deportista.

El entrenador debe aprovechar esas situaciones favorables con un objetivo formativo.

Antes del partido

Antes del partido, el entrenador comunica a sus jugadores la composición de la alineación y asigna a cada uno tareas y acciones particulares y explica la disposición táctica para dicho partido.

El partido a nivel táctico debe prepararse a lo largo de la semana durante los entrenamientos, poniendo de relieve los errores cometidos anteriormente e

indicando las soluciones para eliminarlos. Las disposiciones tácticas precisas deben darse antes del partido, poniendo de relieve las características de los adversarios y el modo en que se pretenden aprovechar a nuestro favor.

El entrenador deberá hablar con un tono de voz calmado, sosegado, como quien está perfectamente seguro de sus afirmaciones. Preparar a los futbolistas para las condiciones del partido no quiere decir crear en ellos estados de excitación, sino infundirles calma y serenidad junto a la concentración sobre el partido.

Durante el partido

Durante el juego, el entrenador debe hacer sentir su presencia a sus futbolistas, y si es necesario proponer algunas sugerencias. Hay que evitar absolutamente gritos y voces continuos desde el banquillo, que seguramente no ayudan a nadie.

Es más provechoso comunicar a un jugador los posibles consejos directamente o a través del capitán.

Durante el descanso

El breve tiempo de descanso concedido en un tiempo y otro debe servir para la recuperación física y psicológica de los futbolistas.

El entrenador puede aprovechar este tiempo para dar alguna indicación, invitar a la calma si es necesario, infundir confianza, despertar a alguno de la apatía o la resignación. En modo alguno deberá dirigirse a sus deportistas con tono de voz alterado ni mostrar una gran contrariedad por una posible marcha negativa del partido. La preparación del segundo

tiempo exige del entrenador capacidad de análisis, equilibrio mental y gran experiencia.

No hay que hacer recriminaciones sobre posibles errores cometidos (probablemente el jugador ya sea consciente de ellos), sino que deben darse indicaciones concretas con respecto a aspectos importantes del juego. Para discutir los errores y sus causas es preferible y útil esperar a hablar en la primera sesión de entrenamiento después del partido.

Después del partido
Inmediatamente después del partido, está bien evitar cualquier comentario, sobre todo si el resultado final ha sido negativo. Igualmente es oportuno abstenerse de manifestaciones exageradas de alegría en caso de victoria, así como de actitudes de desesperación en caso de derrota.

El entrenador deberá impedir que otras personas entren en los vestuarios mientras los futbolistas se encuentren todavía en estado de excitación por el esfuerzo realizado durante el partido. Solo en el siguiente entrenamiento posterior al partido se podrá realizar una valoración objetiva del mismo, basándonos en cómo se ha desarrollado el juego y cómo han visto los futbolistas sus diversas fases.

En este momento, y solo entonces, el entrenador expondrá francamente su punto de vista, ofrecerá su valoración personal, escuchará a los jugadores y discutirá con ellos, buscando llegar a consideraciones generales que hagan posible el consenso y la aprobación de todo el grupo.

Una valoración serena del juego desarrollado, la plena conciencia de posibles errores cometidos y de su origen o causa, constituirá para cada uno una motivación suplementaria para poner empeño en el posterior trabajo de entrenamiento.

Análisis y valoración del juego
Entre las numerosas tareas del entrenador también está la de deber comprender lo que está sucediendo durante el partido y anticipar los acontecimientos. Algunos entrenadores tienen una disposición natural para este tipo de observaciones, otros tienen dificultades para identificar las causas y soluciones de determinadas situaciones.
También los futbolistas deberían tratar de desarrollar esta habilidad, que les permite desempeñar un papel importante en el equipo y en el desarrollo del partido.
Un partido debe entenderse en clave táctica durante su desarrollo si se quiere contribuir eficazmente a determinar su resultado.
Para poder hacer un examen detallado del partido, hay que tener en cuenta algunos hechos, situaciones y comportamientos.
Después de 5-6 minutos, cuál es el equipo que ha asumido el control del juego en términos de:

- Ventaja territorial.
- Posesión del balón.

Cuáles son los motivos que determinan el control del juego:
- Un marcaje estrecho de los jugadores del equipo en cuestión.

- Un marcaje relajado de los adversarios.
- Posibles errores de juego y su naturaleza.
- Superioridad física de algunos elementos.

Las respuestas a estas preguntas sirven para determinar los puntos débiles y fuertes de un equipo.

Hasta qué punto se utilizan o ignoran los principios del juego:
a. Existe un escalonamiento defensivo.
b. Los delanteros muestran variaciones en el juego.
c. El equipo que pierde la posesión del balón busca recuperarlo inmediatamente.

Este análisis puede dar respuestas útiles para formular un juicio sobre el juego y, si es el caso, adoptar las correcciones oportunas.

Si el equipo está demasiado extendido sobre el terreno de juego (desde el defensa más retrasado al delantero más adelantado hay 50-60 m.), cuáles son las causas:
a. Los defensas no están suficientemente cerca de los delanteros.
b. Los delanteros no se retrasan para disminuir las distancias.
c. Los delanteros corren lejos de quien posee el balón.
d. Los defensas se retiran demasiado pronto o demasiado velozmente.

Cuál es la carga de trabajo del equipo y de cada jugador.
En el fútbol, algunos futbolistas trabajan intensamente cuando las cosas van bien y se esconden cuando van mal.

Qué esquema táctico se adopta:
a. Quiénes son los principales distribuidores.
b. En qué zona del campo y cómo obtienen la posesión del balón estos distribuidores.
c. Quiénes son los principales receptores.
d. Cuál es la zona más apropiada para que reciban el balón.

De qué deriva el dominio del juego:
a. Del ritmo del juego.
b. Del trabajo del equipo.
c. De qué forma puede impedirse o molestarse ese dominio.

Al equipo dominante se le concede demasiado tiempo o demasiado espacio. En caso afirmativo:
a. Cuáles son los jugadores a los que hay que someter a un marcaje estrecho.
b. Qué jugadores no saben contener suficientemente el juego.
Algunos futbolistas, cuando se dedican a defender, actúan de forma relajada, por lo que los adversarios disponen de mucho espacio de maniobra.
Todos los adversarios deben estar controlados cuando su equipo tiene la posesión del balón, cada uno de ellos debe verse obligado a realizar un trabajo duro para conseguir lo que se propone.

Por qué lado intenta un equipo penetrar en la defensa adversaria:
a. Qué métodos se emplean para realizar la penetración cerca del área de penalti.
b. El intento de penetración se efectúa de forma repentina e inesperada o mediante maniobras de preparación.

Cuáles son los puntos fuertes y débiles de los jugadores individuales, con referencia particular:
a. A las características técnicas individuales.
b. A las características atléticas y competitivas en la defensa y la administración de los recursos físicos propios.
c. Cuáles son las tareas asignadas a cada uno por el entrenador.

Cómo se juega el balón en las situaciones de balón inactivo:
a. Saques de esquina, se improvisan o están preparados.
b. Saques de faltas, se lanzan directamente o están preparados.
c. Saques de banda, son normales o algún jugador posee dotes particulares en su ejecución.
d. El portero saca con las manos o prefiere usar los pies. Qué distancia alcanza y a quién manda el balón.

LA PROGRESIÓN DIDÁCTICA EN LOS JUVENILES

En el desarrollo formativo que atraviesa toda la carrera deportiva de los jugadores, la atención pasará progresivamente del comportamiento individual al colectivo. Aumentará de modo creciente el número de elementos que caracterizan el contexto del juego (compañeros y adversarios), el espacio a utilizar o controlar y, en general, las dificultades a afrontar. La enseñanza de las capacidades técnico-tácticas se efectúa a través de las siguientes fases:

Entrenamiento motor

- El desarrollo correcto y completo de todas las capacidades coordinativas y motoras más importantes en las diversas edades ayuda a un aprendizaje más correcto y rentable de todos los elementos de la técnica de base.

Entrenamiento técnico

- Busca ampliar el bagaje de fundamentos y su perfeccionamiento. El trabajo repetitivo continuo, organizado bajo los principios de la progresividad didáctica y la corrección

constante de los errores permite poder desarrollar de manera correcta y rentable los elementos de la técnica aplicada.

Entrenamiento técnico-táctico

- Busca el desarrollo del pensamiento táctico individual.

Entrenamiento táctico colectivo

- Estimula la creación y el desarrollo del pensamiento táctico colectivo. El conocimiento de los elementos que caracterizan la técnica aplicada, desarrollados según los principios fundamentales del entrenamiento, permiten al jugador integrarse rápida y eficazmente en cualquier sistema de juego.

Entrenamiento táctico por posición

- Busca instaurar y perfeccionar colaboraciones específicas en función de los puestos y las situaciones. No existe un desarrollo táctico por posición o de equipo eficaz y duradero en el tiempo si los elementos antes descritos no se desarrollan de manera completa y correcta.

LA TÉCNICA

La técnica futbolista es igual que los movimientos con y sin balón que se realizan durante un partido, en el cual las dos fases de juego conocidas comúnmente son:

1. POSESIÓN DEL BALÓN
2. NO POSESIÓN DEL BALÓN

En realidad, es más correcto hablar de 5 fases de juego:

1. POSESIÓN DEL BALÓN
2. NO POSESIÓN DEL BALÓN
3. TRANSICIÓN POSITIVA
4. TRANSICIÓN NEGATIVA
5. BALÓN INACTIVO

Un buen conocimiento técnico permite al futbolista poder efectuar cualquier gesto, ya sea con o sin balón, con el fin de obtener la máxima eficacia para dar ventaja a su equipo.

LOS GESTOS TÉCNICOS son los comportamientos que realiza cada jugador individual cuando entra en contacto con el balón.
Los «fundamentales» se dividen por tanto como si no existiera el contexto de juego, con el fin de

resaltar exclusivamente la **relación del jugador con el balón.**

CONDUCIR/CONTROLAR
CHUTAR
RECIBIR
DEFENDER
CABECEAR
SACAR DE BANDA
TÉCNICA DEL PORTERO

Conducir / Controlar
Requisito fundamental que determina nuestro grado de habilidad en la gestión individual del balón en una situación de contacto estrecho y poco espacio.

Chutar
Gesto específico que evidencia la habilidad de un jugador para dirigir con el pie el balón hacia un objetivo previamente fijado (compañero, portería contraria).

Recibir
Habilidad técnica que consiste en manejar el balón que llega, parándolo u orientándolo, anticipando la elección de la jugada inmediatamente siguiente.

Defender
Tratar de recuperar el balón con una acción de defensa directa o indirecta.

Cabecear
Gesto técnico que evidencia la habilidad de un jugador para dirigir el balón con la cabeza hacia un

objetivo previamente fijado (compañero, portería contraria).

Sacar de banda
Gesto técnico realizado con las manos, por medio del cual se reanuda el juego después de que el balón salga por una banda lateral.

Técnica del portero
Fundamentos propios.

Todos los recursos y todos los movimientos, con o sin balón, que realiza el jugador para que las prestaciones propias resulten útiles, rentables y económicas, teniendo en cuenta a los compañeros, los adversarios y las situaciones del juego, reciben el nombre de **TÁCTICA INDIVIDUAL** o **TÉCNICA APLICADA**.

En la fase de POSESIÓN de balón podemos distinguir los siguientes gestos:

DESMARQUE
CONTROL Y DEFENSA DEL BALÓN
PASE
FINTA
REGATE
TIRO A PUERTA

Desmarque
Habilidad técnica individual que consiste en librarse del marcaje adversario y que termina con la recepción del balón o la creación de un espacio.

Control y defensa del balón
Habilidad individual que permite mantener el dominio del balón en presencia de adversarios.

Pase
Habilidad individual que permite transmitir el balón a un compañero en donde está o al hueco. *No confundir con la técnica fundamental de patear el balón («mecánica» del gesto).*

Finta
Movimiento realizado con o sin balón que no prevé superar a un adversario. Le sigue una fase de conducción, recepción o desmarque.

Regate
Habilidad individual que se realiza en posesión del balón y que busca superar a un adversario.

Tiro a puerta
Habilidad individual que permite acabar con un gol.

En la fase de NO POSESIÓN de balón, podemos distinguir los siguientes gestos:

POSICIONAMIENTO
MARCAJE
INTERCEPCIÓN
DEFENSA
DEFENSA DE LA PORTERIA

Posicionamiento
El posicionamiento o toma de posesión consiste en asumir un desplazamiento que, teniendo en cuenta

la portería propia, el adversario directo y el sector del campo en el que está el balón, ofrece la posibilidad de retrasar u obstaculizar la acción del adversario.

Marcaje
La acción de control directo del adversario.

Intercepción
Interrumpir la acción del adversario actuando directamente sobre el balón. La forma más eficaz de intercepción es anticiparse al adversario.

Defensa
Puede ser directa, si se realiza sobre el jugador que posee el balón, o indirecta, cuando se trata de llevar a una «zona de sombra» a un adversario que no posee el balón.

Defensa de la portería
Principio fundamental de la fase defensiva. La forma típica con la que el defensa aplica este principio consiste en interponerse entre el balón y el espacio de la propia portería.

En realidad, hay más conceptos relacionados con los gestos técnicos aplicados, que son:

Bloqueos y pantallas
Acciones individuales que tienden a interrumpir la continuidad del marcaje del defensor en los enfrentamientos de los compañeros. Los bloqueos se realizan en situaciones casi estáticas, por tanto, sobre todo con el balón inactivo. Las pantallas se

realizan con balón en movimiento, en cualquier momento y situación del juego.

Ayudas verbales
Mensajes codificados de ayuda para el desarrollo seguro de las acciones.

Zona de luz y zona de sombra
Indican la zona donde se puede recibir el balón o donde un adversario cierra la trayectoria de pase.

Balón descubierto y balón cubierto
Es el concepto fundamental sobre el que se basan todos los movimientos defensivos y ofensivos de un jugador, de un puesto o del equipo.
«Balón abierto o descubierto», cuando el adversario que posee el balón puede realizar una jugada peligrosa para nuestra portería.
«Balón cerrado o cubierto», cuando el adversario que posee el balón no puede llevar peligro a nuestra portería.

Lado fuerte y lado débil
Esta distinción viene determinada por la posición de espera que asume el defensa, cuyo lado fuerte corresponde al del pie retrasado, mientras que el lado débil es el del pie avanzado.

Pausa
Con el balón descubierto. Retrasar lo más posible la ofensiva adversaria para recuperarse de una situación de desventaja o inferioridad numérica.

Entrada al balón

Con el balón cubierto. Quitar espacio de juego al adversario.

Desmarque
Movimiento por delante de la línea del balón para poder recibir este de un compañero desde una línea de juego más baja.

Apoyo
Movimiento detrás de la línea del balón para poder recibirlo de un compañero desde una línea de juego más alta.

Internada
Movimiento vertical o diagonal partiendo de detrás de la línea del balón.

Corte
Movimiento (para estrechar o alargar) desmarcándose por delante de la línea del balón.

Superposición
Carrera (interna o externa) rodeando al poseedor del balón. Movimiento desmarcándose delante de la línea del balón.

LA TÁCTICA

La táctica es el movimiento coordinado de dos o más jugadores, de un puesto o de todo el equipo con el objetivo de conseguir un resultado previamente determinado.

Los elementos importantes son:

- **OBJETIVO PREDETERMINADO**
- **MOVIMIENTO COORDINADO**

Objetivo predeterminado

Puede variar en función del modelo de juego (que veremos en el capítulo correspondiente), de los principios del juego y de los subprincipios.

Para un jugador, significa saber siempre cómo comportarse tácticamente (individual y colectivamente) en función de las distintas situaciones de juego.

Movimiento coordinado

Movimiento de los jugadores en función del balón, de los adversarios, de la zona del campo y de la previsión de una situación determinada.

Los movimientos individuales provocan siempre efectos en la organización del juego.

Por esto es importante distinguir dos factores importantes en relación con la táctica en general, que son:

- **La táctica individual o técnica aplicada.**
- **La táctica colectiva.**

El objetivo de la táctica es saber transformar un grupo de jugadores en un equipo que «hable el mismo idioma».

Conseguir que todos entiendan y razonen de la misma forma y al mismo tiempo en función de la misma situación.

A todo esto, lo podemos llamar **ORGANIZACIÓN DEL JUEGO**.

Esta característica, la organización, es un determinante absoluto e imprescindible para un equipo que quiera obtener resultados.

Hay que considerar que, para una buena organización del juego, existen dos elementos fundamentales:

- Técnica y técnica aplicada.
- Tiempo.

La técnica y la técnica aplicada son evidentemente necesarias para dar eficacia a un movimiento táctico individual o colectivo y por tanto se requieren y entrenan siempre en un contexto situacional-

cognitivo, es decir, con ejercicios que tengan un objetivo táctico-estratégico preciso y que obliguen al futbolista a pensar y realizar un gesto técnico apropiado para el contexto táctico.

El tiempo es otro determinante esencial, es la clave del fútbol. Tiempo de marcaje, tiempo de enfrentar, tiempo de pasar, tiempo de colocación en el campo, tiempo de desmarque, etc.

El trabajo de un entrenador se dirige siempre a mejorar los tiempos de juego, trabajando en la lectura e interpretación de estos por los futbolistas.

El inicio de la acción
En el fútbol moderno, el inicio de la acción y la construcción del juego representan elementos muy característicos para los equipos de alto nivel, independientemente de la categoría a la que pertenezcan.
Por inicio de la acción se entienden todas las situaciones tácticas en las que la acción debe organizarse a partir del portero, ya se trate de saques de fondo o de una entrega «en movimiento» con el balón en las manos del último defensa.
Por el contrario, por construcción del juego entendemos la capacidad de un equipo de hilvanar determinadas tramas de juego con el objetivo de acercarse a la portería adversaria para acabar las acciones ofensivas.
Las modalidades para el inicio de la acción y la construcción del juego dependen de algunos factores esenciales:

- La filosofía de juego del entrenador y el consiguiente modelo de juego.
- Las características de los futbolistas a su disposición.
- Las características del próximo adversario al que se han de enfrentar.
- La evolución de la competición, desde el punto de vista técnico-táctico, en relación con estas situaciones de juego.

Estos elementos tienen una fuerte interdependencia.

Solo después de un minucioso análisis podrá el entrenador optar por la situación táctica deseada.

El inicio del juego puede producirse principalmente de dos maneras:

1. Inicio bajo: Se produce con el pase corto del balón por parte del portero, en dirección a uno de los defensores o centrocampistas retrasados encargados de construcción del juego. El inicio bajo del juego es un elemento muy característico de los equipos de alto nivel, en mi opinión imprescindible. El entrenador, basándose en su modelo de juego y las características de los futbolistas, tiene la posibilidad de estudiar y desarrollar la situación de juego más idónea para construir y desarrollar las acciones ofensivas.

2. Inicio largo: Se produce con el lanzamiento largo del portero en dirección a una referencia atacante, generalmente posicionado hacia la mitad defensiva del

campo o más allá. Tras este lanzamiento, el resto del equipo deberá achicar rápidamente el espacio hacia delante siguiendo la referencia del juego zonal, tanto para garantizar el equilibrio como para tratar de conseguir la continuidad del balón.

Como podemos intuir, las dos modalidades posibles de inicio de la acción del juego son diametralmente opuestas, tanto en los principios como en la ejecución. El inicio bajo y corto del juego presenta numerosas ventajas y pocas desventajas.

Entre los puntos fuertes, encontramos sin duda el «control» que puede tener todo el equipo sobre el desarrollo integral del juego. Es posible crear, gracias a la acción táctica individual de los centrocampistas, situaciones continuas de superioridad numérica, garantizando siempre la posibilidad concreta de organizar el juego de forma fluida.

Además, al construir el juego desde la mitad propia del campo, es posible permitir al equipo actuar de modo fluido y funcional en relación con el espacio-tiempo, ocupando y atacando los espacios libres en el momento justo.

Las desventajas de esta situación táctica de juego están sobre todo ligadas al aspecto mental, ya que iniciar la acción desde el portero representa sin duda un riesgo, sobre todo debido a la zona en que se efectúa este desarrollo del juego. Por fin, considero necesario subrayar un concepto. Muchos entrenadores consideran que para construir el juego

a partir del sector defensivo hacen falta futbolistas muy bien dotados técnicamente. Aunque sea verdad, o al menos preferible, sin embargo, hay que afirmar que muy a menudo un buen juego posicional está en disposición de superar la técnica refinada de uno o más futbolistas.

Por el contrario, el inicio largo de la acción es una situación de juego indudablemente mucho menos arriesgada desde el punto de vista defensivo. Sin embargo, al mismo tiempo, es totalmente incontrolable con respecto al éxito en el desarrollo del juego y se confía sobre todo en las características físicas de un futbolista, que debe ganar un balón aéreo y luego en la capacidad del equipo de achicar el espacio hacia delante. Este desarrollo táctico, como se ha subrayado antes, conlleva una agresión clara sobre el espacio que hay por delante, con el doble objetivo de garantizar el equilibrio y de conseguir el balón dividido.

Las ventajas, como acabo de explicar, se encuentran en la ausencia de riesgo y la posibilidad, una vez ganado al menos un enfrentamiento aéreo o haber conseguido el balón dividido, de llegar directamente a la mitad ofensiva del campo.

Las desventajas derivan de la falta total de control de todo el desarrollo del juego, ya que resulta imposible prever dónde cae el balón después del lanzamiento y su posición posterior después de la disputa aérea.

¿Cómo actúan los factores fundamentales antes descritos?

La filosofía del fútbol del entrenador y la consiguiente estructuración de un modelo determinado de juego representan sin duda el primer mandamiento a cumplir.

Todas las fases del juego, incluido el inicio de la acción y la construcción del juego, deben caracterizarse por principios precisos, subprincipios y subsubprincipios de juego, todos necesariamente congruentes entre sí. La elección de estos comportamientos colectivos depende claramente de las características de los jugadores disponibles, pero sin que estos determinen todo el proyecto táctico del equipo.

Por ejemplo, disponer de dos centrocampistas centrales con un gran físico puede ser una solución alternativa a la construcción baja del juego, en determinados casos influyendo incluso en el comportamiento de los adversarios, a condición de que no se especule con dichas características modificando completamente el modelo de juego o parte de él.

La construcción del juego
Sobre la base de lo expuesto anteriormente, resultaría difícil hablar de construcción del juego y de la acción ofensiva después del lanzamiento largo del portero. Pero no hay que descartar esta última hipótesis. Sin embargo, creo que para conseguir un desarrollo eficaz del juego es necesario partir del portero y toda la línea defensiva para luego desarrollar los principios y subprincipios de juego deseados.

Para este fin, dividiremos las fases de ataque organizado (o con posesión del balón) en tres subfases:

1. **Construcción del juego:**
Esta fase de desarrolla justamente en el primer tercio del campo. La acción parte siempre del portero, que tiene el objetivo de entregar en corto el balón a uno de los defensas centrales. En un sistema de juego 1-4-3-2-1, para desarrollar nuestro juego ideal, es necesario desarrollar y potenciar los principios, subprincipios y subsubprincipios del juego. Señalemos cuáles:

Macroprincipio de juego.
Posesión y circulación en corto del balón. El objetivo es atraer a los adversarios a la mitad propia del campo con el fin de desorganizar/desequilibrar su estructura defensiva.

Subprincipio de juego:
Buen juego posicional y creación de superioridad numérica mediante una línea defensiva compuesta por tres hombres: dos defensas centrales abiertos y el centrocampista pivote colocado entre ellos.

Subsubprincipio de juego:
Valoración del riesgo.
Para crear y ocupar espacios libres es necesario que quienes organicen la construcción baja del juego asuman los riesgos en la primera fase de construcción, por ejemplo, la conducción del balón

en caso de que los espacios estuvieran ocupados, con el objetivo de atraer a los adversarios y ocuparlos-atacarlos.

Los defensas centrales deben posicionarse muy abiertos, los defensas laterales, abiertos y en diagonal para garantizar amplitud y profundidad. Uno de los dos centrocampistas centrales, el opuesto al lado del balón, va a ocupar la posición de tercer defensa central colocado entre los dos defensores, que se abren para asegurar una superioridad numérica constante. El otro centrocampista tiene el objetivo de realizar los desmarques en diagonal (abiertos y cerrados) para asegurar líneas de pase fáciles y seguras y espacios propios para la progresión del juego.

Subsubprincipio de juego:
Implicación continua del portero.
Para que sea eficaz el inicio bajo del juego, es necesario que el portero participe continuamente. Es precisamente este futbolista el que la mayoría de las veces garantiza la superioridad numérica necesaria para desarrollar las tramas de juego. El portero debe actuar como un verdadero sostén de la unidad mínima ideal de posesión del balón, dando aire a la fase de posesión.

Un ejemplo reciente de este comportamiento táctico individual es el de Manuel Neuer en el último campeonato del mundo ganado por Alemania.
 2. **Progresión ofensiva o creación:**
 Una vez construido el juego, el equipo tiene el objetivo de progresar hacia la portería

adversaria, creando situaciones efectivas para dar el último toque y posteriormente concluir el juego ofensivo. En esta fase de juego, en mi opinión, el entrenador tiene dos posibilidades:
A) Desarrollar el macroprincipio del ataque directo: el objetivo es el de enfrentarse a los futbolistas más avanzados, colocados en la mitad contraria del campo.
B) Preferir la posesión del balón con el objetivo de acercarse a la portería adversaria: El principal objetivo es el de dar lugar a figuras geométricas continuas, como triángulos y rombos, mediante la creación constante de la unidad ideal mínima de posesión. El objetivo principal es el de facilitar el movimiento rápido y fluido del balón con el objetivo de progresar hacia la portería contraria.
Será precisamente el orden preferencial de dichas posibilidades (definido y desarrollado en el entrenamiento), el que establecerá las tramas del juego de ataque del equipo. Independientemente de la elección de la progresión del juego (ataque directo o desarrollo paciente de la posesión del balón), el equipo debe acatar algunos subprincipios muy importantes del juego:
Buscar agrandar el campo. Se trata de asegurar siempre dos jugadores muy abiertos e igualmente en profundidad.
Alternar el juego entre las líneas en busca de amplitud: entrenar los cortes convergentes de los extremos y los ataques continuos a la estructura defensiva por parte del centrocampista ofensivo es uno de los subprincipios más importantes de este y

otros sistemas de juego. El delantero más peligroso de un equipo es siempre un espacio libre que atacar: Este «entre las líneas» es indudablemente el más peligroso por su difícil lectura por parte de los adversarios.

3. Finalización

Después de haber construido y hecho progresar el juego, resulta importante el subprincipio relativo a la ocupación de zonas peligrosas para la finalización, que desarrollaremos en los capítulos siguientes.

Lo expuesto no es un modelo completo de juego, sino un conjunto de principios, subprincipios y subsubprincipios de juego útiles para desarrollar y potenciar el inicio de la acción y la construcción del juego.

METODOLOGÍAS DE ENTRENAMIENTO

La **metodología** es la disciplina que estudia la evolución (técnico-práctica) del trabajo de investigación sobre la base del método científico. La asunción de un modelo metodológico permite conocer las consecuencias científicas del trabajo propio.

El **método** es el procedimiento dirigido a garantizar, en el plano teórico o práctico, el resultado satisfactorio de un trabajo o un comportamiento.

Las principales metodologías conocidas y usadas en el ámbito futbolístico son:

- MÉTODO TRADICIONAL
- MÉTODO INTEGRADO
- PERIODIFICACIÓN TÁCTICA

METODO TRADICIONAL

Tiene como objetivo principal el entrenamiento físico. Cree en la forma física y en el punto de la fuerza máxima y sobre todo en el segundo principio según el cual el volumen del ejercicio físico es más importante que la intensidad.

VOLUMEN: Cantidad de trabajo.
– Ejercicios que se desarrollan con distinta intensidad máxima relativa.

INTENSIDAD: Calidad de trabajo.
– Intensidad de concentración, sobre todo táctica, que el futbolista debe mantener constante en cada ejercicio, con el objetivo de resolver los problemas de las distintas situaciones del juego.

MÉTODO INTEGRADO

Tiene como objetivo el entrenamiento integral del deportista. Mediante la utilización constante del balón en todos los ejercicios se trata de lograr entrenamiento en las diversas áreas: técnica, táctica, condicional y psicológica. En esta metodología es mucho más importante la INTENSIDAD del trabajo que el volumen. En mi opinión, esta metodología es la más indicada para la formación del futbolista joven, ya que lo prepara para poder entrenar con cualquier metodología, como, por ejemplo, la periodificación táctica.

PERIODIFICACIÓN TÁCTICA

Según esta metodología, el hombre es una unidad biopsicológica en la que es imposible separar cuerpo y mente. Eso significa que para un entrenador que sigue esta metodología es imposible separar la parte condicional de la técnica, táctica y psicológica. Explicada así, podría parecerse mucho a la metodología integrada, pero la diferencia sustancial es que cada entrenamiento, cada ejercicio, está en

función del modelo de juego impuesto por el entrenador. No es importante tener una condición física perfecta o tener capacidades técnico/tácticas excepcionales, sino que es esencial que estas características estén «adaptadas» al modelo de juego. Un ejemplo para aclarar el concepto:
Si un entrenador tiene como principio de juego el de «saltarse» el centro del campo en la fase de posesión del balón para llegar al delantero centro, que tiene como tarea principal pasar el balón a los extremos para esperar el centro, es inútil entrenar la posesión del balón.

Las características de la periodificación táctica

Es importante tener claro el hecho de que mediante esta metodología se trata de lograr una determinada organización del juego o una organización táctica.

PRINCIPIOS	SUBPRINCIPIOS	SUBSUBPRINCIPIOS
En fase de posesión del balón	Ocupación/ataque del espacio (cómo)	Ataque de la profundidad
En fase de no posesión del balón	Escalonamiento con líneas cercanas	Equilibrio
En fase de transición positiva	Juego en vertical, con finalización por el centro	Pases con apoyo central y doblando velozmente
En fase de transición negativa	Pressing «alto» para recuperar rápido el balón	Doblar en el pressing y cobertura del compañero

Ejemplo de ejercicio de un equipo que adopta un sistema de juego 1-4-3-3 y que se enfrenta a un equipo con el mismo sistema, con los siguientes principios de juego:

<u>EN FASE DE POSESIÓN</u>: Posesión del balón para atraer al equipo contrario y poder atacar luego con velocidad en los espacios que se crean a la espalda de las líneas adversarias (para poder realizar este tipo de juego hacen falta jugadores con calidad técnica elevada).

<u>EN FASE DE NO POSESIÓN</u>: Pressing alto para poder recuperar el balón lo antes posible.

<u>EN FASE DE TRANSICIÓN POSITIVA</u>: Ataque directo central con internadas de uno de los centrocampistas (por ejemplo, no hace falta llegar a la línea de fondo por los extremos para realizar un centro si no se tienen jugadores con buena capacidad para el remate de cabeza mientras que se dispone de jugadores hábiles aplicando la técnica y capaces de internarse en los espacios en el momento justo).

<u>EN FASE DE TRANSICIÓN NEGATIVA</u>: Todos los jugadores deben colocarse lo más rápidamente posible detrás del balón (evidentemente, para lograr un pressing rápido y eficaz tendremos jugadores que vayan a doblar y triplicar el marcaje al jugador con el balón sin estar necesariamente detrás de la línea del balón).

Salida lateral defensiva en fase de NO POSESIÓN

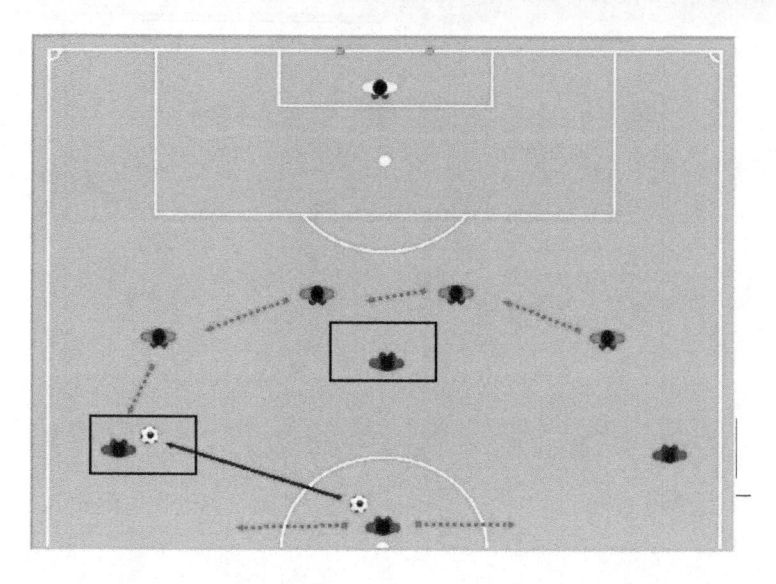

El centrocampista se mueve con el balón al interior del espacio y los defensas se mueven en consecuencia. En el momento del pase a uno de los tres compañeros colocados en un sector determinado, el jugador externo saldrá a presionar con la consiguiente cobertura del compañero de la línea. Es importante no dar ninguna indicación, sino que la señal sea la propia situación real del pase, de modo que la indicación que ordena el movimiento sea común para todos.

Transición positiva en la mitad defensiva del campo

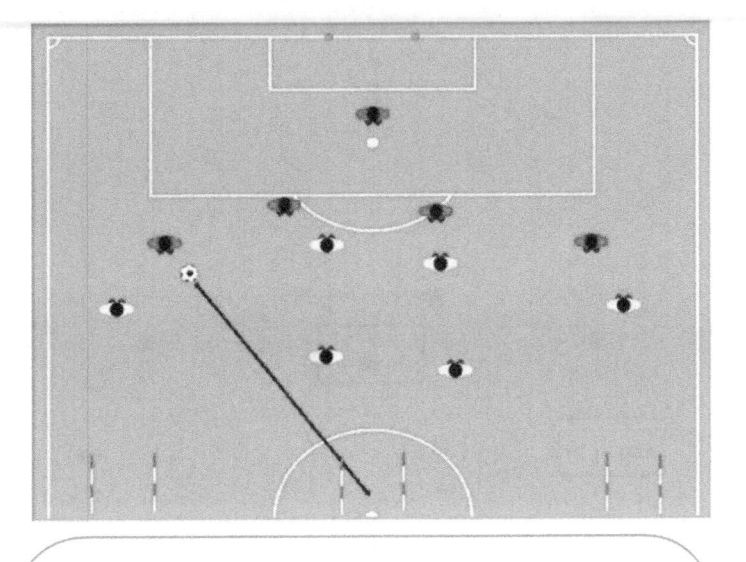

Se juega un 6 contra 4+1. Los amarillos deben tratar de marcar y los rojos deben conseguir el balón. Tras recuperarlo deben marcar (como si fuera un pase) en alguna de las tres porterías colocadas en la mitad del campo, que representan a los tres centrocampistas. Posteriormente será oportuno añadir en la progresión didáctica tres centrocampistas reales. Luego será posible añadir en un primer momento un jugador amarillo que pueda presionar a los tres centrocampistas y finalmente añadir el mismo número de centrocampistas adversarios que se encontrarán en el partido.

Transición positiva en la mitad ofensiva del campo

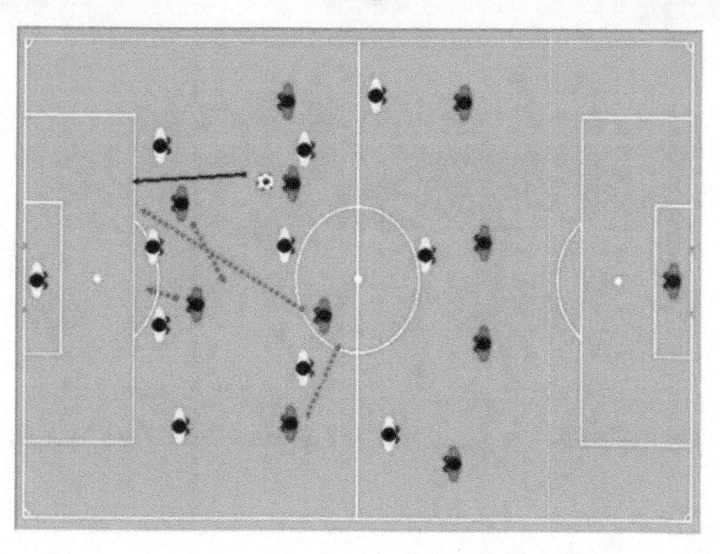

Con los jugadores dispuestos como en un partido, se juega con los defensas amarillos en posesión del balón sin una presión activa de los rojos. Sin embargo, en el momento que recibe el balón uno de los centrocampistas o delanteros, la presión será activa y repentina. Tras conseguir el balón, se realizarán los movimientos del diagrama para atacar en profundidad.

Transición negativa

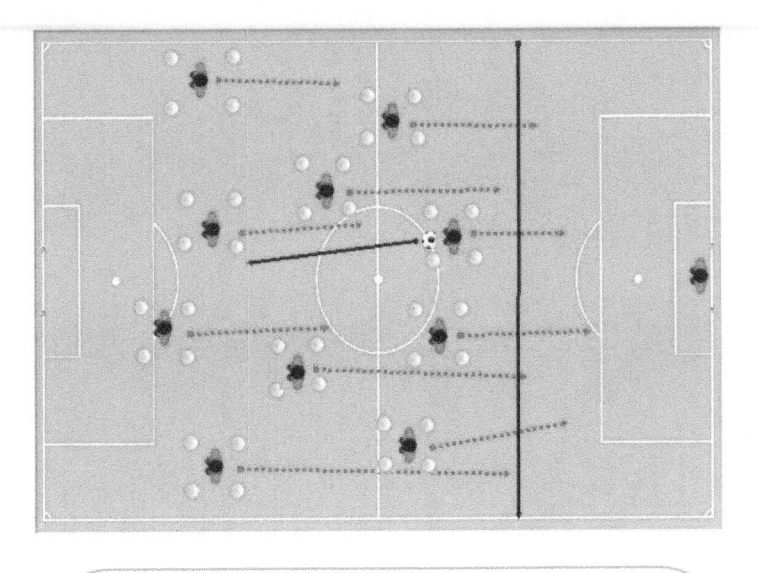

Jugadores dispuestos en el campo cada uno dentro de un cuadrado. Se realizan pases entre los jugadores. Debe realizarse el control sin que el balón salga del cuadrado, igual que el pase. En el momento en el que el pase o el control no se efectúen correctamente, todos los jugadores tendrán un máximo de 5 segundos para correr detrás de la línea negra (que representaría la línea del balón). Este ejercicio, además de poder ser un ejercicio condicional valido, garantizará una precisión en el pase y en el control, ya que los jugadores tratarán de evitar carreras continuas. Además, para evitar el riesgo de error, los pases serán cortos (que es el modelo de juego que se pretende alcanzar).

SISTEMAS DE JUEGO

Por SISTEMA DE JUEGO se entiende la posición en el campo de los jugadores en una situación estática y dónde ocupan estos la zona de defensa, centro del campo y delantera.

No confundir con el MÓDULO DE JUEGO (o modelo de juego), que representa la aplicación dinámica de un sistema de juego con tareas y funciones predefinidas para cada jugador y líneas en cada situación distinta de juego.

El sistema de juego representa y explica la reordenación básica mediante las tareas y las funciones de los jugadores en el campo.

Cualquier sistema de juego que se desee aplicar debe tener en cuenta las características esenciales e indispensables que representan los principios generales de cualquier sistema.

De esto se deduce que un sistema de juego ha de ser:

- **Equilibrado:** Que tenga en consideración del mismo modo y al mismo tiempo las dos fases en cualquier momento del juego.

- **Elástico**: Que se pueda adaptar fácilmente a cualquier adversario, manteniendo siempre los equilibrios.

- **Racional**: Que se adapte a las características de los futbolistas disponibles.

Por ejemplo, un 1-4-4-2 en zona es un sistema capaz de garantizar solidez, equilibrio y seguridad en la fase defensiva y variedad en la ofensiva.

Además, es un sistema de juego que permite mantener al equipo cerca en ambas fases del juego, acosar constantemente al adversario y ocupar los espacios de forma óptima, tratando de aprovechar al máximo las zonas laterales. Es un sistema de juego de fácil comprensión y representa la base de todo sistema de juego. Es por tanto importante que el futbolista joven conozca sus principios.

En mi opinión, este sistema tendría que adoptarse siempre en la fase de no posesión del balón, independientemente del sistema principal de juego adoptado.

Esto avala el principio según el cual un equipo debe estar en disposición de cambiar el sistema de juego también durante el mismo partido, en función de las diversas situaciones de juego y también de las características de los adversarios.

La defensa en zona

Antes se ha especificado que el sistema de juega era un 1-4-4-2 **en zona**.

Vamos pues a explicar qué se entiende por una defensa en zona.

La defensa en zona se opone evidentemente a la defensa al hombre. La característica de este tipo de táctica es sin duda la posición del balón, que se convierte en el punto de referencia, incluso por encima de la posición del adversario, considerada por el contrario como lo primero que hay que tener en cuenta cuando se efectúa una defensa al hombre. Los ejes de un fútbol con defensa en zona son el acoso al poseedor del balón y obtener la superioridad numérica en la zona del balón.

Los futbolistas deberán tener una buena velocidad y un buen sentido de la posición para aplicar de la mejor manera este tipo de estrategia.

Los movimientos típicos de una defensa de cuatro en fase de no posesión del balón son los de un movimiento coordinado dirigido a atacar al poseedor del balón, con posiciones escalonadas y haciendo la cobertura al compañero (como se ha visto por ejemplo en el ejercicio anterior con una defensa de cuatro).

Es obvio que en caso de defensa de tres se hace todavía más necesario el escalonamiento de un centrocampista lateral para cubrir adecuadamente el campo en toda su longitud. El concepto de presión sobre el poseedor del balón es válido también para centrocampistas y delanteros.

Es evidente que, en relación con el sistema de juego aplicado, habrá diferencias sustanciales en los movimientos de los jugadores individuales.

Por ejemplo, si se aplica un sistema con tres delanteros, la presión de los tres será distinta de una presión realizada por uno o dos delanteros (en un **1-4-2-3-1** o **1-4-4-2** etc.).

En concreto, vamos a ver la diferencia de movimiento de los delanteros y los centrocampistas.

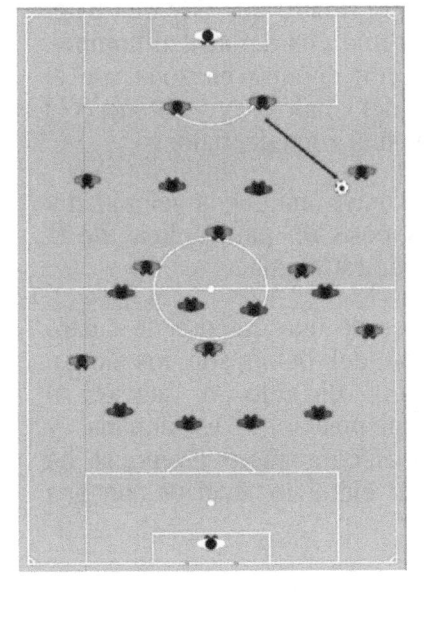

Esta situación, de fácil lectura, explica cuáles serían los movimientos de los jugadores azules en función de un pase lateral por parte de los rojos, en un sistema de juego 1-4-4-2 que se enfrenta a un equipo adopta un 1-4-3-3. Evidentemente, cada entrenador actuará de acuerdo con su visión y su modelo de juego. **Esta es la situación inicial en el momento del pase.**

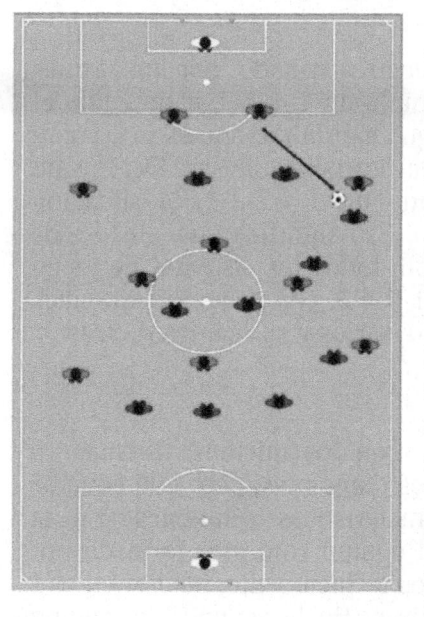

Vemos cómo el primer jugador que va a la presión del receptor del balón es el centrocampista lateral derecho. El centrocampista interior derecho va a cubrir, así como el otro interior. El lateral izquierdo se centra. La línea de defensa sube y el lateral defensivo derecho adopta una posición de cobertura al compañero y de marcaje preventivo al extremo. El delantero azul se coloca de manera que impide el pase al central. **Esta es la situación final tras el pase**.

Si el sistema de juego adoptado por los azules hubiera sido por ejemplo un 1-4-3-3, habría sido el extremo derecho el que habría ido a presionar como hubiera hecho un centrocampista lateral. Del mismo modo, si hubiera sido un 1-4-2-3-1, la situación habría sido la misma. Eso significa que, en fase de no posesión del balón, todos los sistemas de juego se convierten en un 1-4-4-2, con pequeñas variantes en función de los adversarios y sus características.

Ejemplo:

La misma situación, con los mismos sistemas de juego indicados en los diagramas, pero con equipos adversarios con características diferentes. En la primera situación, el equipo rojo está formado por jugadores muy buenos técnicamente, hábiles en el 1 contra 1 y en los pases. En la segunda, el equipo rojo no está particularmente dotado técnicamente, pero es muy fuerte físicamente.

Situación 1

El entrenador deberá preparar el partido buscando evitar dejar al poseedor del balón solo contra un solo jugador. Por tanto, será fundamental la ayuda y el marcaje preventivo sobre posibles receptores del pase. Por tanto, las líneas serán muy cortas y los espacios entre los jugadores bastante reducidos.

Situación 2

No será necesaria la presión con ayuda pues se supone que en el 1 contra 1 probablemente baste con un jugador para recuperar el balón. Será por el contrario importante el movimiento de desmarque de los compañeros con tiempos apropiados en el momento de la recuperación del balón para dar

inmediatamente una salida a quien lo consiga. Se hace sobre todo para dar a quien lo reciba luego la posibilidad de poder tener espacio al recibir y, por tanto, de no tener que pelear a nivel físico con adversarios fuertes en ese aspecto.

Es evidente que esto forma parte de la estrategia de un entrenador y de cómo prepara el partido. Pero era necesario para explicar que hay que adaptar a los movimientos básicos las características de los jugadores propios y las de los adversarios, No basta con saber que el balón es el punto de referencia en una defensa en zona. Hay muchos otros conceptos que un entrenador ha de tener en cuenta.

Otro ejemplo de cómo la estrategia de un entrenador es su capacidad de individualizar las características de los adversarios es el siguiente:

Todos sabemos que, cuando el poseedor del balón se enfrenta un defensa, este último debe tratar de conseguir el balón dirigiendo al delantero hacia el exterior del campo. En la situación del gráfico anterior, por ejemplo, el defensor deberá trata de «empujar» al exterior al adversario con el balón. Pero también sabemos que el defensor debe dirigir al poseedor del balón hacia su lado débil.

Si un zurdo se encuentra en la banda izquierda y se enfrenta a un contrario, ¿deberá este llevarlo al exterior (pero sobre su lado fuerte) o al interior (sobre su lado débil, pero en la zona más peligrosa del campo)?

En mi opinión, esto depende de cuatro factores:

1. Dónde.

2. Cómo

3. Cuándo.

4. Por qué.

Dónde: ¿En qué zona del campo se encuentra? Si estamos en la mitad del campo contrario, será preferible llevar al poseedor del balón al interior, ya que la zona es peligrosa para su equipo y los compañeros del defensor pueden ayudar a recuperar el balón más fácilmente. Además, se evitaría que el poseedor del balón efectúe un pase a lo largo de la banda.

Cómo: ¿La presión será individual o con ayuda o incluso con más jugadores? ¿O bien será una presión de retraso para esperar la ayuda de un compañero o que el equipo recupere sus posiciones?

Por qué: El poseedor del balón es mucho más hábil técnicamente en el 1 contra 1 y por tanto decidirá que el defensor realice una presión de retraso para esperar a que le ayude un compañero. O bien, siguiendo el ejemplo inicial del zurdo, supongamos que juega como lateral en la derecha. En este caso si el defensor le «lleva» al exterior le está forzando también a jugar sobre el lado débil y por tanto parecería la mejor solución. ¿Pero qué sería mejor si este mismo jugador es muy rápido? Entiendo que esta no sería la mejor solución, ya que llevarlo al exterior le facilitaría jugar el balón hacia delante y superar al defensor en velocidad. Un entrenador «reflexivo», en mi opinión, debería indicar al

defensor que dirija a este jugador al interior del campo y busque una ayuda inmediata. Hay que posicionar por tanto a un buen defensor en la cobertura del compañero exterior.

Repito que estos son conceptos que cada entrenador puede compartir en mayor o menor medida. Sin embargo, es importante que sepa reconocer las características de sus jugadores y su momento de forma física.

EJEMPLOS DE SISTEMAS DE JUEGO

Recordemos que por sistema de juego se entiende la posición en el campo de los jugadores en una situación estática donde estos ocupan las zonas de defensa, centro del campo y ataque.

1-4-4-2.

La defensa está compuesta por dos centrales y dos laterales. Uno de los centrales tiene la tarea de dirigir el avance simultáneo de la línea de defensa. La línea de defensa puede organizarse con balón en el extremo, con una o dos líneas de cobertura y con balón central. En este último caso, la cobertura es en embudo.

Los centrocampistas pueden colocarse en línea o en rombo, con uno de los dos pivotes más atrasado y el otro desplegado por detrás de delanteros.

1-5-3-2.

En el caso de 1-5-3-2 con marcaje en zona, los defensores marcan a los delanteros adversarios en sus propias zonas de competencia. Los laterales defensivos pueden convertirse en un cuarto centrocampista (en la fase de posesión del balón) o apoyar ambos el centro del campo.

En la defensa con marcaje mixto, en la zona central, los marcadores tienen asignación al hombre de los delanteros contrarios. El marcaje puede ser fijo o con cambio de marca en la mitad propia del campo (centro derecha o centro izquierda). En defensa central tiene la función de líbero clásico, siempre ligeramente separado de los defensas que tienen la obligación de marcar.

Los laterales deben ocuparse de posibles extremos y, en la fase de posesión del balón, atacar por las bandas.

Lo centrocampistas pueden disponerse con el pivote más retrasado o más avanzado con respecto a los compañeros de línea. La decisión determina una mayor cobertura o una mayor capacidad ofensiva. Los delanteros deben ayudar a los centrocampistas en el exterior.

1-3-4-3 defensa con marcaje en zona

Con solo tres jugadores en defensa hay una zona defensiva del campo más amplia a gestionar, pero las tareas no varían con respecto a la defensa de 4.

En la fase de cobertura, la defensa del sector central se ve ayudada por los exteriores del centro del campo y por un pivote del centro del campo que se inserta en la línea de defensa.

Los centrocampistas se alinean como en centro del campo del 1-4-4-2.

Los delanteros, a su vez, deben ayudar a los centrocampistas en la fase de no posesión del balón.

Las cadenas de juego

En el fútbol, independientemente de si se defiende al hombre o en zona, el fundamento táctico principal debe ser la organización. El objetivo que debe plantearse todo entrenador es el de transferir al grupo sus propios conocimientos e ideas para hacer que todos entiendan lo mismo en la misma

situación, creando así un lenguaje común, para colaborar, cooperar y razonar de modo unívoco.

Al implantar su programa de trabajo, el entrenador no puede dejar de valorar, conocer y enriquecer el bagaje técnico-táctico individual de cada jugador.

Es por tanto indispensable que las habilidades individuales se inserten en el colectivo, creando así la organización del juego. Dentro de esta, la colaboración y la interrelación son de importancia esencial, con el fin de tener un equipo siempre equilibrado, funcional y racional.

Las competencias del entrenador deben ser «absolutas» para hacer así que sus mensajes se conviertan en indicadores claros y precisos, asimilables por todo el grupo.

Definición de «cadenas de juego»

Las «cadenas de juego» se entienden como una colaboración entre varios jugadores cercanos repartidos sobre el terreno por el sistema de juego en sentido horizontal o vertical.

Estos efectuarán movimientos coordinados y funcionales en relación con una situación determinada en un determinado sector del campo.

Las «cadenas» comprenden innumerables soluciones técnico-tácticas, cuya eficacia y multiplicidad dependen de las habilidades técnicas de sus intérpretes, de sus conocimientos técnicos y tácticos, de factores físicos y psicológicos y de las reacciones de los adversarios.

Por ejemplo, en el 1-4-4-2, las «cadenas» de jugadores previstas en sentido vertical para

aprovechar las bandas estarán compuestas por lateral, centrocampista lateral e interior.

Tendremos así en la derecha 2-8-7 y en la izquierda 3-4-11 *(Figura).*

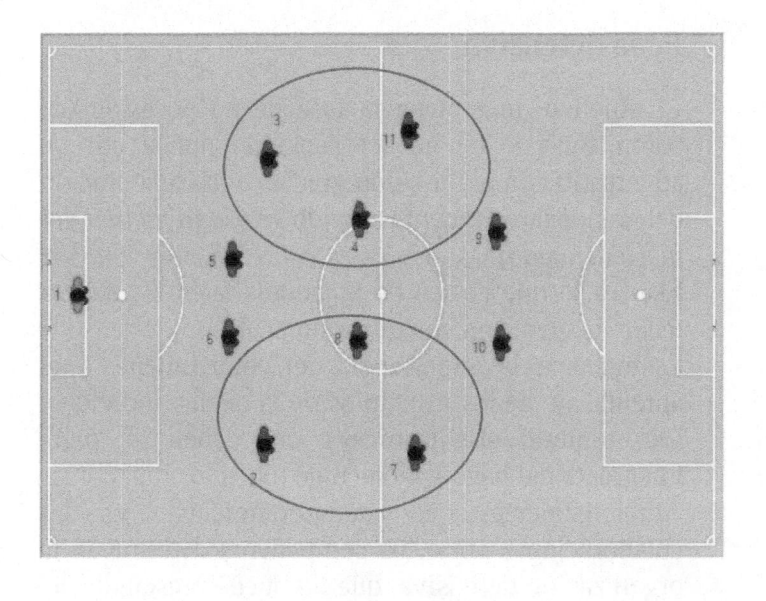

Es fundamental que estos tríos de jugadores interaccionen entre sí moviéndose con sincronía y colaboración, condición principal del juego de cualquier equipo.

Ocupar, dominar y aprovechar las bandas es uno de los requisitos del juego en zona.

En las dos fases del juego deberemos tener absolutamente en cuenta dos factores fundamentales del fútbol: tiempo y espacio.

El objetivo de cualquier entrenador es el de buscar mejorar continuamente estos dos componentes,

porque en cualquier situación ganar o perder tiempo y espacio de juego significa imponerse o sucumbir ante el adversario.

En las siguientes fases examinaremos cómo pueden comportarse e interactuar las «cadenas» laterales en las dos fases del juego.

Fase defensiva

El objetivo general en la fase de no posesión del balón consiste en no ser superado nunca por un adversario con o sin balón gracias a la colaboración del compañero (*excepto cuando se usa la táctica del fuera de juego*).

Esto es lo que el trío de jugadores laterales deberá tener en cuenta en cualquier situación.

Es evidente la importancia del conocimiento y el aprendizaje de los principios de la táctica individual (ver capítulo «La técnica»), que deben ser parte integrante del bagaje técnico de todos los jugadores.

Adicionalmente, el comportamiento y las colaboraciones entre los compañeros determinan la organización defensiva, que no puede prescindir del respeto y mantenimiento de los principios de táctica colectiva en cualquier situación (ver capítulo «La técnica»).

Las «cadenas» de juego deben tomar una multitud de decisiones en situaciones diversas en el menor tiempo posible, por lo que la tarea del entrenador es la de dar a sus jugadores la mayor cantidad posible de conocimiento e instrumentos para hacer que elijan las mejores opciones.

Fase ofensiva

Habilidad técnica en la rapidez de ejecución y velocidad de movimiento con capacidad de leer cualquier situación técnico-táctica son las cualidades requeridas al futbolista por todo entrenador que pretenda desarrollar una maniobra ofensiva eficaz.

Hay que educar y entrenar a los jugadores en el movimiento, en asumir iniciativas sin balón, en hacer estos movimientos combinados y sincronizados con el fin de tener un diseño táctico común.

El fútbol de nuestros días es cada vez más dinámico, los espacios y el tiempo de juego cada vez más pequeños y veloces, por lo que el movimiento sin balón y la velocidad de pensamiento se convierten en elementos fundamentales para la didáctica de cualquier juego de ataque.

Colaborar en la fase ofensiva significa realizar movimientos, moverse en continuidad en función del compañero en posesión del balón para doblar y apoyar siempre de modo que se ofrezcan más posibilidades en el desarrollo de la maniobra.

Conocer la importancia del pase rápido, saber orientarse con el cuerpo de modo tal que se vea la mayor cantidad posible de campo, desmarcarse en el momento justo mediante un contramovimiento, son capacidades que deben incluirse en el bagaje de todo jugador independientemente del puesto que ocupe y del sistema de juego aplicado. **(Esto remite a la importancia de una formación integral de un futbolista en todo los aspectos, técnicos, tácticos, físicos y psicológicos, de modo que se pueda**

adaptar a cualquier sistema, modelo o estrategia de juego).
El pase y el movimiento sin balón deben ser simultáneos.

Es importante hacer comprender a nuestros futbolistas que es el acompañamiento sin balón, mediante su carrera en velocidad y en la dirección deseada, el que indica el pase y no al contrario.

El jugador sin balón deberá entender inmediatamente que, si el compañero en posesión del balón tiene dificultades porque le presionan, hay que realizar un movimiento de ayuda, para lo que deberá moverse ganando campo por delante si el compañero tiene espacio y tiempo a su disposición para jugar.

En este caso, el desmarque se prepara efectuando un contramovimiento: mediante una carrera de traslado, mientras el balón está llegando a nuestro compañero, nos alejamos de la zona previamente escogida y posteriormente, cuando el compañero esté en disposición de realizar el pase, se efectuará un cambio de velocidad y dirección en el espacio libre.

Para desarrollar la maniobra con eficacia y variedad es fundamental saber aprovechar las bandas.

Resulta difícil superar la concentración de una defensa adversaria si no se la obliga a ampliar sus distancias ocupando con velocidad y por sorpresa las bandas.

En la fase ofensiva las bandas laterales deben estar siempre ocupadas mediante movimientos combinados y sincronizados que permitan evitar la trampa del fuera del juego.

En el sistema de juego 1-4-4-2 al que nos referimos, esta tarea se encarga claramente a las «cadenas» laterales que deben moverse coordinadas en el tempo justo y que en diversas situaciones pueden valerse de la ayuda del delantero correspondiente.
En todas las situaciones es necesario respetar los tiempos de la jugada, que se pueden entrenar partiendo de combinaciones libres de tres jugadores trabajando sobre los factores de tiempo y espacio, bajo el concepto «juega con quien veas» y contando con su apoyo (figura siguiente) y en ejercicios de posesión de balón con la posibilidad de variar el objetivo final.

También los ejercicios psicocinéticos, con todas sus diversas aplicaciones, pueden ser de gran importancia, porque obligan y acostumbran a los jugadores y ver y pensar antes, por lo que aceleran la velocidad de pensamiento.

Además, se puede entrenar la fase de ataque mediante planes ofensivos, sin la presencia de adversarios, probando diversas soluciones en las que la presencia de las «cadenas» laterales se convierte en fundamental, prestando particular atención a los tiempos de ejecución y los movimientos,

Además y alternativamente es posible buscar el desarrollo de la acción ofensiva mediante situaciones de juego en superioridad numérica, incluyendo por tanto adversarios activos. Estos pueden ser tanto delanteros que dificultan la construcción del juego de la defensa como defensas que obstaculizan la fase ofensiva. Se puede llegar así a disputar un 11x7 donde buscar un movimiento continuo, velocidad en el pase, visión de juego y colaboración en la fase ofensiva.

Conclusiones

Las soluciones aquí indicadas en el desarrollo del juego de equipo son solo una mínima parte de las innumerables combinaciones posibles creables durante un partido, también porque, como sabemos, la realidad de este es muy distinta de la de un entrenamiento. De hecho, las tensiones nerviosas son diferentes, así como las situaciones de juego. Y sobre todo los adversarios afrontan el partido con su estrategia y por tanto no es fácilmente predecible para preparar las contramedidas adecuadas.

Mediante ejercicios que se ocupen sobre todo de los tiempos, los espacios del movimiento y las colaboraciones entre los jugadores y pasando continuamente de lo sencillo a lo complejo, el entrenador puede transmitir sus ideas y mentalidad de juego, dentro de las cuales el futbolista individual, cada uno con sus propias capacidades, pueda aprovecharlas al máximo.

Competencias, ideas, equilibrio y pasión son cualidades fundamentales para todo entrenador.

Su tarea es la de conseguir transmitir la cultura del entusiasmo por el trabajo cotidiano, sin la cual se hace difícil obtener algo importante.

Entre los muchos lugares comunes en el fútbol, hay uno que considero que es verdadero: «Como te entrenes durante la semana, jugarás el domingo».

Eso no quiere decir que si un grupo trabaja con seriedad, entusiasmo e intensidad en cada entrenamiento consiga vencer siempre, sino que significa que sin duda se tendrá siempre un equipo listo, preparado y concentrado para cualquier situación.

Los jugadores, que son los protagonistas, deben estar plenamente convencidos de lo que se les propone. Solo así será posible tener participación y disponibilidad total con el fin de obtener una organización válida del equipo.

El aspecto más satisfactorio, más allá de los valores técnico-tácticos, es el de conseguir «entrar en la cabeza» de los jugadores y hacerlos partícipes y conscientes de formar parte de un grupo que quiere trabajar, crecer y mejorar juntos.

Está claro que tener a tu disposición no solo buenos jugadores, sino sobre todo hombres inteligentes, altruistas y ambiciosos hará más sencillo el trabajo del entrenador y será más fácil contribuir a producir buen fútbol, eficaz y espectacular.

LA POSESIÓN DEL BALÓN

La estadística más citada de un partido de fútbol es la de la posesión del balón, pero el dato «en bruto» no dice cómo emplea un equipo el tiempo que pasa con el balón en los pies, si lo hace mejor o peor que el equipo al que se enfrenta o a los otros equipos del campeonato. Por tanto, he tratado de relacionar la media de la posesión del balón con la de pases realizados para empezar a tener un cuadro más claro acerca de las capacidades en la gestión del balón de cada equipo.

Un equipo que quiera tener el balón más tiempo lo hará con pases más sencillos y por tanto más precisos, una posesión «conservadora». Una posesión muchas veces en la zona baja, al límite de su propia área de penalti. Evidentemente una presión poco agresiva del equipo adversario ayuda a obtener altos porcentajes de pases realizados.

Esto no significa que quien domine la gestión del balón juegue un «fútbol» mejor.

¿Qué hay que analizar para poder valorar si la posesión del balón es realmente eficaz y productiva?

ZONAS DEL CAMPO

La posesión del balón, si se efectúa en la zona defensiva propia, resulta más sencilla con respecto a la posesión en la zona de ataque.

Esto ocurre porque en la zona defensiva muy a menudo la presión adversaria (como decíamos antes) no es comparable con la realizada en las zonas del centro del campo y la defensa.

JUGADORES AFECTADOS

Dependiendo de la zona del campo donde se mantenga principalmente la posesión de un equipo durante el partido, se deriva que los jugadores afectados sean distintos. Esto comporta que un entrenador inteligente no pretende estructurar su modelo de juego con una posesión de balón en la zona de ataque si no tiene a su disposición jugadores ofensivos con buenas capacidades técnicas y que puedan hacer eficaz esta estrategia. Otro factor importante es saber cuántas veces participa el portero en la posesión del balón.

MODO

Existen equipos que prefieren mantener la posesión del balón en la zona «baja» para hacer que suba el equipo contrario, creando espacio para atacar mediante penetraciones o en profundidad. Por el contrario, otros equipos, en cuanto consiguen la posesión del balón, prefieren mandarlo inmediatamente a los delanteros y mantienen la posesión en la zona de ataque. Es evidente que

ambas modalidades son diferentes y necesitan jugadores con las características propias de la estrategia adoptada.

Por tanto, no es verdad que juegue mejor quien tenga un mayor porcentaje de posesión del balón. A veces puede ser más espectacular asistir a un partido donde un equipo define con pocos pases, pero muy veloces, que ver jugar a un equipo que mantiene constantemente la posesión del balón, pero no consigue llegar a crear situaciones para golear. Sin embargo, una cosa es cierta: Según las estadísticas de las competiciones más importantes, los equipos que ganan o que juegan finales son siempre los que tienen un mayor porcentaje de posesión del balón. Todo esto resulta razonable: Tener el control del balón por más tiempo garantiza un saldo positivo entre las ocasiones creadas y las concedidas.

DIDÁCTICA DE LA POSESIÓN DEL BALÓN

Desde el punto de vista didáctico, el objetivo de los ejercicios debe en principio dirigirse exclusivamente a la fase de posesión.

Por lo que el enfoque se orienta a:

- El desmarque.
- La transmisión del balón, con la obligación del pase raso. Esto no significa que no se realicen pases largos o no rasos. Sin embargo, es evidente que en este caso resulta más difícil mantener la posesión, dado que el control del balón resulta más difícil.

No importa la intensidad del ejercicio si no se apoya en una calidad adecuada de la ejecución. Sobre todo, debe explicarse a los jugadores que la velocidad de carrera en la fase de construcción de la maniobra es distinta y menos intensa con respecto a la fase de recuperación del balón.

Para conseguirlo, es necesario un movimiento continuo por parte de todos los compañeros (ver «Movilidad - Táctica colectiva») y una búsqueda continua de la zona de «luz», es decir, aquella donde el compañero sin balón está en disposición de recibir el pase de quien lo posea, facilitando así el desarrollo del juego.

Después de que el equipo haya aprendido la posesión del balón con base

* 2 x 1.
* 3 x 1.
* 4 x 2.
* 6 x 4.

será posible pasar a la fase evolutiva, que prevé la introducción de un objetico específico para cada ejercicio propuesto.

Por tanto, la posesión del balón se convierte en un instrumento a través del cual el entrenador ejercita principio de juego como la búsqueda de amplitud de campo (ver «Amplitud - Táctica colectiva»)

Es de importancia fundamental para mantener la posesión del balón el mayor tiempo posible, la

recuperación del balón en el momento en que se está en fase de no posesión.

A los defensas de la última generación, se les viene reprochando a menudo que no tienen ya una habilidad muy importante, considerada en el pasado una carcaterística identificativa por ejemplo del fútbol italiano:

El marcaje.

«Entender al adversario» significa saber cómo reaccionar ante una situación de juego con los gestos técnicos necesario (posturas, apoyos, visión periférica), por lo que el problema no es de naturaleza física (contacto), sino cognitiva: Saber dónde «estoy yo, el defensa», dónde están mis compañeros y dónde está mi adversario directo, en referencia a la posición de la portería y el balón.

Con el tiempo se ha cometido el error de pensar que para resolver todo problema era bastante la ejecución sistemática de los movimientos de la línea defensiva (automatismo).

Esto pasa sobre todo a nivel juvenil, donde los entrenadores preparan a los equipos como si fueran de adultos, descuidando fundamentos individuales imprescindibles, como por ejemplo el marcaje (ver «Técnica»).

El defensa debe poder «leer» las posturas del jugador en posesión del balón y, para ser eficaz,

pensar como un delantero, moviéndose con las posturas del delantero.
El marcaje se diferencia en dos situaciones:

1. Marcaje al adversario en posesión del balón.
2. Marcaje al adversario sin balón.

Marcaje al adversario en posesión del balón

En el marcaje del adversario con balón, el principio general es que el defensa debe posicionarse entre la portería y el balón.

Podemos tener acciones de <u>dilación</u> y acciones de <u>enfrentamiento</u>. El defensa debe acercarse los más rápidamente posible al adversario para evitar que este gane espacio por delante y adquiera velocidad.

Antes de que el adversario entre en posesión del balón, el defensa deba estar ya colocado en la posición de proyección **anterior-posterior** (apoyos ligeros, cuerpo en equilibrio y baricentro bajo, nunca fuera de la base de apoyo) con el fin de no ser superado con un cambio de dirección o de velocidad del adversario.

La atención debe dirigirse al balón, para no ser engañado por eventuales fintas con el cuerpo.

En este momento, el defensor debe decidir si:
- Retrasa la acción (por ejemplo, en inferioridad numérica), donde es

fundamental ganar al menos tiempo de juego para permitir una posible cobertura.

- Defender al adversario, si es posible en una posición estratégicamente ventajosa.
- Tratar de recuperar el balón cuando la probabilidad de éxito sea evidente o tiene una cobertura a las espaldas.

Las situaciones de juego que pueden darse son:

Ataque frontal – En el que el defensa debe posicionarse con el cuerpo protegiendo la portería.

Ataque lateral – En el que el defensa debe tratar de dirigir al adversario hacia el exterior. Ambos pies estarán en el interior de la línea de avance del balón (si el adversario tuviera que invertir la dirección, sería anulado).

Ataque con el adversario de espaldas – En este caso, el defensa debe:
- «Ver» siempre el balón.
- En posición anterior-posterior, poner el brazo semiextendido sobre el adversario sin apoyarlo.
- «Entender» si el adversario está cambiando de dirección al girar sobre sí mismo.
- Evitar que se gire y verse atacado frontalmente.
- Si el atacante trata de girarse, enfrentarse a él cuando el poseedor del balón esté en mitad del giro (momento en el que cubre menos el esférico).

- No cometer nunca fallos.

Marcaje al adversario sin balón

En el marcaje del adversario sin balón, la elección del defensa está relacionada principalmente con la «lectura» de las intenciones del poseedor del balón.

Podemos subdividir las acciones del defensa en tres fases:
1. Espera.
2. Anticipación.
3. Defensa de la profundidad.

Espera

En la fase de espera, el jugador debe estar en disposición de valorar las intenciones del jugador en posesión del balón, teniendo en consideración de modo particular a dónde se vuelve la postura del cuerpo y cómo se muestra la oscilación de la pierna en contacto con el balón durante la ejecución del pase que condiciona la decisión entre anticipación y defensa de la profundidad.

De hecho, una oscilación limitada de la pierna predice un pase corto (por falta de potencia), mientras que una oscilación amplia predice un toque de rango medio-largo.

En caso de duda, el defensor debe elegir siempre defender la profundidad.

Anticipación

En la acción de anticipación se presuponen dos posibles intensidades de carrera (a menos que no esté clara y evidente la recuperación del balón): Inicialmente más lenta, casi una fase de estudio, posteriormente de alta intensidad en la ejecución del gesto técnico. En este caso, el jugador debe estar en disposición de elegir el tiempo preciso en el que pasar a enfrentarse para no cometer fallos y para lograr obtener el balón.

Defensa de la profundidad

El defensa, al valorar la distancia a mantener en el enfrentamiento con el adversario (marcaje estrecho o marcaje largo), debe basarse en una serie de factores:

- Distancia del balón al adversario.
- Situación de balón descubierto o cubierto.
- Cobertura a sus espaldas (posición de los compañeros).
- Calidad técnico-física-atlética del adversario directo.
- Estrategia defensiva adoptada por el equipo propio.

En conclusión:

Tener mucha posesión no es garantía de éxito. La posesión del balón es solo un dato en bruto, que puede dar una indicación instantánea sobre quién

está dominando el juego en un momento determinado del partido, Para hacerla significativa ha de estar siempre relacionada con otras informaciones. Por sí sola, la posesión del balón no da ninguna indicación sobre el peligro creado o la posibilidad de victoria de un equipo. Un equipo que logra disfrutar del dominio en la posesión del balón, lo demuestra en las ocasiones de gol que crea. En mi opinión, el factor para hacer eficaz una posesión del balón es la FASE DE TRANSICIÓN POSITIVA, en cuanto que si se recupera el balón en la mitad del campo propio no se puede crear tanto peligro como si se recupera en la zona de ataque.

Por tanto, parece una paradoja, pero para tener una posesión constante y eficaz del balón hay que ser bueno en la NO posesión del balón.

CÓMO PREPARAR UN ENTRENAMIENTO

Para prepara un entrenamiento hay que tener presente un factor importante. Sea cual sea el nivel de los jugadores, su edad y la categoría en la que juegan:
CADA SESIÓN DEBE TENER UN OBJETIVO CLARO.

A menudo nos preocupa qué ejercicios proponer sin pensar en por qué se hacen, si son adecuados para el nivel de los jugadores, su edad biológica, su momento de forma y el momento de la temporada deportiva.

No hay que confundir «preparar el entrenamiento» con «preparar un partido».

A nivel juvenil (hasta unos 14 años) se prepara un entrenamiento. Cada entrenamiento debe estar en función de la mejora técnica, táctica, física y psicológica de cada jugador individual, independientemente del partido que se realizará el fin de semana. El partido debe ser la «piedra de toque» de las mejoras individuales mediante los entrenamientos semanales.

El entrenamiento a nivel agonista será distinto (desde los 15 años). En este caso se puede hablar de «preparación para el partido», por cuanto se supone que los futbolistas ya han adquirido las competencias individuales necesarias.

Por tanto, en este caso, el entrenador deberá preparar el partido del domingo según su modelo de juego y su estrategia.

Será fundamental la programación de los entrenamientos.

El entrenador puede utilizar la ficha de la página 227 para preparar las sesiones de entrenamiento. Como vemos, en ella están indicados todos los elementos fundamentales a entrenar (fundamentos técnicos – táctica individual – táctica colectiva).

De este modo es posible anotar cuáles son las cosas sobre las que se trabajará en la sesión y, además, tener siempre a su alcance estas indicaciones ayuda al entrenador a memorizar más rápidamente la terminología.

Veamos además cómo la ficha presenta tres fases distintas del entrenamiento, que son:

- ANALÍTICA
- SITUACIONAL
- PARTIDO TEMÁTICO
- PARTIDO FINAL

ANALÍTICA

Un ejercicio se considera analítico cuando no está prevista la presencia de un jugador oponente.

SITUACIONAL

En el momento en el que el ejercicio prevé un jugador opuesto a uno o más jugadores, hablamos de situacional. Damos un ejemplo muy sencillo.

En las dos figuras siguiente vemos cómo en la primera hay un jugador que chuta a puerta sin portero (por tanto, sin oponente). Por tanto, está realizando un ejercicio analítico. En el momento en que está presente el portero (oponente), el jugador con el balón no trabaja ya el gesto de chutar el balón, sino el del tiro a puerta (situacional).

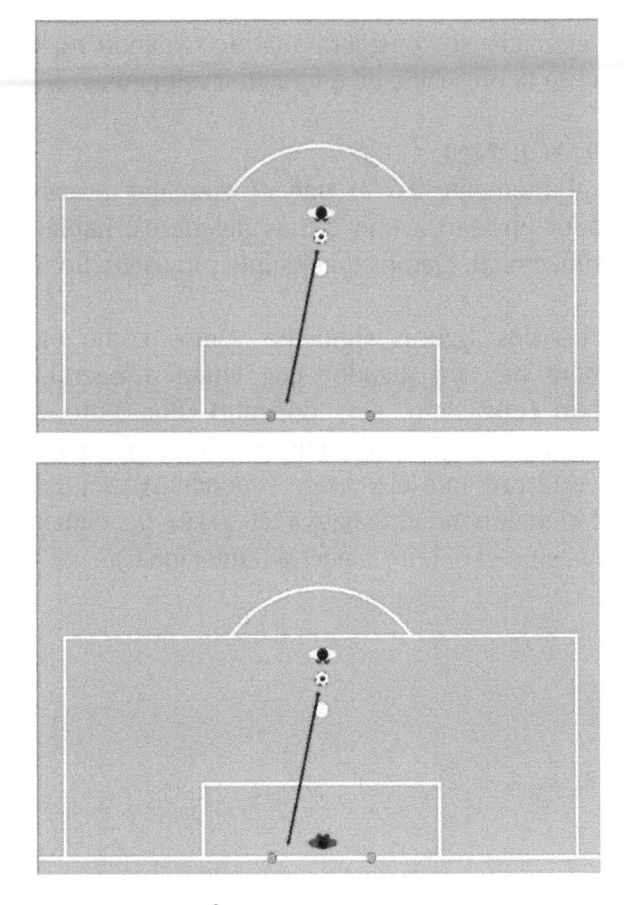

PARTIDO TEMÁTICO
Partido en el cual se introducen una o más reglas relacionadas con el objetivo de la sesión.

PARTIDO FINAL
Sería siempre oportuno acabar con un partido real.

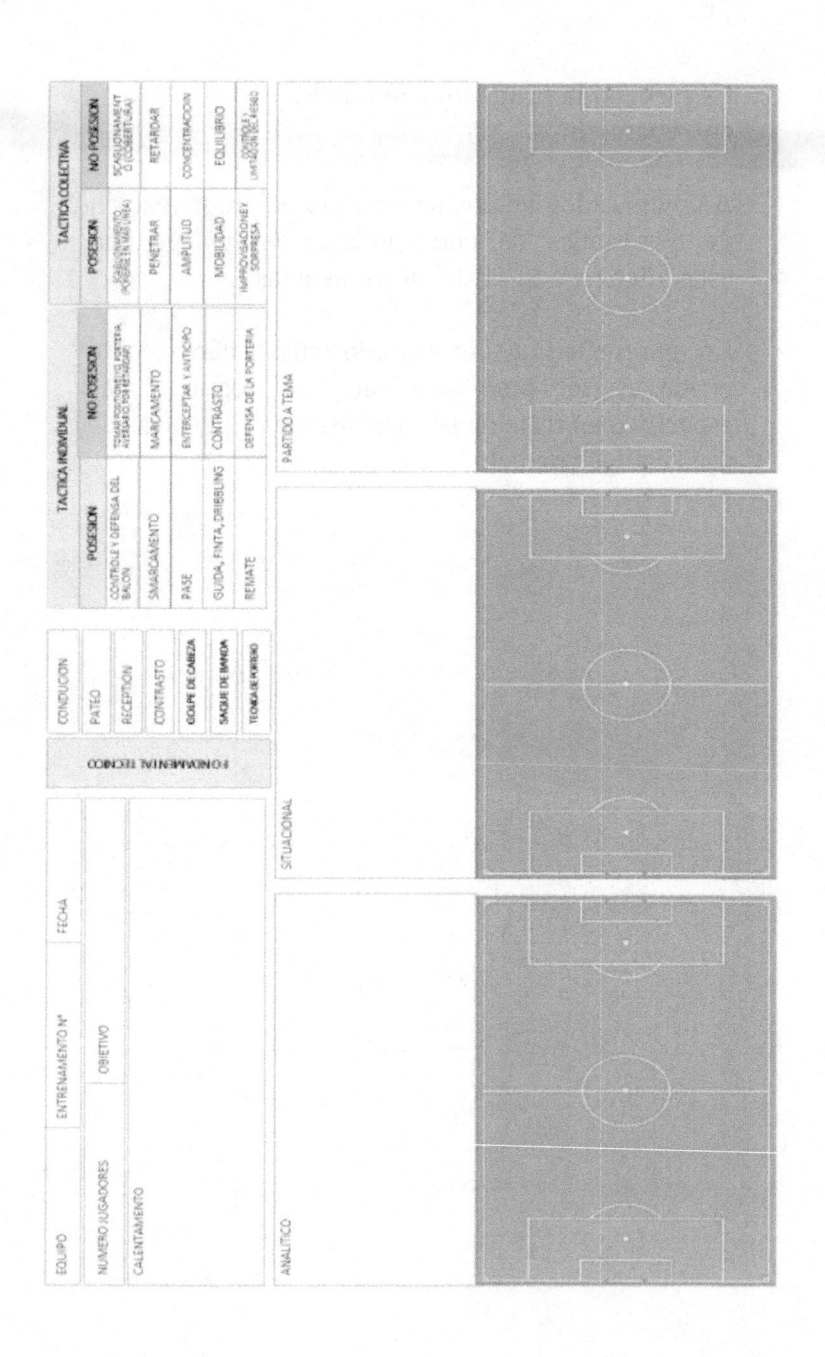

	TACTICA INDIVIDUAL		TACTICA COLECTIVA	
	POSESION	NO POSESION	POSESION	NO POSESION
	CONTROLE Y DEFENSA DEL BALON	TOMAR POSICIONES (EL PORTERA ADELGAZO POR RETARDAR)	ESCALONAMIENTO (POBRE EN 1RA. LINEA)	ESCALONAMIENTO O (COBERTURA)
	SMARCAMENTO	MARCAMENTO	PENETRAR	RETARDAR
	PASE	ENTERCEPTAR Y ANTICIPO	AMPLITUD	CONCENTRACION
	GUIDA, FINTA, DRIBBLING	CONTRASTO	MOBILIDAD	EQUILIBRIO
	REMATE	DEFENSA DE LA PORTERIA	IMPROVISADOONEY SORPRESA	CONTROL Y LIMITACION DEL RIESGO

CONDUCION
PATEO
RECEPTION
CONTRASTO
GOLPE DE CABEZA
SAQUE DE BANDA
TECNIQUE PORTERO

FONDAMENTAL TECNICO

EQUIPO	ENTRENAMIENTO N°	FECHA
NUMERO JUGADORES	OBJETIVO	
CALENTAMIENTO		

ANALITICO

SITUACIONAL

PARTIDO A TEMA

277

Es esencial la programación de los entrenamientos.

A continuación vemos un ejemplo de programación de 6 sesiones de entrenamiento en un periodo específico para tres categorías distintas.

Lo representado es un ejemplo muy genérico, pero puede usarse como guía para un programa más específico en relación con las distintas exigencias de cada equipo concreto.

PROGRAM FROM NOVEMBER

	TRAINING 1			TRAINING 2			TRAINING 3			TRAINING 4			TRAINING 5			TRAINING 6		
	U8	U10/13	U15/16	U8	U10/13	U15/16	U8	U10/13	U15/16	U8	U10/13	U15/16	U8	U10/13	U15/16	U8	U10/13	U15/16
TECNIQUE																		
BALL CONDUCTION																		
KICK	WITH COORD	WITH COORD		WITH COORD	WITH COORD		WITH COORD	WITH COORD		WITH COORD			WITH COORD	WITH COORD	WITH COORD	WITH COORD	WITH COORD	WITH COORD
RECIVE																		
TACKLE																		
HEAD SHOT																	WITH COORD	
THROW IN																		
TECNIQUE OF GK									1V GK				RUN FOR SHOT		1V GK			
INDIVIDUAL TACTIC																		
with ball																		
CONTROL AND DEFENSE BALL																		
UNMARKET																		
PASSING																		
CONDUCTION, FEINT, DRIBLE	WITH COORD			WITH COORD	WITH COORD													
SHOT IN GOL																		
without ball																		
TAKE POSITION	2V1											2V1						
MARKET												2V2			BEHIND/SIDE			BEHIND/SI
INTERCEPT AND ANTICIPATE												2V1			BEHIND/SIDE			BEHIND/SI
TACKLE																		
DEFENSE OF GOALS	2V1								1V1 NO G			TRANSITION						
COLECTIVE TACTIC																		
with ball																		
SCAGLIONAMENTO	2V1											5V3			RECIV BET IN			WAIT MOM
PENETRATION															RECIV BET IN			WAIT MON
AMPLITUDE		T.M. POSS			T.M. POSSE				T.M. POSSE						BACK PASS			WAIT MOM
MOBILITY			FREE SPACE															
IMPROVISATION AND SUR...						TAKE SHOTS						SH. MIN. W/ANT						WAIT MOM
without ball																		
SCAGLIONAMENTO		2V2	1V2									TRANSITION						WAIT MON
DELAY																		
CONCENTRATION					T.M. SHOTS													
BALANCE	T.M. POSS																	
CONTROL AND RISK LIMITA																		

LA GESTIÓN DEL QUE NO JUEGA

Todo entrenador se encuentra todas las semanas debiendo gestionar la situación de quien no ha jugado o ha jugado poco en los partidos anteriores.

Nunca es fácil excluir a un jugador del partido, tanto más cuando se tienen muchos disponibles y a menudo se está obligado a excluir a algunos completamente del partido sin ni siquiera convocarlos.

Evidentemente, la cosa cambia si hablamos de futbolistas jóvenes con respecto a un equipo de adultos. Y si afrontamos el tema en relación con los jugadores profesionales es algo completamente diferente,

Es importante motivar a quien normalmente no juega haciéndole entender lo determinante que puede ser un jugador que entra en el curso de un partido, porque a menudo esto se produce en momentos críticos o difíciles del partido.

El entrenador debe estar dispuesto a asumir la responsabilidad con respecto a sus decisiones. Esas responsabilidades afectan a:
- ✓ Aspectos técnicos.
- ✓ Aspectos tácticos.
- ✓ Aspectos condicionales.

Aspecto técnico

El entrenador debe valorar el nivel técnico de sus jugadores en relación con los adversarios para poder tomar decisiones exclusivamente por el bien del colectivo.

Aspecto táctico

Independientemente del nivel técnico de los jugadores en relación con los adversarios, el entrador debe saber «leer» el comportamiento táctico de dichos adversarios para contraponer una estrategia táctica eficaz. Como se ha descrito en los capítulos anteriores, las características de los jugadores a nuestra disposición influirán en la estrategia y no al contrario. Por tanto, las sustituciones en este caso estarán dictadas por la situación táctica y no la técnica.

Aspecto condicional

Es evidente que un entrenador debe poder reconocer a un jugador con dificultades en el aspecto condicional.

Los padres

En años recientes, el papel de los padres ha asumido un aspecto negativo. Sobre todo en un deporte como el fútbol, a menudo el padre ve en su hijo la solución a los problemas económicos familiares poniendo sobre el hijo una presión notable que a menudo es una causa determinante para el abandono de este deporte por parte de los chicos.

Contrariamente a lo que se podría pensar, es fundamental implicar a los padres en la comprensión de las propuestas educativas a nivel deportivo que se ofrecen a sus hijos. Solo mediante una buena formación de los padres se puede llegar a obtener un ambiente tranquilo para sus hijos.